# Distribution Transformers

## 26307-05

**Twin Falls Hydroelectric Project**

The Snake River is home to numerous hydroelectric power plants that use water power to produce electricity. One such power plant is the Twin Falls Hydroelectric Project in Twin Falls, Idaho. In addition to electricity, it provides many recreational resources, including a boat ramp, overlooks, parks, and picnic areas.

# 26307-05
# *Distribution System Transformers*

# Overview

Voltage levels on power transmission can exceed 800kV. These high levels of voltage are necessary to transmit the generated power over long distances to the usage areas. Once the power is received at distribution substations, it must be stepped down and regulated to a usable level. This is the work performed by distribution system power transformers.

Keep in mind the power formula of $P = EI$ when thinking about transformers. If you increase the voltage from one side of a transformer to the other, you decrease the available current. This is the reason that step-up transformers have limited use; the more you increase the voltage the less current is available to operate a load.

Power transformer windings may be wound and tapped to provide various levels of voltage on the secondary side, or selective connections based on available voltages on the primary side. Varying the point at which connections are made on transformer primary or secondary windings varies the voltage available by changing the turns ratio between the windings.

Control and metering circuits in distribution substations require small transformers called control transformers. These transformers can be used to regulate the voltage supplies to control and metering circuits, or they may be used to reduce monitored high current levels to user-safe metering levels. The *NEC* regulates overcurrent protection, installations, and grounding of all types of distribution transformers.

## Objectives

When you have completed this module, you will be able to do the following:

1. Describe transformer operation.
2. Explain the principle of mutual induction.
3. Describe the operating characteristics of various types of transformers.
4. Connect a multi-tap transformer for the required secondary voltage.
5. Explain *National Electrical Code® (NEC®)* requirements governing the installation of transformers.
6. Compute transformer sizes for various applications.
7. Explain types and purposes of grounding transformers.
8. Connect a control transformer for a given application.
9. Size the maximum load allowed on open delta systems.
10. Describe how current transformers are used in conjunction with watt-hour meters.
11. Apply capacitors and rectifiers to practical applications.
12. Calculate the power factor of any given electrical circuit.

## Trade Terms

Ampere turn
Autotransformer
Capacitance
Current transformer
Flux
Induction
Kilovolt-amperes (kVA)
Loss
Magnetic field

Magnetic induction
Mutual induction
Potential transformer
Power transformer
Reactance
Rectifiers
Transformer
Turn
Turns ratio

## Required Trainee Materials

1. Pencil and paper
2. Appropriate personal protective equipment
3. Copy of the latest edition of the *National Electrical Code®*

## Prerequisites

Before you begin this module, it is recommended that you successfully complete *Core Curriculum; Electrical Level One; Electrical Level Two; Electrical Level Three*, Modules 26301-05 through 26306-05.

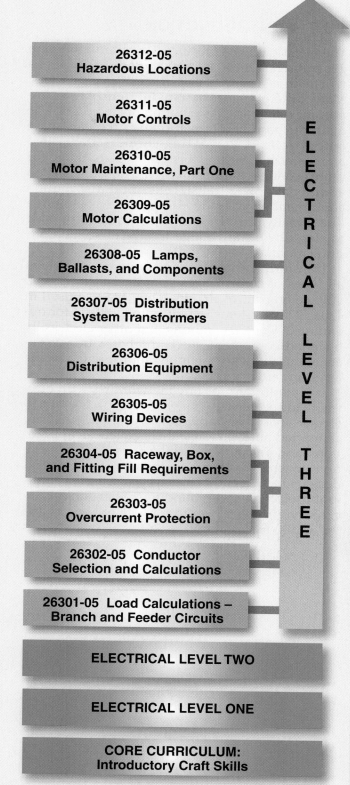

307CMAP.EPS

This course map shows all of the modules in *Electrical Level Three*. The suggested training order begins at the bottom and proceeds up. Skill levels increase as you advance on the course map. The local Training Program Sponsor may adjust the training order.

# 1.0.0 ◆ INTRODUCTION

The electric power produced by alternators in a generating station is transmitted to locations where it is utilized and distributed to users. Many different types of transformers play an important role in the distribution of electricity. The main purpose of a transformer is to change the output voltage. Power transformers are located at generating stations to step up the voltage for more economical transmission. Substations with additional power transformers and distribution equipment are installed along the transmission line. Finally, distribution transformers are used to step down the voltage to a level suitable for utilization.

Transformers are also used quite extensively in all types of control work to raise and lower AC voltage on control circuits. They are also used in 480Y/277V systems to reduce the voltage for operating 208Y/120V lighting and other electrically operated equipment. Buck-and-boost transformers are used for maintaining appropriate voltage levels in certain electrical systems.

It is important for anyone working with electricity to become familiar with all aspects of transformer operation—how they work, how they are connected into circuits, their practical applications, and precautions to take during the installation or while working on them. This module is designed to cover these items, as well as overcurrent protection and grounding. Other subjects include correcting power factor with capacitors and the application of rectifiers.

# 2.0.0 ◆ TRANSFORMER BASICS

A very basic transformer consists of two coils, windings, formed on a single magnetic core, shown in *Figure 1*. Such an arrangement will allow transforming a large alternating current at a low voltage into a small alternating current at a high voltage, or vice versa.

## 2.1.0 Mutual Induction

The term mutual induction refers to the condition in which two circuits are sharing the energy of one of the circuits. It means that energy is being transferred from one circuit to the other.

Consider the diagram in *Figure 2*. Coil A is the primary circuit that obtains energy from the battery. When the switch is closed, the current starts to flow and a magnetic field expands out of coil A. Coil A then changes the electrical energy of the battery into the magnetic energy (induction) of magnetic field. When the field of coil A is expanding, it cuts across coil B, the secondary circuit, inducing a voltage in coil B. The indicator (a galvanometer) in the secondary circuit is deflected and shows that a current, developed by the induced voltage, is flowing in the circuit.

The induced voltage may be generated by moving coil B through the flux of coil A. However, the voltage is induced without moving coil B. When the switch in the primary circuit is open, coil A has no current and no field. As soon as the switch is closed, current passes through the coil, and the magnetic field is generated. This expanding field

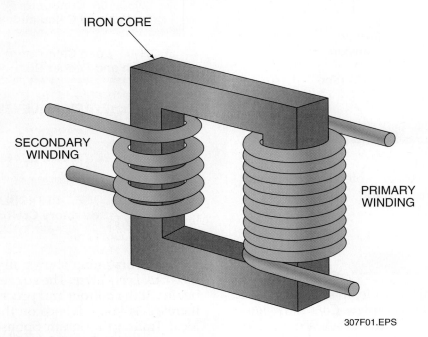

IRON CORE

SECONDARY
WINDING

PRIMARY
WINDING

307F01.EPS

*Figure 1* ◆ Basic components of a transformer.

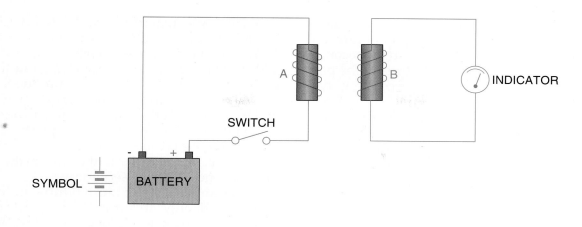

307F02.EPS

*Figure 2* ◆ Mutual induction circuits.

oves or cuts across the wires of coil B, thus in-
icing a voltage without the movement of coil B.
The magnetic field expands to its maximum
rength and remains constant as long as full cur-
nt flows. Flux lines stop their cutting action
ross the **turns** of coil B because the expansion of
e field has ceased. At this point, the indicator
edle on the meter reads zero because the in-
iced voltage no longer exists. If the switch is
ened, the field collapses back to the wires of coil
As it does so, the changing flux cuts across the
ires of coil B, but in the opposite direction. The
rrent present in the coil causes the indicator
edle to deflect, showing this new direction.
erefore, the indicator shows current flow only
en the field is changing, either building up or
llapsing. In effect, the changing field produces
induced voltage in the same way as a magnetic
ld moving across a conductor. This principle of
ducing voltage by holding the coils steady and
rcing the field to change is used in innumerable
plications. The transformer is particularly suit-
le for operation by mutual induction. Trans-
rmers are the ideal components for transferring
d changing AC voltages as needed.
Transformers are generally composed of two
ils placed close to each other but not connected.
fer once more to *Figure 1*. The coil that receives
ergy from the line voltage source is called the
imary, and the coil that delivers energy to a load
called the secondary. Even though the coils are
t physically connected, they manage to convert
d transfer energy as required by a process
own as mutual induction.
Transformers, therefore, enable changing or
nverting power from one voltage to another.
r example, generators that produce moderately
ge alternating currents at moderately high volt-
es use transformers to convert the power to a

very high voltage and proportionately small current in transmission lines, permitting the use of
smaller cable and producing less power **loss.**
When alternating current (AC) flows through a
coil, an alternating magnetic field is generated
around the coil. This alternating magnetic field
expands outward from the center of the coil and
collapses into the coil as the AC through the coil
varies from zero to a maximum and back to zero
again, as discussed in an earlier module. Since the
alternating magnetic field must cut through the
turns of the coil, a self-inducing voltage occurs in
the coil, which opposes the change in current
flow.
If the alternating magnetic field generated by
one coil cuts through the turns of a second coil,
voltage will be generated in this second coil just as
voltage is induced in a coil that is cut by its own
magnetic field. The induced voltage in the second
coil is called the voltage of mutual induction, and
the action of generating this voltage is called
transformer action. In transformer action, electrical energy is transferred from one coil (the primary) to another (the secondary) by means of a
varying magnetic field.

## 2.2.0 Induction in Transformers

As stated previously, a simple transformer consists of two coils located very close together and
electrically insulated from each other. The primary coil generates a magnetic field that cuts
through the turns of the secondary coil and generates a voltage in it. The coils are magnetically
coupled to each other, and consequently, a transformer transfers electrical power from one coil to
another by means of an alternating magnetic field.
Assuming that all the magnetic lines of force
from the primary cut through all the turns of the

secondary, the voltage induced in the secondary will depend on the ratio of the number of turns in the primary to the number of turns in the secondary. For example, if there are 100 turns in the primary and only 10 turns in the secondary, the voltage in the primary will be 10 times the voltage in the secondary. Since there are more turns in the primary than there are in the secondary, the transformer is called a step-down transformer. Transformers are rated in **kilovolt-amperes (kVA)** because they are independent of power factor. *Figure 3* shows a diagram of a step-down transformer with a **turns ratio** of 100:10, or 10:1.

$$\frac{10 \text{ turns}}{100 \text{ turns}} = 0.10 = 0.10 \times 120V = 12V$$

Assuming that all the primary magnetic lines of force cut through all the turns of the secondary, the amount of induced voltage in the secondary will vary with the ratio of the number of turns in the secondary to the number of turns in the primary.

If there are more turns in the secondary winding than in the primary winding, the secondary voltage will be higher than that in the primary and by the same proportion as the number of turns in the winding. The secondary current, in turn, will be proportionately smaller than the primary current. With fewer turns in the secondary than in the primary, the secondary voltage will be propor-

tionately lower than that in the primary, and th secondary current will be proportionately large Since alternating current continually increase and decreases in value, every change in the pr mary winding of the transformer produces a sim ilar change of flux in the core. Every change of flu in the core and every corresponding movement the magnetic field around the core produce a sim ilarly changing voltage in the secondary windin causing an alternating current to flow in the circu that is connected to the secondary.

For example, if there are 100 turns in the se ondary and only 10 turns in the primary, th voltage induced in the secondary will be 10 tim the voltage applied to the primary. See *Figure* Since there are more turns in the secondary tha in the primary, the transformer is called a step-u transformer.

$$\frac{100}{10} = 10 \times 12V = 120V$$

**NOTE**

A transformer does not generate electric power. simply transfers electric power from one coil to another by **magnetic induction**. Transformers are rated in either volt-amperes (VA) or kilovolt-amperes (kVA).

$$\frac{10 \text{ TURNS}}{100 \text{ TURNS}} = 0.10 = 0.10 \times 120V = 12V$$

100 TURNS       10 TURNS

120V       12V

PRIMARY       SECONDARY

$$\text{SECONDARY VOLTAGE} = \frac{10}{100} \times 120V = 12V$$

307F03.EPS

*Figure 3* ◆ Step-down transformer with a 10:1 turns ratio.

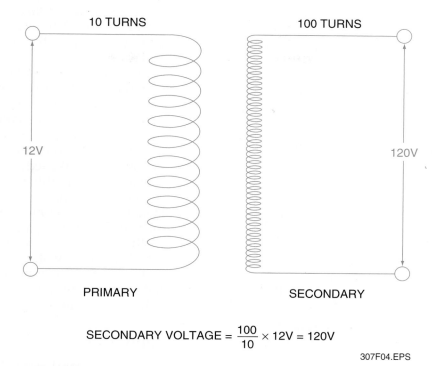

$$\frac{100}{10} = 10 \times 12V = 120V$$

10 TURNS           100 TURNS

12V              120V

PRIMARY           SECONDARY

$$\text{SECONDARY VOLTAGE} = \frac{100}{10} \times 12V = 120V$$

307F04.EPS

*ure 4* ◆ Step-up transformer with a 1:10 turns ratio.

## 3.0 Magnetic Flux in Transformers

*gure 5* shows a cross section of what is known as
nigh-leakage flux transformer. In these trans-
rmers, if no load were connected to the second-
y or output winding, a voltmeter would
dicate a specific voltage reading across the sec-
dary terminals. If a load were applied, the volt-
e would drop, and if the terminals were
orted, the voltage would drop to zero. During
ese circuit changes, the flux in the core of the
nsformer would also change; it is forced out of
e transformer core and is known as leakage flux.
aking flux can actually be demonstrated with
n filings placed close to the transformer core.
the changes take place, the filings will shift
eir position, clearly showing the change in the
x pattern.

What actually happens is that as the current
ws in the secondary, it tries to create its own
gnetic field, which is in opposition to the orig-
l flux field. This action, like a valve in a water
tem, restricts the flux flow, which forces the ex-
s flux to find another path, either through the
or in adjacent structural steel, such as trans-
mer housings or supporting clamps.

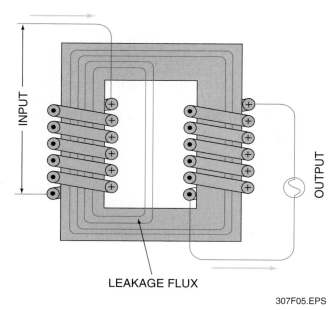

LEAKAGE FLUX

307F05.EPS

*Figure 5* ◆ Transformer with high-leakage flux.

Note that the coils in *Figure 5* are wrapped on
the same iron core but are separated from each
other, while the transformer in *Figure 6* has its
coils wrapped around each other, which results in
a low-leakage transformer design.

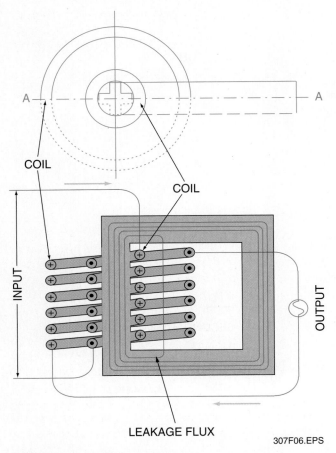

COIL

COIL

INPUT

OUTPUT

LEAKAGE FLUX

307F06.EPS

*Figure 6* ◆ Low-leakage transformer.

## 3.0.0 ◆ TRANSFORMER CONSTRUCTION

Transformers that are designed to operate on low frequencies have their coils, called windings, wound on iron cores. Since iron offers little resist-ance to magnetic lines, nearly all the magnet field of the primary flows through the iron co and cuts the secondary.

Iron cores of transformers are constructed three basic types: the open core, the closed co and the shell type. See *Figure 7*. The open core is t least expensive to manufacture because the p mary and secondary are wound on one cylindri core. The magnetic path, as shown in *Figure 7*, partially through the core and partially throu; the surrounding air. The air path opposes t magnetic field so that the magnetic interaction linkage is weakened. Therefore, the open cc transformer is highly inefficient.

The closed core improves the transformer ef ciency by offering more iron paths and a reduc air path for the magnetic field. The shell-type cc further increases the magnetic coupling, a therefore, the transformer efficiency is greater d to two parallel magnetic paths for the magne field, providing maximum coupling between t primary and the secondary.

## 3.1.0 Cores

Special core steel is used to provide a controll path for the flow of magnetic flux generated i transformer. In most practical applications, t transformer core is not a solid bar of steel but constructed of many layers of thin sheet st called laminations. Although the specifications the core steel are primarily of interest to the tra former design engineer, the electrical worl should at least have a conversational knowled of the materials used.

The steel used for transformer core laminatic will vary with the manufacturer, but a popu

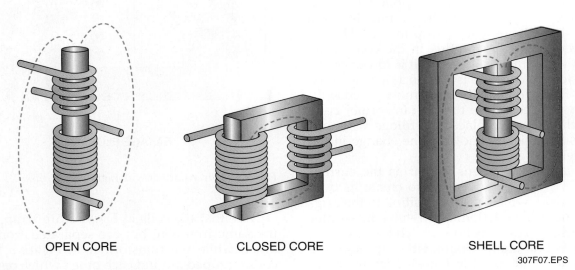

OPEN CORE

CLOSED CORE

SHELL CORE

307F07.EPS

*Figure 7* ◆ Three types of iron core transformers.

ze is 0.014" thick and is called 29-gauge steel. It
processed from silicon iron alloys containing
pproximately 3¼% silicon. The addition of silicon
the iron increases its ability to be magnetized
nd also renders it essentially non-aging.

The most important characteristic of electrical
eel is core loss. It is measured in watts per pound
a specified frequency and flux density. The core
ss is responsible for the heating in the trans-
rmer and also contributes to the heating of the
indings. Much of the core loss is a result of eddy
rrents that are induced in the laminations when
e core is energized. To hold this loss to a mini-
um, adjacent laminations are coated with an in-
ganic varnish.

Cores may either be of the core type, as shown
Figure 8, or the shell type, as shown in Figure 9.
f the two, the core type is favored for dry-type
ansformers for the following reasons:

- Only three core legs require stacking, which reduces cost.
- Steel does not encircle the two outer coils; this
  provides better cooling.
- The required floor space is reduced.

## 3.2.0 Types of Cores

Transformer cores are normally available in three
types:

- Butt
- Wound
- Mitered cores

The butt-and-lap core is shown in *Figure 10*. Only
two sizes of core steel are needed in this type of core
due to the lap construction shown at the top and
right side. For ease of understanding, the core
strips are shown much thicker than the 0.014"
thickness mentioned earlier. Each strip is carefully
cut so that the air gap indicated in the lower left
corner is as small as possible. The permeability of
steel to the passage of flux is about 10,000 times as
effective as air, hence, the air gap must be held to
the barest minimum to reduce the **ampere turns**
necessary to achieve adequate flux density. Also,
the amount of sound produced by a transformer is
a function of the flux density, which produces a difference between this construction and other types.

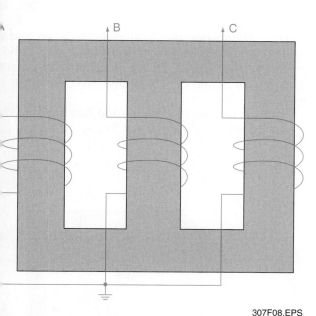

307F08.EPS

*ure 8* ◆ Core-type transformer construction.

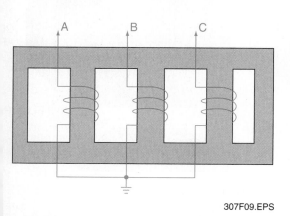

307F09.EPS

*ure 9* ◆ Shell-type transformer core.

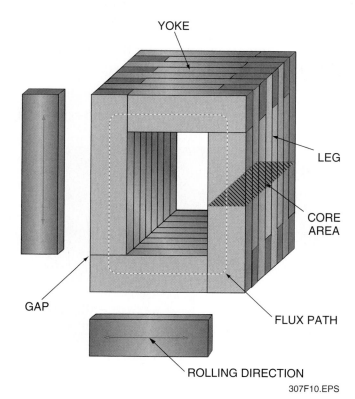

307F10.EPS

*Figure 10* ◆ Butt-and-lap transformer core.

Another phenomenon in core steel is that the flux flows more easily in the direction in which the steel was rolled. This also varies between hot-rolled steel and cold-rolled steel. For example, the core loss due to flux passing at right angles to the rolling direction is almost 1½ times as great in hot-rolled steel and 2½ times as great in cold-rolled steel when compared with the core loss in the direction of rolling. The difference in exciting current is more dramatic, with ratios of two to one in hot-rolled steel and almost 40 to 1 in cold-rolled steel. These are primarily the designer's concern, but you should know that there is a difference.

Eddy currents are restricted from passage from one lamination to another due to the inorganic insulating coating. However, the magnetic lines of flux easily transfer at adjacent laminations in the lap area, but in so doing, they are forced to cross at an angle to the preferred direction.

### 3.3.0 Wound Cores

Because of the unique characteristics of core steel, some core designs are made to take advantage of these differences. One such type is shown in *Figure 11.* The core loops are cut to predetermined lengths so that the gap locations do not coincide. These cuts permit assembling the core around a prewound coil that passes through both openings. Another design, now discontinued because of unfavorable cost, used a continuous core with no cuts. Separate coils had to be wound on each of the vertical legs of the completed core. You may encounter transformers of this type in existing installations.

### 3.4.0 Mitered Cores

*Figure 12* shows a mitered core design. It is bas[i]cally a butt-lap core with the joints made at 4[5] degree angles.

There are two benefits derived from this type [of] joint:

- It eliminates all cross grain flux, thereby impro[v]ing the core loss and exciting current values.
- It reduces the flux density in the air gap, resu[lt]ing in lower sound levels.

This type of core is normally used only wi[th] cold-rolled, grain-oriented steel and permits th[e] steel to be used to its fullest capability.

### 3.5.0 Transformer Characteristics

In a well-designed transformer, there is very lit[tle] magnetic leakage. The effect of the leakage is [to] cause a decrease of secondary voltage when t[he] transformer is loaded. When a current flo[ws] through the secondary in phase with the seconda[ry] voltage, a corresponding current flows through t[he] primary in addition to the magnetizing curre[nt]. The magnetizing effects of the two currents a[re] equal and opposite.

In a perfect transformer (one having no ed[dy] current losses, no resistance in its windings, a[nd]

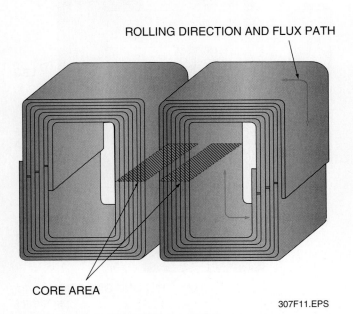

ROLLING DIRECTION AND FLUX PATH

CORE AREA

307F11.EPS

*Figure 11* ◆ Wound transformer coil.

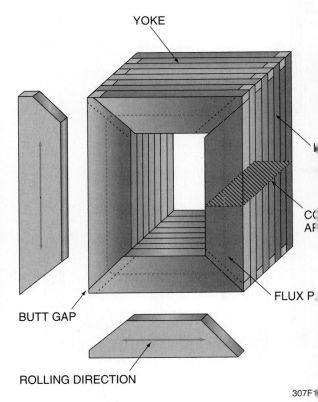

YOKE

C[O]
A[R]

FLUX P[...]

BUTT GAP

ROLLING DIRECTION

307F1[...]

*Figure 12* ◆ Mitered transformer core.

magnetic leakage), the magnetizing effects of the primary load current and the secondary current neutralize each other, leaving only the constant primary magnetizing current effective in setting up the constant flux. If supplied with a constant primary pressure, such a transformer would maintain constant secondary pressure at all loads. Obviously, the perfect transformer has yet to be built; the best transformers available today have a very small eddy current loss where the drop in pressure in the secondary windings is not more than 1% to 3%, depending on the size of the transformer.

## 10.0 ◆ TRANSFORMER TAPS

If the exact rated voltage could be delivered at every transformer location, transformer taps would be unnecessary. However, this is not possible, so taps are provided to either increase or decrease the secondary voltage.

Generally, if a load is very close to a substation or power plant, the voltage will consistently be above normal. Near the end of the line, the voltage may be below normal.

In large transformers, it would naturally be very inconvenient to move the thick, well-insulated primary leads to different tap positions when changes in source voltage levels make this

necessary. Therefore, taps are used, such as those shown in the wiring diagram in *Figure 13*. In this transformer, the permanent high-voltage leads would be connected to $H_1$ and $H_2$, and the secondary leads, in their normal fashion, to $X_1$ and $X_2$, and $X_3$ and $X_4$. Note, however, the tap arrangements available at taps 2 through 7. Until a pair of these taps is interconnected with a jumper wire, the primary circuit is not completed. If this were a typical 7,200V primary, the transformer would normally have 1,620 turns. Assume 810 of these turns are between $H_1$ and $H_6$ and another 810 between $H_3$ and $H_2$. Then, if taps 6 and 3 are connected with a flexible jumper on which lugs have already been installed, the primary circuit is completed, and we have a normal ratio transformer that could deliver 120/240V from the secondary.

Between taps 6 and either 5 or 7, 40 turns of wire exist. Similarly, between taps 3 and either 2 or 4, 40 turns are present. Changing the jumper from 3 to 6 to 3 to 7 removes 40 turns from the left half of the primary. The same condition would apply on the right half of the winding if the jumper were between taps 6 and 2. Either connection would boost secondary voltage by 2½%. Had taps 2 and 7 been connected, 80 turns would have been omitted, and a 5% boost would result. Placing the jumper between taps 6 and 4 or 3 and 5 would reduce the output voltage by 5%.

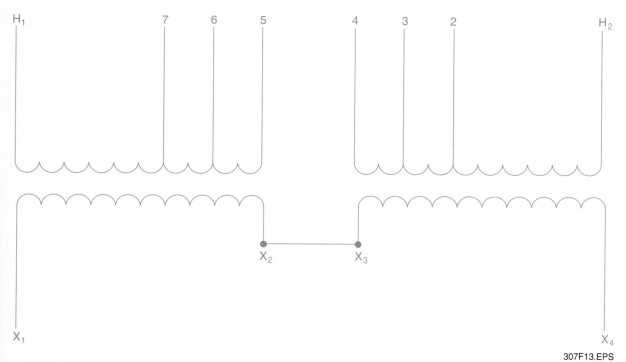

307F13.EPS

*Figure 13* ◆ Transformer taps to adjust secondary voltage.

# 5.0.0 ◆ BASIC TRANSFORMER CONNECTIONS

Transformer connections are many, and space does not permit the description of all of them here. However, an understanding of a few connection types will give the basic requirements and make it possible to use manufacturer's data for others should the need arise.

## 5.1.0 Single-Phase Light and Power Systems

*Figure 14* is a single-phase transformer line diagram showing a connection used primarily for residential and small commercial applications. It is the most common single-phase distribution transformer in use today. It is known as a three-

wire, 120/240V, single-phase system. Because its configuration, it is easy to balance the load between the two coils. The kVA of a single-phase transformer is calculated by dividing the total V by 1,000.

## 5.2.0 Three-Phase Power Systems

The following factors need to be considered when choosing a three-phase power system:

- The load(s) to be supplied
- The voltages needed for the application
- Future expansion

There are advantages and disadvantages associated with the different types of three-phase systems. The wye system can be used for both single-phase and three-phase loads. Because of configuration, it is easy to balance the single-phase loads while still having the ability to use for three-phase loads. Transformers installed this type of system are sized by first dividing total single-phase load in kVA by three, then taking this result and adding it to the total three-phase load in kVA divided by three. The result these two loads added together identifies the required kVA rating of the transformer. The nominal voltage levels provided by this type of system 120/208V or 277/480V. Note that 240V is not option, and this may prove to be a disadvantage in many applications since 240V is a common operating voltage.

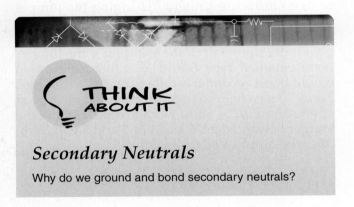

**THINK ABOUT IT**

*Secondary Neutrals*

Why do we ground and bond secondary neutrals?

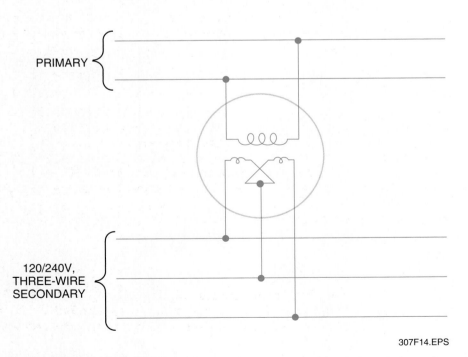

PRIMARY

120/240V, THREE-WIRE SECONDARY

307F14.EPS

*Figure 14* ◆ Single-phase transformer connection.

## 5.2.1 Delta-Wye Transformers

One of the most common transformer systems found in today's commercial and industrial settings is the delta primary, wye secondary transformer system (*Figure 15*). This is a three-phase, four-wire system that has the advantage of both providing three-phase power and also allowing lighting to be connected between any of the secondary phases and the neutral.

In *Figure 15*, the system is basically made up of three typical single-phase, step-down transformers with the interconnections between each individual transformer's primary and secondary coils determining the output voltage on the secondary side. However, this does not mean that any three single-phase transformers can be developed into a functional three-phase, delta-wye system for power and lighting. The coils must be rated for the loads to be served, as well as the primary voltage level to be connected. Power and light delta-wye transformers are universally found in both commercial and industrial installations as floor-mounted, dry-type transformers.

Although this transformer provides the convenience of three-phase and single-phase power, as well as each phase of the 208V system sharing the neutral to supply three legs of 120V lighting circuits, remember that the three-phase and single-phase power availability is at the 208V level and not 240V. Should a power requirement specifically call for 240V and not permit a 208V supply, this type of transformer is not the best selection.

## 5.2.2 Delta-Delta Transformers

The delta-delta system in *Figure 16* operates a little differently from the delta-wye system. Whereas the wye-connected system is formed by connecting one terminal from each of three equal voltage transformer windings together to make a common terminal, the delta-connected system has its windings connected in series, forming a triangle, or the Greek symbol delta (Δ). In *Figure 17*, a center-tapped terminal is used on one winding to ground the system. A 120/240V system has 120V between the center-tapped terminal and each ungrounded terminal on either side such as phases A and C, and 240V across the full winding of each phase.

Refer to *Figure 17* and note the high leg. This is also known as the wild leg. This high leg has a higher voltage to ground than the other two phases. The voltage of the high leg can be determined by multiplying the voltage to ground of either of the other two legs by the square root of 3, which we round to a value of 1.732. Therefore, if the voltage between phase A to ground is 120V, the voltage between phase B to ground may be determined as follows:

$$120V \times 1.732 = 207.84V = 208V$$

From this, it should be obvious that no single-pole breakers should be connected to the high leg of a center-tapped, four-wire, delta-connected system. In fact, *NEC Section 110.15* requires that the phase busbar or conductor having the higher

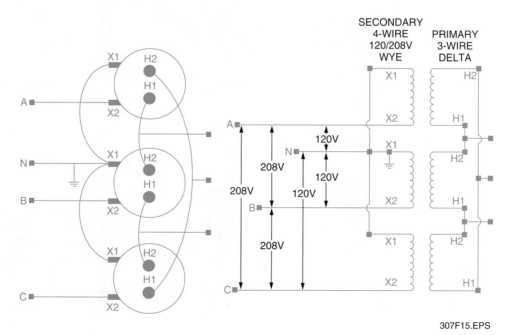

307F15.EPS

*Figure 15* ◆ Delta-wye transformer system.

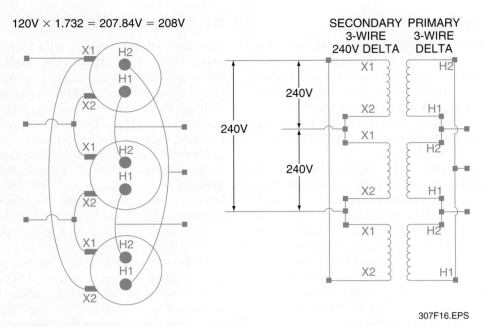

$120V \times 1.732 = 207.84V = 208V$

*Figure 16* ◆ Delta-connected secondary.

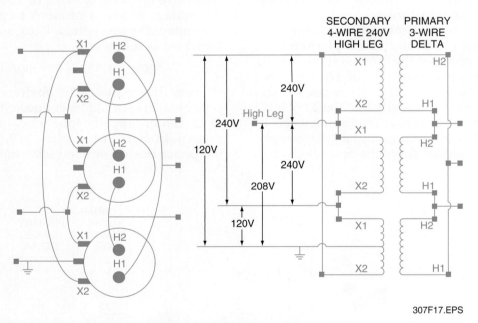

*Figure 17* ◆ Characteristics of a center-tapped, delta-connected system.

voltage to ground be durably and permanently marked by an outer finish that is orange in color, or by other effective means. This prevents future workers from connecting 120V single-phase loads to this high leg, which would probably damage any equipment connected to the circuit. Remember the color orange; no line-to-neutral loads are to be connected to this phase.

 **WARNING!**
Always use caution when working on a center-tapped, four-wire, delta-connected system. Phase B has a higher voltage to ground than phases A and C. Never connect 120V circuits to the high leg. Doing so will result in damage to the circuits and equipment.

### 5.2.3 Open Delta Transformers

Three-phase, delta-connected systems may be connected so that only two transformers are used; this arrangement is known as an open delta system, as shown in *Figure 18*. It is frequently used on a delta system when one of the three transformers becomes damaged. The damaged transformer is disconnected from the circuit, and the remaining two transformers carry the load. In doing so, the three-phase load carried by the open delta bank is only 86.6% of the combined rating of the remaining two equally sized units. It is only 57.7% of the normal full-load capability of a full bank of transformers. In an emergency, however, this capability permits single-phase and three-phase power at a location where one unit burned out and a replacement was not readily available. The total load must be curtailed to avoid another burnout.

### 5.3.0 Parallel Operation of Transformers

Transformers will operate satisfactorily in parallel on a single-phase, three-wire system if the terminals with the same relative polarity are connected together. However, the practice is not very economical because the individual cost and losses of the smaller transformers are greater than one larger unit giving the same output. Therefore, paralleling of smaller transformers is usually done only in an emergency. In large transformers, however, it is often practical to operate units in parallel as a regular practice. See *Figure 19*.

When connecting large transformers in parallel, especially when one of the windings is for a comparatively low voltage, the resistance of the joints and interconnecting leads must not vary

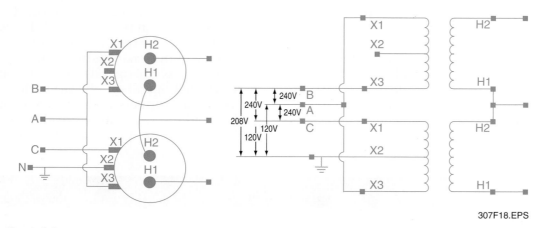

307F18.EPS

*Figure 18* ◆ Open delta system.

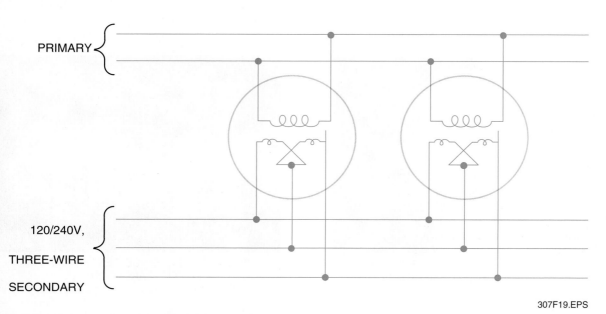

307F19.EPS

*Figure 19* ◆ Parallel operation of single-phase transformers.

significantly between the different transformers, or it will cause an unequal division of load.

Two three-phase transformers may also be connected in parallel, provided they have the same winding arrangement, are connected with the same polarity, and have the same phase rotation. If two transformers, or two banks of transformers, have the same voltage ratings, the same turns ratios, the same impedances, and the same ratios of reactance to resistance, they will divide the load current in proportion to their kVA ratings with no phase difference between the currents in the two transformers. However, if any of the preceding conditions are not met, then it is possible for the load current to divide between the two transformers in proportion to their kVA ratings. There may also be a phase difference between currents in the two transformers or banks of transformers.

Some three-phase transformers cannot be operated properly in parallel. For example, a transformer having both its primary and secondary windings connected in delta cannot be connected in parallel with another transformer that is connected either with a primary delta or a secondary wye. However, a transformer with a delta primary and a wye secondary can be made to parallel with transformers having their windings joined in certain ways; that is, a wye primary connection and a delta secondary connection.

To determine whether or not three-phase transformers will operate in parallel, connect them as shown in *Figure 20*, leaving two leads on one of the transformers unjoined. Test with a voltmeter across the unjoined leads. If there is no voltage between the points shown in the drawing, the polarities of the two transformers are the same, and the connections may then be made and the transformer put into service.

If a reading indicates a voltage between the points indicated in the drawing (either one of the two or both), the polarities of the two transformers are different. Should this occur, disconnect transformer lead A successively to mains 1, 2, and 3, as shown in *Figure 20*, and at each connection test with a voltmeter between b and B and the leg of the main to which lead A is connected. If with any trial connection the voltmeter readings between b and B and either of the two legs is found to be zero, the transformer will operate with leads b and B connected to those two legs. If no system of connections can be discovered that will satisfy this condition, the transformer will not operate in parallel without changes to its internal connections, or it may not operate in parallel at all.

In parallel operation, the primaries of the two or more transformers involved are connected together, and the secondaries are also connected together. With the primaries so connected, the

### Transformers

These photos show single-phase and three-phase transformers. Note the orange marking on the high leg of the three-phase transformer in accordance with *NEC Sections 110.15 and 215.8.*

100kVA SINGLE-PHASE TRANSFORMER
480V PRIMARY, 120V/240V SECONDARY

300kVA THREE-PHASE CENTER-TAPPED
DELTA TRANSFORMER
480V PRIMARY, 120V/240V SECONDARY

307P0701.EPS

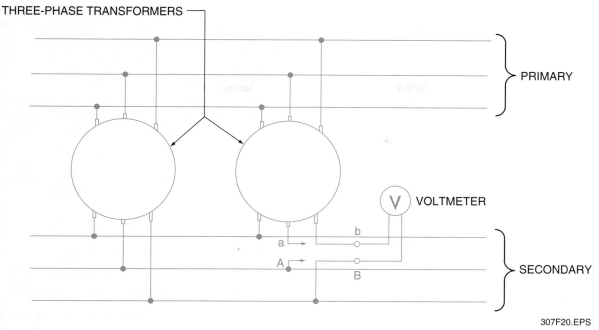

THREE-PHASE TRANSFORMERS

PRIMARY

VOLTMETER

SECONDARY

307F20.EPS

*Figure 20* ◆ Testing three-phase transformers for parallel operation.

voltages in both primaries and secondaries will be in certain directions. It is necessary that the secondaries be so connected that the voltage from one secondary line to the other will be in the same direction through both transformers. Proper connections to obtain this condition for single-phase transformers of various polarities are shown in *Figure 21*. In *Figure 21(A)*, both transformers A and B have additive polarity; in *Figure 21(B)*, both transformers have subtractive polarity; and in *Figure 21(C)*, transformer A has additive polarity and B has subtractive polarity.

Transformers, even when properly connected, will not operate satisfactorily in parallel unless their transformation ratios are very close to being equal and their impedance voltage drops are also approximately equal. A difference in transformation ratios will cause a circulating current to flow, even at no load, in each winding of both transformers. For example, in a loaded parallel bank of two transformers of equal capacities, if there is a difference in the transformation ratios, the load circuit will be superimposed on the circulating current. The result in such a case is that in one transformer, the total circulating current will be added to the load current; whereas in the other transformer, the actual current will be the difference between the load current and the circulating current. This may lead to unsatisfactory operation. Therefore, the transformation ratios of transformers for parallel operation must be definitely known.

When two transformers are connected in parallel, the circulating current caused by the difference in the ratios of the two is equal to the difference in the open circuit voltage divided by the sum of the transformer impedances. This is because the current is circulated through the windings of both transformers due to this voltage difference. To illustrate, let I represent the amount of circulating current, in percent of full-load current, and the equation will be:

$$I = \frac{\text{percent voltage difference} \times 100}{\text{sum of percent impedances}}$$

Assume an open circuit voltage difference of 3% between two transformers connected in parallel. If each transformer has an impedance of 5%, the circulating current, in percent of full-load current, is:

$$I = \frac{3 \times 100}{5 + 5} = 30\%$$

A current equal to 30% of the full-load current therefore circulates in both the high-voltage and low-voltage windings. This current adds to the load current in the transformer having the higher induced voltage and subtracts from the load current of the other transformer. Therefore, one transformer will be overloaded, while the other may or may not be, depending on the phase angle difference between the circulating current and the load current.

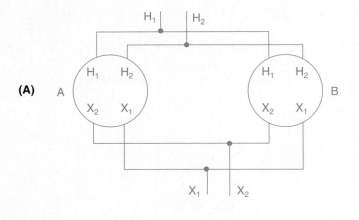

**(A)**

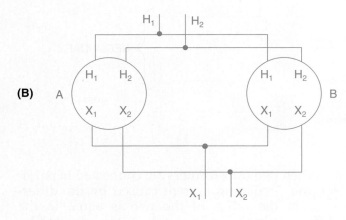

**(B)**

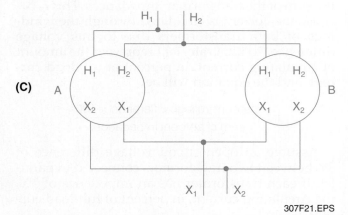

**(C)**

307F21.EPS

*Figure 21* ◆ Transformers connected in parallel.

## 5.3.1 Impedance in Parallel-Operated Transformers

Impedance plays an important role in the successful operation of transformers connected in parallel. The impedance of the transformers must be such that the voltage drop from no load to full load is the same in all transformer units in both magnitude and phase. In most applications, you will find that the total resistance drop is relatively small when compared with the reactance drop and the total percent impedance drop can be taken as approximately equal to the percent reactance drop. If the percent impedances of the given transformers at full load are the same, they will, of course, divide the load equally.

The following equation may be used to obtain the division of loads between two transformer banks operating in parallel on single-phase systems:

$$Power = \frac{kVA_1 \div Z_1}{(kVA_1 \div Z_1) + (kVA_2 \div Z_2)} \times total\ kVA\ load$$

*Where:*

$kVA_1$ = kVA rating of transformer 1
$kVA_2$ = kVA rating of transformer 2
$Z_1$ = percent impedance of transformer 1
$Z_2$ = percent impedance of transformer 2

In this equation, it can be assumed that the ratio of resistance to reactance is the same in all units since the error introduced by differences in this ratio is usually so small as to be negligible.

The preceding equation may also be applied to more than two transformers operated in parallel by adding to the denominator of the fraction the kVA of each additional transformer divided by its percent impedance.

## 5.3.2 Parallel Operation of Three-Phase Transformers

Three-phase transformers, or banks of single-phase transformers, may be connected in parallel provided each of the three primary leads in one three-phase transformer is connected in parallel with a corresponding primary lead of the other transformer. The secondaries are then connected in the same way. The corresponding leads are the leads that have the same potential at all times and the same polarity. Furthermore, the transformers must have the same voltage ratio and the same impedance voltage drop.

When three-phase transformer banks operate in parallel and the three units in each bank are similar, the division of the load can be determined by the same method previously described for single-phase transformers connected in parallel on a single-phase system.

In addition to the requirements of polarity, ratio, and impedance, paralleling of three-phase transformers also requires that the angular displacement between the voltages in the windings be taken into consideration when they are connected together.

Phasor diagrams of three-phase transformers that are to be paralleled greatly simplify matters. With these, all that is required is to compare the two diagrams to make sure they consist of phasors that can be made to coincide and then to connect the terminals corresponding to coinciding voltage phasors. If the phasor diagrams can be made to coincide, leads that are connected together will have the same potential at all times. This is one of the fundamental requirements for paralleling. Phasor diagrams are covered in more detail later in this module.

## 6.0.0 ◆ AUTOTRANSFORMERS

An autotransformer is a transformer whose primary and secondary circuits have part of a winding in common; therefore, the two circuits are not isolated from each other. See *Figure 22.* The application of an autotransformer is a good choice where a 480Y/277V or 208Y/120V, three-phase, four-wire distribution system is used. Some of the advantages are:

Lower purchase price
Lower operating cost due to lower losses
Smaller size, easier to install
Better voltage regulation
Lower sound levels

For example, when the ratio of transformation from the primary to the secondary voltage is small, the most economical way of stepping down the voltage is by using autotransformers, as

shown in *Figure 23.* For this application, it is necessary that the neutral of the autotransformer bank be connected to the system neutral, similar to a wye connection.

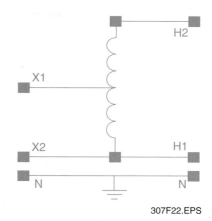

307F22.EPS

*Figure 22* ◆ Step-down autotransformer.

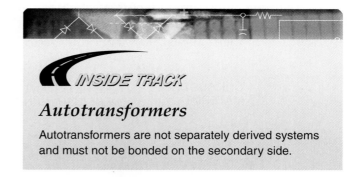

### Autotransformers

Autotransformers are not separately derived systems and must not be bonded on the secondary side.

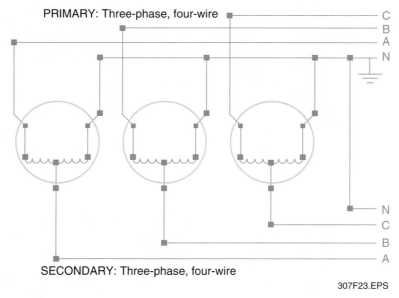

307F23.EPS

*Figure 23* ◆ Autotransformers supplying power from a three-phase, four-wire system.

## 7.0.0 ◆ DRY-TYPE TRANSFORMER CONNECTIONS

Electricians performing work on commercial and industrial installations will be concerned with the installation and connections of dry-type transformers. Dry-type transformers are available in both single-phase and three-phase types with a wide range of sizes from small control transformers to those rated at 500kVA or more. Such transformers have wide application in electrical systems of all types.

*NEC Section 450.11* requires that each transformer must be provided with a nameplate giving the manufacturer, rated kVA, frequency, primary and secondary voltage, impedance of transformers 25kVA and larger, required clearances for transformers with ventilating openings, and the amount and type of insulating liquid (where used). In addition, the nameplate of each dry-type transformer must include the temperature class for the insulation system. See *Figure 24.*

In addition, most manufacturers include a wiring diagram and a connection chart, as shown in *Figure 25* for a 480V delta primary to 208Y/120V

wye secondary. It is recommended that all transformers be connected as shown on the manufacturer's nameplate.

In general, this wiring diagram and accompanying table indicate that the 480V, three-phase, three-wire primary conductors are connected to terminals $H_1$, $H_2$, and $H_3$, respectively, regardless of the desired voltage on the primary. A neutral conductor, if required, is carried from the primary through the transformer, to the secondary. Two variations are possible on the secondary side of this transformer: 208V, three-phase, three-wire or four-wire or 120V, single-phase, two-wire. To connect the secondary side of the transformer as a 208V, three-phase, three-wire system, the secondary conductors are connected to terminals $X_1$, $X_2$, and $X_3$; the neutral is carried through with conductors usually terminating at a solid neutral bus in the transformer.

Another popular dry-type transformer connection is the 480V primary to 240V delta/120V secondary. This configuration is shown in *Figure 26.* Again, the primary conductors are connected to transformer terminals $H_1$, $H_2$, and $H_3$. The secondary connections for the desired voltages are made as indicated in the table.

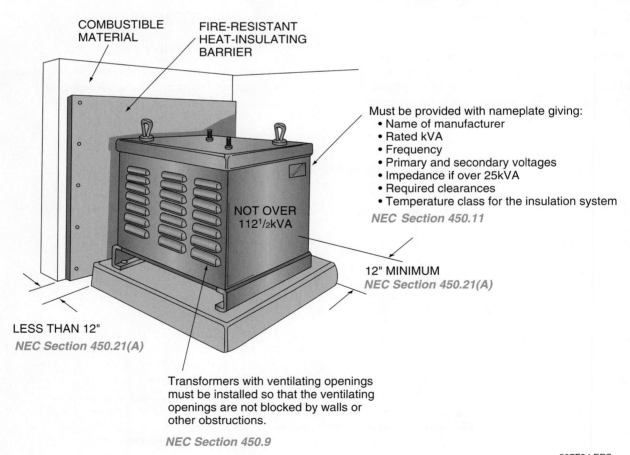

COMBUSTIBLE MATERIAL

FIRE-RESISTANT HEAT-INSULATING BARRIER

Must be provided with nameplate giving:
- Name of manufacturer
- Rated kVA
- Frequency
- Primary and secondary voltages
- Impedance if over 25kVA
- Required clearances
- Temperature class for the insulation system

*NEC Section 450.11*

NOT OVER 112½kVA

12" MINIMUM
*NEC Section 450.21(A)*

LESS THAN 12"
*NEC Section 450.21(A)*

Transformers with ventilating openings must be installed so that the ventilating openings are not blocked by walls or other obstructions.

*NEC Section 450.9*

307F24.EPS

*Figure 24* ◆ Dry-type transformer installed indoors.

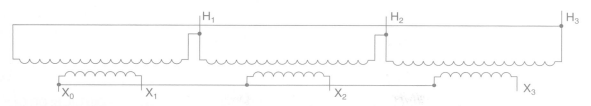

| PRIMARY VOLTS | CONNECT PRIMARY LINES TO | CONNECT SECONDARY LINES TO |
|---|---|---|
| 480V | $H_1$, $H_2$, $H_3$ | ——— |
| SECONDARY VOLTS | | |
| 208V | ——— | $X_1$, $X_2$, $X_3$ |
| 120V SINGLE-PHASE | ——— | $X_1$ to $X_0$ $X_2$ to $X_0$ $X_3$ to $X_0$ |

307F25.EPS

*Figure 25* ◆ Typical manufacturer's wiring diagram for a delta-wye transformer.

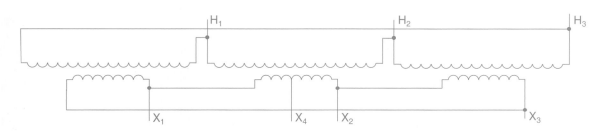

| PRIMARY VOLTS | CONNECT PRIMARY LINES TO | CONNECT SECONDARY LINES TO |
|---|---|---|
| 480V | $H_1$, $H_2$, $H_3$ | ——— |
| SECONDARY VOLTS | | |
| 240V | ——— | $X_1$, $X_2$, $X_3$ |
| 120V | ——— | $X_1$, $X_4$ or $X_2$, $X_4$ |

307F26.EPS

*Figure 26* ◆ 480V delta to 240V delta transformer connections.

## .1.0 Zig-Zag Connections

here are many situations in which it is desirable o upgrade a building's lighting system from 20V fixtures to 277V fluorescent fixtures. Often, ese buildings have a 240/480V, three-phase, ur-wire delta system. One way to obtain 277V om a 240/480V system is to connect 240/480V ansformers in a zig-zag fashion, as shown in *igure 27*. In doing so, the secondary of one phase connected in series with the primary of another hase, thus changing the phase angle.

The zig-zag connection may also be used as a grounding transformer where its function is to obtain a neutral point from an ungrounded system. With a neutral being available, the system may then be grounded. When the system is grounded through the zig-zag transformer, its sole function is to pass ground current. A zig-zag transformer is essentially six impedances connected in a zig-zag configuration.

The operation of a zig-zag transformer is slightly different from that of the conventional

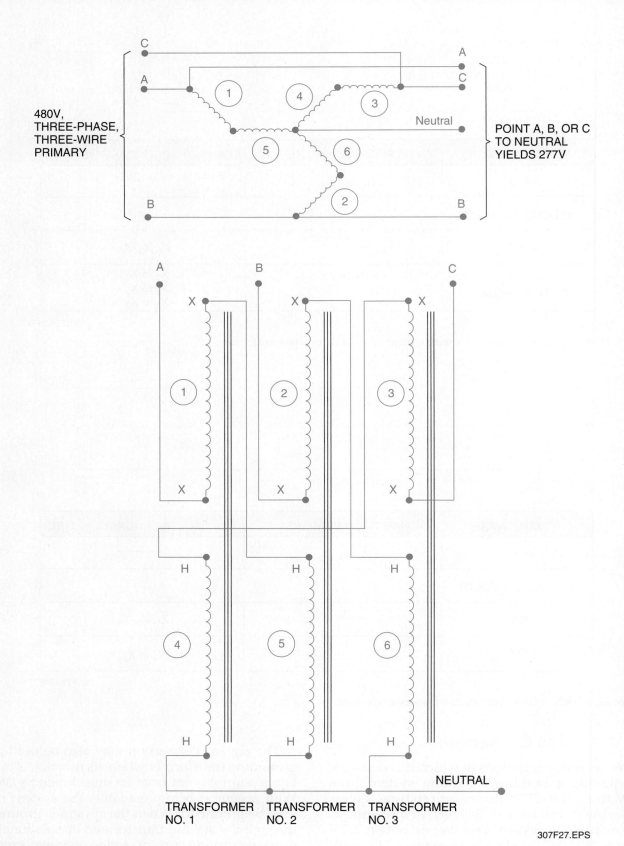

480V,
THREE-PHASE,
THREE-WIRE
PRIMARY

Neutral

POINT A, B, OR C
TO NEUTRAL
YIELDS 277V

TRANSFORMER
NO. 1

TRANSFORMER
NO. 2

TRANSFORMER
NO. 3

NEUTRAL

307F27.EPS

*Figure 27* ◆ Zig-zag connection.

ansformer. We will consider current rather than voltage. While a voltage rating is necessary for the connection to function, this is actually line voltage and is not transformed. It provides only exciting current for the core. The dynamic portion of the zig-zag grounding system is the fault current. To understand its function, the system must also be viewed backward; that is, the fault current will flow into the transformer through the neutral, as shown in *Figure 28*.

The zero sequence currents are all in phase in each line (they all hit the peak at the same time). In reviewing *Figure 28*, we see that the current leaves the motor, goes to ground, flows up the neutral, and splits three ways. It then flows back down the line to the motor through the fuses, which then open, shutting down the motor.

The neutral conductor will carry full fault current and must be sized accordingly. It is also time rated (0–60 seconds) and can therefore be reduced in size. This should be coordinated with the manufacturer's time/current curves for the fuse. See the Level Three module entitled *Overcurrent Protection*.

To determine the size of a zig-zag grounding transformer, proceed as follows:

*Step 1* Calculate the system line-to-ground asymmetrical fault current.

*Step 2* If relaying is present, consider reducing the fault current by installing a resistor in the neutral. If fuses or circuit breakers are the protective device, you may need all the fault current to quickly open the overcurrent protective devices.

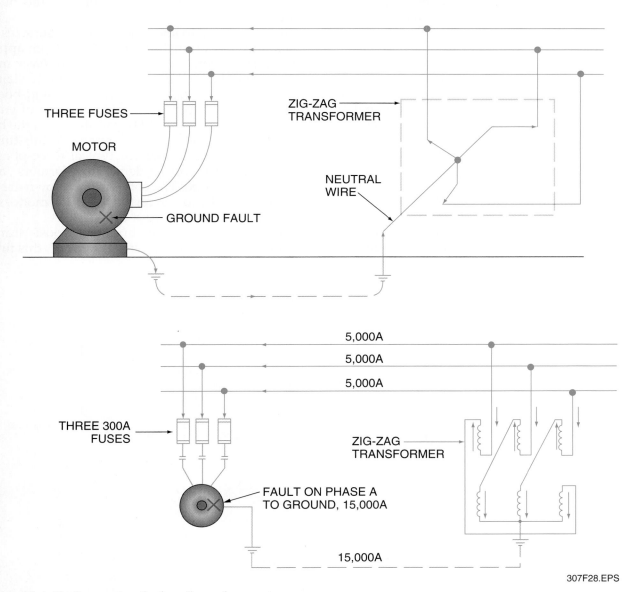

307F28.EPS

*Figure 28* ◆ Fault current paths for a three-phase system.

**Step 3** Obtain the time/current curves of the relay and the fuses or circuit breakers.

**Step 4** Select the zig-zag transformer for:
- Fault current (line-to-ground fault)
- Line-to-line voltage
- Duration of fault (determined from time/current curves)
- Impedance per phase at 100% (for any other, contact the manufacturer)

## 7.2.0 Buck-and-Boost Transformers

The buck-and-boost transformer is a very versatile unit for which a multitude of applications exist. Buck-and-boost transformers, as the name implies, are designed to raise (boost) or lower (buck) the voltage in an electrical system or circuit. In their simplest form, these insulated units will deliver 12V or 24V when the primaries are energized at 120V or 240V, respectively. However, their prime use and value lies in the fact that the primaries and secondaries can be interconnected, permitting their use as an autotransformer.

Assume that an installation is supplied with a 208Y/120V service, but one piece of equipment in the installation is rated for 230V single phase. A buck-and-boost transformer may be used to increase the voltage from 208V to 230V (*Figure 29*). With this connection, the transformer is in the boost mode and delivers 228.8V at the load. This is close enough to 230V that the load equipment will function properly.

If the connections were reversed, this would also reverse the polarity of the secondary with the

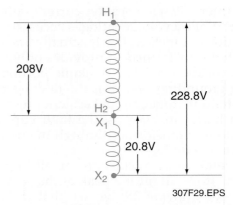

*Figure 29* ◆ Buck-and-boost transformer connected to a 208V system to obtain 230V.

result being a voltage of 208V − 20.8V = 187.2V The transformer is now operating in the buc mode.

It is important to know how to calculate sizes of buck-and-boost transformers for any given appl cation. However, due to the amount of basic m terial covered in this module, advanced sizin and application techniques for buck-and-boos transformers are presented in Level Four of you training. Still, you should be familiar with the ba sic buck-and-boost wiring diagrams at this time Transformer connections for typical three-phase buck-and-boost, open delta transformers ar shown in *Figure 30*. The connections shown are i the boost mode; to convert to the buck mode, re verse the input and output connections.

Another three-phase buck-and-boost trans former connection is shown in *Figure 31*; this tim

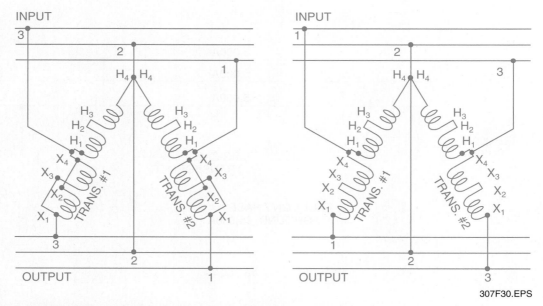

*Figure 30* ◆ Open delta, three-phase, buck-and-boost transformer connections.

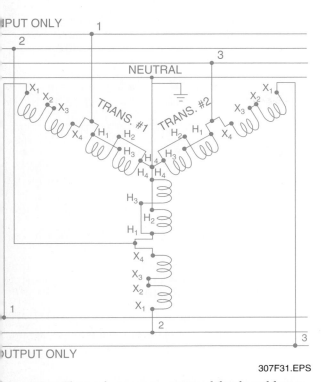

INPUT ONLY

OUTPUT ONLY

307F31.EPS

*Figure 31* ◆ Three-phase, wye-connected, buck-and-boost transformer in the boost mode.

is a wye-connected type. While the open delta transformers (*Figure 30*) can be converted from buck to boost or vice versa by reversing the input/output connections, this is not the case with the three-phase, wye-connected transformer. The connection shown in *Figure 31* is for the boost mode only.

Several typical single-phase, buck-and-boost transformer connections are shown in *Figure 32.* Other diagrams may be found on the transformer's nameplate or in the manufacturer's instructions supplied with each new transformer.

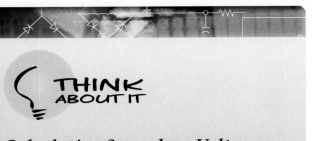

## THINK ABOUT IT

## Calculating Secondary Voltages

Given a turns ratio of 10:1 and an input voltage of 208V, determine what the secondary voltage should be for each of the connections shown in *Figure 32.*

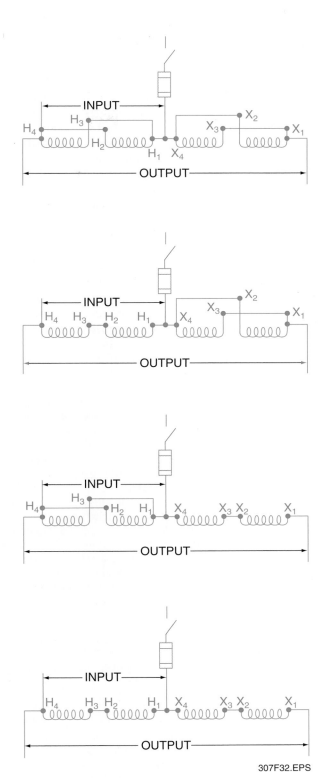

307F32.EPS

*Figure 32* ◆ Typical single-phase, buck-and-boost transformer connections.

## 8.0.0 ◆ CONTROL TRANSFORMERS

Control transformers are available in numerous types, but most are dry-type, step-down units with the secondary control circuit isolated from the primary line circuit to ensure maximum safety. See *Figure 33*. Industrial control transformers are designed to accommodate the momentary current inrush caused when electromagnetic components are energized without sacrificing secondary voltage stability beyond practical limits. Refer to *Table 1* for control circuit transformer requirements.

Other types of control transformers, sometimes referred to as control and signal transformers, are constant-potential, air-cooled transformers. Their purpose is to supply the proper reduced voltage for control circuits of electrically operated switches, signal circuits, or other equipment. These transformers do not normally require the industrial regulation characteristics found in other transformers. Some are of the open type

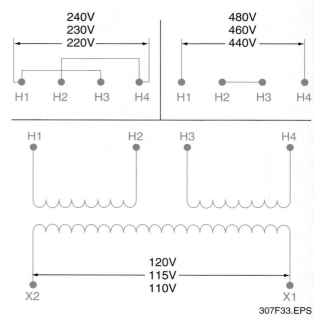

307F33.EPS

*Figure 33* ◆ Typical control transformer wiring diagram.

**Table 1**  Summary of *NEC*® Transformer Installation and Overcurrent Protection Requirements

| Application | NEC® Regulation | NEC® Reference |
|---|---|---|
| Location | Transformers must be readily accessible to qualified personnel for maintenance and inspection. | *NEC Section 450.13* |
| | Dry-type transformers rated at 112½kVA or less may be located out in the open provided they are separated from combustible material by 12" or a suitable fire/heat barrier. | *NEC Section 450.21(A)* |
| | Dry-type transformers rated at more than 112½kVA must be installed in a transformer room of fire-resistant construction. | *NEC Section 450.21(B)* |
| | Dry-type transformers not exceeding 600V and 50kVA are not required to be readily accessible and are permitted in fire-resistant hollow spaces of a building under the conditions specified in the *NEC*®. | *NEC Sections 450.13(A) and (B)* |
| | Dry-type transformers installed outdoors must have a weatherproof enclosure. | *NEC Section 450.22* |
| | Liquid-filled transformers must be installed as specified in the *NEC*® and usually in vaults when installed indoors. | *NEC Section 450.23* |
| Overcurrent protection | The primary protection must be rated or set as follows:<br>• 9A or more—125%<br>• Less than 9A—167%<br>• Less than 2A—300%<br>If the primary current (line side) is 9A or more, the next higher standard size overcurrent protective device greater than 125% of the primary current is used. For example, if the primary current is 15A, 125% of 15A = 18.75A. The next standard size circuit breaker is 20A. Therefore, this size, 20A, may be used.<br>Conductors on the secondary side of a single-phase transformer with a two-wire secondary may be protected by the primary overcurrent device under certain *NEC*® conditions. | *NEC Table 450.3(B)* |
| Transformers used in motor control circuits | Special rules apply to these circuits for the various types of transformers. | *NEC Section 430.72(C)* |
| Over 600V | Special *NEC*® rules apply to transformers operating at over 600V. | *NEC Table 450.3(A)* |

with no protective casing over the windings; others are enclosed within a metal casing.

When choosing control transformers for any application, the loads must be calculated and completely analyzed before the proper transformer selection can be made. This analysis must consider every electrically energized component in the control circuit. To select an appropriate control transformer, first determine the voltage and frequency of the supply circuit. Next, determine the total inrush volt-amperes (watts) of the control circuit. In doing so, do not neglect the current requirements of indicating lights and timing devices that do not have inrush volt-amperes but are energized at the same time as the other components in the circuit. Their total volt-amperes should be added to the total inrush volt-amperes.

Again, control transformers will be covered in more detail in Level Four, as will other types of transformers. The material presented in this module is designed to introduce you to these devices; additional study of practical applications is forthcoming.

## 9.0.0 ◆ POTENTIAL AND CURRENT TRANSFORMERS

In general, a **potential transformer** (*Figure 34*) is used to supply voltage to devices, such as voltmeters, frequency meters, power factor meters, watt-hour meters, and protective relays. The voltage is proportional to the primary voltage, but it is small enough to be safe for the test instrument. The secondary of a potential transformer may be designed for several different voltages, but most are designed for 120V. The potential transformer is primarily a distribution transformer especially designed for voltage regulation so that the secondary voltage (under all conditions) will be as close as possible to a specified percentage of the primary voltage.

A **current transformer** is used to supply current to an instrument connected to its secondary with the current being proportional to the primary current but small enough to be safe for the instrument. The secondary of a current transformer is usually designed for a rated current of 5A.

A current transformer operates in the same way as any other transformer in that the same relationship exists between the primary current and the secondary current. A current transformer uses the circuit conductors as its primary winding. The secondary of the current transformer is connected to current devices, such as ammeters, wattmeters, watt-hour meters, power factor meters, some forms of relays, and the trip coils of some types of circuit breakers.

When no instruments or other devices are connected to the secondary of the current transformer, a short circuit device or shunt is placed across the secondary to prevent the secondary circuit from being opened while the primary winding is carrying current.

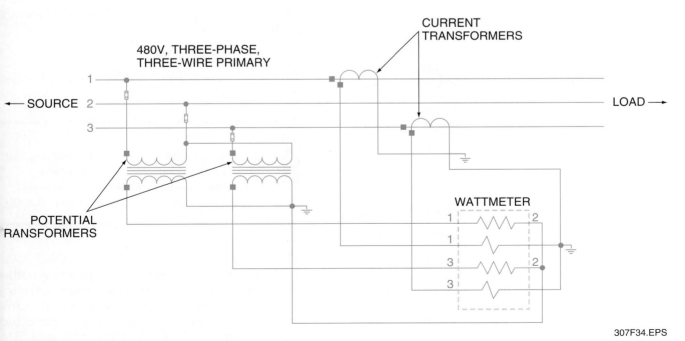

307F34.EPS

*Figure 34* ◆ Current and potential transformers connected for power metering of a three-phase circuit.

## 10.0.0 ◆ *NEC®* REQUIREMENTS

Transformers must normally be accessible for inspection, except for dry-type transformers under certain specified conditions. Certain types of transformers with a high voltage or kVA rating are required to be enclosed in transformer rooms or vaults when installed indoors. The construction of these vaults is covered in *NEC Sections 450.41 through 450.48* and described in *Figure 35* and *Table 1.*

In general, the *NEC®* specifies that the walls and roofs of vaults must be constructed of materials that have adequate structural strength for the conditions with a minimum fire resistance of three hours. However, where transformers are protected with an automatic sprinkler system, water spray, carbon dioxide, or halon, the fire resistance construction may be lowered to only one hour. The floors of vaults in contact with the earth must be of concrete and not less than 4" thick. If the vault is built with a vacant space or other floors (stories) below it, the floor must have adequate structural strength for the load imposed thereon and a minimum fire resistance of three hours. Again, if the fire extinguishing facilities are provided, as outlined above, the fire resistance construction need only be one hour. The *NEC®* does not permit the use of studs and wallboard construction for transformer vaults.

## 10.1.0 Overcurrent Protection for Transformers (600V or Less)

The overcurrent protection for transformers is based on their rated current, not on the load to be served. The primary circuit may be protected by a device rated or set at not more than 125% of the rated primary current of the transformer for transformers with a rated primary current of 9A or more.

Instead of individual protection on the primary side, the transformer may be protected only on the secondary side if all of the following conditions are met:

- The overcurrent device on the secondary side is rated or set at not more than 125% of the rated secondary current.
- The primary feeder overcurrent device is rated or set at not more than 250% of the rated primary current.

For example, if a 12kVA transformer has a primary voltage rating of 480V, calculate the amperage as follows:

$$\frac{12{,}000VA}{480V} = 25A$$

With a secondary voltage rated at 120V, the amperage becomes:

$$\frac{12{,}000VA}{120V} = 100A$$

The individual primary protection must be set at

$$1.25 \times 25A = 31.25A$$

In this case, a standard 30A cartridge fuse rated at 600V could be used, as could a circuit breaker approved for use on 480V. However, if certain conditions are met, individual primary protection for the transformer is not necessary if the feeder overcurrent protective device is rated at not more than:

$$2.5 \times 25A = 62.5A$$

In addition, the protection of the secondary side must be set at not more than:

$$1.25 \times 100A = 125A$$

In this case, a standard 125A circuit breaker could be used.

The requirements of *NEC Section 450.3* cover only transformer protection; in practice, other components must be considered when applying circuit overcurrent protection. Circuits with transformers must meet the requirements for conductor protection in *NEC Articles 240 and 310*

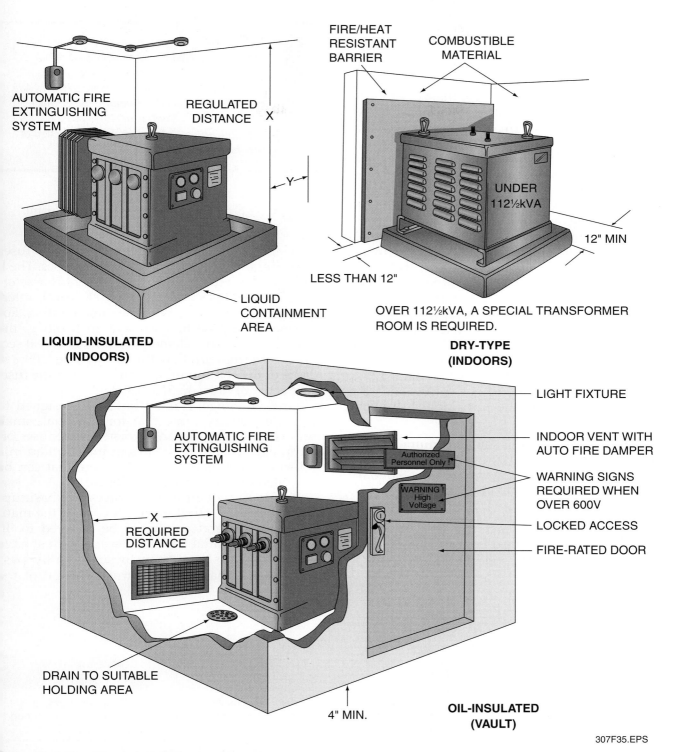

AUTOMATIC FIRE
EXTINGUISHING
SYSTEM

REGULATED
DISTANCE    X

Y

LIQUID
CONTAINMENT
AREA

**LIQUID-INSULATED
(INDOORS)**

FIRE/HEAT
RESISTANT
BARRIER

COMBUSTIBLE
MATERIAL

UNDER
112½kVA

12" MIN

LESS THAN 12"

OVER 112½kVA, A SPECIAL TRANSFORMER
ROOM IS REQUIRED.

**DRY-TYPE
(INDOORS)**

AUTOMATIC FIRE
EXTINGUISHING
SYSTEM

Authorized
Personnel Only !

WARNING
High
Voltage

X

REQUIRED
DISTANCE

LIGHT FIXTURE

INDOOR VENT WITH
AUTO FIRE DAMPER

WARNING SIGNS
REQUIRED WHEN
OVER 600V

LOCKED ACCESS

FIRE-RATED DOOR

DRAIN TO SUITABLE
HOLDING AREA

4" MIN.

**OIL-INSULATED
(VAULT)**

307F35.EPS

*Figure 35* ◆ Transformer installation requirements.

Panelboards must meet the requirements of *NEC Article 408*.

- *Primary fuse protection only* – If secondary fuse protection is not provided, then the primary fuses must not be sized larger than 125% of the transformer primary full-load amperes (FLA), except if the transformer primary FLA is that shown in *NEC Table 450.3(B)*. See *Figure 36*. Individual transformer primary fuses are not necessary where the primary circuit fuse provides this protection.

- *Primary and secondary protection* – According to *NEC Table 450.3(A)*, a transformer with a primary voltage over 600V, located in unsupervised areas, is permitted to have the primary fuse sized at a maximum of 300%. If the secondary is also over 600V, the secondary fuses can be sized at a maximum of 250% for transformers with impedances not greater than 6% and 225% for transformers with impedances greater than 6% and not more than 10%. If the secondary is 600V or below, the secondary fuses can be sized at a maximum of 125%. Where these settings do not correspond to a standard fuse size, the next higher standard size is permitted.

In supervised locations, the maximum settings are as shown in *Figure 37*, except for secondary voltages of 600V or below, where the secondary fuses can be sized at a maximum of 250%.

- *Primary protection only* – In supervised locations, the primary fuses can be sized at a maximum of 250% or the next larger standard size if 250% does not correspond to a standard fuse size.

### 10.1.1 Overcurrent Protection for Small Power Transformers

Low-amperage, E-rated, medium-voltage fuse are general-purpose, current-limiting fuses. The I rating defines the melting time current character istic of the fuse and permits electrical inter changeability of fuses with the same E rating. Fo a general-purpose fuse to have an E rating, th current responsive element shall melt in 300 sec onds at an rms current within the range of 200% t 240% of the continuous current rating of the fuse fuse refill, or link (*ANSI C37.46*).

Low-amperage, E-rated fuses are designed t provide primary protection for potential, sma service, and control transformers. These fuses of fer a high level of fault current interruption in self-contained, non-venting package that can b mounted indoors or in an enclosure.

As for all current-limiting fuses, the basic ap plication rules found in the *NEC*® and the man ufacturer's literature should be adhered to. I addition, potential transformer fuses must hav sufficient inrush capacity to successfully pas through the magnetizing inrush current of th

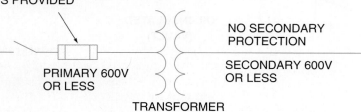

FUSE MUST NOT BE LARGER THAN 125% OF TRANSFORMER PRIMARY FLA WHEN NO TRANSFORMER SECONDARY PROTECTION IS PROVIDED

NO SECONDARY PROTECTION

PRIMARY 600V OR LESS

SECONDARY 600V OR LESS

TRANSFORMER

| PRIMARY CURRENT | PRIMARY FUSE RATING |
|---|---|
| 9A or more | 125% or next higher standard rating if 125% does not correspond to a standard fuse size |
| 2A to 9A | 167% maximum |
| Less than 2A | 300% maximum |

307F36.EP

*Figure 36* ◆ Transformer circuit with primary fuse only.

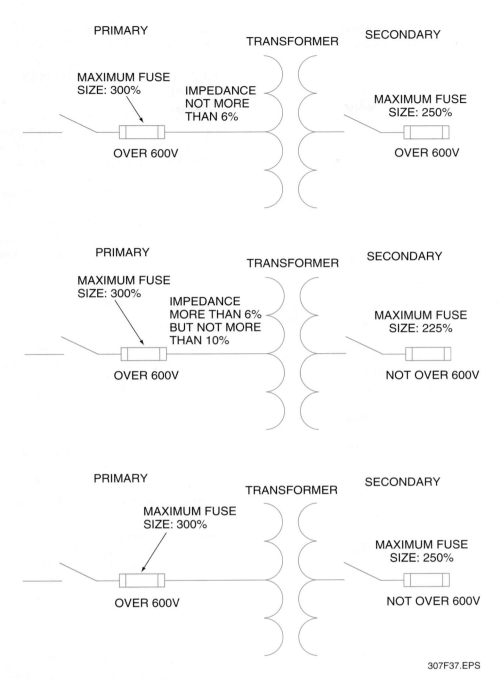

PRIMARY

TRANSFORMER

SECONDARY

MAXIMUM FUSE
SIZE: 300%

IMPEDANCE
NOT MORE
THAN 6%

MAXIMUM FUSE
SIZE: 250%

OVER 600V

OVER 600V

PRIMARY

TRANSFORMER

SECONDARY

MAXIMUM FUSE
SIZE: 300%

IMPEDANCE
MORE THAN 6%
BUT NOT MORE
THAN 10%

MAXIMUM FUSE
SIZE: 225%

OVER 600V

NOT OVER 600V

PRIMARY

TRANSFORMER

SECONDARY

MAXIMUM FUSE
SIZE: 300%

MAXIMUM FUSE
SIZE: 250%

OVER 600V

NOT OVER 600V

307F37.EPS

*Figure 37* ◆ Minimum overcurrent protection for transformers in supervised locations.

transformer. If the fuse is not sized properly, it will open before the load is energized. The maximum magnetizing inrush currents to the transformer at system voltage and the duration of this inrush current vary with the transformer design. Magnetizing inrush currents are usually denoted as a percentage of the transformer full-load current (10X, 12X, 15X, etc.). The inrush current duration is usually given in seconds.

Where this information is available, an easy check can be made on the appropriate minimum melting curve to verify proper fuse selection. In lieu of transformer inrush data, the rule of thumb is to select a fuse size rated at 300% of the primary full-load current or the next larger standard size.

For example, a transformer manufacturer states that an 800VA, 2,400V, single-phase potential transformer has a magnetizing inrush current of 12X lasting for 0.1 second. Therefore:

$$I = \frac{800VA}{2,400V} = 0.333A$$

$$\text{current} = 12A \times 0.333A = 4A$$

Since the voltage is 2,400V, we can use either a JCW or a JCD fuse. Using the 300% rule of thumb:

$$300\% \text{ of } 0.333A = 0.999A$$

Therefore, we would choose a JCW-1E or JCD-1E fuse.

Typical potential transformer connections can be grouped into two categories:

- Those connections that require the fuse to pass only the magnetizing inrush of one potential transformer (*Figure 38*)
- Those connections that must pass the magnetizing inrush of more than one potential transformer (*Figure 39*)

Fuses for medium-voltage transformers and feeders are E-rated, medium-voltage fuses, which are general-purpose, current-limiting fuses. The fuses carry either an E or an X rating, which defines the melting time current characteristic of the fuse. The ratings are used to allow electrical interchangeability among different manufacturers' fuses.

For a general-purpose fuse to have an E rating, the following conditions must be met:

- Current responsive elements with ratings 100A or below shall melt in 300 seconds at an rms current within the range of 200% to 240% of the continuous current rating of the fuse unit (*ANSI C37.46*).

- Current responsive elements with rating above 100A shall melt in 600 seconds at an rms current within the range of 220% to 264% of the continuous current rating of the fuse unit (*ANSI C37.46*).

A fuse with an X rating does not meet the electrical interchangeability for an E-rated fuse, but it offers the user other ratings that may provide better protection for the particular application.

Transformer protection is the most popular application of E-rated fuses. The fuse is applied to the primary of the transformer and is solely used to prevent rupture of the transformer due to short circuits. It is important, therefore, to size the fuse so that it does not clear on system inrush or

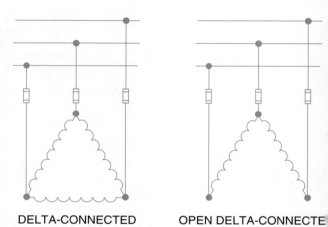

DELTA-CONNECTED     OPEN DELTA-CONNECTE

307F39.EP

*Figure 39* ◆ Connections requiring fuses to pass the magnetizing inrush of more than one transformer.

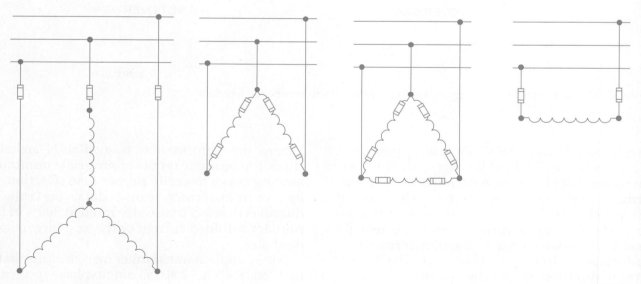

307F38.EPS

*Figure 38* ◆ Connections requiring fuses to pass only the magnetizing inrush of one transformer.

## Transformers

permissible overload currents. Magnetizing inrush must also be considered when sizing a fuse. In general, power transformers have a magnetizing inrush current of 12X, which is the full-load rating for a duration of ¹⁄₁₀ second.

### 10.2.0 Transformer Grounding

Grounding is necessary to remove static electricity and also as a precautionary measure in case the transformer windings accidentally come in contact with the core or enclosure. All transformers should be grounded and bonded to meet *NEC*® requirements and also local codes where applicable.

The case of every power transformer should be grounded to eliminate the possibility of obtaining static shocks from it or being injured by accidental grounding of the winding to the case. A grounding lug is provided on the base of most transformers for the purpose of grounding the case and fittings.

The *NEC*® specifically states the requirements for grounding and should be followed in every respect. Furthermore, certain advisory rules recommended by manufacturers provide additional protection beyond that of the *NEC*®. In general,

the code requires that separately derived alternating current systems be grounded as stated in *NEC Section 250.30.*

### 11.0.0 ◆ POWER FACTOR

Power factor was covered in the Level Two module entitled *Alternating Current,* so a brief review of the subject should suffice here. The equation for power factor is:

$$\text{Power factor (pf)} = \frac{kW}{kVA}$$

*Where:*

kW = kilowatts

kVA = kilovolt-amperes

Calculating the power factor of an electrical system requires that the true power, inductive reactance, and capacitive reactance of the system be determined. An analogy should enhance your understanding of these terms.

Imagine a farm wagon to which three horses are hitched, as shown in *Figure 40.* The horse in the middle (#1) is pulling straight ahead; we will call

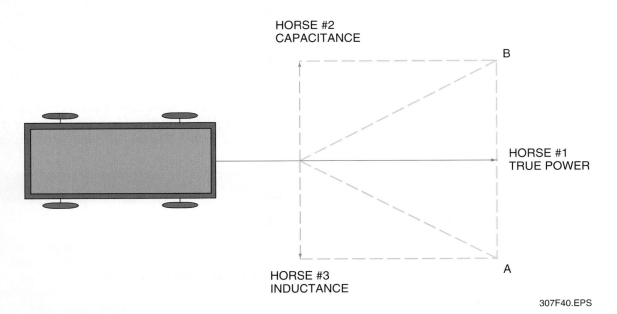

307F40.EPS

*Figure 40* ◆ Depicting power factor.

this horse true power because all of the effort is in the direction that the work should be done. Horse #2 wants to nibble at the grass growing along the side of the road. This horse does not contribute an ounce of pull in the desired direction and causes a problem by pulling the wagon toward the ditch. We will call horse #2 inductance. The third horse has about the same strength as horse #2 and enjoys the grass on the opposite side of the road, which causes this horse to pull in the exact opposite direction of horse #2. Horse #3 also contributes nothing to the forward motion. This horse is called **capacitance.**

We will forget about horse #3 for the moment. If only horse #1 and horse #2 were pulling, the wagon would go in the direction of dotted line A. Notice that the length of that line is greater than the line to #1, so the horse named inductance has an effect on the final result. The direction and length of A might well be called apparent power and happens to be the hypotenuse (or diagonal) of a right angle triangle.

If the #2 horse were unhitched, then horses #1 and #3 would cause the wagon to move in the direction of line B, and the length of that line would also be apparent power. If all three horses were pulling, horses #2 and #3 would cancel one another out, and the only useful animal would be reliable horse #1, true power.

In an AC circuit, there are always three forces working in varying lengths. Inductance (horse #2) is present in every magnetic circuit and always works at a 90° angle with true power. Therefore, we have a power factor of less than 100% because the wagon does not move straight ahead, but travels toward the right due to the pull of horse #2. However, we can improve the power factor by adding horse #3, capacitance, which tends to cancel out the pull of inductance, enabling the wagon to travel straight ahead.

## 11.1.0 Capacitors

*NEC Article 460* states specific rules for the installation and protection of capacitors other than surge capacitors or capacitors that are part of an other apparatus. The chief use of capacitors is to improve the power factor of an electrical installation or an individual piece of electrically operated equipment. In general, this efficiency lowers the cost of power. The *NEC*® requirements for capacitors operating under 600V are summarized in *Table 2.*

Since capacitors may store an electrical charge and hold a voltage that is present even when a capacitor is disconnected from a circuit, capacitors must be enclosed, guarded, or located so that persons cannot accidentally contact the terminals. In most installations, capacitors are installed out of reach or are placed in an enclosure accessible only to qualified persons. The stored charge of a capacitor must be drained by a discharge circuit either permanently connected to the capacitor or automatically connected when the line voltage of the capacitor circuit is removed. The windings of a motor or a circuit consisting of resistors and reactors will serve to drain the capacitor charge.

Capacitor circuit conductors must have an ampacity of not less than 135% of the rated current of the capacitor. This current is determined from the VA rating of the capacitor as for any other load. For example, a 100kVA (100,000VA), three-phase capacitor operating at 480V has a rated current of

$$I = \frac{100{,}000\text{VA}}{1.732 \times 480\text{V}} = 120.3\text{A}$$

The minimum conductor ampacity is then:

$$I = 1.35 \times 120.3\text{A} = 162.4\text{A}$$

When a capacitor is switched into a circuit, a large inrush current results to charge the capacitor to the circuit voltage. Therefore, an overcurrent protective device for the capacitor must be rated or set high enough to allow the capacitor to charge. Although the exact setting is not specified in the *NEC*®, typical settings vary between 150% and 250% of the rated capacitor current.

In addition to overcurrent protection, a capacitor must have a disconnecting means rated at not less than 135% of the rated current of the

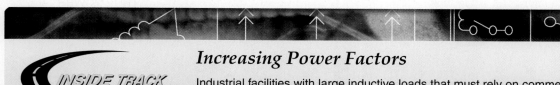

### *Increasing Power Factors*

*INSIDE TRACK*

Industrial facilities with large inductive loads that must rely on commercial power to operate pay a rate depending on power factor and consumption. The rate increases when the power factor is low because the utility must supply additional kVARs not metered by the watt-hour meter. In order to decrease the cost of electricity caused by these inductive loads, capacitors are often installed to increase the power factor.

**Table 2** *NEC®* Capacitor Installation Requirements

| Application | NEC® Regulation | NEC® Reference |
|---|---|---|
| Enclosing and guarding | Capacitors must be enclosed, located, or guarded so that persons cannot come into accidental contact or bring conducting materials into accidental contact with exposed energized parts, terminals, or buses associated with them. However, no additional guarding is required for enclosures accessible only to authorized and qualified persons. | *NEC Section 460.2(B)* |
| Stored charge | Capacitors must be provided with a means of draining the stored charge. The discharge circuit must be either permanently connected to the terminals of the capacitor or capacitor bank or provided with automatic means of connecting it to the terminals of the capacitor bank on removal of voltage from the line. Manual means of switching or connecting the discharge circuit shall not be used. | *NEC Section 460.6* |
| Capacitors on circuits over 600V | Special *NEC®* regulations apply to capacitors operating at over 600V. | *NEC Articles 460, Part II and 490* |
| Conductor ampacity | The ampacity of capacitor circuit conductors must not be less than 135% of the rated current of the capacitor. | *NEC Section 460.8(A)* |
| Capacitors on motor circuits | The ampacity of conductors that connect a capacitor to the terminals of a motor or to motor circuit conductors shall not be less than one-third the ampacity of the motor circuit conductors and in no case less than 135% of the rated current of the capacitor. | *NEC Section 460.8(A)* |
| Overcurrent protection | Overcurrent protection is required in each ungrounded conductor unless the capacitor is connected on the load side of a motor running overcurrent device. The setting must be as low as practicable. | *NEC Section 460.8(B)* |
| Disconnecting means | A disconnecting means is required for a capacitor unless it is connected to the load side of a motor controller. The rating must be not less than 135% of the rated current of the capacitor. | *NEC Section 460.8(C)* |
| Overcurrent protection for improved power factor | If the power factor is improved, the motor running overcurrent device must be selected based on the reduced current draw, not the full-load current of the motor. | *NEC Section 460.9* |
| Grounding | Capacitor cases must be grounded except when the system is designed to operate at other than ground potential. | *NEC Section 460.10* |

apacitor unless the capacitor is connected to the load side of the motor running overcurrent device. In this case, the motor disconnecting means would serve to disconnect the capacitor and the motor.

A capacitor connected to a motor circuit serves to increase the power factor and reduce the total kVA required by the motor capacitor circuit. As stated earlier, the power factor (pf) is defined as the true power in kilowatts divided by the total kVA, or:

$$pf = \frac{kW}{kVA}$$

A power factor of less than one represents a lagging current for motors and inductive devices. The capacitor introduces a leading current that reduces the total kVA and raises the power factor to a value closer to unity (one). If the inductive load of the motor is completely balanced by the capacitor, a maximum power factor of unity results, and all of the input energy serves to perform useful work.

The capacitor circuit conductors for a power factor correction capacitor must have an ampacity of not less than 135% of the rated current of the capacitor. In addition, the ampacity must not be less than one-third the ampacity of the motor circuit conductors.

The connection of a capacitor reduces the current in the feeder up to the point of connection. If the capacitor is connected on the load side of the motor running overcurrent device, the current through this device is reduced, and its rating must be based on the actual current, not on the full-load current of the motor.

## 11.2.0 Resistors and Reactors

*NEC Article 470* covers the installation of separate resistors and reactors on electric circuits. However, this article does not cover such devices that are component parts of other machines and equipment.

In general, *NEC Section 470.2* requires resistors and reactors to be installed where they will not be exposed to physical damage. Therefore, such devices are normally installed in a protective enclosure, such as a controller housing or other type of cabinet. When these enclosures are constructed of metal, they must be grounded as specified in *NEC Article 250*. Furthermore, a thermal barrier must be provided between resistors and/or reactors and any combustible material that is less than 12" away. A space of 12" or more between the devices and combustible material is considered a sufficient distance so as not to require a thermal barrier.

Insulated conductors used for connections between resistors and motor controllers must be rated at not less than 90°C (194°F) except for motor starting service. In this case, other conductor insulation is permitted, provided other sections of the *NEC*® are not violated.

## 11.3.0 Diodes and Rectifiers

The diode and the rectifier are the simplest form of electronic components. The major difference between the two is their current rating. A component that is rated less than 1A is called a diode; a similar component rated above 1A is called a rectifier. The main purpose of either device is to convert or rectify alternating current to direct current.

Diodes and rectifiers are composed of two types of semiconductor materials and are classified as either P or N types. One has free electrons, the other has a shortage of electrons. When the two types of material are bonded together, a solid state component is produced that will allow electrons to flow in one direction and act as an insulator when the voltage is reversed.

Diodes and rectifiers are used extensively in control circuits. For example, *Figure 41* shows an AC voltage supplying a control transformer that must supply a DC electronic controller. Consequently, two rectifiers are installed on the secondary side of the transformer to change AC to DC. The rectifiers allow current to flow in one direction but will not allow the normal alternating current reversal, simulating direct current.

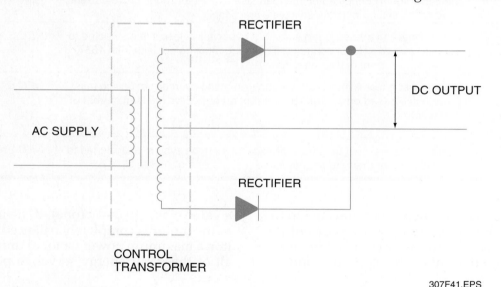

307F41.EPS

*Figure 41* ◆ Rectifiers used in a control circuit to change AC to DC.

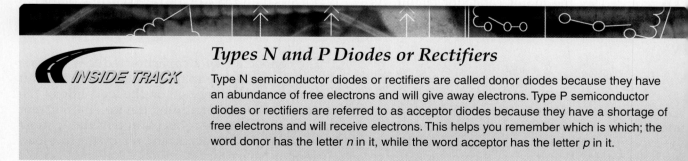

### Types N and P Diodes or Rectifiers

Type N semiconductor diodes or rectifiers are called donor diodes because they have an abundance of free electrons and will give away electrons. Type P semiconductor diodes or rectifiers are referred to as acceptor diodes because they have a shortage of free electrons and will receive electrons. This helps you remember which is which; the word donor has the letter *n* in it, while the word acceptor has the letter *p* in it.

## 2.0.0 ◆ VECTORS

The theoretical study of transformers includes the use of phasor diagrams, or vectors, that graphically represent voltages and currents in transformer windings.

A vector or phasor diagram is a line with direction and length. Reading a vector diagram is like reading a road map and is not much more difficult, just a bit more refined. For example, road directions that instruct you to go east 40 miles and then south 30 miles to get to your destination are simple to understand. In other words, you had to drive 70 miles to get there. However, had you been able to drive as the crow flies, the distance would have been shorter—only 50 miles. See *Figure 42(A)*. If the miles were converted into electrical terms, this same triangle would be the classic 3/4/5 triangle or the 80% power factor relationship, as shown in *Figure 42(B)*.

Referring to *Figure 42(B)*, if the working current (line A-B) is 4A and the inductive current (line B-C) is 3A, then the diagonal line A-C, or hypotenuse, will be 5A. This value may be proven by drawing lines A-B and B-C to scale and then connecting line A-C and measuring it. However, the same results may be obtained mathematically using the Pythagorean theorem, which states that the hypotenuse is equal to the square root of the sum of the squares of the other two sides:

$$AC = \sqrt{AB^2 + BC^2}$$
$$AC = \sqrt{4^2 + 3^2} = \sqrt{16 + 9} = \sqrt{25}$$
$$AC = 5$$

In this example, the working current is related to kilowatts (kW), and the total current is related to kVA. The ratio between the two is $4 \div 5 = 0.80$. Since the power factor equals $kW \div kVA$, the power factor of this circuit is 80%.

## 12.1.0 Practical Applications of Phasor Diagrams

When three single-phase transformers are used as a three-phase bank, the direction of the voltage in each of the six phase windings may be represented by a voltage phasor. A voltage phasor diagram of the six voltages involved provides a convenient way to study the relative direction and amounts of the primary and secondary voltages.

The same is true for one three-phase transformer, which also has six voltages to be considered, because its phase windings on the high-voltage and low-voltage sides are connected together in the same way as the phase windings of three single-phase transformers.

To show how a phasor diagram is drawn, consider the three-phase transformer shown in *Figure 43*. Here we have a wye/delta-connected, three-phase transformer with three legs, with each leg carrying a high-voltage and a low-voltage winding. The high-voltage windings are connected in wye (with a common neutral point at N) with the leads to the high-voltage terminals designated $H_1$, $H_2$, and $H_3$. The three low-voltage windings are connected in delta. The junction points of the three windings serve as low-voltage terminals $X_1$, $X_2$, and $X_3$.

The voltages in the low-voltage windings are assumed to be equal to each other in amount but are displaced from each other by 120 degrees.

When drawing the phasor diagram for the low-voltage windings, phasor $X_1X_2$ is drawn first in any selected direction and to any convenient scale. The arrowhead indicates the instantaneous direction of the alternating voltage in winding $X_1X_2$, and the length of the phasor represents the amount of voltage in the winding. The broken lines that extend past the arrowheads represent reference lines for phase angles.

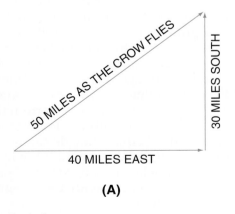

**(A)**

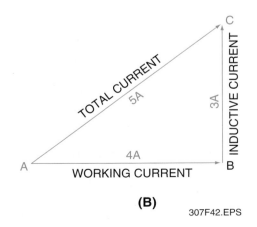

**(B)**

307F42.EPS

*Figure 42* ◆ Typical vectors.

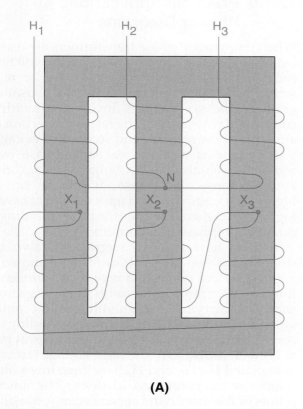

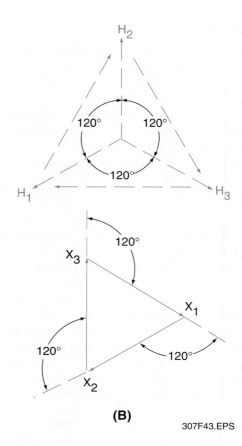

**Figure 43** ◆ Windings and phasor diagrams of a three-phase transformer.

307F43.EPS

Since winding $X_2X_3$ is physically connected to the end of $X_2$ in the $X_1X_2$ winding, phasor $X_2X_3$ will be started at point $X_2$, 120 degrees out of phase with phasor $X_1X_2$ in the clockwise direction. The length of phasor $X_2X_3$ is equal to the length of phasor $X_1X_2$. Winding $X_3X_1$ is drawn in a similar manner.

The high-voltage phasor comes next. Since the low-voltage winding $X_1X_2$ is wound on the same leg as the high-voltage winding $NH_1$, the voltages in these two windings are in phase and are represented by parallel voltage phasors. Therefore, the phasor $NH_1$ is drawn from a selected point N parallel to $X_1X_2$. Note that all three high-voltage windings are physically connected to a common point N. Therefore, the phasors representing the voltages $NH_1$, $NH_2$, and $NH_3$ will all start at the common point (point N in the phasor diagram). Again, the high-voltage phasors are all of the same length but are displaced from each other by 120 degrees as shown.

The high-voltage phasors have the same length as the low-voltage phasors. Each phase of the high voltage is, however, proportional to the low voltage in the same phase according to the turns ratio, making the line voltage 1.732 times higher than

the phase voltage in any one winding. It can b geometrically proven, for example, that $H_1H_2$ > $NH_1 = 1.732 \times NH_2$ and so forth for each lin voltage.

When comparing three-phase transformers fo possible operation in parallel, draw the voltag phasor diagram for transformer bank A, and mar the terminals as shown in *Figure 44(A)*. Next, drav the phasor diagram for bank B on drafting o other transparent paper; then draw a heavy refer ence line m-n as shown in *Figure 44(B)*. Cut th transparent diagram into two parts as indicatec by the dashed lines in the drawing. The two part of the reference line are now marked m and n Place diagram m on the high-voltage diagram i *Figure 44(A)* so that the terminals that are desirec to be connected together coincide. Place diagran n on the low-voltage diagram in *Figure 44(A)* s that the heavy reference line of n is parallel to th heavy reference line of m. If the terminals of n ca be made to coincide with the low-voltage termi nals, the terminals that coincide can be connectec together for parallel operation. If the low-voltag terminals cannot be made to coincide, parallel op eration is not possible with the assumed high voltage connection.

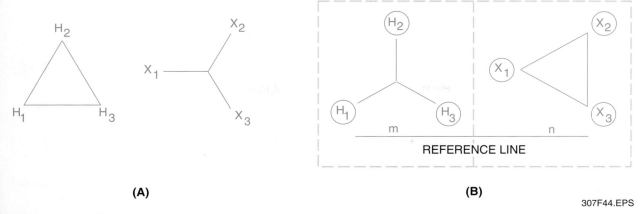

(A)

(B)

307F44.EPS

*Figure 44* ◆ Phasor diagrams for three-phase transformer banks in parallel.

## 2.2.0 Voltage Drop

*Figure 45* shows a simple 100% power factor circuit in which a $1\Omega$ resistance appears between the source of power and the load. The current in this series circuit is 10A, and the voltage at the source is 120V. Because Ohm's law states that $E = IR$, we must have a voltage drop across the resistance equal to 10 times 1, or 10V. With the voltage and current in phase, only 110V will be available at the load because we must subtract the resistance drop from the source voltage. Voltage drop was covered more thoroughly earlier in your training.

Voltage drop, however, becomes a little more complicated when inductance is introduced into the circuit, as shown in *Figure 46*. In this case, the load voltage will be equal to the source voltage minus the voltage drops through R and X, but they cannot be added arithmetically. The vector diagram in *Figure 47* shows that the dotted line A-C is the combination of the two voltages across R and X and represents the voltage drop in the line only.

*Figure 47* shows that line G-A, which is the load voltage $E_L$, is less than the source voltage G-C due to the voltage drop in line A-C. Because of the effect of the reactance in the line, this voltage drop cannot be subtracted arithmetically from the source voltage to obtain the load voltage; vectors must be used.

Calculations of impedance can be simplified by using equivalent circuits. The reactance voltage drop is governed by the leakage flux, and the voltage regulation depends on the power factor of the load. To determine transformer efficiency at various loads, it is necessary to first calculate the core loss, hysteresis loss, eddy current loss, and load loss.

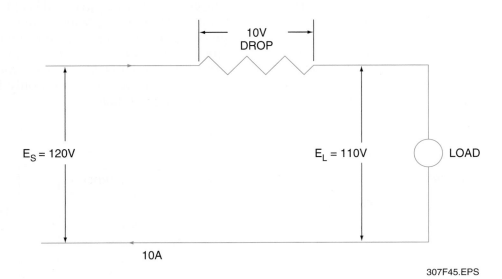

307F45.EPS

*Figure 45* ◆ Circuit containing resistance only.

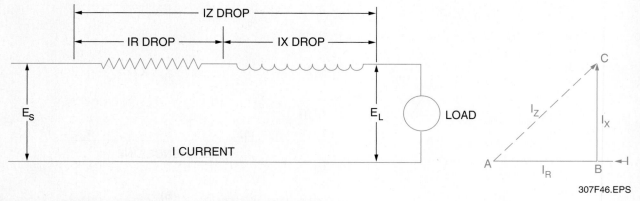

*Figure 46* ◆ Electrical circuit with both resistance and inductance.

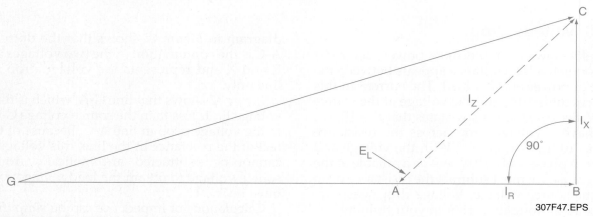

*Figure 47* ◆ Effect of voltage drop in an AC circuit.

However, for all practical purposes in electrical construction applications, a transformer's efficiency may be considered to be 100%. Therefore, for our purposes, a transformer may be defined as a device that transfers power from its primary circuit to the secondary circuit without any significant loss.

Since apparent power (VA) equals voltage (E) times current (I), if $E_PI_P$ represents the primary apparent power and $E_SI_S$ represents the secondary apparent power, then $E_PI_P = E_SI_S$ (the subscript

P = primary, and the subscript S = secondary. See *Figure 48*. If the primary and secondary voltages are equal, the primary and secondary currents must also be equal. Assume that $E_P$ is twice as large as $E_S$. For $E_PI_P$ to equal $E_SI_S$, $I_P$ must be one half of $I_S$. Therefore, a transformer that steps voltage down always steps current up. Conversely, a transformer that steps voltage up always steps current down. However, transformers are classified as step-up or step-down only in relation to their effect on voltage.

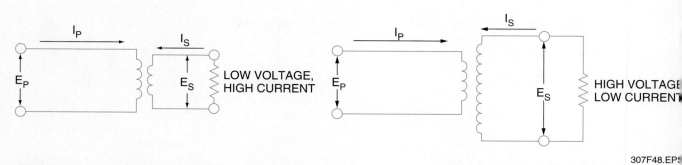

*Figure 48* ◆ Voltage-current relationship in a transformer.

# 3.0.0 ◆ TROUBLESHOOTING

Since transformers are an essential part of every electrical installation, electricians must know how to test and locate problems that develop in transformers, especially in the smaller power supply or control transformers. The procedure for accomplishing this is commonly known as troubleshooting.

The term troubleshooting, as used in this module, covers the investigation, analysis, and corrective action required to eliminate faults in electrical systems, including circuits, components, and equipment. Most problems are simple and easily corrected, such as an open circuit, a ground fault or short circuit, or a change in resistance.

There are many useful troubleshooting charts available. Most charts list the complaint on the left side of the chart, then the possible cause, followed by the proper corrective action.

When troubleshooting, think before acting, study the problem thoroughly, then ask yourself these questions:

What were the warning signs preceding the trouble?
What previous repair and maintenance work has been done?
Has similar trouble occurred before?
If the circuit, component, or piece of equipment still operates, is it safe to continue operation before further testing?

The answers to these questions can usually be obtained by:

Questioning the owner of the equipment
Taking time to think the problem through
Looking for additional symptoms
Consulting troubleshooting charts
Checking the simplest things first
Referring to repair and maintenance records
Checking with calibrated instruments
Double-checking all conclusions before beginning any repair

**NOTE**

Always check the easiest and most obvious things first; following this simple rule will save time and trouble.

## 3.1.0 Double-Check Before Beginning

The source of many problems can be traced not to one part alone but to the relationship of one part with another. For instance, a tripped circuit breaker may be reset to restart a piece of equipment, but what caused the breaker to trip in the first place? It could have been caused by a vibrating hot conductor momentarily coming into contact with a ground, a loose connection, or any number of other causes.

Too often, electrically operated equipment is completely disassembled in search of the cause of a certain complaint and all evidence is destroyed during disassembly. Check again to be certain an easy solution to the problem has not been overlooked.

## 13.2.0 Find and Correct the Basic Cause of the Trouble

After an electrical failure has been corrected in any type of electrical circuit or piece of equipment, be sure to locate and correct the cause so the same failure will not be repeated. Further investigation may reveal other faulty components.

Also be aware that although troubleshooting charts and procedures greatly help in diagnosing malfunctions, they can never be complete. There are too many variations and solutions for any given problem.

To solve electrical problems consistently, you must first understand the basic parts of electrical circuits, how they function, and for what purpose. If you know that a particular part is not performing its job, then the cause of the malfunction must be within this part or series of parts.

## 13.3.0 Troubleshooting Transformers

This section discusses common transformer problems.

### 13.3.1 Open Circuit

Should one of the windings in a transformer develop a break or open condition, no current can flow, and therefore, the transformer will not deliver any output. The main symptom of an open circuit in a transformer is that the circuits that derive power from the transformer are de-energized or dead. Use an AC voltmeter or a volt-ohm-milliammeter (VOM) to check across the transformer output terminals, as shown in *Figure 49*. A reading of zero volts indicates an open circuit.

Next, take a voltage reading across the input terminals. If a voltage reading is present, then the conclusion is that one of the windings in the transformer is open. However, if no voltage reading is on the input terminals either, then the conclusion is that the open is elsewhere on the line side of the circuit; perhaps a disconnect switch is open.

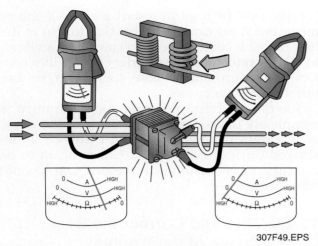

307F49.EPS

***Figure 49*** ◆ Checking a transformer for an open winding using a VOM to measure voltage.

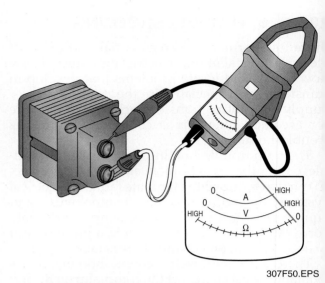

307F50.EPS

***Figure 50*** ◆ Checking for an open winding with a continuity test using a VOM.

 **WARNING!**

Make absolutely certain that your testing instruments are designed for the job and are calibrated for the correct voltage. Never test the primary side of any transformer over 600V unless you are qualified and have the correct high-voltage testing instruments and the test is made under the proper supervision. Always set the range selector switch on the test equipment to the highest setting, and decrease it in increments until the most accurate reading is indicated.

If voltage is present on the line or primary side and is not present on the secondary or load side, open the switch to de-energize the circuit, and place a warning tag (tagout and lock) on this switch so that it is not inadvertently closed again while someone is working on the circuit. Disconnect all of the transformer primary and secondary leads; then check each winding in the transformer for continuity, as indicated by a resistance reading taken with an ohmmeter (*Figure 50*).

Continuity is indicated by a relatively low resistance reading on control transformers; an open winding will be indicated by an infinite resistance reading on the ohmmeter. In most cases, small transformers will have to be replaced unless the break is accessible and can be repaired.

### 13.3.2   Shorted Turns

Sometimes a few turns in the secondary winding of a transformer will acquire a partial short, which in turn will cause a voltage drop across the secondary. The symptom of this condition is usually overheating of the transformer caused by large circulating currents flowing in the shorted windings. The most accurate way to check for this condition is with a transformer turns ratio tester (TTR). However, another way to check for this condition is with a VOM set at the proper voltage scale (*Figure 51*). Take a reading on the line or primary side of the transformer first to make certain normal voltage is present; then take a reading on the secondary side. If the transformer has a partial short or ground fault, the voltage reading should be lower than normal.

Replace the faulty transformer with a new one and again take a reading on the secondary. If the voltage reading is now normal and the circuit operates satisfactorily, leave the replacement

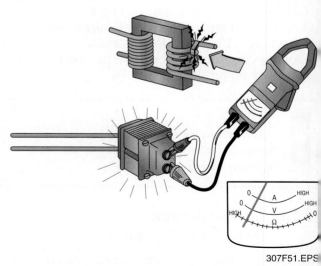

307F51.EPS

***Figure 51*** ◆ Transformers that overheat usually have a partial short in the windings.

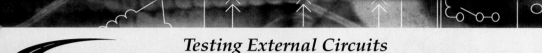

## Open and Unbonded Neutrals

What is the difference between an open neutral and an unbonded neutral?

## Testing External Circuits

*INSIDE TRACK*

Always retest the external circuits supplied by the transformer before energizing a replacement transformer. This is done to avoid damaging or destroying the replacement due to a shorted external circuit, which may have caused the original transformer to burn out.

ansformer in the circuit, and either discard or re-
air the original transformer.

A highly sensitive ohmmeter may also be used
 test for this condition when the system is de-
ergized and the leads are disconnected; a lower
an normal reading on the ohmmeter indicates
is condition. However, the difference will usu-
ly be so slight that the average ohmmeter is not
nsitive enough to detect it. Therefore, the rec-
mmended method is to use the voltmeter test.

### 3.3.3 Complete Short

ccasionally, a transformer winding will become
mpletely shorted. In most cases, this will acti-
ate the overload protective device and de-
ergize the circuit, but in other instances, the
ansformer may continue trying to operate with
xcessive overheating due to the very large circu-
ting current. This heat will often melt the wax or
sulation inside the transformer, which is easily
etected by the odor. Also, there will be no voltage
utput across the shorted winding, and the circuit
cross the winding will be dead.

The short may be in the external secondary cir-
uit, or it may be in the transformer's winding. To
etermine its location, disconnect the external secndary circuit from the winding, and take a read-
g with a voltmeter. If the voltage is normal with
e external circuit disconnected, then the prob-
m lies within the external circuit. However, if the
oltage reading is still zero across the secondary
ads, the transformer is shorted and will have to
 replaced.

### 13.3.4 Grounded Windings

Insulation breakdown is quite common in older transformers, especially those that have been over-loaded. At some point, the insulation breaks or deteriorates, and the wire becomes exposed. The exposed wire often comes into contact with the transformer housing and grounds the winding.

If a winding develops a ground and a point in the external circuit connected to this winding is also grounded, part of the winding will be shorted out. The symptoms will be overheating, which is usually detected by heat or a burning smell and a low resistance reading from the secondary winding to the core (case), as indicated on the VOM in *Figure 52*. In most cases, transformers with this condition will have to be replaced.

A megohmmeter (megger) is the best test instrument to check for this condition. Disconnect the leads from both the primary and secondary windings. Tests can then be performed on either winding by connecting the megger negative test lead to an associated ground and the positive test lead to the winding to be measured.

**WARNING!**

Do not use a megger unless you are qualified and properly supervised.

The insulation resistance should then be measured between the windings themselves. This is accomplished by connecting one test lead to the primary and the second test lead to the secondary and ground. After that, connect the first lead to the secondary and the second test lead to the primary and ground. All such tests should be noted on record card under the proper identifying labels.

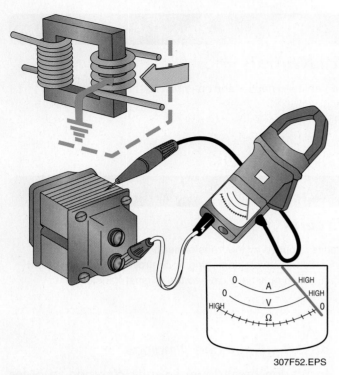

307F52.EPS

*Figure 52* ◆ Testing a transformer for a ground fault by measuring resistance using a VOM.

1. The main purpose of a transformer is to _____.
   a. change the current
   b. improve the power factor
   c. change the output voltage
   d. enter impedance into the circuit

2. The three parts of a basic transformer are the _____.
   a. housing, lifting hooks, and base
   b. dry, oil-filled, and gas-filled chambers
   c. shell, open winding, and closed winding
   d. primary winding, secondary winding, and core

3. When AC flows through a transformer coil, a _____ field is generated around the coils.
   a. magnetic
   b. non-magnetic
   c. high-impedance
   d. rotating

4. When the field from one coil cuts through the turns of a second coil, _____.
   a. the second coil will not be affected
   b. the coils will rotate
   c. voltage will be generated
   d. no current will flow in the circuit

5. What causes voltage to be induced in a transformer?
   a. Transformer taps
   b. Mutual induction
   c. Reluctance
   d. Capacitance

6. In a transformer with a turns ratio of 5:1 (the primary has five times the number of turns as the secondary), what will be the voltage on the secondary if the primary voltage is 120V?
   a. 12V
   b. 24V
   c. 48V
   d. 60V

7. The three basic types of iron core transformers are _____.
   a. dry, oil-filled, and auto
   b. closed core, open core, and shell
   c. control, power, and lighting
   d. metal, nonmetallic, and high-temperature

8. One effect caused by magnetic leakage in transformers is a _____.
   a. reactance voltage drop
   b. low impedance
   c. higher secondary voltage
   d. lower secondary voltage

9. A symptom of a transformer with an open circuit is _____.
   a. high voltage on the secondary
   b. excessive overheating
   c. no output on the secondary
   d. voltage drop across the secondary

10. A(n) _____ should be used to measure insulation resistance.
    a. ammeter
    b. megger
    c. voltmeter
    d. TTR

# Summary

This module covered the basic components and applications of distribution system transformers. When the AC voltage needed for an application is lower or higher than the voltage available from the source, a transformer is used. The essential components of a transformer are the primary winding, which is connected to the source, and the secondary winding, which is connected to the load. Both are wound on an iron core. The two windings are not physically connected, with the exception of autotransformers. The alternating voltage in the primary winding induces an alternating voltage in the secondary winding. The ratio of the primary and secondary voltages is equal to the ratio of the number of turns in the primary and secondary windings. Transformers may step up the voltage applied to the primary winding and have a higher voltage at the secondary terminals, or they may step down the voltage applied to the primary winding and have a lower voltage available at the secondary terminals.

# Notes

# Trade Terms
# Introduced in This Module

*Ampere turn:* The product of amperes times the number of turns in a coil.

*Autotransformer:* Any transformer in which primary and secondary connections are made to a single winding. The application of an auto-transformer is a good choice where a 480Y/277V or 208Y/120V, three-phase, four-wire distribution system is used.

*Capacitance:* The storage of electricity in a capacitor or the opposition to voltage change. Capacitance is measured in farads (F) or microfarads (μF).

*Current transformer:* A single-phase instrument transformer connected in series in a line that carries the full-load current. The turns ratio is designed to produce a reduced current in the secondary suitable for the current coil of standard measuring instruments and in proportion to the load current.

*Flux:* The rate of energy flow across or through a surface. Also a substance used to promote or facilitate soldering or welding by removing surface oxides.

*Induction:* The production of magnetization or electrification in a body by the mere proximity of magnetized or electrified bodies, or the production of an electric current in a conductor by the variation of the magnetic field in its vicinity.

*Kilovolt-amperes (kVA):* 1,000 volt-amperes (VA).

*Loss:* The power expended without doing useful work.

*Magnetic field:* The area around a magnet in which the effect of the magnet can be felt.

*Magnetic induction:* The number of magnetic lines or the magnetic flux per unit of cross-sectional area perpendicular to the direction of the flux.

*Mutual induction:* The condition of voltage in a second conductor because of current in another conductor.

*Potential transformer:* A special transformer designed for use in measuring high voltage; normally, the secondary voltage is 120V.

*Power transformer:* A transformer that is designed to transfer electrical power from the primary circuit to the secondary circuit(s) to step up the secondary voltage at less current or step down the secondary voltage at more current, with the voltage-current product being constant for either the primary or secondary.

*Reactance:* The opposition to AC due to capacitance and/or inductance.

*Rectifiers:* Devices used to change alternating current to direct current.

*Transformer:* A static device consisting of one or more windings with a magnetic core. Transformers are used for introducing mutual coupling by induction between circuits.

*Turn:* The basic coil element that forms a single conducting loop comprised of one insulated conductor.

*Turns ratio:* The ratio between the number of turns between windings in a transformer; normally the primary to the secondary, except for current transformers, in which it is the ratio of the secondary to the primary.

This module is intended to present thorough resources for task training. The following reference works are suggested for further study. These are optional materials for continued education rather than for task training.

*American Electrician's Handbook.* Terrell Croft an Wilfred I. Summers. New York, NY: McGraw Hill, 1996.

*National Electrical Code® Handbook,* Latest Edition Quincy, MA: National Fire Protection Associa tion.

The NCCER makes every effort to keep these textbooks up-to-date and free of technical errors. We appreciate your help in this process. If you have an idea for improving this textbook, or if you find an error, a typographical mistake, or an inaccuracy in NCCER's *Contren®* textbooks, please write us, using this form or a photocopy. Be sure to include the exact module number, page number, a detailed description, and the correction, if applicable. Your input will be brought to the attention of the Technical Review Committee. Thank you for your assistance.

*Instructors* – If you found that additional materials were necessary in order to teach this module effectively, please let us know so that we may include them in the Equipment/Materials list in the Annotated Instructor's Guide.

**Write:** Product Development
National Center for Construction Education and Research
P.O. Box 141104, Gainesville, FL 32614-1104

**Fax:** 352-334-0932

**E-mail:** curriculum@nccer.org

Craft

Module Name
_____

Copyright Date      Module Number            Page Number(s)
_____

Description
_____

_____

_____

_____

(Optional) Correction
_____

_____

_____

(Optional) Your Name and Address
_____

_____

_____

# Specialty Transformers
## 26406-05

**Steven F. Udvar-Hazy Center**
**National Air and Space Museum**
Chantilly, Virginia
Mega-Projects Over $100 Million Award Winner
Hensel Phelps Construction Co.

# 26406-05
# *Specialty Transformers*

*Topics to be presented in this module include:*

## Overview

When a circuit is connected to the secondary winding of a transformer and a AC voltage is applied to the primary, induced current will flow through the secondary winding and any circuits connected to it. Specialty transformers apply the same basic fundamentals of transformer induction, but they use different coil arrangements and access points (taps) to obtain unique voltage levels at the transformer secondary.

The basic electrical frequency generated by power plants in the U.S. is sixty cycles per second (60 Hz), which graphically appears as a near perfect sinusoidal waveform on a scope meter. Most equipment or electrical loads are considered linear loads, meaning that they operate over the entire sine wave generated by sixty cycles. However, certain loads, such as fluorescent lamps and high-performance electronic equipment used in computers, operate on sharp, irregular pulses drawn from the sixty-cycle frequency. These types of loads are referred to as non-linear loads. The resulting effect on the sixty-cycle sinusoidal waveform caused by non-linear loads is a distorted wave, where distortion occurs in multiples of the basic sixty-cycle pattern. These harmonic currents can flow back to the source transformer, causing overheating and other problems. In installations where harmonics are a problem, the ampacity of the supply transformers must be derated, or a specially designed transformer must be used to avoid overheating.

## Objectives

When you have completed this module, you will be able to do the following:

1. Identify power transformer connections.
2. Identify specialty transformers.
3. Size and select buck-and-boost transformers.
4. Connect current and potential transformers.
5. Calculate and install overcurrent protection for specialty transformers.
6. Ground specialty transformers in accordance with *National Electrical Code® (NEC®)* requirements.
7. Size, install, and connect control, shielded, constant-current, and other specialty transformers.
8. Derate transformers to account for the effects of harmonics.

## Trade Terms

Ampere turn
Autotransformer
Bank
Core loss
Eddy currents

Harmonic
Hysteresis
Impedance
Isolation transformer
Reactance

## Required Trainee Materials

1. Pencil and paper
2. Appropriate personal protective equipment
3. Copy of the latest edition of the *National Electrical Code®*

## Prerequisites

Before you begin this module, it is recommended that you successfully complete *Core Curriculum; Electrical Level One; Electrical Level Two; Electrical Level Three; Electrical Level Four,* Modules 26401-05 through 26405-05.

This course map shows all of the modules in *Electrical Level Four.* The suggested training order begins at the bottom and proceeds up. Skill levels increase as you advance on the course map. The Local Training Program Sponsor may adjust the training order.

26411-05 High-Voltage Terminations/Splices

26410-05 Motor Maintenance, Part Two

26409-05 Heat Tracing and Freeze Protection

26408-05 HVAC Controls

26407-05 Advanced Motor Controls

26406-05 Specialty Transformers

26405-05 Fire Alarm Systems

26404-05 Basic Electronic Theory

26403-05 Standby and Emergency Systems

26402-05 Practical Applications of Lighting

26401-05 Load Calculations – Feeders and Services

ELECTRICAL LEVEL THREE

ELECTRICAL LEVEL TWO

ELECTRICAL LEVEL ONE

CORE CURRICULUM: Introductory Craft Skills

ELECTRICAL LEVEL FOUR

406CMAP.EPS

# 1.0.0 ◆ INTRODUCTION

When the AC voltage needed for an application is lower or higher than the voltage available from the source, a transformer is used. The essential parts of a transformer are the primary winding (which is connected to the source) and the secondary winding (which is connected to the load), both wound on an iron core. The two windings are not physically connected.

The alternating voltage in the primary winding induces an alternating voltage in the secondary winding. The ratio of the primary and secondary voltages is equal to the ratio of the number of turns in the primary and secondary windings.

Transformers may step up the voltage applied to the primary winding and have a higher voltage at the secondary terminals, or they may step down the voltage applied to the primary winding and have a lower voltage at the secondary terminals.

**NOTE**

Transformers are applied in AC systems only and would not work in DC systems because the induction of voltage depends on the rate of change in the current.

A transformer can be constructed as a single-phase or three-phase apparatus. A three-phase transformer, such as the one shown in *Figure 1*, has three primary and three secondary windings, which may be connected in either a delta (Δ) or wye (Y) configuration. Combinations such as Δ-Δ, Δ-Y, Y-Δ, and Y-Y are possible. The first letter indicates the connection of the primary winding, and the second letter indicates that of the secondary winding.

A **bank** of three single-phase transformers can serve the same purpose as one three-phase transformer. The connections between the three primary windings and the three secondary windings are again Δ or Y, and they are available in all combinations.

## 1.1.0 Types of Transformers

Large transformers used in transmission systems are called power transformers. They may step up the voltage produced in the generator to make it suitable for commercial transmission, or they may step down the voltage in a transmission line to make it practical for distribution. Power transformers are usually installed outdoors in generating stations and substations. The transformer shown in *Figure 2* is a liquid-filled power transformer with radiators that disperse the heat from the transformer.

Another type of transformer is the distribution transformer, which steps down the voltage at various points of a power distribution system for better utilization.

An **autotransformer** is a transformer with only one winding, which serves as both a primary and a secondary. Autotransformers are economical, space saving, and especially practical if the difference between the primary and secondary voltage is relatively small.

Three-winding, single-phase transformers have two secondary windings so that they can deliver two different secondary voltages.

In many applications of electrical measuring instruments, the voltage or current in the circuit to be measured is too high for the instruments. In such situations, instrument transformers are used to ensure safe operation of the instruments. An instrument transformer is either a current transformer, a

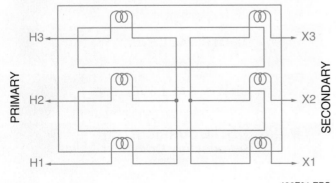

406F01.EPS

*Figure 1* ◆ Typical three-phase transformer.

406F02.EPS

*Figure 2* ◆ Typical liquid-filled, three-phase power transformer.

## Transformer Management Systems

Some manufacturers provide monitoring and diagnostic systems for large liquid-filled power transformers used in substations or in large industrial applications. These systems are used to obtain warnings of impending faults and as a predictor for scheduling maintenance shutdowns. The systems use data from sensors incorporated in the transformers. The sensors monitor the following conditions:

- Dissolved gas-in-oil
- Top and bottom oil temperature
- Gas pressure
- Ambient temperature
- Oil level
- Winding temperature
- Load and meter values
- Bushing activity

This data is transmitted via a network to a computer and used with IEEE or IEC analytical modeling software offline to access the condition of the equipment and diagnose impending failures. This includes moisture-in-insulation modeling, predictive insulation aging rate, cumulative aging, partial discharge activity, overflux (overvoltage), fault event recording, harmonic monitoring, cooling system efficiency, and other trending information.

own in *Figure 3*, or a potential (voltage) transformer, as shown in *Figure 4*. For example, if the current in a line is approximately 100A and the ammeter is rated at 5A, a bar-type current transformer with a current ratio of 100:5 can be connected in series with the line. The secondary winding is then connected to the ammeter. The current in the secondary is proportional to the current in the line. With the toroid current transformer, an insulated line passes through the center, and proportional current is induced in the toroid winding for application to the meter.

Similarly, the potential transformer reduces the voltage in a high-voltage line to the 120V for which the voltmeter is normally rated. The potential transformer is always connected across the line to be measured. Sometimes it is important to indicate the polarity of the current in both the instrument and the transformer. The polarity is the instantaneous direction of current at a specific moment. Wires with the same polarity usually contain a small black block or cross in electrical diagrams, as shown in *Figure 4*.

## 2.0 Internal Connections in Three-Phase Transformers

Various combinations of primary and secondary three-phase voltages are possible with the proper combination of delta and wye internal connections

BAR-TYPE CURRENT TRANSFORMER

TOROID (DONUT-TYPE)
CURRENT TRANSFORMERS

406F03.EPS

*Figure 3* ◆ Two types of current transformers.

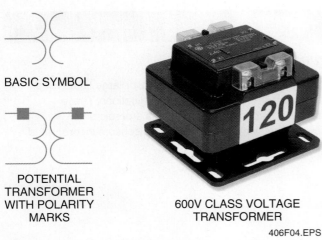

BASIC SYMBOL

POTENTIAL
TRANSFORMER
WITH POLARITY
MARKS

600V CLASS VOLTAGE
TRANSFORMER

406F04.EPS

*Figure 4* ◆ Voltage (potential) transformer.

of three-phase transformers or with banks o single-phase transformers.

See *Figure 5*. In all examples, it is assumed tha the primary line voltages between lines A, B, an C are all 1,000V and that the transformation rati is 10:1. The primary connections are shown by th upper three windings, and the Δ or Y next to th winding indicates how the winding is connected

In the Δ connections, as in *Figure 5(A)* an *Figure 5(D)*, the phase voltages of the primarie are the same as the line voltage or 1,000V. In the connections of the primaries, as in *Figure 5(B)* an *Figure 5(C)*, the phase voltages are 0.577 times th line voltages or 577V. The wye point (N) is ind cated as a common point if the windings are wy connected.

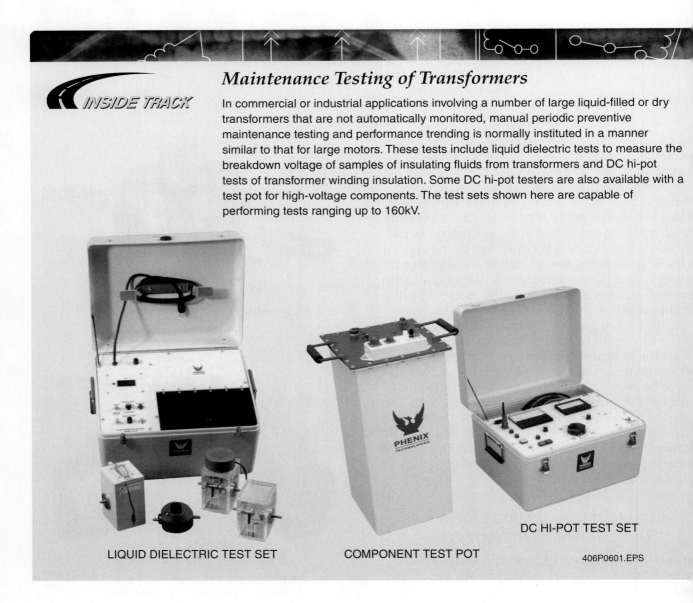

## Maintenance Testing of Transformers

*INSIDE TRACK*

In commercial or industrial applications involving a number of large liquid-filled or dry transformers that are not automatically monitored, manual periodic preventive maintenance testing and performance trending is normally instituted in a manner similar to that for large motors. These tests include liquid dielectric tests to measure the breakdown voltage of samples of insulating fluids from transformers and DC hi-pot tests of transformer winding insulation. Some DC hi-pot testers are also available with a test pot for high-voltage components. The test sets shown here are capable of performing tests ranging up to 160kV.

LIQUID DIELECTRIC TEST SET

COMPONENT TEST POT

DC HI-POT TEST SET

406P0601.EPS

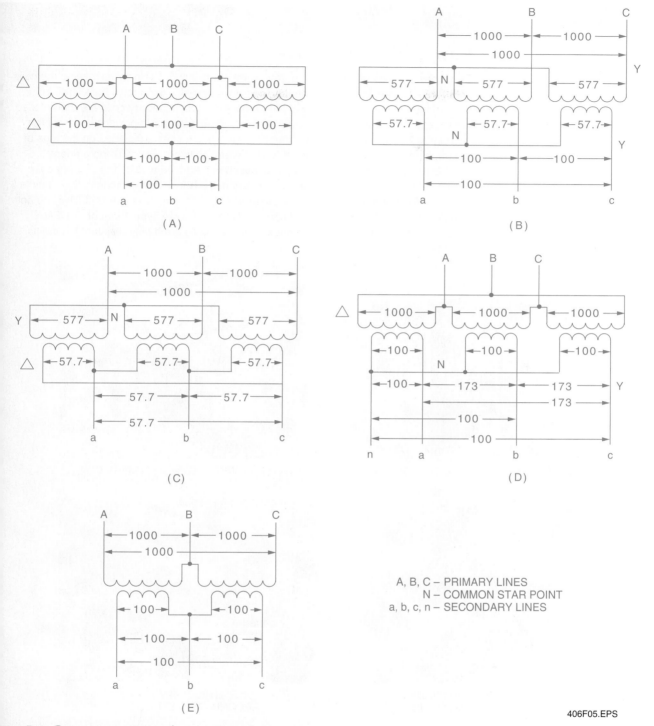

A, B, C – PRIMARY LINES
N – COMMON STAR POINT
a, b, c, n – SECONDARY LINES

406F05.EPS

*Figure 5* ◆ Common power transformer connections.

The secondaries are shown in the lower row of windings, and their connections are also indicated by the symbol Δ or Y. Each secondary phase winding has only ⅟₁₀ of the turns used in the corresponding primary phase winding and therefore supplies a phase voltage that is ⅟₁₀ of the primary phase voltage. In *Figure 5(A)* and *Figure 5(D)*, the secondary phase voltages are $1,000 \div 10 = 100$V, and in *Figure 5(B)* and *Figure 5(C)*, they are $577 \div 10 = 57.7$V. The secondaries are delta connected in *Figure 5(A)* and *Figure 5(C)*, and their line voltages or the voltages between the secondary line wires (a, b, and c) are the same as the secondary phase windings. When the secondaries are wye

## Cast-Coil Transformers

Some newer types of power transformers are made without using wire to wind the coils of the transformer. In the three-phase, step-down transformer shown here, strip foil technology is used to wind each of the primary coils. The primary coils are then placed in molds and encased with a mixture of epoxy resin and quartz powder under a high vacuum to remove any moisture. After heat curing, the coils are placed on the legs of the transformer core. Then, concentric secondary coils are wound using a sheet conductor. These secondary coils are encased in the same way as the primary coils. After curing, they are placed over the primary coils. Transformers made in this manner are capable of operating at temperatures ranging from −40°C to +180°C. They do not require liquid cooling or vaults and can be placed in NEMA Type 1 indoor or NEMA Type 3R outdoor enclosures. The epoxy-encased coils are highly resistant to caustic and humid environments.

CAST-COIL THREE-PHASE TRANSFORMER

STRIP-FOIL WINDING OF A PRIMARY COIL

SHEET-CONDUCTOR WINDING OF
A SECONDARY COIL

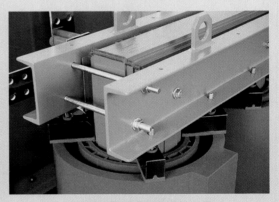

CONCENTRIC PRIMARY AND
SECONDARY CAST COILS

406P0602.EPS

connected, as in *Figure 5(B)* and *Figure 5(D)*, they have a common wye point (N) and the secondary line voltages are 1.732 times the phase voltage. In *Figure 5(B)*, the voltages between lines a, b, and c are 1.732 × 57.7 = 100V, and in *Figure 5(D)*, they are 1.732 × 100 = 173V. In addition, a fourth secondary wire (n) is brought out from the wye point

(N) in *Figure 5(D)*, and the secondary voltage between any of the lines (a, b, or c and n) is equal to the secondary phase voltage or 100V.

As you become more experienced in reading electrical diagrams, you should be able to immediately recognize the differences between delta and wye connections in any three-phase system f the three windings have a common point, it is a Y connection, and the line voltages are 1.732 times higher than the individual phase voltages. If the three windings build a closed path, it is a delta connection, and the line voltages are the same as the phase voltages.

A connection using two single-phase transformers for a three-phase system is shown in Figure 5(E). This is an open delta connection that provides a three-phase secondary with only two transformers.

# 2.0.0 ◆ SPECIALTY TRANSFORMERS

A transformer may be specially designed for a specific purpose. The principle of operation is the same for all transformers, but the forms, connections, and auxiliary devices differ widely. Among the many transformers designed for a specific purpose are single-phase transformers with two secondaries, single-phase transformers with three windings, autotransformers, constant-current transformers, series transformers, rectifier transformers, network transformers, and step-voltage regulators.

## 2.1.0 Transformers with Multiple Secondaries

One common type of transformer is a single-phase transformer with two secondaries (*Figure 6*). The first secondary has terminals $X_1$ and $X_2$ and is connected internally in series with the other secondary, which has terminals $X_3$ and $X_4$. Terminals

$X_1$ and $X_4$ are connected to outside leads, and terminals $X_2$ and $X_3$ are connected together, with the junction point connected to a third outside lead. Such transformers are commonly used as distribution transformers where three-wire service is needed from a two-wire, single-phase supply. The rated secondary voltage (120V in *Figure 6*) is obtained between either outside lead and the middle lead or neutral. In addition, double voltage (240V in *Figure 6*) is available between the two outside leads. This higher voltage is usually needed for HVAC equipment, electric ranges, and dryers, while lamps and small appliances are operated on 120V.

### 2.1.1 Three-Winding Transformers

Another widely used type of transformer is a three-winding, single-phase transformer. A third winding can be added to a transformer, and voltages will be induced in this winding proportional to the number of turns, the same as in the other windings. As a matter of fact, there is theoretically no limit to the number of windings that may be provided in a transformer. Practically, however, there is a limit because of the greater complexity, and transformers are seldom provided with more than four windings.

Three-winding transformers are used when a third voltage is desired at a given point. For example, a transformation may be desired from 132kV down to 66kV, with provision for supplying a 12kV circuit for local power distribution. Instead of using two transformers, one transforming from 13kV to 66kV and the other transforming from 66kV to 12kV, all three voltages may be obtained from one three-winding transformer.

A three-winding transformer, with the third winding connected in a delta configuration, may be used for Y-Y-connected banks for the suppression of third **harmonic** voltages. The third harmonic voltages and currents are induced in windings and superimposed on the normal voltages and currents. They have a frequency three times that of the rated frequency. Three-winding transformers are also sometimes used to tie together three transmission systems; they permit the flow of power in any direction with good voltage regulation.

Three-winding transformers are built in the same way as two-winding transformers, and they may be either the core or shell types. In the core construction, the additional winding is usually arranged so that it is concentric with the other two. In a shell transformer, the third winding is interleaved with the other two, which makes it more flexible than the core form.

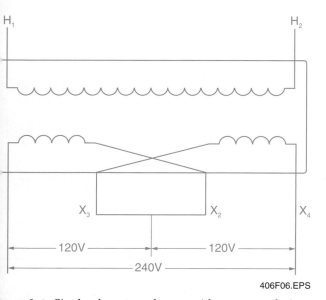

406F06.EPS

*Figure 6* ◆ Single-phase transformer with two secondaries.

## Multiple-Secondary Transformers

INSIDE TRACK

The two multiple-secondary transformers shown here are liquid-filled for cooling and insulation purposes and have internal, manually switched voltage taps. They are used for single-phase residential 120V/240V service.

PAD-MOUNTED TRANSFORMER

POLE-MOUNTED TRANSFORMER

406P0603.EPS

### 2.2.0 Autotransformers

The usual transformer has two windings that are not physically connected. In an autotransformer, one of the windings is connected in series with the other, thereby forming the equivalent of a single winding, as shown in *Figure 7*. This illustration represents a step-up autotransformer, so called because the secondary voltage is higher than the voltage supplied to the primary.

The primary voltage ($E_P$) is applied to the primary or common winding. The secondary or series winding is connected in series with the primary at the junction terminal. This point may be obtained by a tap, which will divide a single winding into a primary and a secondary.

A voltage induced in the secondary winding adds to the voltage in the primary winding, and the secondary voltage ($E_s$) is higher than the applied voltage. The ratio of transformation depends on the turns ratio, as in a two-winding transformer.

The primary current ($I_p$) branches into current $I_c$ through the common winding and the current $I_s$ through the series winding, as indicated by the arrows in *Figure 7*. The values of currents $I_c$ and $I_s$

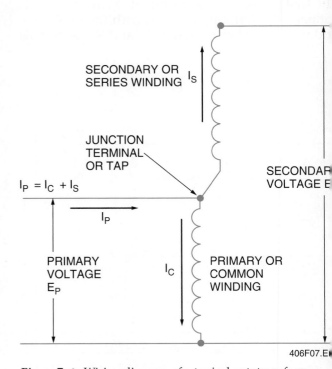

SECONDARY OR SERIES WINDING $I_S$

JUNCTION TERMINAL OR TAP

$I_P = I_C + I_S$

$I_P$

SECONDARY VOLTAGE E

PRIMARY VOLTAGE $E_P$

$I_C$

PRIMARY OR COMMON WINDING

406F07.E

*Figure 7* ◆ Wiring diagram of a typical autotransformer.

## Three-Winding Control Transformers

Small three-winding transformers may be used in control systems. The one shown here has separate 24V and 26V secondary windings and a 120V primary winding.

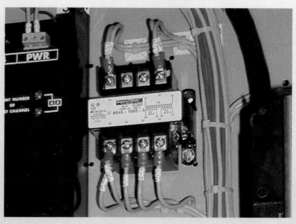

406P0604.EPS

## Advantages of Autotransformers

Autotransformers are less costly than conventional two-winding transformers and have better voltage regulation and a better ratio of energy output to input (efficiency). They are used in motor starters so that a voltage lower than the line voltage may be applied during the starting period.

inversely proportional to the ratio of turns in the two windings and the primary current ($I_p = I_s$ $I_c$). Since the currents $I_s$ and $I_c$ oppose each other, the secondary current is lower than the primary current.

Autotransformers may be used economically to connect individual loads requiring voltages other than those available in the distribution system. An example would be increasing the voltage in a branch circuit from a 120V/208V panel to 240V for more effective utilization of a motor or resistive load.

An autotransformer, however, cannot be used in a 240V or 480V, three-phase, three-wire delta system. A grounded neutral phase conductor must be available in accordance with *NEC Section 210.9*, which states that branch circuits shall not be supplied by autotransformers unless the system supplied has a grounded conductor that is electrically connected to a grounded conductor of the system supplying the autotransformer.

In general, the *NEC®* requires that separately derived alternating current systems be grounded. The secondary of an isolation transformer is a separately derived system. Therefore, it must be grounded in accordance with *NEC Section 250.30*. See *Figure 8*. In the case of an autotransformer, the grounded conductor of the supply is brought into the transformer to the common terminal and the ground is established to satisfy the *NEC®*.

### 2.3.0 Constant-Current Transformers

Constant-current transformers are used to supply series airport lighting and street lighting circuits in which the current must remain constant while the number of lamps in series varies because of burnout or bypass switching. This type of transformer has a stationary primary coil connected to a source of alternating voltage and a movable secondary coil connected to the lamp circuit. To allow it to move freely, the secondary coil is suspended

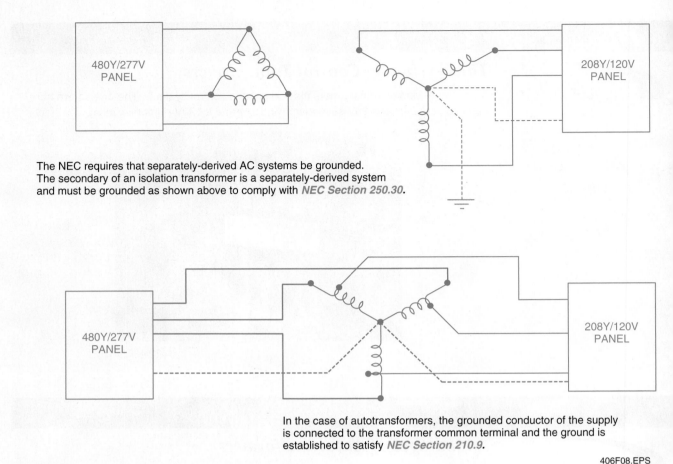

The NEC requires that separately-derived AC systems be grounded. The secondary of an isolation transformer is a separately-derived system and must be grounded as shown above to comply with *NEC Section 250.30.*

In the case of autotransformers, the grounded conductor of the supply is connected to the transformer common terminal and the ground is established to satisfy *NEC Section 210.9.*

406F08.EPS

*Figure 8* ◆ *NEC*® grounding requirements for isolation and autotransformers.

from a shaft and rod attached to a rocker arm on which hinges are attached. The tendency of the secondary coil to move downward due to gravity is opposed by both the counterweight and the magnetic repulsion between the coils caused by the current in them.

The constant secondary current is usually between 4A and 7.5A, depending on the current rating of the lamps. In order to maintain a constant secondary current, the voltage of the secondary must vary directly with the number of lamps in series. If the resistance of the secondary is reduced by decreasing the number of lamps in series because of burnout or bypass switching, the current in the transformer will momentarily increase. This will increase the force of repulsion between the coils, which will move apart. The increase in distance between the coils increases the leakage **reactance** of the transformer and causes a greater voltage drop in the transformer, with a consequent decrease in the secondary voltage. The coil will continue to move until the current in the secondary winding reaches its original value, at which position the mechanical forces

acting on the secondary coil are again balance Incandescent lamps used in series lighting circui have a film cutout in the socket. When a lam burns out, the full transformer secondary volta appears between two spring contacts separate by a thin insulation film in the socket. The volta punctures the film, causing the series circuit to k re-established.

### 2.4.0 Control Transformers

Control transformers and their connections we covered in your Level Three training. Howeve due to the number of control transformers used industrial establishments (both in new constru tion and in existing installations), and the impo tance of having a basic knowledge of how to si: these transformers for any given application, w will review the process briefly.

In general, the selection of a proper contr circuit transformer must be made from a determ nation of the maximum inrush VA and the ma> mum continuous VA to which it is subjected. Th data can be determined as follows:

**tep 1** Determine the inrush and sealed VA of all coils to be used.

**tep 2** Determine the maximum sealed VA load on the transformer.

**tep 3** Determine the maximum inrush VA load on the transformer at 100% of the secondary voltage. Add this value to any sealed VA present at the time inrush occurs.

**tep 4** Calculate the power factor of the VA load obtained in Step 3. The actual coil power factor should be used. If this value is unknown, an inrush power factor of 35% may be assumed.

**tep 5** Select a transformer with a continuous VA rating equal to or greater than the value obtained in Step 2 and whose maximum

inrush VA from Step 3 at the calculated load power factor falls on or below the corresponding curve in *Figure 9*.

The regulation curves in *Figure 9* indicate the maximum permissible inrush loads (volt-amperes at 100% of the secondary voltage), which, if applied to the transformer secondary, will not cause the secondary voltage to drop below 85% of the rated voltage when the primary voltage has been reduced to 90% of the rated voltage.

## 2.5.0 Series Transformers

A power or distribution transformer is normally used with each of its primary terminals connected across the line. When a transformer is used in series with the main line, the term series transformer is applied.

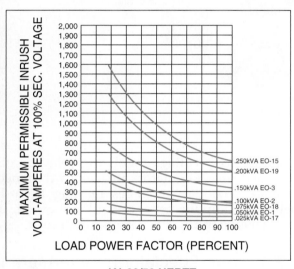

**(A) 60/50 HERTZ**

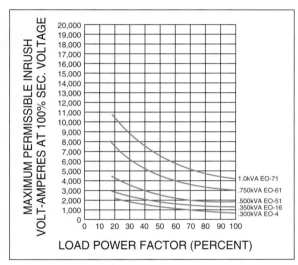

**(B) 60/50 HERTZ**

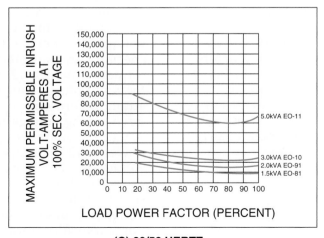

**(C) 60/50 HERTZ**

406F09.EPS

*igure 9* ◆ Regulation curves.

## *Control Power Transformers*

The control power transformer shown here is rated for use in medium-voltage applications, including switchgear, with primary voltage ranges from 5kV to 34kV. Standard output voltages are 120V/240V for single-phase units and 208V/120V for three-phase units. Some versions can be mounted vertically to conserve space.

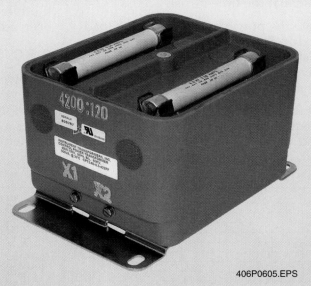

406P0605.EPS

A common application of a series transformer is its use in an airport system that has runway lamps connected in series. A small transformer is used with one or more lamp(s). The primary is connected in series with the line, and the secondary is connected across the lamp(s). The secondary winding is automatically short-circuited if a lamp burns out. The short circuit is obtained by a film cutout. When the circuit opens and the voltage across the secondary rises, it punctures the film, thereby short-circuiting the transformer secondary.

Series transformers are used in load tap changing circuits and with step-voltage regulators to reduce the operating voltage to ground when it is too high for the tap changes or to reduce the current in the tap changer contacts when the current exceeds the tap changer rating. These series transformers usually serve the purpose of an auxiliary transformer mounted in the main transformer tank.

## 2.6.0 Step-Voltage Regulators

Regulators of the step-voltage type are transformers provided with load tap changers. They are used to raise or lower the voltage of a circuit in response to a voltage-regulating relay or othe control device. Regulators are usually designed provide secondary voltages ranging from 10° below the supply voltage to 10% above it, or total change of 20% in 32 steps of ⅝% each.

## 2.7.0 Other Specialty Transformers

Specialty transformers make up a large class transformers and autotransformers used fc changing a line voltage to some particular valu best adapted to the load device. The primar voltage is generally 600V or less. Examples c specialty transformers are sign lighting tran: formers in which 120V is stepped down to 25 for low-voltage tungsten sign lamps; arc-lam autotransformers in which 240V is steppe down to the voltage required for best operatio of the arc; and transformers used to change 240 power to 120V for operating portable tools, fan welders, and other devices. Also included in th specialty class are neon sign transformers tha step 120V up to between 2,000V and 15,000V fc the operation of neon signs. Many special ste down transformers are used for small work, suc as doorbells or other signaling systems, batter charging rectifiers, and individual low-voltag amps. Practically all specialty transformers are self-cooled and air-insulated. Sometimes the cases are filled with a special compound to prevent moisture absorption and to conduct heat to the enclosing structure.

# .0.0 ◆ INSTRUMENT TRANSFORMERS

Instrument transformers are so named because they are usually connected to an electrical instrument, such as an ammeter, voltmeter, wattmeter,

or relay. As mentioned earlier, instrument transformers are of two types: current and potential (voltage).

The primary winding of a current transformer is connected in series in a line connecting the power source and the load, and it carries the full-load current. The turns ratio is designed to produce a rated current of 5A (or some other specified value) in the secondary winding when the rated current flows in the primary winding. The current transformer provides a small current suitable for the current coil of standard instruments and

## Voltage Regulators

Depending on size, individual single-phase step-voltage regulators can be pole- or pad-mounted and are available in sizes up to 830kVA at voltages from 2,500V to 19,920V. The step-voltage regulator shown here is liquid-filled and has both remote and local digital switching control for tap changing. It uses a switching reactor with equalizer windings to balance reactor voltage. An internal voltage supply furnishes power to the switching motor and control devices. Another type of voltage-adjusting transformer is the automatic voltage regulator. It continuously senses and self-adjusts to maintain a selected output voltage level at ±1% for critical loads including computer, medical, communications, and industrial process equipment. These are dry-type units with a variable-ratio autotransformer consisting of a rotor and stator. The rotor only turns 180° to add or subtract from the supply voltage and is driven by a reversible motor. Because these units regulate by transformer action instead of impedance change, no waveform distortion occurs. The regulators are available in single- and three-phase versions in sizes up to 1,000kVA at voltages from 120V to 480V.

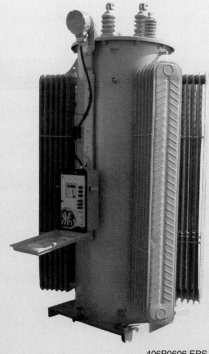

406P0606.EPS

proportional to the load current. The low-voltage, low-current secondary winding providing the current may be grounded for safety and economy in the secondary wiring and instruments.

A potential transformer is connected from one power line to another. Its secondary winding provides a low voltage, usually up to 120V, that is proportional to the line voltage. This low voltage is suitable for the voltage coil of standard instruments. The low-voltage secondary winding may be grounded for the safety of the secondary wiring and the instrument, regardless of the power line voltage.

When connecting instrument transformers to wattmeters, watt-hour meters, power factor meters, etc., it is necessary to know the polarity of the leads. One primary lead and one secondary lead of the same polarity are clearly marked on all instrument transformers, usually by a white spot or white marker on the leads.

The direction of current in the two leads of the same polarity is such that, if it is toward the transformer in the marked primary lead, it is away from the transformer in the marked secondary lead.

In diagrams, the polarity mark is usually indicated in one of three ways, as shown in *Figure 10*.

## 3.1.0 Current Transformers

A current transformer is always a single-phase transformer. If current transformers are used in a three-phase system, one current transformer is inserted into each phase line between the power

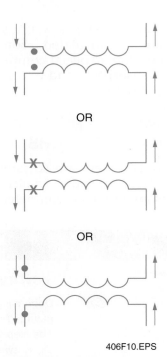

406F10.EPS

*Figure 10* ◆ Polarity marks on transformers.

supply and the instrument. A connection of current transformer into a single-phase, two-wir line is shown in *Figure 11*.

The primary winding of a current transforme must be connected in series with one of the mai power lines; thus, the main line load current flow through the primary winding. The secondar winding at the current transformer is connected t a current-responsive instrument. The secondar

### Instrument Transformers

INSIDE TRACK

Instrument transformers are classified according to the following factors:

- *Service* – Instrument transformers are designated for either metering or relaying service.
- *Burden* – The burden represents the size and characteristics of the load connected to the transformer secondary. For potential (voltage) transformers, the burden is expressed in VA at a specified power factor and voltage. For current transformers, the burden is expressed in total impedance at specified values of resistance and inductance. Generally, a transformer must perform as rated within the limits of its burden.
- *Accuracy* – For a metering transformer, an accuracy rating representing the amount of uncertainty (inaccuracy) is assigned for each rated burden of the transformer. For example, a transformer may have an accuracy rating of 0.3 at burden X and 0.6 at burden Y. Standard accuracy classes for instrument transformers are 0.3, 0.6, 1.2, and 2.4.

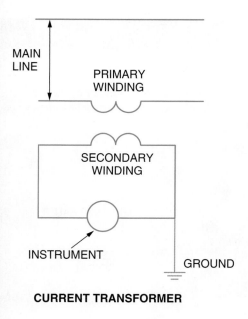

**CURRENT TRANSFORMER**

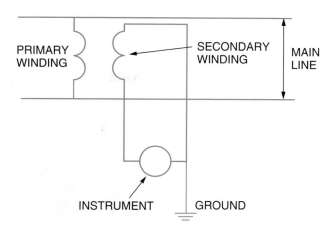

**POTENTIAL TRANSFORMER**

406F11.EPS

*Figure 11* ◆ Connection of instrument transformers.

urrent is grounded for safety. Instruments that require a current transformer may include amme-rs, wattmeters, watt-hour meters, power factor eters, some forms of relays, and trip coils of cir-uit breakers. One current transformer can be sed to operate several instruments.

The current transformer is designed for a cer-in rated apparent power or VA rating. The volt-mperes of the secondary circuit are theoretically qual to the volt-amperes of the primary circuit. he value of the secondary voltage is obtained as e product of the secondary current and the mpedance of the secondary circuit. This imped-nce, measured in ohms, consists of the imped-nces of all the instruments connected to the econdary terminals of the current transformer. Vhen no instruments are connected to the current ansformer, a short circuit connection must be laced across the secondary terminals; this results a secondary voltage of 0V.

**.1.1 Using Current Transformers**

efore disconnecting an instrument, the second-y of the current transformer must be short-rcuited. If the secondary circuit is opened while e primary winding is carrying current, there ill be no secondary **ampere turns** to balance the rimary ampere turns. Therefore, the total pri-ary current will become exciting current and agnetize the core to a high flux density, which ill produce a high voltage across both the pri-ary and secondary windings.

> **WARNING!**
>
> The secondary circuit of a current transformer should never be opened while the primary is carrying current.

Because current transformers are designed for accuracy, the normal exciting current is only a small percentage of the full-load current. The volt-age produced with the secondary open circuited is high enough to endanger the life of anyone coming in contact with the meters or leads. The high secondary voltage may also overstress the secondary insulation and cause a breakdown. Still other damage may be caused by operation with the secondary open circuited—the transformer core may become permanently magnetized, impairing the accuracy of the transformer. If this occurs, the core may be demagnetized by passing about 50% excess current through the primary, with the secondary connected to an adjustable high resistance that is gradually reduced to zero.

**3.2.0 Potential Transformers**

Potential or voltage transformers are single-phase transformers. If used on three-phase circuits, sets of two or three potential transformers are applied. The primary winding of a potential transformer is always connected across the main power lines.

A connection to a single-phase, two-wire circuit is shown in *Figure 11*. The primary of the potential

## Three-Phase Current Transformers

A three-phase toroidal current transformer unit with the leads to a motor contactor passing through the center holes is shown here. The ground fault sensor is a similar type of transformer.

GROUND FAULT SENSOR

THREE-PHASE TOROIDAL CURRENT TRANSFORMER

406P0607.EPS

## Voltage Transformers

This voltage transformer has a fused input and a primary rated for medium-voltage applications up to 34.5kV.

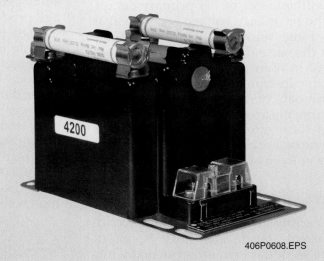

4200

406P0608.EPS

transformer is connected across the main line, and the secondary is connected to an instrument. For safety, the secondary circuit is grounded.

The main circuit voltage exists across the primary winding. The secondary of the potential transformer is connected to one or more voltag responsive devices, such as voltmeters, wat meters, watt-hour meters, power factor meters, some forms of relays or trip coils. The voltag across the secondary terminals of the potenti transformer is always lower than the primary voltage and is rated at 120V. For example, if a potential transformer with a turns ratio of 12:1 is connected to a 1,380V main line, the voltage in the instrument connected across the secondary terminals will be about 120V.

### 3.2.1 Types of Potential Transformers

All potential transformers have a wound primary and a wound secondary. Mechanically, their construction is similar to that of wound current transformers. Their secondary thermal kVA rating seldom exceeds 1.5kVA.

Potential transformers are available in both oil-filled and dry types. In both types, the primary high-voltage leads are terminated at bushings and the housing contains the secondary low-voltage terminations. When supplied as part of a switchgear assembly, they occupy dedicated spaces.

In certain small services, both current and potential transformers are packaged into a metering unit that is a single enclosure. This reduces the assembly time in field installations.

## 4.0.0 ◆ SIZING BUCK-AND-BOOST TRANSFORMERS

Manufacturers of buck-and-boost transformers normally offer easy-to-use selector charts that allow you to quickly select a buck-and-boost transformer for practically any application. These charts may be obtained from electrical equipment suppliers or ordered directly from the manufacturer—often at no charge. Instructions accompanying these charts will enable anyone familiar with transformers and electrical circuits to use them. An overview of the principles involved in using buck-and-boost transformers is given here.

When reviewing the selector charts, it may surprise you to discover that these transformers can handle loads that are much greater than their nameplate ratings. For example, a typical 1kVA buck-and-boost transformer can easily handle an 11kVA load when the voltage boost is only 10%. We will see how this is possible. First, we will examine an isolation transformer that will be incorporated as part of an autotransformer to form a buck-and-boost transformer.

### INSIDE TRACK

#### Buck-and-Boost Transformers

A small buck-and-boost transformer is shown here. It is a single-phase compound-filled unit rated at 0.05kVA. However, depending on the percentage of voltage buck or boost required, it can be used in circuits with much higher loads.

406P0609.EPS

Assume that we have a 1kVA (1,000VA) isolation transformer that is designed to transform 208V to 20.8V (see *Figure 12*). This results in a transformer winding ratio of 10:1. The primary current may be found using the following equation:

$$\text{Primary current} = \frac{1{,}000\text{VA}}{208\text{V}} = 4.8\text{A}$$

Because the transformation ratio is 10 to 1, the secondary amperes will be 48A (4.8A × 10 = 48A), or the amperage may be determined using the following equation:

$$\text{Secondary current} = \frac{1{,}000\text{VA}}{20.8\text{V}} = 48\text{A}$$

*Figure 13* shows how the windings are connected in series to form an autotransformer. Because we started with 208V at the source and now add 20.8V to it, the load is now 208V + 20.8V = 228.8V. To find the kVA rating of the system at the load, use the following equation:

$$\begin{aligned}\text{kVA} &= \frac{\text{volts}}{1{,}000} \times \text{amps} \\ &= \frac{228.8\text{V}}{1{,}000} \times 48\text{A} \\ &= 11\text{kVA}\end{aligned}$$

Ten kVA is conducted from the source, and 1kVA is transformed from the source. The total kVA rating is 10kVA + 1kVA = 11kVA.

The $H_1H_2$ winding is rated at 4.8A, and the $X_1X_2$ winding is rated at 48A. Therefore, the line

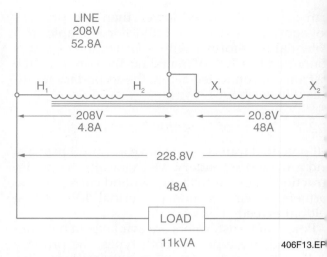

*Figure 13* ◆ Boost transformer connection.

current at 208V would be 4.8A + 48A = 52.8A. Th input kVA rating is as follows:

$$\begin{aligned}\text{kVA} &= \frac{\text{volts}}{1{,}000} \times I \\ &= \frac{208\text{V}}{1{,}000} \times 52.8\text{A} \\ &= 11\text{kVA}\end{aligned}$$

The diagrams shown in *Figures 12* and *13* ar usually simplified even more in a line diagram, a shown in *Figure 14*. Actually, all three wiring di₄ grams indicate the same thing, and following th connections on any of these drawings will pro duce the same results at the load. *Figure 14* show the calculations for a 240V source.

It should now be evident how a 1kVA buck and-boost transformer, when connected in the cir cuit as described previously, can actually carr 11kVA in its secondary winding.

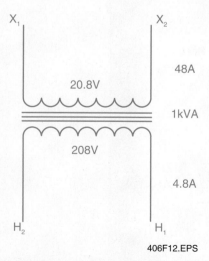

*Figure 12* ◆ Isolation transformer.

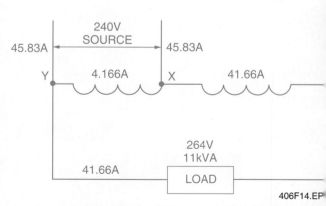

*Figure 14* ◆ Typical line diagram of a transformer circuit.

# 5.0.0 ◆ HARMONICS

Harmonics are the byproducts of modern electronics. They are especially prevalent wherever there are large numbers of personal computers (PCs), adjustable-speed drives, and other types of equipment that draw current in short pulses.

This equipment is designed to draw current only during a controlled portion of the incoming voltage waveform. Although this dramatically improves efficiency, it causes harmonics in the load current. This results in overheated transformers and neutrals, as well as tripped circuit breakers.

The problem is evident when you look at a waveform. A normal 60-cycle power line voltage appears on the oscilloscope as a near sine wave, as shown in *Figure 15(A)*. When harmonics are present, the waveform is distorted, as shown in *Figure 15(B)* and *Figure 15(C)*. These waves are described as non-sinusoidal. The voltage and current waveforms are no longer simply related—hence the term nonlinear.

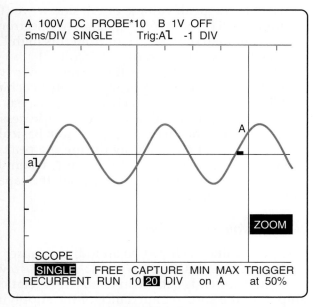

**(A) NEAR SINE WAVE**

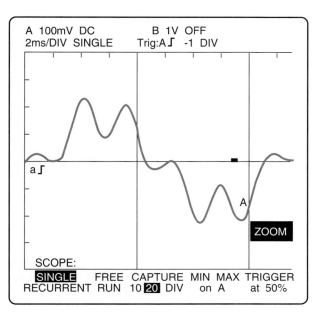

**(B) DISTORTED WAVEFORM**

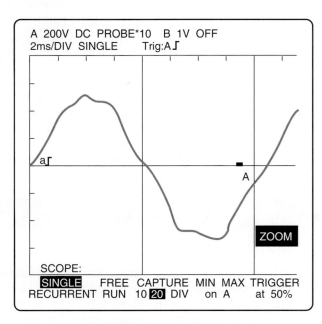

**(C) DISTORTED WAVEFORM**

406F15.EPS

*Figure 15* ◆ Voltage waveforms.

## Harmonics

If you were to listen to an ordinary 60-cycle power line, you would hear a monotone hum or buzz. When harmonics are present, you hear a different tune, rich with high notes.

Finding the problem is relatively easy once you know what to look for and where to look. Harmonics are usually anything but subtle. This section will give you some basic pointers on how to find harmonics and some suggested ways to address the problem. However, in many cases, consultants must be called in to analyze the operation and design a plan for correcting the problem.

**CAUTION**

As part of a regular maintenance program, pay careful attention to overheating of the neutral conductors in distribution systems. Harmonics may cause deterioration of the insulation.

### 5.1.0 Defining the Problem

Harmonics are currents or voltages with frequencies that are integer multiples of the fundamental power frequency. For example, if the fundamental frequency is 60Hz, then the second harmonic is 120Hz, the third is 180Hz, and so on.

Harmonics are created by nonlinear loads that draw current in abrupt pulses rather than in a smooth sinusoidal manner. These pulses cause distorted current waveshapes, which in turn cause harmonic currents to flow back into other parts of the power system. This phenomenon is especially prevalent with equipment that contains diode/capacitor input or solid-state switched power supplies, such as personal computers, printers, and medical test equipment.

In a diode/capacitor, the incoming AC voltage is diode rectified and is then used to charge a large capacitor. After a few cycles, the capacitor is charged to the peak voltage of the sine wave (for example, 168V for a 120V line). The electronic equipment then draws current from this high DC voltage to power the rest of the circuit.

The equipment can draw the current down to a regulated lower limit. Typically, before reaching that limit, the capacitor is recharged to the peak in the next half cycle of the sine wave. This process is repeated over and over. The capacitor basically draws a pulse of current only during the peak of the wave. During the rest of the wave, when the voltage is below the capacitor residual, the capacitor draws no current.

### 5.1.1 Voltage Harmonics

The power line itself can be an indirect source of voltage harmonics. The harmonic current drawn by nonlinear loads acts in an Ohm's law relationship with the source impedance of the supplying transformer to produce the voltage harmonics. The source impedance includes both the supplying transformer and the branch circuit components. For example, a 10A harmonic current being drawn for a source impedance of $0.1\Omega$ will generate a harmonic voltage of 1.0V. Any loads sharing a transformer or branch circuit with a heavy harmonic load can be affected by the voltage harmonics generated.

Many types of devices are very susceptible to voltage harmonics. The performance of the diode/capacitor power supply is critically dependent on

## Nonlinear Loads

The diode/capacitor or solid-state switched power supplies found in office equipment typically consist of single-phase, nonlinear loads. In industrial plants, the most common causes of harmonic currents are three-phase, nonlinear loads. These include electronic motor drives, uninterruptible power supplies (UPSs), HID lighting, and welding machines.

he magnitude of the peak voltage. Voltage harmonics can cause flat-topping of the voltage waveform, lowering the peak voltage. In severe cases, the computer may reset due to insufficient peak voltage.

In an industrial environment, the induction motor and power factor correction capacitors can also be seriously affected by voltage harmonics.

Power correction capacitors can form a resonant circuit with the inductive parts of a power distribution system. If the resonant frequency is near that of the harmonic voltage, the resultant harmonic current can increase substantially, overloading the capacitors and blowing the capacitor fuses. Fortunately, the capacitor failure detunes the circuit and the resonance disappears.

### .1.2 Classification of Harmonics

Each harmonic has a name, frequency, and sequence. The sequence refers to phasor rotation with respect to the fundamental (F); that is, in an induction motor, a positive sequence harmonic would generate a magnetic field that rotates in the same direction as the fundamental. A negative sequence harmonic would rotate in the reverse direction. The first nine harmonics, along with their effects, are shown in *Table 1*.

### .2.0 Office Buildings and Plants

Harmonics have a significant effect in office buildings and industrial establishments. Symptoms of harmonics usually show up in the power distribution equipment that supports the nonlinear loads. There are two basic types of nonlinear loads: single phase and three phase. Single-phase loads are prevalent in offices; three-phase loads are widespread in industrial plants.

Each component of the power distribution system manifests the effects of harmonics a little differently, but they are all subject to damage and inefficient performance.

### 5.2.1 Neutral Conductors

In a three-phase, four-wire system, the neutral conductor can be severely affected by nonlinear loads connected to the 120V branch circuits. Under normal conditions for a balanced linear load, the fundamental 60Hz portion of the phase currents will cancel in the neutral conductor.

In a four-wire system with single-phase, nonlinear loads, certain odd-numbered harmonics called triplens—odd multiples of the third harmonic: 3rd, 9th, 15th, etc.—do not cancel, but rather add together in the neutral conductor. In systems with many single-phase, nonlinear loads, the neutral current can actually exceed the phase current. The danger here is excessive overheating because there is no circuit breaker in the neutral conductor to limit the current as there are in the phase conductors.

Excessive current in the neutral conductor can also cause higher voltage drops between the neutral conductor and ground at the 120V outlet.

### 5.2.2 Circuit Breakers

Common thermal-magnetic circuit breakers use a bimetallic trip mechanism that responds to the heating effect of the circuit current. They are designed to respond to the true root-mean-square (rms) value of the current waveform and therefore will trip when they get too hot. This type of breaker has a better chance of protecting against harmonic current overloads.

A peak sensing electronic trip circuit breaker responds to the peak of the current waveform. As a result, it will not always respond properly to harmonic currents. Since the peak of the harmonic current is usually higher than normal, this type of circuit breaker may trip prematurely at a low current. If the peak is lower than normal, the breaker may fail to trip when it should.

**Table 1**    Harmonic Rates and Effects

| Name | F | 2nd | 3rd | 4th | 5th | 6th | 7th | 8th | 9th |
|------|----|-----|-----|-----|-----|-----|-----|-----|-----|
| Frequency | 60 | 120 | 180 | 240 | 300 | 360 | 420 | 480 | 540 |
| Sequence | + | — | 0 | + | — | 0 | + | — | 0 |

| Sequence | Rotation | Effects (skin effect, eddy currents, etc.) |
|----------|----------|--------------------------------------------|
| Positive | Forward | Heating of conductors and circuit breakers |
| Negative | Reverse | Heating as above, plus motor problems |
| Zero | None | Heating, plus add-in neutral of three-phase, four-wire system |

### 5.2.3 Busbars and Connecting Lugs

Neutral busbars and connecting lugs are sized to carry the full value of the rated phase current. They can become overloaded when the neutral conductors are overloaded with the additional sum of the triplen harmonics.

### 5.2.4 Electrical Panels

Harmonics in electrical panels can be quite noisy. Panels that are designed to carry 60Hz current can become mechanically resonant to the magnetic fields generated by high-frequency harmonic currents. When this happens, the panel vibrates and emits a buzzing sound at the harmonic frequencies.

### 5.2.5 Telecommunications

Telecommunications cable is commonly run right next to power cables. To minimize the inductive interference from phase current, telecommunications cables are run closer to the neutral wire. Triplens in the neutral conductor commonly cause inductive interference that can be heard on a phone line. This is often the first indication of a harmonic problem and gives you a head start in detecting the problem before it causes major damage.

### 5.2.6 Transformers

Commercial buildings commonly have a 120V/208V transformer in a delta-wye configuration, as shown in *Figure 16*. These transformers commonly feed receptacles in a commercial building. Single-phase, nonlinear loads connected to the receptacles produce triplen harmonics that algebraically add up in the neutral. When this neutral current reaches the transformer, it is reflected into the delta primary winding, where it circulates and causes overheating and transformer failures.

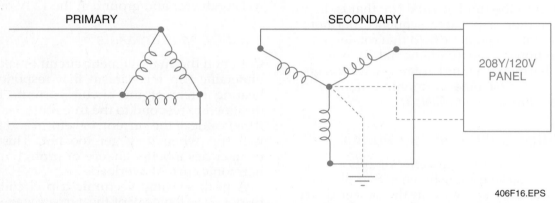

*Figure 16* ◆ Three-phase, delta-wye transformer configuration.

### K-Rated and Zig-Zag Transformers

Specially designed transformers that reduce or compensate for harmonic current include K-rated and zig-zag transformers. To prevent overheating, K-rated three-phase transformers for delta-to-wye connections are sized to handle 100% of the normal 60Hz load plus a specified nonlinear load defined by a K number. Manufacturers' specifications define the K numbers for various types of loads. If the various harmonics are known, a specific transformer can be custom built. The inherent phase shift of a K-rated transformer will cancel 5th and 7th harmonics but not the triplens. Because triplens are not cancelled, the neutral of the secondary is normally oversized at 200% of the maximum current rating of one of the phase connections. A zig-zag phase shift transformer cancels triplens and other harmonics at the load side of the transformer by using six windings in the secondary. An extra winding for each phase is connected in series with another phase to produce a phase shift. This type of transformer works well if the loads are balanced. A drawback is that zig-zag transformers use more material in the windings and are heavy. Other techniques such as active filters or ferroresonant transformers are also used for harmonic current suppression in certain applications.

Another transformer problem results from **core loss** and copper loss. Transformers are normally rated for a 60Hz phase current load only.

High-frequency harmonic currents cause increased core loss due to **eddy currents** and **hysteresis,** resulting in more heating than would occur at the same 60Hz current. These heating effects demand that transformers be derated for harmonic loads or replaced with specially designed transformers.

### 5.2.7 Generators

Standby generators are subject to the same types of overheating problems as transformers. Because they provide emergency backup for harmonics-producing loads such as data processing equipment, they are often even more vulnerable. In addition to overheating, certain types of harmonics produce distortion at the zero crossing of the current waveform, which causes interference and instability in the generator control circuits.

## 5.3.0 Survey the Situation

A quick survey will help to determine whether or not you have a harmonics problem and where it is located. The survey procedure should include the following:

*Step 1* Take a walking tour of the facility and look at the types of equipment in use. If there are a lot of personal computers and printers, adjustable-speed motors, solid-state heater controls, and certain types of fluorescent lighting, there is a good chance that harmonics are present.

*Step 2* Locate the transformers feeding the nonlinear loads and check for excess heating. Also, make sure that the cooling vents are unobstructed.

*Step 3* Use a true rms meter to check transformer currents.
- Verify that the voltage ratings for the test equipment are adequate for the transformer being tested.
- Measure and record the transformer secondary currents in each phase and in the neutral (if used).
- Calculate the kVA delivered to the load, and compare it to the nameplate rating. If harmonic currents are present, the transformer can overheat, even if the kVA delivered is less than the nameplate rating.
- If the transformer secondary is a four-wire system, compare the measured

neutral current to the value predicted from the imbalance in the phase currents. (The neutral current is the vector sum of the phase currents and is normally zero if the phase currents are balanced in both amplitude and phase.) If the neutral current is unexpectedly high, triple harmonics are likely, and the transformer may need to be derated.
- Measure the frequency of the neutral current. 180Hz would be a typical reading for a neutral current consisting of mostly third harmonics.

*Step 4* Survey the subpanels that feed harmonic loads. Measure the current in each branch neutral, and compare the measured value to the rated capacity for the wire size used. Check the neutral busbar and feeder connections for heating or discoloration.

*Step 5* Neutral overloading in receptacle branch circuits can sometimes be detected by measuring the neutral-to-ground voltage at the receptacle. Measure the voltage when the loads are on. A reading of 2V or less is normal. Higher voltages can indicate trouble, depending on the length of the run, quality of the connections, etc. Measure the frequency. 180Hz would suggest a strong presence of harmonics. 60Hz would suggest that the phases are out of balance. Pay special attention to under-carpet wiring and modular office panels with integrated wiring that use a neutral shared by three-phase conductors. Because the typical loads in these two areas are computer and office machines, they are often trouble spots for overloaded neutrals.

### 5.3.1 Meters

Having the proper equipment is crucial to diagnosing harmonics problems. The type of equipment used varies with the complexity of measurements required.

To determine whether you have a harmonics problem, you need to measure the true rms value and the instantaneous peak value of the waveshape. For this test, you need a true rms clamp-on multimeter or a handheld digital multimeter that makes true rms measurements and has a high-speed peak hold circuit.

The term true rms refers to the root-mean-square or equivalent heating value of a current or voltage waveshape. True distinguishes the measurement from those taken by average responding meters.

The vast majority of low-cost, portable clamp-on ammeters are average responding. These instruments give correct readings for pure sine waves only and will typically read low when confronted with a distorted current waveform. The result is a reading that can be up to 50% low.

True rms meters give correct readings for any waveshape within the instrument's crest factor and bandwidth specifications.

### 5.3.2 Crest Factor

The crest factor of a waveform is the ratio of the peak value to the rms value. For a sine wave, the crest factor is 1.414. A true rms meter will have a crest factor specification. This specification relates to the level of peaking that can be measured without errors.

A quality true rms handheld digital multimeter has a crest factor of 3.0 at full scale. This is more than adequate for most power distribution measurements. At half scale, the crest factor is double. For example, a meter may have a crest factor specification of 3.0 when measuring 400VAC and a crest factor of 6.0 when measuring 200VAC.

**NOTE**

Most true rms meters cannot be used for signals below 5% of scale because of the measurement noise problem. Use a lower range if it is available.

The crest factor can be easily calculated using true rms meter with a peak function or a cres function. A crest factor other than 1.414 indicate the presence of harmonics. In typical single-phas cases, the greater the difference from 1.414, th greater the harmonics. For voltage harmonics, th typical crest factor is below 1.414 (i.e., a flat-to waveform). For single-phase current harmonics the typical crest factor is well above 1.414. Three phase current waveforms often exhibit th double-hump waveform; therefore, the crest fac tor comparison method should not be applied t three-phase load currents.

After you have determined that harmonics ar present, you can make a more in-depth analysis o the situation using a harmonics analyzer.

## Power Quality Analyzers

*INSIDE TRACK*

Portable power quality analyzers like the one shown here can be used to determine harmonics, as well as to make power measurements (kW, VA, and VAR), power factor and displaced power factor measurements, voltage and current readouts and waveforms, inrush current and duration recording, transient measurements, and sag and swell recording. Extensive power quality measurements can be made continuously using the software provided with most energy management systems.

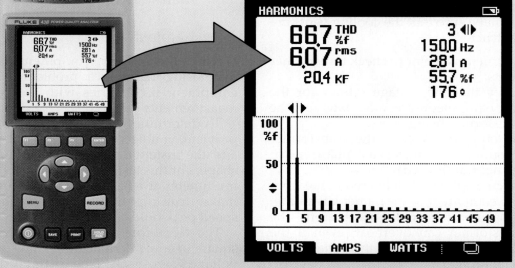

406P0610.EPS

## Four-Wire Systems

**What condition might cause some conductors of a four-wire system to feel hot to the touch?**

## .4.0 Solving the Problem

he following are some suggested ways of ddressing some typical harmonics problems. efore taking any measures, you should consult a ower quality expert to analyze the problem and esign a plan tailored to your specific situation.

### .4.1   Harmonics in Overloaded Neutrals

n a three-phase, four-wire wye system, the 60Hz ortion of the neutral current can be minimized y balancing the loads in each phase. *NEC Section 20.61* prohibits reduced sizing of neutral conduc- ors serving nonlinear loads. The triplen harmon- s neutral current can be reduced by adding armonic filters at the load. If neither of these olutions is practical, you can pull in extra neu- als (ideally one neutral for each phase) or you an install an oversized neutral to be shared by the ree conductors.

In new construction, under-carpet wiring and nodular office partition wiring should be speci- ed with individual neutrals and possibly an iso- ted ground separate from the safety ground.

### .4.2   Derating Transformers

ne way to protect a transformer from harmonics to limit the amount of load placed on it. This is lled derating the transformer. The most rigor- us derating method is described in *ANSI/IEEE tandard C57.110-1986*. This method is somewhat npractical because it requires extensive loss data om the transformer manufacturer, plus a com- lete harmonics spectrum of the load current.

The Computer and Business Equipment Manu- cturers' Association (CBEMA) has recom- ended a second method that involves several traightforward measurements that you can get sing common test equipment. It appears to give asonable results for 208V/120Y receptacle trans- rmers that supply the low-frequency odd har- onics (3rd, 5th, and 7th) commonly generated y computers and office machines.

The test equipment you use must be capable of king both the true rms phase current and the

instantaneous peak phase current for each phase of the secondary.

To determine the derating factor for the trans- former, take the peak and true rms current mea- surements for the three-phase conductors. If the phases are not balanced, average the three mea- surements and plug that value into the following equation:

Transformer harmonics derating factor (THDF) =

$$\frac{1.414 \times \text{true rms phase current}}{\text{instantaneous peak phase current}}$$

This equation generates a value between 0 and 1.0 (typically between 0.5 and 0.9). If the phase currents are purely sinusoidal (undistorted), the instantaneous current peaks at 1.414 times the true rms value and the derating factor is 1.0. If that is the case, no derating is required.

However, with harmonics present, the trans- former rating is the product of the nameplate kVA rating times the THDF:

Derated kVA = THDF × nameplate kVA

For example, a modern office building dedicated primarily to computer software development contains a large number of PCs and other elec- tronic office equipment. These electronic loads are fed by a 120V/208V transformer configured with a delta primary and a wye secondary. The PCs are fairly well distributed throughout the building, except for one large room that contains several machines. The PCs in this room, used exclusively for testing, are served by several branch circuits.

The transformer and main switchgear are located in a ground floor electrical room. An inspection of this room immediately reveals two symptoms of high harmonic currents:

- The transformer is generating a substantial amount of heat.
- The main panel emits an audible buzzing sound. The sound is not the chatter commonly associ- ated with a faulty circuit breaker, but rather a deep, resonant buzz that indicates the mechani- cal parts of the panel itself are vibrating.

**Table 2** Current Measurements

| Conductor Name | Multimeter (true rms) | Average Responding Multimeter | Instantaneous Peak Current |
|---|---|---|---|
| Phase 1 | 410A | 328A | 804A |
| Phase 2 | 445A | 346A | 892A |
| Phase 3 | 435A | 355A | 828A |
| Neutral | 548A | 537A | 762A |

The ductwork installed directly over the transformer to carry off some of the excess heat keeps the room temperature within reasonable limits.

Current measurements (see *Table 2*) are taken on the neutral and on each phase of the transformer secondary using both a true rms multimeter and an average responding unit.

A 600A, clamp-on current transformer accessory is connected to each meter to allow the meters to make high current readings.

The presence of harmonics is obvious by a comparison of the phase current and neutral current measurements. As *Table 2* shows, the neutral current is substantially higher than any of the phase currents, even though the phase currents are relatively well balanced. The average responding meter consistently shows readings that are approximately 20% low on all phases. Its neutral current readings are only 2% low.

The waveforms explain the discrepancy. The phase currents are badly distorted by large amounts of triplen harmonics, while the neutral current is not affected. The phase current readings listed in *Table 2* clearly demonstrate why true rms measurement capability is required to accurately determine the value of harmonic currents.

The next step is to calculate the transformer harmonic derating factor, or THDF, as explained previously.

The results indicate that, with the level of harmonics present, the transformer should be derated to 72.3% of its nameplate rating to prevent overheating. In this case, the transformer should be derated to 72.3% of its 225kVA rating, c 162.7kVA.

The actual load is calculated to be 151.3kVA Although this figure is far less than the nameplat rating, the transformer is operating close to it derated capacity.

Next, a subpanel that supplies branch circuit for the 120V receptacles is also examined. The cu rent in each neutral is measured and shown i *Table 3*.

**Table 3** Neutral Loads

| Neutral Conductor Number | Current (Amps) |
|---|---|
| 01 | 5.0 |
| 02 | 11.3 |
| 03 | 5.0 |
| 04 | 13.1 |
| 05 | 12.4 |
| 06 | 15.0 |
| 07 | 1.8 |
| 08 | 11.7 |
| 09 | 4.5 |
| 10 | 11.8 |
| 11 | 9.6 |
| 12 | 11.5 |
| 13 | 11.3 |
| 14 | 6.7 |
| 15 | 7.0 |
| 16 | 2.3 |
| 17 | 2.6 |

**THINK ABOUT IT**

*True RMS Meters*

Why is it important to use a true rms meter?

When a marginal or overloaded conductor is identified, the associated phase currents and the neutral-to-ground voltage at the receptacle are also measured. When a check of neutral No. 6 reveals 15A in a conductor rated for 16A, the phase currents of the circuits (No. 25, No. 27, and No. 29) that share that neutral are also measured. See *Table 4*.

Note that each of the phase currents of these three branch circuits is substantially less than 15A and the same phase conductors have significant neutral-to-ground voltage drops.

In the branch circuits that have high neutral currents, the relationship between the neutral and the phase currents is similar to that of the transformer secondary. The neutral current is higher than any of the associated phase currents. The danger here is that the neutral conductors could become overloaded and not offer the warning signs of tripped circuit breakers.

**Table 4** Phase Currents and Neutral-to-Ground Voltages

| Circuit Number | Phase Current | Neutral-to-Ground Voltage Drop at Receptacle |
|---|---|---|
| 25 | 7.8A | 3.75V |
| 27 | 9.7A | 4.00V |
| 29 | 13.5A | 8.05V |

The recommendations are:

- Refrain from adding additional loads to the receptacle transformer unless steps are taken to reduce the level of harmonics.
- Pull extra neutrals into the branch circuits that are heavily loaded.
- Monitor the load currents on a regular basis using true rms test equipment.

1. What is the name given to the large transformers used in transmission systems to step voltage up and down?
   a. Control transformers
   b. Power transformers
   c. Instrument transformers
   d. Potential transformers

2. The purpose of the two secondary windings in a three-winding, single-phase transformer is _____.
   a. so the transformer may be used on systems with different primary voltages
   b. to produce a non-magnetic field
   c. to produce a high-impedance field
   d. to produce two secondary voltages

3. How many windings are normally found in an autotransformer?
   a. One
   b. Two
   c. Three
   d. Four

4. What type of transformer is normally used with metering equipment when the current is too high for the metering equipment?
   a. Potential transformer
   b. Reactance transformer
   c. Current transformer
   d. Autotransformer

5. What type of transformer is normally used with metering equipment when the line voltage is too high for the metering equipment?
   a. Potential transformer
   b. Reactance transformer
   c. Current transformer
   d. Autotransformer

6. What is a transformer called when it is connected in series with the main line?
   a. Reactance transformer
   b. Series transformer
   c. High-voltage transformer
   d. Low-ampere transformer

7. A(n) _____ is always a single-phase transformer.
   a. power transformer
   b. reactance transformer
   c. current transformer
   d. autotransformer

8. The secondary thermal kVA rating of a conventional potential transformer seldom exceeds _____.
   a. 1kVA
   b. 1.5kVA
   c. 1,500kVA
   d. 15,000kVA

9. What type of transformer is normally able to handle a load that is much greater than its nameplate rating?
   a. Potential transformer
   b. Reactance transformer
   c. Current transformer
   d. Buck-and-boost transformer

10. The problem of harmonics is often first detected by the presence of inductive interference in _____ systems.
    a. lighting
    b. heating
    c. telecommunications
    d. emergency power

11. Potential transformers are available in _____ types.
    a. oil-filled and hydraulic
    b. oil-filled and dry
    c. dry and chemical
    d. dry and coiled

12. Regulators are usually designed to provide a total secondary voltage range of _____ of the supply voltage.
    a. 20%
    b. 35%
    c. 45%
    d. 55%

**13.** Each harmonic has a _____.
   a.  name only
   b.  name and frequency only
   c.  name, frequency, and sequence
   d.  name, frequency, and rotation

**14.** Neutral busbars and connecting lugs are sized to carry _____ of the rated phase current.
   a. 75%
   b. 80%
   c. 90%
   d. 100%

**15.** For a sine wave, the crest factor is _____.
   a.  1.000
   b.  1.414
   c.  2.212
   d.  2.414

# Summary

Transformers are used in numerous applications to alter the output voltage to serve various purposes. This module covered types of specialty transformers, including:

- Power transformers
- Buck-and-boost transformers
- Current and potential transformers
- Transformers with multiple secondaries
- Autotransformers
- Constant-current transformers

- Control transformers
- Series transformers
- Rectifier transformers
- Step-voltage regulators

It also discussed the problem of harmonics and its associated symptoms and possible solutions. A complete understanding of transformer selection, application, and troubleshooting techniques is essential to the proper installation and servicing of electrical systems.

# Notes

# Trade Terms
# Introduced in This Module

*Ampere turn:* The product of amperes times the number of turns in a coil.

*Autotransformer:* Any transformer in which the primary and secondary connections are made to a single winding. The application of an autotransformer is a good choice where a 480Y/277V or 208Y/120V, three-phase, four-wire distribution system is used.

*Bank:* An installed grouping of a number of units of the same type of electrical equipment, such as a bank of transformers, a bank of capacitors, or a meter bank.

*Core loss:* The electric loss that occurs in the core of an armature or transformer due to conditions such as the presence of eddy currents or hysteresis.

*Eddy currents:* The circulating currents that are induced in conductive materials by varying magnetic fields; they are usually considered undesirable because they represent a loss of energy and produce excess heat.

*Harmonic:* An oscillation whose frequency is an integral multiple of the fundamental frequency.

*Hysteresis:* The time lag exhibited by a body in reacting to changes in the forces affecting it; hysteresis is an internal friction.

*Impedance:* The opposition to current flow in an AC circuit; impedance includes resistance (R), capacitive reactance $(X_C)$, and inductive reactance $(X_L)$. It is measured in ohms $(\Omega)$.

*Isolation transformer:* A transformer that has no electrical metallic connection between the primary and secondary windings.

*Reactance:* The imaginary part of impedance; also, the opposition to alternating current due to capacitance $(X_C)$ and/or inductance $(X_L)$.

## Additional Resources

This module is intended to present thorough resources for task training. The following reference works are suggested for further study. These are optional materials for continuing education rather than for task training.

*American Electrician's Handbook,* Terrell Croft an Wilfred I. Summers. New York, NY: McGraw Hill, 1996.

*National Electrical Code® Handbook,* Latest Edition Quincy, MA: National Fire Protection Associa tion.

# CONTREN® LEARNING SERIES — USER FEEDBACK

The NCCER makes every effort to keep these textbooks up-to-date and free of technical errors. We appreciate your help in this process. If you have an idea for improving this textbook, or if you find an error, a typographical mistake, or an inaccuracy in NCCER's *Contren®* textbooks, please write us, using this form or a photocopy. Be sure to include the exact module number, page number, a detailed description, and the correction, if applicable. Your input will be brought to the attention of the Technical Review Committee. Thank you for your assistance.

*Instructors* – If you found that additional materials were necessary in order to teach this module effectively, please let us know so that we may include them in the Equipment/Materials list in the Annotated Instructor's Guide.

**Write:**  Product Development
National Center for Construction Education and Research
P.O. Box 141104, Gainesville, FL  32614-1104

**Fax:**  352-334-0932

**E-mail:**  curriculum@nccer.org

Craft _____  Module Name _____

Copyright Date _____  Module Number _____  Page Number(s) _____

Description _____

_____

_____

_____

(Optional) Correction _____

_____

_____

(Optional) Your Name and Address _____

_____

_____

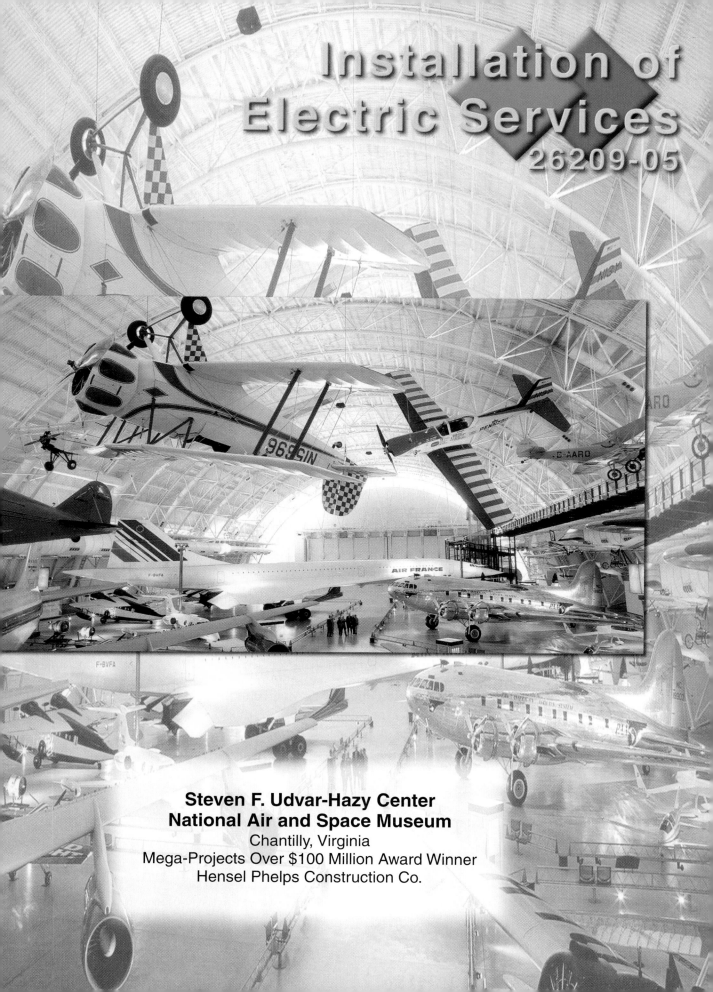

# Installation of Electric Services

## 26209-05

**Steven F. Udvar-Hazy Center**
**National Air and Space Museum**
Chantilly, Virginia
Mega-Projects Over $100 Million Award Winner
Hensel Phelps Construction Co.

# 26209-05

# *Installation of Electric Services*

*Topics to be presented in this module include:*

# Overview

Commercial power becomes the responsibility of the customer at the electr service. Electricians install the electric service but do not generally make t connections at the point where the commercial power connects. This is usual the job of the electric utility provider.

If the commercial power connects to the electric service overhead, the i coming service supply is referred to as a service drop. On the other hand, if t lines are supplied underground, the service supply is said to be a service la eral. The *National Electrical Code*® regulates the installation of both service dro and service laterals, including minimum requirements related to overhead co ductor heights, burial depths, raceways, and other installation conditions.

Building an electric service at the consumer's location requires knowled of materials and service installation skills. If the service supply is a servi drop, the service conductors enter the service raceway through a service he or weatherhead, which is designed to keep rain out of the service equipme Separate service-entrance conductors are usually installed in the service rac way and these connect to the service drop at the point of attachment to t service raceway. The service equipment includes the electrical meter enclosu service disconnecting means, main circuit breaker panelboard, and groundi system.

## Objectives

When you have completed this module, you will be able to do the following:

1. Describe various types of electric services for commercial and industrial installations.
2. Read electrical blueprints and diagrams describing service installations.
3. Calculate and select service-entrance equipment.
4. Explain the role of the *NEC®* in service installations.
5. Install main disconnect switches, panelboards, and overcurrent protection devices.
6. Identify the circuit loads, number of circuits required, and installation requirements for distribution panels.
7. Explain the types and purposes of service grounding.
8. Explain the purpose and required location(s) of ground fault circuit interrupters.
9. Describe single-phase service connections.
10. Describe both wye- and delta-connected three-phase services.

## Trade Terms

Delta-connected
Load center
Service
Service conductors
Service drop
Service entrance
Service equipment
Service lateral
Service raceway
Substation
Wye-connected

## Required Trainee Materials

1. Pencil and paper
2. Appropriate personal protective equipment
3. Copy of the latest edition of the *National Electrical Code®*

## Prerequisites

Before you begin this module, it is recommended that you successfully complete *Core Curriculum; Electrical Level One; Electrical Level Two,* Modules 26201-05 through 26208-05. You should also read *NEC Article 230.*

This course map shows all of the modules in *Electrical Level Two.* The suggested training order begins at the bottom and proceeds up. Skill levels increase as you advance on the course map. The local Training Program Sponsor may adjust the training order.

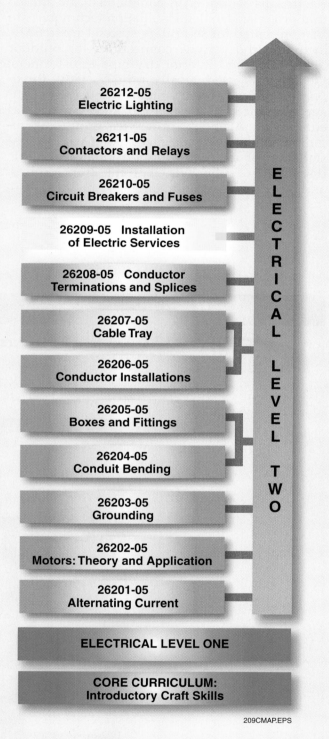

209CMAP.EPS

## 1.0.0 ◆ INTRODUCTION

This module is designed to cover most electric **service** applications that will be encountered by electricians working on commercial and industrial projects. Detailed installation techniques are also presented for secondary systems up to 600V, including the various connections for outdoor distribution and interior dry-type transformers; the latter is used mostly on 277/480V, three-phase, **wye-connected** systems where lower voltage is required to operate 120/208V outlets and equipment. A review of service grounding requirements is also presented, along with the installation of main distribution panels, multiple disconnects, subpanels, current transformers, and other service equipment.

Electric services can range in size from a small 120V, single-phase, 15A service, which is the minimum allowed by *NEC Section 230.79(A)*, for a roadside vegetable stand, to huge industrial installations involving **substations** dealing with thousands of volts and amperes. Regardless of the size, all electric services are provided for the same purpose: to deliver electrical energy from the supply system to the wiring system on the premises served. Consequently, all establishments containing equipment that utilizes electricity require an electric service.

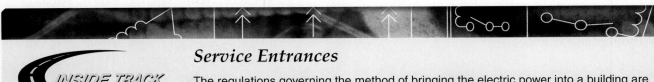

INSIDE TRACK

### Service Entrances

The regulations governing the method of bringing the electric power into a building are established by the local utility company. These regulations can vary considerably between utility companies and regional areas.

209P0901.EPS

*Figure 1* shows the basic components of a typical commercial electric service. In this illustration, note that the high-voltage lines terminate on a power pole near the building being served. A bank of transformers is mounted on the pole to reduce the transmission voltage to a usable level (in this case, 120/208V, three-phase, wye-connected). The remaining sections are:

- *Service drop* – The overhead conductors through which electrical service is supplied between the last power company pole and the point of their connection to the service-entrance conductors located at the building or other support used for the purpose.
- *Service entrance* – All components between the point of termination of the overhead service drop or underground **service lateral** and the building's main disconnecting device, except for metering equipment.

- *Service conductors* – The conductors between the point of termination of the overhead service drop or underground service lateral and the main disconnecting device in the building or on the premises.
- *Service equipment* – The necessary equipment, usually consisting of a circuit breaker or switch and fuses and their accessories, located near the point of entrance of supply conductors to a building and intended to constitute the main control and cutoff means for the electric supply to the building.

When the service conductors to the building are routed underground, as shown in *Figure 2*, these conductors are known as the service lateral, which are the underground conductors through which service is supplied between the power company's distribution facilities and the first point of their connection to the building or area service facilities located at the building or other support used for the purpose.

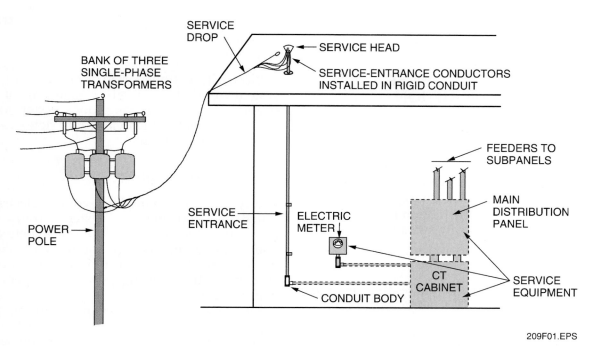

209F01.EPS

*Figure 1* ◆ Typical three-phase overhead service.

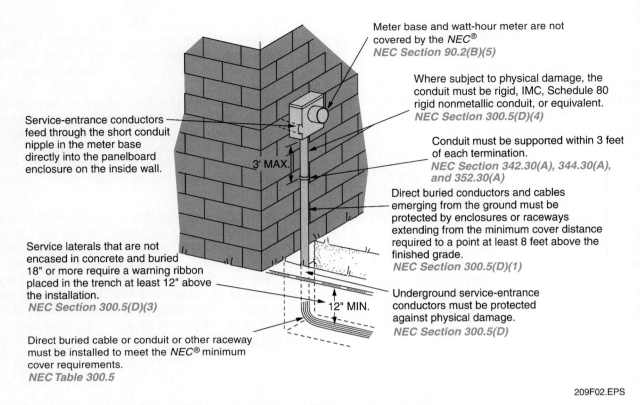

Meter base and watt-hour meter are not covered by the *NEC®*
*NEC Section 90.2(B)(5)*

Where subject to physical damage, the conduit must be rigid, IMC, Schedule 80 rigid nonmetallic conduit, or equivalent.
*NEC Section 300.5(D)(4)*

Conduit must be supported within 3 feet of each termination.
*NEC Section 342.30(A), 344.30(A), and 352.30(A)*

Direct buried conductors and cables emerging from the ground must be protected by enclosures or raceways extending from the minimum cover distance required to a point at least 8 feet above the finished grade.
*NEC Section 300.5(D)(1)*

Underground service-entrance conductors must be protected against physical damage.
*NEC Section 300.5(D)*

Service-entrance conductors feed through the short conduit nipple in the meter base directly into the panelboard enclosure on the inside wall.

3' MAX.

Service laterals that are not encased in concrete and buried 18" or more require a warning ribbon placed in the trench at least 12" above the installation.
*NEC Section 300.5(D)(3)*

12" MIN.

Direct buried cable or conduit or other raceway must be installed to meet the *NEC®* minimum cover requirements.
*NEC Table 300.5*

209F02.EPS

*Figure 2* ◆ Single-phase underground service lateral for small commercial building.

## 2.0.0 ◆ ELECTRICAL GENERATION AND DISTRIBUTION

A review of electrical distribution systems is the best foundation for understanding alternating current and the purpose of electric services.

The essential elements of an AC electrical system capable of producing useful power include generating stations, transformers, substations, transmission lines, and distribution lines. *Figure 3* shows these elements and their relationships.

### 2.1.0 Generation

Electricity is produced at the generating plant at voltages ranging between 2,400V and 13,200V. Transformers are also located at the generating plant to step up the voltage to hundreds of thousands of volts for transmission.

Electricity is transported from one part of th[e] system to another by cables made up of man[y] strands of wire. The continuous system of co[n]ductors through which electricity flows is calle[d] the distribution circuit.

### 2.2.0 Transmission

The system for moving high-voltage electricity [is] called the transmission system. Transmissio[n] lines are interconnected to form a network [of] lines. Should one line fail, another will take ov[er] the load. Such interconnections provide a reliab[le] system for transporting power from generatin[g] plants to communities.

Most transmission lines installed by pow[er] companies utilize three-phase current—three se[p]arate streams of electricity traveling on separa[te]

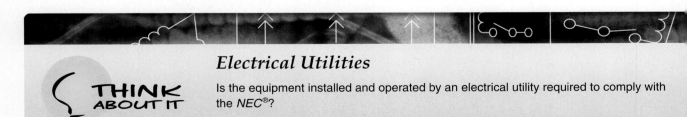

### *Electrical Utilities*

**THINK ABOUT IT**

Is the equipment installed and operated by an electrical utility required to comply with the *NEC®*?

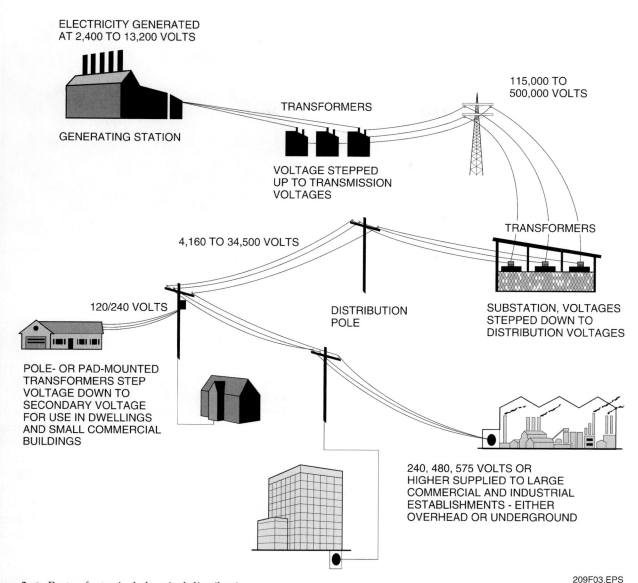

ELECTRICITY GENERATED
AT 2,400 TO 13,200 VOLTS

GENERATING STATION

TRANSFORMERS

VOLTAGE STEPPED
UP TO TRANSMISSION
VOLTAGES

115,000 TO
500,000 VOLTS

TRANSFORMERS

4,160 TO 34,500 VOLTS

120/240 VOLTS

DISTRIBUTION
POLE

SUBSTATION, VOLTAGES
STEPPED DOWN TO
DISTRIBUTION VOLTAGES

POLE- OR PAD-MOUNTED
TRANSFORMERS STEP
VOLTAGE DOWN TO
SECONDARY VOLTAGE
FOR USE IN DWELLINGS
AND SMALL COMMERCIAL
BUILDINGS

240, 480, 575 VOLTS OR
HIGHER SUPPLIED TO LARGE
COMMERCIAL AND INDUSTRIAL
ESTABLISHMENTS - EITHER
OVERHEAD OR UNDERGROUND

209F03.EPS

*Figure 3* ◆ Parts of a typical electrical distribution system.

onductors. This is an efficient way to transport
arge quantities of electricity. At various points
along the way, transformers step down the transmission voltage at facilities known as substations.

## 3.0 Substations

ubstations can be small buildings or fenced-in
ards containing switches, transformers, and
ther electrical equipment and structures. Substa-
ons are convenient places to monitor the system
nd adjust circuits. Devices called regulators,
hich maintain system voltage as the demand for
ectricity changes, are also installed in substa-
ons. Another device, which momentarily stores
nergy, is called a capacitor, and is sometimes in-
alled in substations; this device reduces energy

losses and improves voltage regulation. Within
the substation, rigid tubular or rectangular bars,
called busbars or buses, are used as conductors.

At the substation, the transmission voltage is
stepped down to voltages below 35,000V, which
feed into the distribution system.

The distribution system delivers electrical energy to the user's energy-consuming equipment
(i.e., lighting, motors, machines, and appliances).

Conductors called feeders radiate in all directions from the substation, carrying the power from
the substation to various distribution centers. At
key locations in the distribution system, the voltage is stepped down by transformers to the level
needed by the customer. Distribution conductors
on the high-voltage side of a transformer are
called primary conductors or primaries; those on

the low-voltage side are called secondary conductors or secondaries.

Transformers are actually smaller versions of substation distribution transformers that are installed on poles, on concrete pads, or in transformer vaults throughout the distribution system.

Distribution lines carry either three-phase or single-phase current. Single-phase power is normally used for residential and small commercial occupancies, while three-phase power serves most of the other users.

## 2.4.0 Underground

Most power companies now utilize transmission systems that include both overhead and underground installations. In general, the terms and devices are the same for both. In the case of the underground system, distribution transformers are installed at or below ground level. Those mounted on concrete slabs are called padmounts (*Figure 4*), while those installed in underground vaults are called submersibles.

Buried conductors (cables) are insulated to protect them from soil chemicals and moisture. Many overhead conductors do not require such protective insulation.

When underground transmission or distribution cables terminate and connect with overhead conductors at buses or on the tops of poles, special devices called potheads or cable terminators are employed. See *Figure 5*. These devices prevent moisture from entering the insulation of the cable and also serve to separate the conductors to prevent arcing between them. The cable installation along the length of the pole is known as the cable riser.

209F04.EF

*Figure 4* ◆ Padmount transformer.

## 2.5.0 Secondary Systems

From a practical standpoint, most of your wor[k] will be involved with the power supply on th[e] secondary (usage) side of the transformer.

Two general arrangements of transformers an[d] secondaries are in common use. The first arrang[e]ment is the sectional form, in which a unit of loa[d] such as one city street or city block, is served b[y] secondary conductors, with the transformer l[o]cated in the middle. The second arrangement [is] the continuous form, in which the primary is in[s]talled in one long continuous run, with tran[s]formers spaced along it at the most suitable poin[ts] to form the secondaries. As the load grows [or] shifts, the transformers spaced along it can b[e] moved or rearranged, if desired. In a section[al]

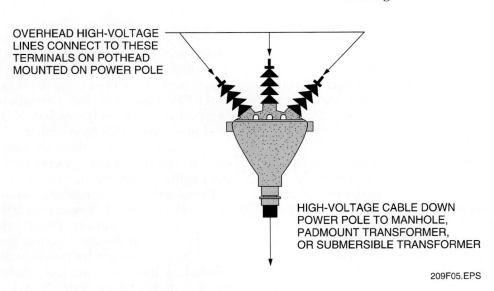

OVERHEAD HIGH-VOLTAGE LINES CONNECT TO THESE TERMINALS ON POTHEAD MOUNTED ON POWER POLE

HIGH-VOLTAGE CABLE DOWN POWER POLE TO MANHOLE, PADMOUNT TRANSFORMER, OR SUBMERSIBLE TRANSFORMER

209F05.EPS

*Figure 5* ◆ Typical pole-mounted pothead.

rrangement, such a load can be increased only by hanging to a larger size of transformer or installing an additional unit in the same section.

One of the greatest advantages of the secondary ank is that the starting currents of motors are divided among transformers, reducing voltage drop nd diminishing the resulting lamp flicker at the arious outlets.

Power companies all over the United States and Canada are now trying to incorporate networks nto their secondary power systems, especially in reas where a high degree of service reliability is ecessary. Around cities and industrial applicaons, most secondary circuits are three-phase, ither 120/208V or 277/480V, and are wye-onnected. Usually, two to four primary feeders re run into the area and the transformers are alernately connected to them. The feeders are interconnected in a grid or network so that if any eeder goes out of service, the load is still carried y the remaining feeders.

The primary feeders supplying networks are un from substations at the usual primary voltage or the system, such as 4,160V, 4,800V, 6,900V, or 3,200V. Higher voltages are practical if the loads re large enough to warrant them.

## .6.0 Common Power Supplies

he most common power supply used for residential and small commercial applications is 20/240V, single-phase, three-wire service; it is sed primarily for light and power, including ngle-phase motors up to about 7½ horsepower

(hp). A diagram of this service is shown in *Figure 6*.

Four-wire, **delta-connected** secondaries (*Figure 7*) and four-wire, wye-connected secondaries (*Figure 8*) are common in industrial and commercial applications.

The characteristics of the electric service and the equipment connected to the service must match. Also, the characteristics of an electric service will often dictate those for the electrical equipment or vice versa.

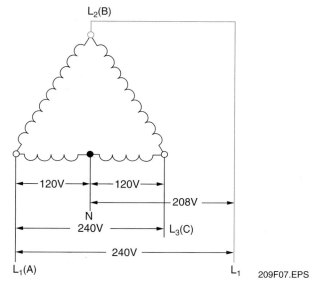

*Figure 7* ◆ Three-phase, four-wire, delta-connected secondary.

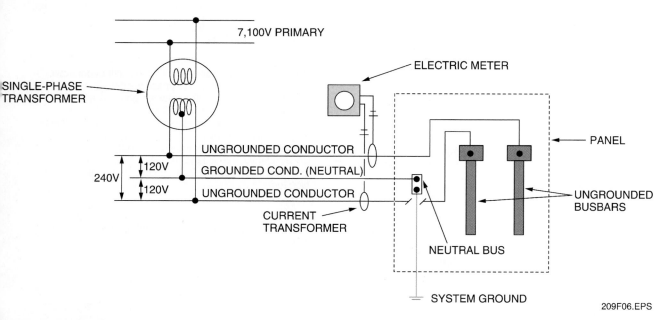

*gure 6* ◆ Single-phase, three-wire, 120/240V electric service.

Referring again to the three-phase, wye-connected service in *Figure 8*, note that the voltage between any one of the three conductors (legs $L_1$, $L_2$, and $L_3$) and the grounded (neutral or N) conductor is 120V. Consequently, you might assume that the voltage between any two of the phase conductors would be 240V. However, this is not the case. When dealing with any three-phase wye system, a factor—the square root of 3 ($\sqrt{3}$ o 1.73)—must be applied to determine the phase-to phase voltage. Therefore, to find the voltage be tween any two phase conductors, multiply th voltage of one phase conductor to ground (120V by the square root of 3:

$$120 \times \sqrt{3} = 207.84V \text{ (approx. 208V)}$$

Therefore, feeder and branch circuits connecte to 120/208V, three-phase, four-wire systems ca supply the following loads:

- 120V, single-phase, two-wire
- 208V, single-phase, two-wire
- 208V, three-phase, three-wire
- 120/208V, three-phase, four-wire

The 120/208V, three-phase, four-wire syster yields an electrical supply for loads rated a 120/208V, such as HVAC equipment, cookin units, washers, and dryers.

Another popular wye-connected system is th three-phase, four-wire, 277/480V system.

Feeder and branch circuits connected to 277 480V, three-phase, four-wire systems can suppl the following loads:

- 277V, single-phase, two-wire
- 480V, single-phase, two-wire
- 480V, three-phase, three-wire
- 277/480V, three-phase, four-wire

The delta-connected system in *Figure 9* operate a little differently. While the wye-connected sy: tem is formed by connecting one terminal froi three equal voltage transformer windings t gether to make a common terminal, the delt connected system has its windings connected

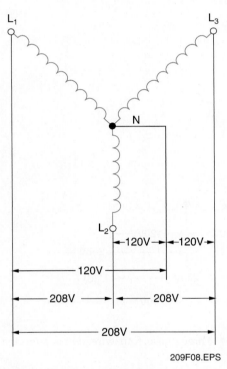

209F08.EPS

*Figure 8* ◆ Four-wire, wye-connected secondary.

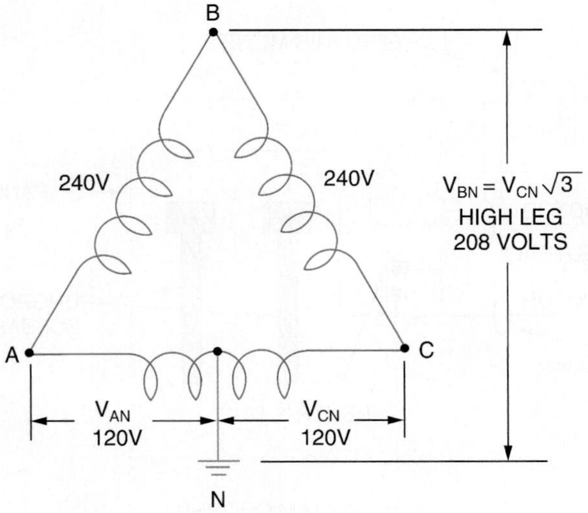

On a three-phase, four-wire 120/240V delta-connected system, the midpoint of one phase winding is grounded to provide 120V between phase A and ground; also between phase C and ground. Between phase B and ground, however, the voltage is higher and may be calculated by multiplying the voltage between C and ground (120V) by the square root of 3 or 1.73. Consequently, the voltage between phase B and ground is approximately 208V (thus, the name *high leg*).

The *NEC* ® requires that conductors connected to the high leg of a four-wire delta system be color coded with orange insulation or tape.

209F09.EPS

*Figure 9* ◆ Characteristics of a center-tap, delta-connected system.

## Four-Wire, Delta-Connected Secondary

**THINK ABOUT IT**

You are connecting 120V lighting branch circuits in a panelboard equipped with a neutral bus. One of the conductors feeding the panel has an orange finish. Can a bus connected to this feeder be used in conjunction with the neutral to supply a 120V branch lighting circuit?

orm a triangle or the Greek delta symbol Δ. Note n *Figure 9* that a center-tap terminal is used on ne winding to ground the system. On a 120/40V system, 120V is available between the enter-tap terminal and each ungrounded termi- al on either side, while 240V is available across he full winding of each phase.

Refer again to *Figure 9*. Point B is known as the igh leg or wild leg. This high leg has a higher oltage to ground than the other two phases. The oltage of the high leg can be determined by mul- iplying the voltage to ground of either of the ther two legs by the square root of 3. Therefore, the voltage between phase A and ground is 20V, the voltage between phase B and ground ay be determined as follows:

$$120 \times \sqrt{3} = 207.84\text{V (approx. 208V)}$$

From this, it should be obvious that no single- ole breakers should be connected to the high leg f a center-tapped, four-wire, delta-connected ystem. In fact, *NEC Sections 230.56 and 408.3(E)* tate that the phase busbar or conductor having he higher voltage to ground must be perma- ently marked by an outer finish that is orange in olor. This prevents future workers from connect- ng 120V single-phase loads to this high leg, vhich would probably result in damaging any quipment connected to the circuit. Remember he color orange: No 120V loads are to be con- ected to this phase.

## .0.0 ◆ SERVICE COMPONENTS

lectricians who work mostly on commercial rojects will be involved with the service installa- on from the power company's point of attach- ient to the building's service equipment, ncluding all wiring and components in between, rith the possible exception of the electric meter.

To understand the function of each part of an lectric service, we will examine an actual in- :allation—a commercial retail store. Assume nat you are in charge of the project and this is our first day on the job. The contractor's super-

intendent stops by the project site and hands you a set of working drawings and written spec- ifications. It is up to you to determine how the service is to be installed. Furthermore, you will be required to compile a materials list and order all the necessary items to complete the service installation.

This particular project consists of a rectangular building that is a part of a shopping center com- plex. The concrete block walls have been erected and the building is under roof. The concrete floor will not be poured until all electrical and plumb- ing work has been installed. However, the perma- nent electric service is to be installed immediately to provide temporary power for the workers. The remaining wiring in the building will be in- stalled later.

### 3.1.0 Consulting the Construction Documents

The first order of business is to consult the work- ing drawings and then read the appropriate sec- tions in the written specifications. The floor plan of the building appears as shown in *Figure 10*. Note that the standard panel symbol is used (a solid rectangle) to indicate the location of Panel *A*, the only power panel used on this project. The panel symbol indicates that the panel is to be surface-mounted on the inside rear wall of the building in the storage area. The electric meter, as well as a time clock for controlling night and out- side lighting, are also shown on this floor plan. The meter is installed on the outside rear wall, while the time clock is installed on the inside rear wall, next to Panel *A*.

Notes and callout arrows on this floor plan re- fer to a power-riser diagram and also a panel- board schedule on the same drawing sheet; these appear in *Figures 11* and *12,* respectively. This drawing sheet showing the floor plan, power- riser diagram, and panelboard schedule pro- vides most of the required information so that the service can be installed to meet the project specifications.

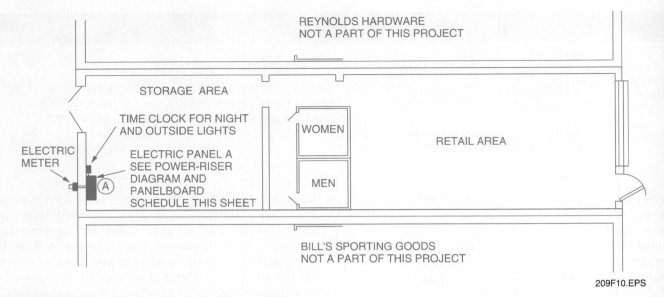

**Figure 10** ◆ Floor plan of an example commercial facility.

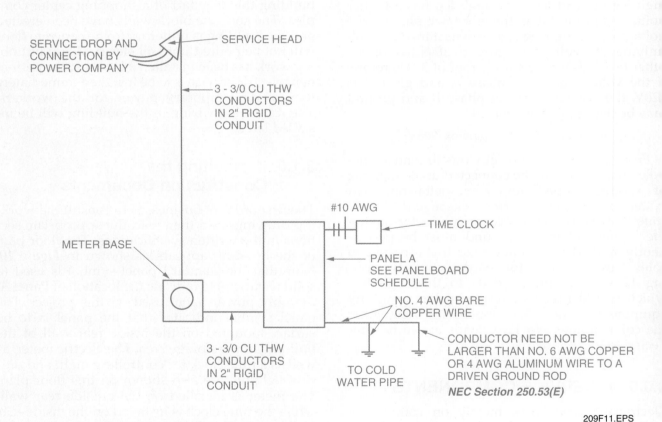

**Figure 11** ◆ Power-riser diagram for sample facility.

In most cases, electrical workers are not required to design electrical systems; rather, they are required to interpret the engineer's designs. Consequently, panelboard schedules will vary with each designer. However, once you have a feel for interpreting electrical working drawings, you should have little difficulty in reading schedules

The written specifications should also be rea to make certain that no conflicts exist, and to fur ther verify the information found on the workin drawings. A sample specification appears i *Figure 13.*

| PANELBOARD SCHEDULE | | | | | | | | | | |
|---|---|---|---|---|---|---|---|---|---|---|
| PANEL NO. | CABINET TYPE | PANEL MAINS | | | | 1P | 2P | 3P | PROT. | FRAME | ITEMS FED OR REMARKS |
| | | AMPS | VOLTS | PHASE | | | | | | |
| A | SURFACE | 200A | 120/240 | 1φ, 3 - W | 12 | - | - | 20A | 70A | LTS., RECEPTS, W.C. |
| | | | | | - | 1 | - | 60A | 100A | CONDENSING UNIT |
| | | | | | - | 1 | - | 30A | 70A | WATER HEATER |
| | | | | | - | 1 | - | 20A | 70A | AIR-HANDLING UNIT |
| | | | | | - | 2 | - | 20A | 70A | TOILET HEATERS |
| | | | | | 8 | - | - | - | 70A | PROVISIONS ONLY |
| | | | | | | | | | | |
| | | | | | | | | | | |

209F12.EPS

*Figure 12* ◆ Panelboard schedule for sample facility.

From the information obtained from the drawings and specifications, we know that the service for this project is single-phase, three-wire, 120/240V, 200A. The main panel (Panel A) is a surface-mounted Square D Type NQO (or equivalent) with a 200A main circuit breaker. Furthermore, we can determine the number of spaces required in the panel by totaling the number of circuit breakers listed in the panelboard schedule as follows:

    12 single-pole, 20A breakers = 12 spaces
    1 two-pole, 60A breaker = 2 spaces
    1 two-pole, 30A breaker = 2 spaces
    3 two-pole, 20A breakers = 6 spaces
    8 provisions only = 8 spaces
    Total = 30 spaces

Therefore, a surface-mounted panel (Square D and type NQO with 200A main circuit breaker and provisions for 30 spaces) can be ordered. The required circuit breakers should also be ordered and installed at the same time. This will meet with the project specifications.

## 3.2.0 Service Head

Referring again to *Figure 11,* start at the top of the service riser. The first item shown is the service head, sometimes called the weatherhead. *NEC Section 230.54(A)* requires the **service raceway** in our example to be equipped with a raintight service head at the point of connection to the service drop conductors.

A service head (*Figure 14*) is a fitting that prevents water from entering the service raceway. This is accomplished by bending the service conductors contained in the raceway downward as they exit from the service head so that any water

or moisture will drip from the outside conductors before entering the service head. These conductors are also protected by a plastic or fiber strain insulator or bushing placed at the entrance of the service head to separate the service conductors as required by *NEC Section 230.54(E).* Two types of service heads are in common use: one type has internal threads that enable the service head to be screwed directly onto the conduit; the other type utilizes a clamp with retaining screws. In the latter type, the service head is placed on top of the service raceway and the clamp is tightened with the retaining screws.

Further protection from water and moisture is provided by drip loops, as specified in *NEC Section 230.54(F).* Service heads are required to be located above the service drop attachment. Drip loops are then formed where the service drop conductors are connected to the service conductors, and these drip loops must be located below the service head. *Figure 14* shows how drip loops prevent water from entering the service raceway; that is, water will not flow uphill into the service head, so the water drips from the conductors at the lowest point of the drip loop.

The service-entrance conductors must have a minimum length of 3½' after they leave the service head. This is to ensure a good drip loop and to provide adequate length for splicing onto the service drop.

**NOTE**

Some states allow a shorter minimum length after leaving the service head. Always check and follow local codes.

## PANELBOARDS-CIRCUIT BREAKER

### A. GENERAL:

Furnish and install circuit breaker panelboards as indicated in the panelboard schedule and where shown on the drawings. The panelboard shall be a dead-front safety-type equipped with molded case circuit breakers and shall be the type as listed in the panelboard schedule. Service-entrance panelboards shall include a full capacity box bonding strap and be approved for service entrance. The acceptable manufacturers of the panelboards are ITE, General Electric, Cutler-Hammer, and Square D, provided that they are fully equal to the type listed on the drawings. The panelboard shall be listed by Underwriters' Laboratories and bear the UL Label.

### B. CIRCUIT BREAKERS:

Provide Type NQO circuit breakers of frame, trip rating, and interrupting capacity as shown on the schedule. Also, provide the number of spaces for future circuit breakers as shown in the schedule. The circuit breakers shall be quick-make, quick-break, thermal-magnetic, trip indicating, and have a common trip on all multipole breakers with internal tie mechanisms.

### C. WIRING TERMINALS:

Terminals for feeder conductors to the panelboard mains and neutral shall be suitable for the type of conductor specified. Terminals for branch circuit wiring, both breaker and neutral, shall be suitable for the type of conductor specified.

### D. CABINETS AND FRONTS:

The panelboard bus assembly shall be enclosed in a steel cabinet. The size of the wiring gutters and gauge of steel shall be in accordance with NEMA Standards. The box shall be fabricated from galvanized steel or equivalent rust-resistant steel. Fronts shall include door and have flush, brushed stainless steel, spring-loaded door pulls. The flush lock shall not protrude beyond the front of the door. All panelboard locks shall be keyed alike. Fronts shall not be removable with the door in the locked position.

### E. DIRECTORY:

On the inside of the door of each cabinet, provide a typewritten directory which will indicate the location of the equipment or outlets supplied by each circuit. The directory shall be mounted in a metal frame with a nonbreakable transparent cover. The panelboard designation shall be typed on the directory card and panel designation stenciled in 1-1/2" high letters on the inside of the door.

### F. PANELBOARD INSTALLATION

(1) Before installing panelboards check all of the architectural drawings for possible conflict of space and adjust the location of the panelboard to prevent such conflict with other items.

(2) When the panelboard is recessed into a wall serving an area with accessible ceiling space, provide and install an empty conduit system for future wiring. All 1-1/4" conduit shall be stubbed into the ceiling space above the panelboard and under the panelboard if such accessible ceiling space exists.

(3) The panelboards shall be mounted in accordance with *NEC Article 312.* The Electrical Contractor shall furnish all material for mounting the panelboards.

209F13.EPS

*Figure 13* ◆ Sample panelboard specifications.

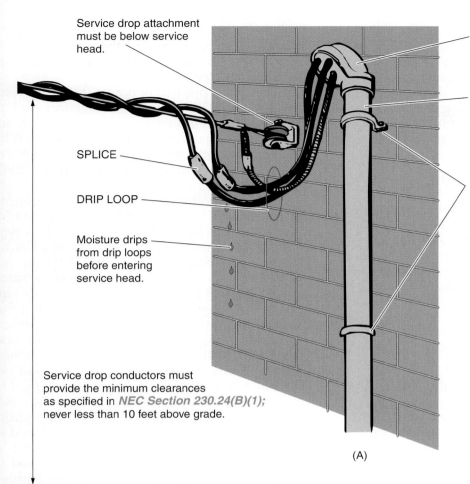

Service drop attachment must be below service head.

SPLICE

DRIP LOOP

Moisture drips from drip loops before entering service head.

Service drop conductors must provide the minimum clearances as specified in *NEC Section 230.24(B)(1)*; never less than 10 feet above grade.

A raintight service head must be installed.
*NEC Section 230.54(A)*

Rigid conduit must be supported within 3 feet of the service head.
*NEC Section 342.30(A), 344.30(A), and 352.30(A)*

Conduit must be supported in accordance with *NEC Sections 342.30(B), 344.30(B), and 352.30(B),* as applicable.

(A)

209F14A.EPS

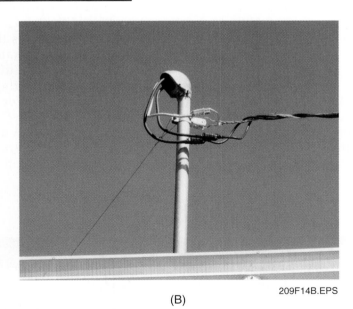

(B)

209F14B.EPS

*Figure 14* ◆ Service head and related components.

## 3.3.0 Service-Entrance Conductors

The 3/0 AWG, Type THW conductors shown in the power-riser diagram in *Figure 11* are service-entrance conductors. These conductors are run from the main disconnect breaker through the meter to the service head and terminate with splices onto the service drop. The conductors must not be spliced at any place between these points except for the following:

- Clamped or bolted connections in metering equipment
- Where service-entrance conductors are tapped to supply two to six disconnecting means that are grouped at a common location
- Where service conductors are extended from a service drop to an outside meter location and returned to connect to the service-entrance conductors of an existing installation
- Where the service-entrance conductors consist of a busway, connections are permitted as required to assemble the various sections and fittings

Service conductors are normally installed in two different ways: in a raceway system or in a cable assembly. In our sample, the conductors are installed in 2" rigid conduit and extend from the service head down to the threaded weatherproof hub on top of the meter base. The *NEC*® permits the conductors to be spliced at this point, that is, connected to the bolted terminals on the meter base. However, no splices are permitted from the service head to the meter base.

## 3.4.0 Service Equipment

Equipment and components falling under the heading of service equipment include the main disconnect switch or breaker, circuit breakers, fuses, and other items necessary to control and disconnect the power supply.

## 3.4.1 Metering Equipment

A watt-hour meter is used by the power company to determine the amount of electrical energy consumed by the customer.

Energy is the product of power (kilowatts) and time (hours). The type of meter connected to most residential and small commercial occupancies provides a reading in kilowatt-hours (kWh). For example, if the meter reads a usage of 500W for a period of six hours, it would register 3kWh $(0.5 \times 6 = 3)$.

There are several different types of metering devices in use. The type used in our sample building is known as the feed-through type. This type of meter is used mostly for services up to 200A, although feed-through meters up to 400A are not uncommon in many locations. Services rated above 400A will almost always use separate current transformers enclosed in a current transformer cabinet (CT cabinet). Current transformers are discussed in greater detail later in this module.

A typical watt-hour meter consists of a combination of coils, conductors, and gears—all encased in a housing, as shown in *Figure 15*. The coils are constructed on the same principle as a split-phase induction motor, in that the stationary current coil and the voltage coil are placed so that they produce a rotating magnetic field. A disc near the center of the meter is exposed to the rotating magnetic field. The torque applied to the disc is proportional to the power in the circuit, and the braking action of the eddy current in the disc makes the speed of the rotation proportional to the rate at which the power is consumed. The disc, through a train of gears, moves the pointers on the register dials to record the amount of power used directly in kilowatt hours.

Most watt-hour meters use five dials (see *Figure 15*). The dial farthest to the right on the meter counts the kilowatt hours singly. The second dial

### Service Mast Installations

*INSIDE TRACK*

*NEC Sections 342.30(A) and 344.30(A)* do not require above-the-roof terminations of metal conduit service masts to be secured within 3' of the service head.

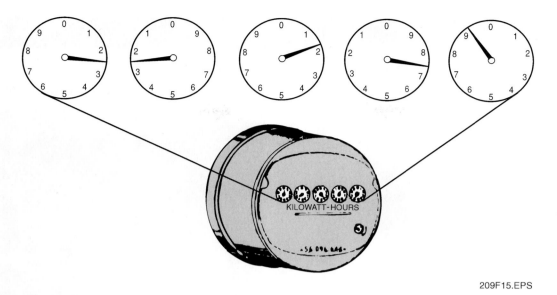

209F15.EPS

*Figure 15* ◆ Typical watt-hour meter.

om the right counts by tens, the third dial by undreds, the fourth dial by thousands, and the ft-hand dial by ten-thousands. The dials may em a little strange at first, but they are actually ery simple to read. The number which the dial as passed is the reading. For example, look at the ial on the far left. Note that the pointer is about alfway between the number 2 and the number 3. nce it has passed the number 2, but has not yet ached 3, the dial reading is 2. The same is true of e second dial from the left; that is, the pointer is etween 2 and 3. Consequently, the reading of this ial is also 2. Following this same procedure, the omplete reading for the meter in *Figure 15* is 2,179 kilowatt-hours.

Although knowing how to read an electric meter is interesting, most electricians will be involved only with installing the meter base and making the connections therein. Once these connections are made and inspected, the local power company will install and seal the meter.

Meter bases should be installed securely with anchors sufficient to hold the weight of the meter as well as the raceway system resting upon the meter base. In our example, this base must support the 2" conduit, service head, and copper conductors. Although the conduit will be supported with conduit straps, most of the weight will rest upon the meter base; the straps are used mainly to keep the conduit from moving sideways.

## Meter Types

Watt-hour meters are available in both analog and digital forms, as shown here.

209P0903.EPS

(A) ANALOG

209P0904.EPS

(B) DIGITAL

Most single-phase, feed-through meter bases are arranged as shown in *Figure 16*. The ungrounded service conductors from the service drop terminate in the top terminals. These conductors are once again picked up from the bottom terminals. Clips are provided on these terminals to clamp in the meter itself, allowing current from the ungrounded conductors to pass through the meter for a reading. Since the grounded conductor (neutral) is not metered, one terminal is provided for both the incoming and outgoing conductors.

### 3.4.2 Service Disconnecting Means

A service disconnecting means is a device that enables the electric service from the power company to be disconnected from the building or premises. Several different configurations are possible. In our sample building, a single panel with a 200A main circuit breaker acts as the disconnecting means. This arrangement and another possibl service configuration for the same project appea in *Figure 17*.

Service switches, load centers, or main distr bution panelboards are normally installed at th point where the service-entrance conductors er ter the building. Branch circuits and feeder par elboards (as well as the main service pane when required) are usually grouped together a one or more centralized locations to keep th length of the branch circuit conductors at a prac tical minimum and to lower the initial installa tion costs.

Distribution panelboards are generally in tended to carry and control electrical current, bu are not intended to dissipate or use energy. The re quirements of *NEC Article 230, Part VI* must b met for service disconnects. In addition, the fo lowing factors influence the selection of distribu tion equipment:

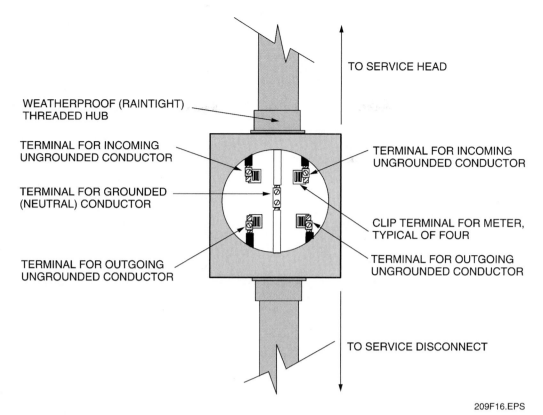

TO SERVICE HEAD

WEATHERPROOF (RAINTIGHT) THREADED HUB

TERMINAL FOR INCOMING UNGROUNDED CONDUCTOR

TERMINAL FOR GROUNDED (NEUTRAL) CONDUCTOR

TERMINAL FOR OUTGOING UNGROUNDED CONDUCTOR

TERMINAL FOR INCOMING UNGROUNDED CONDUCTOR

CLIP TERMINAL FOR METER, TYPICAL OF FOUR

TERMINAL FOR OUTGOING UNGROUNDED CONDUCTOR

TO SERVICE DISCONNECT

209F16.EPS

*Figure 16* ◆ Arrangement of conductors in a typical single-phase meter base.

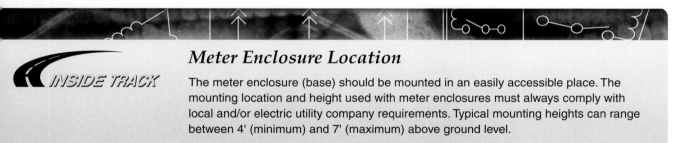

### Meter Enclosure Location

*INSIDE TRACK*

The meter enclosure (base) should be mounted in an easily accessible place. The mounting location and height used with meter enclosures must always comply with local and/or electric utility company requirements. Typical mounting heights can range between 4' (minimum) and 7' (maximum) above ground level.

*Codes and standards* – Suitability for installation and use, in conformity with the provisions of the *NEC*® and all local codes, must be considered. Suitability of equipment may be evidenced by listing or labeling.

*Mechanical protection* – Mechanical strength and durability, including the adequacy of the protection provided, must be considered.

*Wiring space* – Wire bending and connection space is provided according to UL standards in all distribution equipment. When unusual wire arrangements or connections are to be made, then extra wire bending space, gutters, and terminal cabinets should be investigated for use.

*Electrical insulation* – All distribution equipment carries labels showing the maximum volt-age level that should be applied. The supply voltage should always be equal to or less than the voltage rating of distribution equipment.

- *Heat* – Heating effects under normal conditions of use and also under abnormal conditions likely to arise in service must be constantly considered. Ambient heat conditions, as well as wire insulation ratings, along with the heat rise of the equipment, must all be evaluated during selection.

- *Arcing effects* – The normal arcing effects of overcurrent protective devices must be considered when the application is in or near combustible materials or vapors. Enclosures are selected to prevent or contain fires created by the equipment.

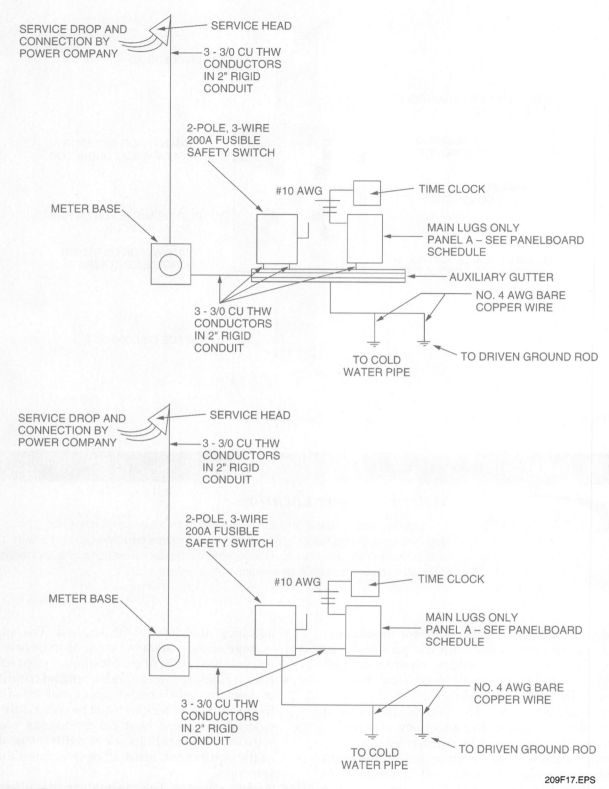

*Figure 17* ◆ Two possible service configurations for the sample facility.

209F17.EPS

## Dual Services

Some large installations have two services. Dual services are provided with separate disconnects, as shown here.

209P0905.EPS

## Service Disconnects

Some local codes allow service-entrance conductors to be run within a building up to a specified length to terminate at the service disconnect. Depending on the specific state or locality, the allowable length can vary anywhere from one or two feet to several feet. When service conductors are run inside a building, they should always be kept to a minimum length, because power utilities provide limited overcurrent protection and, in the event of a fault, the service conductors could ignite nearby combustible materials.

*Classification* – Classification according to type, size, voltage, current capacity, interrupting capacity, and specific use must be considered when selecting distribution equipment. Loads may be continuous or noncontinuous, and the demand factor must be determined before distribution equipment can be selected.

- *Personal protection* – Other factors that contribute to the practical safeguarding of a person using or likely to come in contact with the equipment must be considered. The equipment selected for use by qualified persons may be different from the equipment used or applied where unqualified people may come in contact with it.

In electrical wiring installations, overcurrent protective devices, consisting of fuses or circuit breakers, are sometimes factory-assembled in a metal cabinet; the entire assembly is commonly called a panelboard. At other times, the panelboards will be delivered unassembled, consisting of an enclosure (can), the interior busbars, and the trim. Circuit breakers are then installed as the project dictates.

Sometimes the main service disconnecting means will be made up on the job by assembling individually enclosed fused switches or circuit breakers on a length of metal auxiliary gutter, as shown in one of the views in *Figure 17*.

## 3.5.0 Grounding and Bonding

*NEC Article 250* covers the requirements for grounding and bonding electric services. In general, the *NEC®* requires that a premises' wiring system supplied by an AC service be grounded by a grounding electrode conductor connected to a grounding electrode. The grounding electrode conductor must be bonded to the grounded service conductor (neutral) at any accessible point from the load end of the service drop or service lateral up to and including the terminal bus to which the grounded service conductor is connected at the service disconnecting means. A grounding connection must not be made to any grounded circuit conductor on the load side of the service disconnecting means.

Most applications require the grounded service conductor to be bonded to one or more electrodes according to *NEC Section 250.50*.

*Table 1* gives the required sizes of grounding conductors for various sizes of electric services.

Referring to this table, since the service in our sample building is 200A, requiring 3/0 THW copper conductors, a No. 4 AWG copper or No. 2 AWG aluminum wire must be used for the grounding electrode conductor. Refer to *Figure 18* and the module on grounding for additional details on grounding electric services.

## 4.0.0 ◆ MATERIAL TAKEOFF

After reviewing the details of construction and the *NEC®* requirements so far, all the necessary information required for a complete material takeoff of the service installation has been gathered, with the exception of the height of the service raceway. Our sample building has a flat, built-up gravel roof with a parapet wall around the roof perimeter. The height of the back wall where the service raceway will be installed, along with other details of construction, are shown on the architect's elevation views of the building. If no plans are available, the wall height can be measured, or since 8" high concrete blocks are used for the construction of the wall, one column of blocks may be counted and the height of the wall determined by the following equation:

$$\frac{\text{Number of blocks} \times 8}{12} = \text{total feet}$$

A rear elevation view of our sample building is shown in *Figure 19*.

Note that the total height of the rear wall from ground level is 20', including the parapet wall. However, a loading platform is 4' above grade and since the meter can be read from this platform, the meter can be installed 4' above the loading dock grade or 8' above ground level.

| Table 1 | Sizes of Grounding Electrode Conductors for AC Systems | | | |
|---|---|---|---|---|
| **Size of Largest Service-Entrance Conductor or Equivalent for Parallel Conductors** | | | **Size of Grounding Electrode Conductor** | |
| **Copper** | **Aluminum or Copper-Clad Aluminum** | **Copper** | **Aluminum or Copper-Clad Aluminum** |
| 2 or smaller | 1/0 or smaller | 8 | 6 |
| 1 or 1/0 | 2/0 or 3/0 | 6 | 4 |
| 2/0 or 3/0 | 4/0 or 250 kcmil | 4 | 2 |
| Over 3/0 through 350 kcmil | Over 250 kcmil through 500 kcmil | 2 | 1/0 |
| Over 350 kcmil through 600 kcmil | Over 500 kcmil through 900 kcmil | 1/0 | 3/0 |
| Over 600 kcmil through 1,100 kcmil | Over 900 kcmil through 1,750 kcmil | 2/0 | 4/0 |
| Over 1,100 kcmil | Over 1,750 kcmil | 3/0 | 250 kcmil |

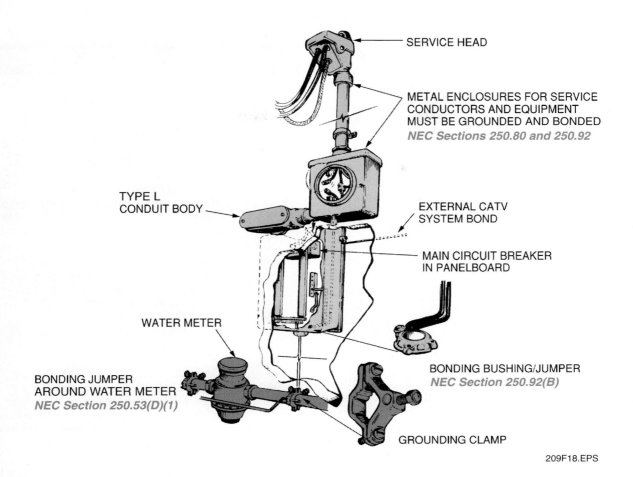

SERVICE HEAD

METAL ENCLOSURES FOR SERVICE
CONDUCTORS AND EQUIPMENT
MUST BE GROUNDED AND BONDED
*NEC Sections 250.80 and 250.92*

TYPE L
CONDUIT BODY

EXTERNAL CATV
SYSTEM BOND

MAIN CIRCUIT BREAKER
IN PANELBOARD

WATER METER

BONDING JUMPER
AROUND WATER METER
*NEC Section 250.53(D)(1)*

BONDING BUSHING/JUMPER
*NEC Section 250.92(B)*

GROUNDING CLAMP

209F18.EPS

*Figure 18* ◆ Summary of *NEC®* service grounding regulations.

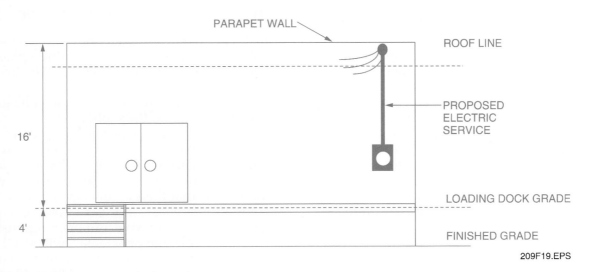

PARAPET WALL

ROOF LINE

PROPOSED
ELECTRIC
SERVICE

16'

LOADING DOCK GRADE

4'

FINISHED GRADE

209F19.EPS

*Figure 19* ◆ Rear elevation of sample building.

Consequently, one 10' length of 2" conduit will put the service raceway and service head at the very top of the wall, leaving plenty of room for the power company to connect the service drop below the service head to comply with *NEC Section 230.54(C)*. Furthermore, the service drop will be more than 10' above the deck—complying with *NEC Sections 230.24 and 230.26.*

Once the service configuration has been laid out, it is best to verify the layout with the local power company. This is also a good time to request the meter base that will have to be installed by the electrician on the job.

This is also a good time to start thinking about the tool requirements. Since the service raceway extends 16' above the loading dock, workers will need a 24' extension ladder. A rotary hammer will be needed to drill the holes for the lead anchors and to penetrate the concrete block to insert the 2" nipple between the meter base and the panelboard on the inside wall. Cable cutters will speed up the work when cutting the 3/0 service conductors and a bucket of wire-pulling lubricant will facilitate the installation of the 3/0 conductors into the 2" conduit. For this short length of pull, no special cable-pulling apparatus should be required. The conductors are merely cut to length, and then two workers feed these conductors from the top of the service raceway down to the meter base for connection to the meter base terminals. The same is true of the short run between the meter base and the panelboard on the opposite wall.

Much time can be saved on any project if careful planning is exercised before beginning any work. Even if the material is already on the job site, as taken from the electrical estimator's list, the electricians on the job must know how to utilize this material to its best advantage. Traditionally, more time has been wasted on electrical jobs because of material or tool shortages than any other causes. Therefore, before a project is started, make sure that all the necessary materials and tools are at hand. If not, order them immediately. Any time saved on any project, in most cases, means a savings to someone.

Before continuing with this module, complete the takeoff list in *Table 2*. The purpose of this exercise is to prepare a complete list of materials for the service described for our sample commercial building. Since grounding details have not been covered, the items required to ground the system have been listed. In general, two 1" grounding clamps and a bonding jumper are required around the water meter.

Another 1" grounding clamp is required to connect the grounding electrode conductor to the 1" water pipe, and a ⅝" grounding clamp is required

**Table 2**  Material Takeoff Exercise

| Quantity | Item |
|---|---|
| 1 | 2" service head |
| — | 2" rigid conduit |
| — | 2" rigid conduit strap(s) |
| — | 200A meter base (obtain from power company) |
| — | Raintight hub(s) for meter base |
| — | 2" Type L conduit body |
| — | 2" conduit nipple(s) (10" long) |
| — | 4" chase nipple(s) (from meter hub to Type L conduit body) |
| — | 2" locknut(s) |
| — | Grounding bushing(s) |
| — | Square D NQO panelboard(s) |
| — | One-pole, 20A circuit breaker(s) |
| — | Two-pole, 60A circuit breaker(s) |
| — | Two-pole, 30A circuit breaker(s) |
| — | Two-pole, 20A circuit breaker(s) |
| — | ¼-20 lead anchor(s) and ¼-20 machine screw(s) 1½" long |
| — | No. 3/0 THW copper wire |
| 3 | Grounding clamp(s) for 1" pipe |
| 1 | Grounding clamp(s) for ⅝" ground rod |
| 20' | No. 4 AWG bare copper wire |
| 1 | ⅝" copperweld grounding rod(s), 8' in length |

to connect the grounding electrode conductor to a driven ground rod. This requires 20' of No. 4 AWG bare copper wire. Also refer to *Figure 18* to better visualize exactly what is required for the grounding of this service.

## 5.0.0 ◆ THREE-PHASE SERVICES

Most services encountered on commercial and industrial projects will consist of three-phase systems with voltage ratings as low as 120/208V to a high as perhaps 4,160V or more.

In single-phase current, only one voltage curve is generated, while three-phase current indicates that there are three voltage curves present on the system simultaneously. There is very little difference between installing a single-phase service (just described) and a three-phase service. The main difference is that there is an extra service conductor for a three-phase, four-wire system, requiring that the service head have four openings instead of three. Of course, the panelboard will also have to be arranged for a three-phase system—requiring an extra ungrounded busbar. Other than these changes, the installation process is essentially the same as that described for the single-phase system.

To illustrate, *Figure 20* shows the power-riser diagram for a 1,200A, three-phase, wye-connected

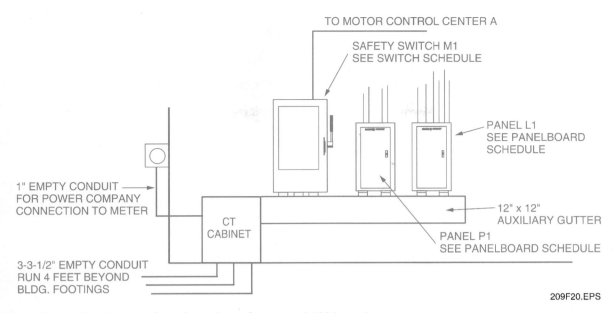

TO MOTOR CONTROL CENTER A

SAFETY SWITCH M1
SEE SWITCH SCHEDULE

PANEL L1
SEE PANELBOARD
SCHEDULE

1" EMPTY CONDUIT
FOR POWER COMPANY
CONNECTION TO METER

CT
CABINET

12" x 12"
AUXILIARY GUTTER

PANEL P1
SEE PANELBOARD SCHEDULE

3-3-1/2" EMPTY CONDUIT
RUN 4 FEET BEYOND
BLDG. FOOTINGS

209F20.EPS

*Figure 20* ◆ Power-riser diagram for a three-phase, four-wire, 1,200A service.

service. Note that the service lateral consists of three 3½" empty conduit runs to be installed from the CT (current transformer) cabinet to 4' beyond the building's footings. These are provided for the power company's service lateral.

The service conductors continue through the CT cabinet and terminate in an auxiliary gutter. Three service equipment taps are made in this gutter to feed the following:

- One 800A fusible safety switch, which feeds a motor control center
- One 200A power panel with a main circuit breaker
- One 200A lighting panel with a main circuit breaker

We will take a look at the individual components for this service.

## 5.1.0 Current Transformers

Meters used by power companies to record the amount of current used by customers usually respond to a current that varies from 0A to 5A. To respond to the actual current of the service, each meter is provided with current transformers. If the peak demand of the service is 100A, a 100:5 current transformer is used. If the peak current demand is expected to be 200A, a 200:5 current transformer is used.

Services above 400A usually utilize a group of current transformers, one for each ungrounded conductor or set of conductors. There are two basic types of current transformers: the busbar type

and the doughnut type. The doughnut-type current transformer encircles the ungrounded conductors in the system to read the current flow, much the same as a clamp-on ammeter. See *Figure 21*. The busbar-type current transformer has each transformer connected in series with a busbar and does not encircle the conductor.

Current transformers are normally enclosed in a CT cabinet. *Figure 22* shows a typical CT cabinet with current transformers and their related wiring. In some cases, the current transformers may be mounted exposed on overhead conductors, but this is more the exception than the rule.

Power companies have different requirements for sizes of CT cabinets, but the dimensions shown in *Table 3* are typical for several service sizes.

Power companies also have different specifications for the location and wiring of CTs and CT cabinets, depending on the locale. The following are the requirements of one power company. However, always check the local requirements.

- The meter base and meter may be located on either the side or top of the current transformer cabinet, or they may be located at a distance away, if approved by the power company and as long as the conduit containing the instrument wiring is run exposed.
- In no instance shall more than one set of conductors terminate in the instrument transformer cabinet. Subfeeders and branch circuits are to terminate at the customer's distribution panel. The instrument transformer cabinet shall not be used as a junction box.

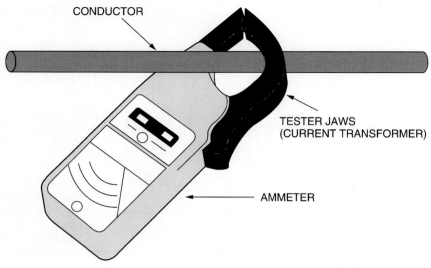

CONDUCTOR

TESTER JAWS
(CURRENT TRANSFORMER)

AMMETER

209F21.EPS

*Figure 21* ◆ Clamp-on ammeters operate on the same principle as doughnut-type current transformers.

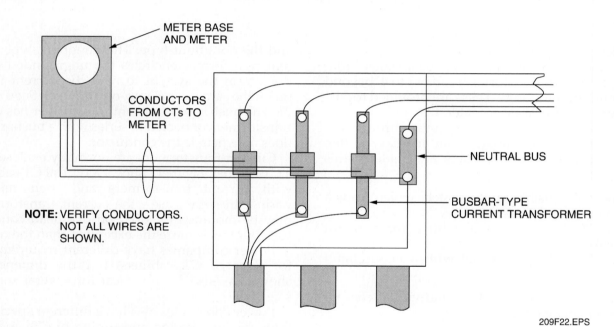

METER BASE
AND METER

CONDUCTORS
FROM CTs TO
METER

NEUTRAL BUS

BUSBAR-TYPE
CURRENT TRANSFORMER

**NOTE:** VERIFY CONDUCTORS.
NOT ALL WIRES ARE
SHOWN.

209F22.EPS

*Figure 22* ◆ Typical CT cabinet arrangement.

**Table 3**   Typical CT Cabinet Sizes

| Phase | Service Characteristics | Cabinet Size |
|---|---|---|
| Single-phase | 120/240V, three-wire | 10" × 24" × 32" |
| Three-phase | 120/240V, four-wire | 10" × 36" × 42" |
| Three-phase | 120/208V, four-wire | 10" × 36" × 42" |
| Three-phase | 480V, three-wire | 10" × 36" × 42" |
| Three-phase | 277V/480, four-wire | 10" × 36" × 48" |

- When service-entrance conductors enter or leave through the back of the cabinet, the size of the CT cabinet must be increased to provide additional working space.
- For services at higher voltages, additional space must be provided in the transformer cabinet for mounting potential transformers. Consult the local power company for dimensions.
- If recording demand instruments are required, increase the height of the meter mounting from 36" to 48".

## 5.2.0 Gutters

Auxiliary gutters are used to route the service conductors and to provide an enclosure for tapping these conductors for safety switches and panels. In this type of arrangement, appropriate connectors are normally used to make the taps. However, many electrical contractors have found that a bussed gutter saves labor and provides for a neater installation.

A bussed gutter is an assembly of busbars in an enclosure. The enclosure may be rated for outdoor (weatherproof) or indoor installations. Busbars installed in the gutter may be made of aluminum or copper and must have an ampacity rating for the application; that is, if the service conductors are rated for 1,200A (as in our sample building), the busbars must be rated for at least the same ampacity. Furthermore, they must be UL listed.

From an installation or a maintenance/modification viewpoint, bussed gutters are one of the most common types of wiring methods for use with multiswitch services. One advantage of a bussed gutter is the ease of installation and modification. Adding disconnect switches or changing switches is relatively easy. No connectors have to be untaped and reconnected, as with systems using wire connectors on the conductors for taps.

In our example, with a service conductor ampacity of 1,200A, the rating of the busbars in bussed gutters must also be 1,200A if bussed gutters are to be used. See *Figure 23*. Furthermore, the bussed gutter must be rated for the available fault current and must have sufficient wire bending space per *NEC Sections 110.3(A)(3) and 312.(A) through (C).*

### 5.2.1 Bus Bracing

One characteristic of fault currents is an induced torque in conductors carrying the fault. Because of this torque, the busbars in a bussed gutter must be attached to the enclosure in such a manner as to prevent their being dislodged and/or making contact with the gutter frame during the fault. When busbars are attached in such a manner as to withstand the torque created by the available amount of fault current, they are said to be *braced* for that amount of current. For instance, busbars may be braced for 20,000A, 30,000A, or whatever level of fault current is required, up to 200,000A. The bussed gutter must be labeled by the manufacturer for the amount of fault current the buses are braced to withstand.

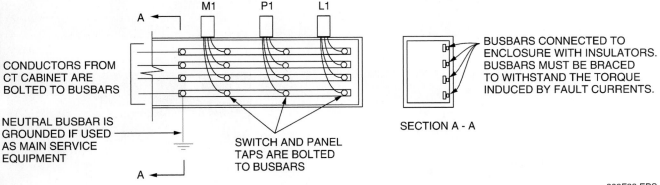

209F23.EPS

*Figure 23* ◆ Three-phase bussed gutter.

## *Three-Phase Busduct*

Three-phase busduct is a modular type of power distribution system that provides power directly through a set of system busbars rather than using power cable. It allows for easy system expansion because whenever a new piece of equipment is added, a new switch can simply be plugged into place and the equipment supplied without the need to run additional power cable through the plant.

209P0906.EPS

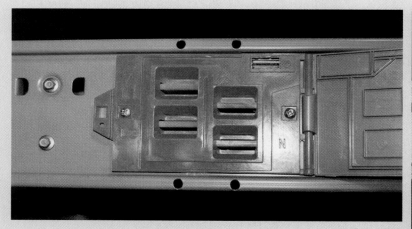

209P0907.EPS

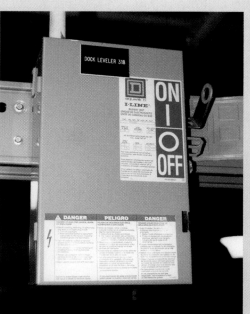

209P0908.EPS

# .0.0 ◆ 277/480V SERVICES

Wye-connected, 277/480V services are common in medium to large commercial projects. This type of service is also frequently used in industrial applications to power motors for driving machinery and other apparatus. Such installations frequently use switchgear enclosures such as the one shown in *Figure 24*. Service equipment of this type is made up of vertical sections that connect to a common bus system within the enclosure. These sections contain fusible switches or circuit breakers, metering equipment, or other devices related to the electric service.

*NEC Section 230.71(A)* allows a maximum of six service disconnecting means per service grouped in any one location. If there are more than six switches or circuit breakers in the switchboard, then a main switch or circuit breaker must be provided to disconnect all service conductors in the building or structure from the power supply.

209F24.EPS

*Figure 24* ◆ Typical switchgear.

Typically, the metering equipment (CTs, potential transformers, etc.) is installed in the same enclosure as the main disconnecting means; additional space is usually provided in the switchgear for this equipment. Furthermore, taps are normally provided in the main bus in a barriered section for connection to emergency switches, such as for fire alarm systems, emergency lighting, etc., as allowed by *NEC Section 230.82(5)*.

## 6.1.0 Practical Applications

*Figure 25* shows a plot plan of a shopping center facility that utilizes a 277/480V, wye-connected, three-phase service to supply numerous tenant areas. In general, a padmount transformer installed on the property perimeter reduces the distribution voltages to 277/480V. An underground service is installed from this padmount transformer to a switchgear room in one section of the shopping center. A single-line diagram of the electrical system for this project is shown in *Figure 26*. Note that there are only six fusible switches in the main switchgear, so no main disconnecting means is necessary. Each of these six feeders supplies a bussed gutter system (discussed previously), each of which contains six meter bases and a fused safety switch that feeds a 277/480V panel for lighting and HVAC equipment. This latter panel also feeds a 480V to 120/208V dry transformer, which in turn furnishes power to a 120/208V panel for feeding tenant receptacles and display lighting.

In general, this system records the amount of power used by each tenant so that tenants may be billed accordingly. A 277V fluorescent lighting system provides general illumination, which is fed from the 277/480V panel in each tenant space. However, some 120V display lighting is employed. It is fed from the 120/208V panel.

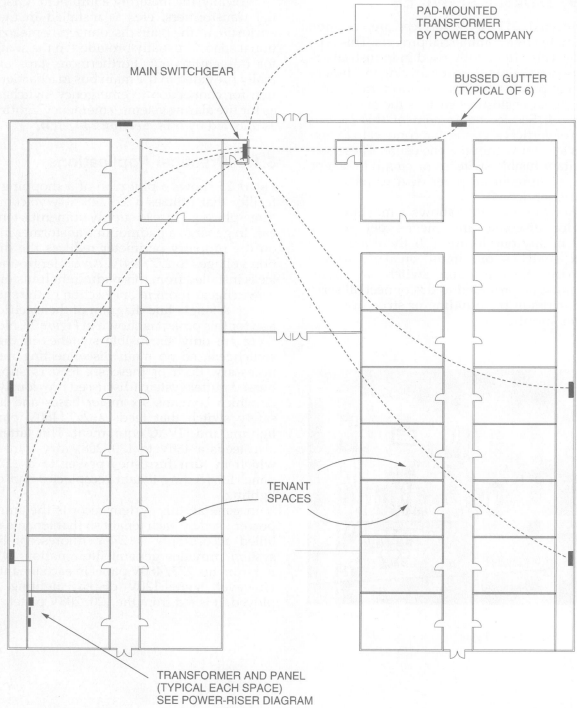

PAD-MOUNTED
TRANSFORMER
BY POWER COMPANY

MAIN SWITCHGEAR

BUSSED GUTTER
(TYPICAL OF 6)

TENANT
SPACES

TRANSFORMER AND PANEL
(TYPICAL EACH SPACE)
SEE POWER-RISER DIAGRAM

209F25.EPS

*Figure 25* ◆ Plot plan of shopping center installation.

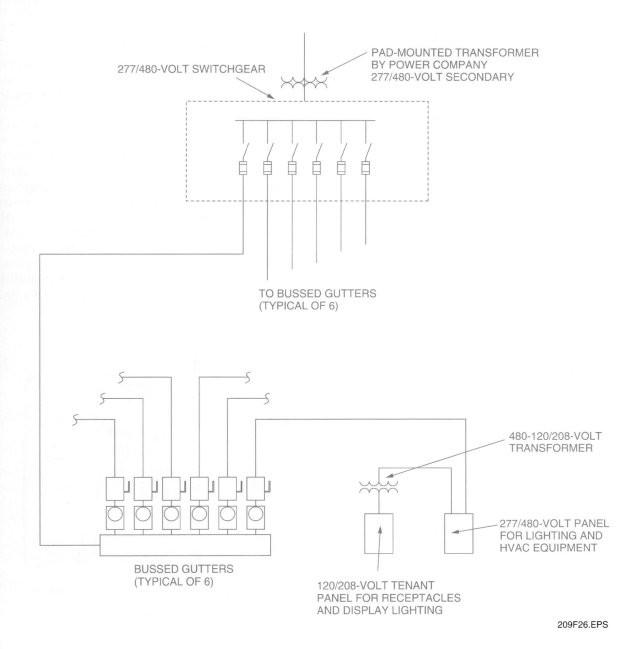

277/480-VOLT SWITCHGEAR

PAD-MOUNTED TRANSFORMER
BY POWER COMPANY
277/480-VOLT SECONDARY

TO BUSSED GUTTERS
(TYPICAL OF 6)

480-120/208-VOLT
TRANSFORMER

277/480-VOLT PANEL
FOR LIGHTING AND
HVAC EQUIPMENT

BUSSED GUTTERS
(TYPICAL OF 6)

120/208-VOLT TENANT
PANEL FOR RECEPTACLES
AND DISPLAY LIGHTING

209F26.EPS

*Figure 26* ◆ Power-riser diagram for shopping center installation.

## .0.0 ◆ SWITCHES, PANELBOARDS, AND LOAD CENTERS

Panelboards consist of assemblies of overcurrent protection devices in a metal cabinet, with or without disconnecting devices. The cabinet includes a cover or trim with one or two doors to allow access to the overcurrent and disconnecting devices and, in some types, access to the wiring space in the panelboard.

There is some confusion concerning the differences between load centers and panelboards.

Typically, load centers are fuse or circuit breaker cabinets used on residential or small commercial projects. They are preassembled units with the interior buses installed at the factory. Upon installation, the required number of plug-in circuit breakers or fuse holders are installed, the circuit conductors terminated, and the front cover installed.

Many electricians classify panelboards as enclosures for overcurrent protection devices that are used on larger commercial and industrial installations. Furthermore, the can or housing usually consists of unpainted galvanized metal. Frequently, the circuit breakers are factory-installed using bolt-in circuit breakers.

You would probably be correct in calling all load centers panelboards, but remember, not all panelboards are load centers.

Panelboards fall into two mounting classifications: flush mounting (*Figure 27*), wherein the trim extends beyond the outside edges of the cabinet to provide a neat finish with the wall surface; and surface mounting (*Figure 28*), wherein the edge of the trim is flush with the edge of the cabinet.

Panelboards fall into two general classifications with regard to overcurrent devices: circuit breaker types and fusible types. Small circuit breaker and fusible panelboards, commonly referred to as load centers, are manufactured for use in residential, small commercial, and small industrial occupancies.

## 7.1.0 Panel Installation

Prior to installing a panel, the selected location must be examined to verify that proper clearances exist and that the environment is proper for the panel installation.

In general, all panelboards must have a rating of not less than the minimum feeder capacity required for the load computed in accordance with *NEC Article 220.* Panelboards must be durably marked by the manufacturer with the voltage and current rating and the number of phases for which they are designed. They must also include the manufacturer's name or trademark in such a manner as to be visible after installation without disturbing the interior parts or wiring. All panelboard circuits and circuit modifications shall be legibly identified as to purpose or use on a circuit

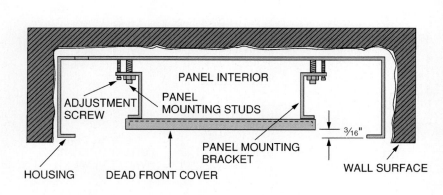

209F27.EPS

*Figure 27* ◆ Flush-mounted panelboard.

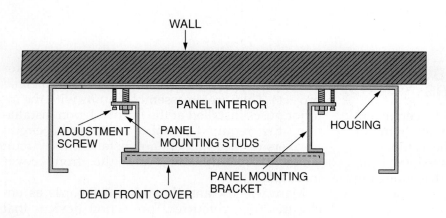

209F28.EPS

*Figure 28* ◆ Surface-mounted panelboard.

irectory located on the face or on the inside of the panel doors (*NEC Section 408.4*). The working height near panelboards is 6.5'. See *Figure 29*.

Once a proper location has been determined, the panel is removed from its packing boxes, assembled, and installed. When removing the panel from its packing, verify that all necessary components have been delivered and make sure that any tray packing material has been removed from the panel. Check to make sure that the right panel is to be installed. A checklist might include the following items:

Is the panel to be top fed or bottom fed? This information should be obtained from the drawings or from the project supervisor.
• Check to verify that the voltage rating of the panel is as specified in the drawings.
• Check to verify that the ampacity of the panel is as specified in the drawings.
• Check to verify that the phase and number of conductors is as specified in the drawings.
• Verify that the panel was not damaged during shipping.
• Verify that the lugs supplied with the panel will fit the conductors being installed.

### 7.1.1 Installing Flush-Mounted Enclosures

Flush-mounted enclosures installed in noncombustible material must be mounted so that the front edge of the enclosure is not set back farther than ¼" from the finished surface. If installed in other than noncombustible walls, the panel edge must be flush with the finished wall (*NEC Section 312.3*).

### 7.1.2 Installing Surface-Mounted Enclosures

Surface-mounted enclosures must be securely fastened in place. If the wall structure offers little structural support, as in the case of ¼" wood paneling or ½" gypsum board, the enclosure must be located so that it may be attached to framing members inside the wall covering. In some cases, a framing structure will have to be built to support the panel.

### 7.1.3 Installing the Panel Interior

Prior to installing the panel interior, check to verify that the enclosure is securely fastened in place and is free of all foreign material. Obtain and study the specifications and instructions that are included with the panel. If no instructions are available, the following is a general installation procedure that may be used:

**Step 1** Mount the interior to the enclosure using the four mounting studs installed on the enclosure back.

**Step 2** Adjust the depth of the interior with the adjustment screws. The dead front cover should be no farther than ³⁄₁₆" from the wall surface for a flush panel, or the same distance from the enclosure face for a surface-mounted panel.

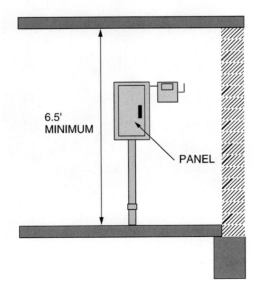

HEADROOM

The minimum headroom of working spaces about service equipment is 6.5 feet.
*NEC Section 110.26(E)*

The *Exception* to this requirement states that service equipment under 200 amperes in existing dwellings does not require this much headroom.

209F29.EPS

*Figure 29* ◆ *NEC*® headroom requirements.

## Panelboards

The selection of the components used in a panelboard is based on the following criteria:

- Feeder voltage and amperage
- Phase (single or three-phase) and number of conductors
- Type of busbar material (copper or aluminum)
- Number of required spaces or blanks
- Whether the panelboard is configured as a main breaker type of panel or main-lugs only (MLO) type of panel

**NOTE**

MLO panels do not have a MAIN circuit breaker.

After the panelboard is assembled, the appropriate number and type of circuit breakers must be ordered separately and installed in the panel.

209P0909.EPS

.series of concentric or eccentric circular partial penings are usually cut in the top, bottom, and des of both load center and panelboard housngs; some may also be cut in the back. These penings are cut in such a manner that they may e removed by tapping (knocking) them out, usully with a screwdriver blade or punch and hamer, just as you would in a device or fixture box *Figure 30*).

The direction from which the knockouts can be emoved alternates from inside the enclosure to utside the enclosure; that is, ½" knockouts are nocked outward from inside the enclosure; ¾" nockouts are knocked inward from outside the nclosure; 1" knockouts are knocked outward om inside the enclosure, etc. See *Figure 31*.

In most cases, raceways connected to panelbards using the concentric knockout openings ave poor equipment grounding connections. onsequently, *NEC Section 250.92(B)* requires nding jumpers to be used around concentric r eccentric knockouts that are punched or therwise formed so as to impair the electrical

connection to ground. This is accomplished by using a grounding locknut or bushing and then connecting a bonding jumper either to another grounding locknut or bushing, or else to the equipment grounding terminal inside the panelboard.

## 7.2.0  Panel Connections

Electrical connections in a panelboard fall under two categories:

- Line connections, including termination and routing of service and feeder conductors
- Load connections, including termination and routing of branch circuit and feeder conductors

**WARNING!**
Even though the main breaker handle is in the OFF position, the line side of the switch is still energized.

Prior to terminating aluminum conductors, verify that the lugs are stamped CU-AL or a label inside the panel states that the connection of aluminum conductors is permitted.

*NEC Section 408.3(E)* requires the phase arrangement on three-phase buses to be A, B, and C from front to back, top to bottom, or left to right, as viewed from the front of the panel. The B phase must be the phase with the highest voltage to ground on a three-phase, four-wire, delta-connected system. See *Figure 32*.

## 7.3.0  Enclosures

The majority of overcurrent devices (fuses and circuit breakers) are used in some type of enclosure (i.e., panelboards, switchboards, motor control centers, individual enclosures, etc.).

NEMA has established enclosure designations because individually enclosed overcurrent protection devices are used in so many different types of locations, weather and water conditions, dust

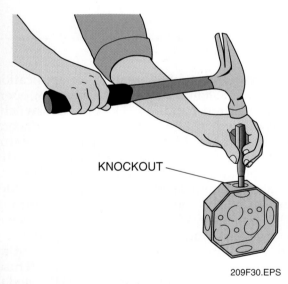

KNOCKOUT

209F30.EPS

*gure 30* ◆ Removing knockouts.

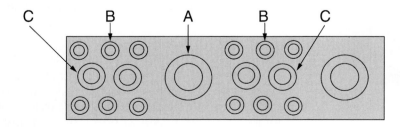

A = Two 2" or 2-1/2" knockouts; space for two 3-1/2" knockouts

B = Twelve 1/2" or 3/4" knockouts

C = Four 3/4" or 1" knockouts

209F31.EPS

*gure 31* ◆ Typical knockouts in top of panelboard.

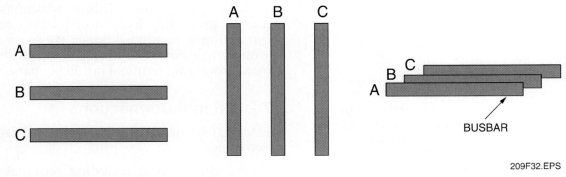

*Figure 32* ◆ *NEC®-approved phase arrangements.*

209F32.EPS

and other contaminating conditions, etc. The NEMA designations were recently revised to obtain a clearer and more precise definition of the enclosure needed to meet various standard requirements.

For example, a NEMA Type 12 enclosure can now be substituted in many installations in place of a NEMA Type 5 enclosure. The advantage of this substitution is that the NEMA Type 12 enclosure is much less expensive than the NEMA Type 5 enclosure. *Figure 33* shows two types of NEMA enclosures and *Table 4* provides a brief explanation of NEMA enclosure specifications.

### 7.4.0 Safety Switches

Most manufacturers of safety switches have at least two complete lines to meet industrial, commercial, and residential requirements. Both types usually have visible blades and safety handles. With visible blades, the contact blades are in full

view so you can clearly see their position. Safet handles are always in complete control of th switch blades, so whether the cover is open c closed, when the handle is in the OFF position, th switch is always OFF, that is, on the load side c the switch. See *Figure 34*.

 **WARNING!**
Even though a safety switch handle is in the OFF position, the line side of the switch is still energized.

Heavy-duty switches are used for applicatior where the switch is subjected to frequent opera tion and rough handling. Heavy-duty switche are also used in atmospheres where a genera duty switch would be unsuitable. Heavy-dut switches are widely used by most heavy indu trial applications; motors and HVAC equipmer will also be controlled by such switches. Mo heavy-duty switches are rated at 30A throug 1,200A, 240V to 600V (AC-DC). The switches wi horsepower ratings are able to interrupt approx mately six times the full-load, motor current ra ings. When equipped with Class J or Class R fuse many heavy-duty safety switches are UL listed fe use on systems with up to 200,000A available fau current. Heavy-duty switches are available wi NEMA Types 1, 3R, 4, 5, 7, 9, and 12 enclosures.

### 7.4.1 Switch Contacts

There are two types of switch contacts used in to day's safety switches. One is the butt contac which is similar to those used in circuit break devices; the other is a knife blade and jaw typ The knife blade type is considered to be superic to other types on the market.

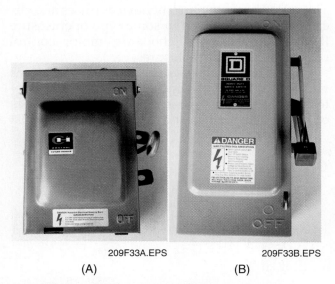

209F33A.EPS    209F33B.EPS
(A)          (B)

*Figure 33* ◆ NEMA enclosures. (A) General-duty safety switch. (B) Heavy-duty safety switch.

**Table 4** NEMA Enclosure Specifications

| Enclosure | Explanation |
|---|---|
| NEMA Type 1 General Purpose | To prevent accidental contact with enclosed apparatus. Suitable for use indoors where not exposed to unusual service conditions. |
| NEMA Type 3 Weatherproof (Weather Resistant) | Protects against specified weather hazards. Suitable for use outdoors. |
| NEMA Type 3R Raintight | Protects against entrance of water from rain. Suitable for general outdoor applications not requiring protection against sleet. |
| NEMA Type 4 Watertight | Designed to exclude water applied in the form of a hose stream. Protects against stream of water during cleaning operations. |
| NEMA Type 5 Dusttight | Constructed so that dust will not enter the enclosed area. Being replaced in some equipment by NEMA Type 12. |
| NEMA Type 7 Hazardous Locations A, B, C, or D Class I– air break letter(s) following type number indicate particular groups of hazardous locations per the *NEC*®. | Designed to meet application requirements of the *NEC*® for Class I, hazardous locations (explosive atmospheres). Circuit interruption occurs in the air. |
| NEMA Type 9 Hazardous Locations E, F, or G Class II– letter(s) following type number indicate particular groups of hazardous locations per the *NEC*®. | Designed to meet application requirements of the *NEC*® for Class II hazardous locations (combustible dusts, etc.). |
| NEMA Type 12 Industrial Use | For use in those industries where it is necessary to exclude dust, fibers, and filings, or oil or coolant seepage. |

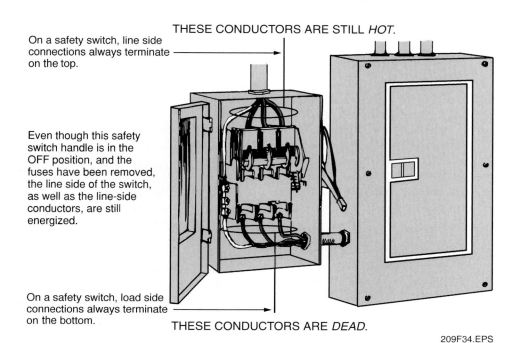

On a safety switch, line side connections always terminate on the top.

THESE CONDUCTORS ARE STILL *HOT*.

Even though this safety switch handle is in the OFF position, and the fuses have been removed, the line side of the switch, as well as the line-side conductors, are still energized.

On a safety switch, load side connections always terminate on the bottom.

THESE CONDUCTORS ARE *DEAD*.

209F34.EPS

*Figure 34* ◆ Using a safety switch as a panelboard disconnect.

All current-carrying parts of safety switches are usually plated with tin, cadmium, or nickel to reduce heating by keeping metal oxidation at a minimum. The switch blade and jaws are made of copper for high conductivity. With knife blade construction, the jaws distribute a uniform clamping pressure over the entire blade-to-jaw contact surface. In the event of a high current fault, the electromagnetic forces that develop tend to squeeze the jaws tightly against the blade. In the butt-type contact, these forces tend to force the contacts apart, causing them to burn severely.

Fuse clips are also plated to control corrosion and keep heating to a minimum. All heavy-duty fuse clips have steel reinforcing springs to increase their mechanical strength and provide a firmer contact pressure. As a result, fuses will not work loose due to vibration or rough handling.

### 7.4.2  Insulating Materials

As the voltage rating of switches is increased, arc suppression becomes more difficult and the choice of insulation material becomes a more critical problem. The arc suppressors used by many manufacturers consist of a housing made of insulation material and one or more magnetic suppressor plates. All arc suppressors are tested to ensure proper control and extinguishing of arcing.

### 7.4.3  Operating Mechanism

Heavy-duty safety switches have spring-driven, quick-make, quick-break mechanisms. The quick-break action is necessary if a switch is to be safely switched to OFF under a heavy load. The spring action, in addition to making the operation quick-make, quick-break, firmly holds the switch blades in an ON or OFF position. The operating handle is an integral part of the switching mechanism, so if the springs should fail, the switch can still be operated. When the handle is in the OFF position, the switch is always OFF.

A one-piece crossbar is usually employed to offer direct control over all blades simultaneously.

The one-piece crossbar provides stability an strength, plus proper alignment for uniform blad operation.

Dual cover interlocks are also standard on a heavy-duty switches. The dual interlock preven the enclosure door from being opened when th switch is ON and also keeps the switch from bein turned ON while the door is open.

### 7.4.4  General-Duty Safety Switches

General-duty switches are for residential an light commercial applications where the pric of the device is a limiting factor. General-dut switches are meant to be used where operatio and handling are moderate and where the avai able fault current is less than 10,000A. Som examples of general-duty switch applications i clude: residential HVAC equipment, light-dut fan coil circuit disconnects for commercial pro ects, and the like.

General-duty switches are rated up to 600A 240V (AC only) in general-purpose (NEMA Typ 1) and rainproof (NEMA Type 3R) enclosure These switches are horsepower-rated and capab of opening a circuit with approximately six tim a motor's full-load current rating.

All current-carrying parts of general-dut switches are plated with either tin or cadmium reduce heating. Switch jaws and blades are mac of plated copper for high conductivity. A steel r inforcing spring increases the mechanical streng of the jaws and ensures firm contact pressure b tween the blade and jaw.

### 7.4.5  Double-Throw Safety Switches

Double-throw switches are used as transf switches and are not intended as motor circu switches; therefore, they are not horsepower-rate

Safety switches are manually operated and a available as either fused or unfused device These switches have quick-make, quick-brea action, plated current-carrying parts, a ke controlled interlock mechanism, and screw-typ lugs. Arc suppressors are supplied on all switch rated above 250V.

## 7.5.0  Main Lugs

Main lugs load centers provide distribution electrical power where a main disconnect wi overcurrent protection is provided separate from the load center. All terminals are suitable f aluminum or copper conductors.

Many main-lugs only (MLO) load centers rated t 125A and up have interiors that are reversible or either top or bottom feed. The cover does not need to be reversed when the interior is reversed. Load centers of 125A and above are commonly available in 14" wide boxes for more wire bending space. Some single-phase, three-wire load centers are also approved for three-phase grounded B-type systems at 240VAC. A main lugs load center can also be converted to a main breaker load center provided that it has approved breakers. Follow the manufacturer's instructions.

## .6.0 Main Breaker Load Centers

Main breaker load centers typically have the following characteristics:

The main breakers are factory-installed, cutting installation costs. There are no lugs to remove; no screws, nuts, or washers to misplace; and no expensive main breakers to lose. Factory-assembled main disconnects also ensure a proper and safe electrical connection.

Boxes that are 14" wide are available in 100A to 225A main breaker load centers. This offers more side gutter space for wiring and permits flush load center installation between 16" centered studs without an extra mounting support to hold the box in place.

The line side terminals of the main breakers are suitable for use with copper or aluminum conductors.

## .7.0 Panelboards

Switchgear manufacturers offer complete lines of lighting and distribution panelboards, most of which are available either unassembled from distributor stock or factory-assembled. All types should be UL listed and meet *Federal Specification WP-115a*.

NQO panelboards are rated for use on the following AC services: 120/240V, single-phase, three-wire; 240V, three-phase, three-wire delta; 240V, three-phase delta with grounded B phase; and 120/208V, three-phase, four-wire wye. They carry no DC rating. NQO panelboards are available either factory-assembled or unassembled.

This type of panelboard is suitable for use in industrial buildings, schools, offices, and commercial buildings and institutions in which the largest branch breaker does not exceed 150A and the system voltage is not greater than 240VAC.

NQO panelboards have maximum ratings of 00A (main breaker or main lugs). Branch circuit breakers may be catalog prefix QO, QO-H, QH, Q1, or Q1-H, and one-, two-, or three-pole—having a maximum rating of 150A and featuring plug-in bus connections. QO and Q1 circuit breakers are standard with 10,000 amperage interrupting capacity (AIC) rating and QH breakers with 65,000 AIC rating. Other ratings for specific applications are also available.

Branch circuit breakers with ground fault circuit interruption may also be supplied in Type NQO panelboards. Rated 10,000 AIC symmetrical, these devices provide GFCI ground fault protection as well as overload and short circuit protection for branch circuit wiring.

NQO unassembled panelboards are available as follows:

- Branch breakers
- Interior with solid neutral
- Box (14" wide × 4" deep, 14" wide × 5¾" deep, or 20" wide × 5¾" deep)
- Mono-flat front with door and flush lock
- Accessories

NQO factory-assembled panelboards are identical in construction to the unassembled type. Main ratings and branch circuits are the same. Unlike unassembled panelboards, however, the branches are factory-installed.

Assembled and unassembled NQO boxes are constructed of galvanized steel. Several types of knockouts are provided in each end wall. Interiors having a maximum main lugs rating of 225A are available in 14" × 4", 14" × 5¾", or 20" × 5¾" boxes. 14" × 5¾" or 20" × 5¾" boxes are required for panelboards having a main circuit breaker. Boxes for interiors having 400A mains (breakers or lugs) are 20" × 5¾".

Interiors for standard-width panelboards having a maximum rating of 225A are of the single-bus construction. In this construction, one-, two-, and three-pole catalog prefix Q1 breakers extend the full width of the panelboard and cannot be mounted opposite each other. QO, QO-H, and QH circuit breakers twin-mount on the bus assembly. In other words, a three-pole QO requires three-pole spaces, but a three-pole Q1 requires six QO spaces.

Interiors of 400A panelboards utilize a double-row bus construction. This type of construction consists of two sets of busbars mounted on a single pan. The respective phase buses of each set are paralleled with each other by means of insulated, solid connectors. QO and Q1 breakers mount on a one-for-one basis (i.e., a three-pole QO requires the same spaces as a three-pole Q1).

All current-carrying parts are plated for maximum corrosion resistance and minimum heating at contact surfaces. Main lugs are UL listed for use with either copper or aluminum cable. Main lugs may be replaced by the appropriate crimp lug, when required. Lug catalog numbers and crimping tools are called out on the panelboard wiring diagram. Box-type lugs for circuits on both branch breakers and the solid neutral permit maximum convenience and speed in wiring and are also UL listed for use with either copper or aluminum cable.

## 8.0.0 ◆ MAINTENANCE

The first requirement in a satisfactory maintenance program for electrical panelboards and switches is safety, including the use of the proper lockout/tagout procedures.

The second is good equipment that has been properly installed. No one can do a good maintenance job on equipment that is not appropriate for the job or that has been installed haphazardly with no eye to future maintenance requirements. If such conditions exist, they should be brought to the attention of the proper party and corrected, rather than trying to establish a maintenance program for them.

The third requirement for a good maintenance program is proper maintenance personnel. Persons who must maintain equipment should have a thorough knowledge of the equipment's operation and have the ability to make thorough inspections and minor repairs of that equipment.

The fourth requirement of a good maintenance program is the establishment of preventive maintenance. This is an all-inclusive phrase for the continuing inspection of equipment, the report and recording of the condition of the equipment, and the repair of the equipment.

The term preventive maintenance has come to mean a system of routine inspections of equipment that is properly recorded for future reference on some type of inspection records. More specifically, the term stands for the heading-off of future equipment problems by making minor repairs in advance of major operating difficulties. In electrical panelboards and switches, a simple tightening of a lug early on can prevent a serious short circuit or a heated terminal later. Due to the aspect of recording all such inspections, some electricians believe that preventive maintenance is merely a system of records. Actually, the records supplement the inspection and are designed to take the place of the maintenance technician's memory. In such extreme cases where only one maintenance worker services a particularly small plant or building, records might be entirely disregarded, although this is not recommended. However, where a number of maintenance personnel are servicing large systems, records are vital to the proper operation of the maintenance inspection routine.

Electrical equipment is more prone to damage by operating conditions than almost any other piece of equipment. Water, dust, heat, cold, humidity, vibration, and countless other conditions can affect the proper operation of electrical equipment. Because of this, there are three cardinal rules to follow in maintaining electrical apparatus. These are:

- Keep it clean.
- Keep it dry.
- Keep it tight.

One of the greatest problems existing in panelboards, switchgear, load centers, and the like are loose connections at both the main lugs and at circuit breakers and/or fuse blocks. Loose connections cause overheating and eventual failure of the terminals and/or conductors. This condition is especially prevalent where aluminum conductors are used. Therefore, periodic checks should be made to ensure that all connections are tight.

## Improper Maintenance Procedures Can Be Dangerous

A group of electricians were performing maintenance on AC switchgear. The equipment was placed in the maintenance mode by opening the primary 20kV interrupter switch. This switch was housed in the upper compartment of a two-compartment cabinet. Each compartment had its own door. One of the electricians was assigned to clean the lower compartment, but he began to clean the upper compartment as well. He sprayed cleaning fluid from an aerosol can onto the circuitry. When the aerosol spray contacted the line side of the primary switch, it provided a conductive plasma for the current. The current passed through the spray, spray can, and the electrician's body, which had apparently made contact with one of the switch blades, causing him to be electrocuted and badly burned.

**The Bottom Line:** This accident could have been prevented if proper safety and maintenance procedures had been followed. No electrician should attempt to work on any equipment, regardless of voltage, without first getting permission from the supervisor and only after having received proper training for the task at hand. This includes training in the use of special tools and safety equipment required for the task.

## *Putting It All Together*

Examine the service at your home or workplace. Is the service entrance properly installed and protected? Is the service-entrance cable cracked or frayed? What about the electrical panel? Are the breakers properly labeled? Is there a main service disconnect switch?

1. Which of the following best describes the components between the service drop and the building's main disconnecting device?
   a. Wye connection
   b. Service entrance
   c. Service union
   d. Service lateral

2. The most common electric service for residential and small commercial applications is _____.
   a. single-phase, 120V, two-wire service
   b. single-phase, 120/240V, three-wire service
   c. three-phase, 208/120V, four-wire service
   d. three-phase, 277V/480, four-wire service

3. The approximate voltage between ground and the high leg of a 120/240V delta-connected service with a center tap is _____.
   a. 120V
   b. 163V
   c. 208V
   d. 240V

4. What is used in conjunction with a watt-hour meter to measure the power used in services over 400A?
   a. An autotransformer
   b. A current transformer
   c. An ohmmeter
   d. An ammeter

5. Which of the following is used on most working drawings to give details of the panelboards and overcurrent protective devices used on the project?
   a. A panelboard schedule
   b. An appliance schedule
   c. A cross-sectional detail drawing
   d. A site plan

6. How must overhead service-entrance conductors be arranged from the point where they leave the service head to the point where they are connected to the service drop?
   a. They must be absolutely straight with no sag.
   b. They must terminate in a pothead.
   c. A drip loop must be provided.
   d. They must be color-coded yellow, green, and orange.

7. A(n) _____ is used to determine the amount of electricity consumed by the customer.
   a. ammeter
   b. wattmeter
   c. watt-hour meter
   d. ohmmeter

8. The minimum size copper grounding electrode conductor allowed when used with copper service-entrance cables No. 2 AWG or smaller is _____.
   a. No. 2
   b. No. 4
   c. No. 6
   d. No. 8

9. When a metal water pipe is used as a grounding electrode, a _____ must be provided at the water meter.
   a. bonding jumper
   b. floor drain
   c. grounding locknut
   d. grounding bushing

10. Which of the following is considered to be a part of the metering equipment in a 277/480V, wye-connected service?
    a. Subpanels
    b. Service-entrance conductors
    c. Potential transformers
    d. Autotransformers

## Summary

Regardless of the size or complexity, all electric services serve the same purpose: to deliver electrical energy from the supply system to the wiring system on the premises served. The basic components of a commercial electric service include a transformer to convert the transmission voltage to a usable level; a service drop, which includes the conductors that are used to connect the service from the power pole to the service facilities at the building; a service entrance, which includes all components between the termination of the overhead service drop and the building's main disconnecting device, except for the metering equipment; service conductors, which are the conductors used in the service entrance; and service equipment, which provides overcurrent protection, a means of disconnect, and a point of attachment for the metering equipment. *NEC Article 230* covers the requirements for electric services.

## Notes

# Trade Terms Introduced in This Module

*Delta-connected:* A three-phase transformer connection in which the terminals are connected in a triangular shape like the Greek letter delta ($\Delta$).

*Load center:* A specific type of panelboard designed for light-duty, single- or three-phase applications, such as residential or light commercial installations.

*Service:* The electric power delivered to the premises.

*Service conductors:* The conductors between the point of termination of the overhead service drop or underground service lateral and the main disconnecting device in the building or on the premises.

*Service drop:* The overhead conductors through which electrical service is supplied between the last power company pole and the point of their connection to the service-entrance conductors located at the building or other support used for the purpose.

*Service entrance:* All components between the point of termination of the overhead service drop or underground service lateral and the building's main disconnecting device, except for metering equipment.

*Service equipment:* The necessary equipment, usually consisting of a circuit breaker or switch and fuses and their accessories, located near the point of entrance of supply conductors to a building and intended to constitute the main control and cutoff means for the electric supply to the building.

*Service lateral:* The underground service conductors between the street main, including any risers at a pole or other structure or from transformers, and the first point of connection to the service-entrance conductors in a terminal box, meter, or other enclosure with adequate space, inside or outside the building wall.

*Service raceway:* The rigid conduit, IMC, or other raceway that encloses the service entrance conductors.

*Substation:* An installation or area where an assembly of devices and apparatus are used to monitor, control, transform, or modify electrical power. Substations are normally installed at a point on the system where transmission voltages are reduced to distribution voltages.

*Wye-connected:* A three-phase transformer connection in which all three phases are connected at a central point, forming a Y configuration.

his module is intended to present thorough re-
urces for task training. The following reference
orks are suggested for further study. These are
tional materials for continued education rather
an for task training.

*American Electrician's Handbook,* Latest Edition. New York: Croft and Summers, McGraw-Hill.

*National Electrical Code® Handbook,* Latest Edition. Quincy, MA: National Fire Protection Association.

# Load Calculations— Feeders and Service

## 26401-05

**Ponnequin Wind Farm**

Ponnequin Wind Farm generates electrical power from the wind. The site is located on the plains of eastern Colorado just south of the Wyoming border. It consists of 44 wind turbines and can generate up to 30 megawatts of electricity. Each wind turbine cost about $1 million to build and is capable of generating 700 kilowatts of electricity. The turbines begin operating with wind speeds as low as 7 mph and shut themselves down at speeds over 55 mph. Each turbine weighs nearly 100 tons and stands 181 feet tall. The turbine blades are attached on the top of the turbine and have a diameter of 159 feet.

# 26401-05
# *Load Calculations – Feeders and Services*

*Topics to be presented in this module include:*

## Overview

Rules and regulations pertaining to branch circuit, feeder, and service calculations are covered in *National Electrical Code Article 220*. Load calculation must be performed and documented before service equipment, panelboard circuit breakers, or conductors are installed because all of these electrical components depend on the calculated loads. Calculating the connected load is no as simple as listing the amperage ratings found on equipment labels. Fo instance, general lighting loads must be calculated based on the square footag of occupied space. General lighting loads include both general-purpose recep tacles and lighting.

The general lighting load is added to the total load calculations for all othe equipment. In residential occupancies, these loads include small appliance HVAC equipment, cooking appliances, laundry room appliances, and an other individual load not included in the general lighting load calculation Total loads for commercial and industrial facilities are calculated in a simila manner. However, demand factors may be applied to reduce the total name plate loads in locations such as apartment complexes, commercial laundr facilities, and commercial kitchens because not all of the equipment will b used at the same time.

## Objectives

When you have completed this module, you will be able to do the following:

1. Size feeders and services in accordance with *National Electrical Code*® (*NEC*®) requirements.
2. Calculate loads and ampacities for single-phase and three-phase feeders.
3. Understand and apply derating factors to size feeders.
4. Size feeder overcurrent protection devices (circuit breakers and fuses) for noncontinuous duty and continuous duty loads.
5. Understand and apply tap rules.
6. Calculate loads for a retail store with a show window.
7. Calculate loads for an office building.
8. Calculate loads for both single-family and multi-family dwellings.
9. Calculate loads for a restaurant.
10. Calculate loads for hotels and motels.
11. Calculate loads for schools and other institutional projects.
12. Perform feeder and service calculations for farms.
13. Calculate the power and supply feeders for marinas and boatyards.
14. Calculate electric motor loads on feeders.

## Prerequisites

Before you begin this module, it is recommended that you successfully complete *Core Curriculum; Electrical Level One; Electrical Level Two; Electrical Level Three.*

This course map shows all of the modules in *Electrical Level Four.* The suggested training order begins at the bottom and proceeds up. Skill levels increase as you advance on the course map. The local Training Program Sponsor may adjust the training order.

## Required Trainee Materials

1. Pencil and paper
2. Appropriate personal protective equipment
3. Copy of the latest edition of the *National Electrical Code*®

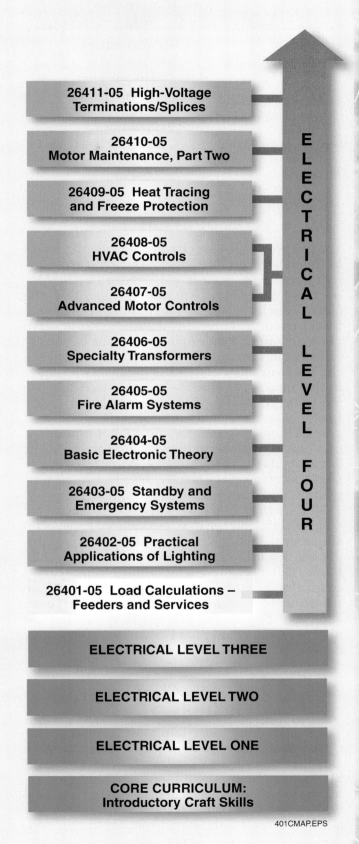

26411-05  High-Voltage Terminations/Splices

26410-05 Motor Maintenance, Part Two

26409-05  Heat Tracing and Freeze Protection

26408-05 HVAC Controls

26407-05 Advanced Motor Controls

26406-05 Specialty Transformers

26405-05 Fire Alarm Systems

26404-05 Basic Electronic Theory

26403-05  Standby and Emergency Systems

26402-05  Practical Applications of Lighting

26401-05  Load Calculations – Feeders and Services

ELECTRICAL LEVEL FOUR

ELECTRICAL LEVEL THREE

ELECTRICAL LEVEL TWO

ELECTRICAL LEVEL ONE

CORE CURRICULUM: Introductory Craft Skills

401CMAP.EPS

# 1.0.0 ◆ INTRODUCTION

The purpose of **feeder** circuit load calculations is to determine the size of feeder circuit overcurrent protection devices and feeder circuit conductors using *NEC®* requirements. Once the feeder circuit load is accurately calculated, feeder circuit components may be sized to serve the load safely. Feeder circuits typically supply transformers, motor control centers, and subpanels. The load calculations and methods presented in this module follow the same pattern and use the same equations that were presented in the *Load Calculations – Branch Circuits* module in Level Three. Some of the information presented previously will be reviewed in this module; however, it is strongly suggested that you review *Load Calculations – Branch Circuits* prior to proceeding with this module.

*NEC Article 215* covers feeder circuits. *NEC Section 215.2* states that feeders shall have an ampacity that is no less than that required to supply the load, as computed in *NEC Article 220, Parts III, IV, and V.* The minimum feeder-circuit conductor size, before the application of any adjustment or correction factors, shall have an allowable ampacity of not less than 100% of the noncontinuous load plus 125% of the continuous load.

# 2.0.0 ◆ BASIC CALCULATION PROCEDURES

The *NEC®* establishes minimum standards for electrical calculations. Since most electrical exams are based upon the minimum *NEC®* requirements, this module will focus on those requirements. Common practice in the electrical industry is to design and plan electrical systems to make allowance for future expansion. Providing conduit and raceways larger than the minimum required by the *NEC®* may reduce the labor required in pulling conductors, which may offset the higher cost of the larger conduit. Services are frequently sized larger than the minimum required by the *NEC®* so that future expansion of the electrical system will be possible.

It should be stressed once more that the journeyman and master electrician examinations are in most cases based upon calculations using *NEC* minimum requirements, without an allowance for future expansion or ease of installation.

## 2.1.0 Load Calculations – Basic Considerations

Electrical calculations can be divided into three sections:

- Branch circuits
- Feeders
- Services

The total load connected to the branch circuit determines the load on feeders, and the total feeder load determines the load on the **service conductors** and equipment. When calculating loads, the logical sequence is to determine the load on branch circuits, calculate the feeder load, and then determine the service load. Branch circuit calculations were covered in your Level Three training, and you are strongly urged to review that material before proceeding because the information presented in this module is based upon the calculations developed using branch circuit calculations.

## 2.2.0 Conductor Adjustments

The allowable current-carrying capacity (ampacity) of conductors may require adjustment due to several conditions. After complying with *NEC Section 110.14(C)*, the conductors selected may have to be increased in size to accommodate the altered allowable ampacity for that conductor. Feeder conductor size is adjusted when:

- The load to be supplied is a continuous duty load per *NEC Section 215.2(A)(1)*.
- There are more than three current-carrying conductors in a raceway per *NEC Table 310.15(B)(2)(a)*.
- The ambient temperature that the conductor will pass through exceeds the temperature ratings for conductors listed in *NEC Table 310.16*.
- Although not mandatory, an increase in conductor size may be made when there is a voltage drop exceeding 3% for feeders or 5% for the combination of the feeder and branch circuit that was caused by excessive voltage drop per *NEC Section 215.2(A)(3), FPN No. 2.*

## 2.1 Continuous Duty, Raceway Fill, and Ambient Temperature

Feeder conductors are adjusted when the load or a part of the load connected to the feeder is a continuous duty load; that is, it operates without interruption for more than three hours consecutively. NEC Table 310.16 lists allowable ampacities for insulated conductors rated at 0 to 2,000V. The ampacities listed apply when no more than three current-carrying conductors are installed in a raceway or are part of a cable assembly. The ampacities are based upon an ambient temperature of 30°C (86°F). If the number of current-carrying conductors in the conduit or cable exceeds three, the ampacity of the conductors must be adjusted using NEC Table 310.15(B)(2)(a). If the ambient temperature exceeds 30°C (86°F), the ampacity of the conductors must be adjusted using the temperature correction factors listed at the bottom of NEC Table 310.16.

When derating conductors, it is permitted to use the allowable ampacity listed for the temperature rating of the conductor instead of the selection ampacity, which is restricted to the 60°C or 75°C column. For example, the minimum size of THHN copper permitted to supply a load of 125A is No. 1 AWG copper, based on the 75°C column of NEC Table 310.16. When derating this conductor, the ampacity used will be the 150A, as shown in the 90°C column.

> **NOTE**
>
> The selection ampacity for choosing a conductor to carry a load is taken from either the 60°C or 75°C column of NEC Table 310.16 as required by NEC Section 110.14(C). When determining the ability of that conductor to carry the load under adverse conditions, the allowable ampacity of the conductor is used based on its actual temperature rating.

The size of a conductor may also be increased when the length of the feeder conductor requires a larger circular mil area to ensure a low enough resistance to allow the needed current to flow.

*Example 1:*

What is the adjusted ampacity for each of six No. 4/0 THHN copper current-carrying conductors in a single conduit?

Per NEC Table 310.16, the ampacity of No. 4/0 THHN is 260A. Per NEC Table 310.15(B)(2)(a), the ampacity must be adjusted by 80% (four through six current-carrying conductors).

$$260A \times 80\% = 208A \text{ for each conductor}$$

*Example 2:*

What is the maximum adjusted ampacity for each of nine No. 3/0 current-carrying THWN copper conductors in a single conduit?

Per NEC Table 310.16, the ampacity of No. 3/0 THWN is 200A. Per NEC Table 310.15(B)(2)(a), the ampacity must be adjusted by 70% (seven through nine current-carrying conductors).

$$200A \times 70\% = 140A \text{ for each conductor}$$

*Example 3:*

A feeder is being installed to supply a load of 375A. The feeder must be routed through a room with an ambient temperature of 98°F. Will 500 kcmil THHN copper conductors be able to carry the load under these conditions?

Per NEC Table 310.16, 500 kcmil THHN conductors have an ampacity of 430A. Per the correction factors of NEC Table 310.16, the ampacity of a type THHN conductor must be multiplied by a factor of 0.91 to account for the ambient temperature.

$$430A \times 0.91 = 391.3A$$

The 500 kcmil THHN conductors will meet the requirements of the NEC®.

*Example 4:*

What is the minimum size THHN copper conductor required for a feeder supplying a continuous load of 85A and a noncontinuous load of 105A while in an ambient temperature of 34°C and with a total of four current-carrying conductors in the same raceway?

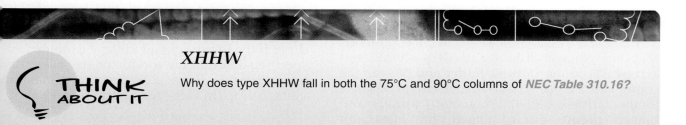

**XHHW**

THINK ABOUT IT

Why does type XHHW fall in both the 75°C and 90°C columns of *NEC Table 310.16?*

To select a feeder conductor, multiply the continuous load by 125%:

$$85A \times 125\% = 106.25A$$

Add the noncontinuous load:

$$106.25A + 105A = 211.25A$$

Per *NEC Table 310.16,* No. 4/0 THHN is selected to carry the load of 211.25A using the 75°C column.

The connected load before any adjustments are made is:

$$85A + 105A = 190A$$

Per *NEC Table 310.16,* the ampacity of a type THHN conductor when in an ambient temperature of 35°C must be multiplied by a factor of 0.96. The allowable ampacity of No. 4/0 THHN copper is 260A.

$$260A \times 0.96 = 249.6A$$

Per *NEC Table 310.15(B)(2)(a)* the allowable ampacity of a conductor run in a raceway with four to six current-carrying conductors must be reduced by 80%.

$$249.6A \times 80\% = 199.68A$$

The No. 4/0 THHN conductors at 199.68A will be able to carry the load of 190A under these adverse conditions. This conductor satisfies the requirements of *NEC Section 215.2(A)(1).*

#### 2.2.2 Voltage Drop

*NEC Section 215.2(A)(3), FPN No. 2* recommends that the voltage drop for feeders should not exceed 3% to the farthest outlet and 5% for the combination of feeder and branch circuit distance to the farthest outlet. When both feeders and branch circuits are combined, the maximum voltage drop allowed for the branch circuits usually 3%, and the voltage drop allowed for the feeder is 2%. There are two formulas used to calculate voltage drop for single-phase circuits with resistive loads (power factor = 1.0).

Formula 1:

$$VD = \frac{2 \times L \times R \times I}{1,000}$$

Formula 2:

$$VD = \frac{2 \times L \times K \times I}{CM}$$

*Where:*

    L = one-way length in feet

    R = conductor resistance
        *(NEC Chapter 9, Table 8)*

    K = constant (12.9 for copper conductors or 21. for aluminum conductors)

    I = load (in amps)

  CM = conductor size in circular mils
        *(NEC Chapter 9, Table 8)*

  VD = voltage drop (in volts)

To calculate the percentage of voltage drop divide the voltage drop (VD) by the applied voltage (V) and multiply by 100:

$$Percent\ voltage\ drop = (VD \div V) \times 100$$

The result is divided by circuit voltage and the multiplied by 100 to determine the % voltage drop. If the branch circuit voltage drop exceeds specified amount, the conductor size is increased to compensate. For a 120V circuit, the maximum voltage drop (in volts) for a permitted 3% drop i

$$120V \times 3\% = 3.6V$$

## The K Factor

To find the K factor, multiply the resistance per foot of the conductor (found in *NEC Chapter 9, Table 8*) by the circular mils of the conductor and divide by 1,000. For example, No. 6 AWG = 26,240 CM × 0.491 = 12,883.84 ÷ 1,000 = 12.88 (round to 12.9).

For a 240V, single-phase (Ø) feeder combined with branch circuits, the maximum voltage drop (in volts) would normally be:

$$240V \times 2\% = 4.8V$$

In commercial fixed load applications, if the feeder load is not concentrated at the end of the feeder but is spread out along the feeder due to multiple taps, the load center length of the feeder should be calculated and used in the voltage drop formulas. This is because the total current does not flow the complete length of the feeder. If the full length is used in computing the voltage drop, the drop determined will be greater than what would actually occur. The load center length of a feeder is that point in the feeder where, if the load were concentrated at that point, the voltage drop would be the same as the voltage drop to the farthest load in the actual feeder. To determine the load center length of a feeder with multiple taps, as shown in *Figure 1*, multiply each tap load by its actual physical routing distance from the supply end of the feeder. Add these products for all loads fed from the feeder and divide this sum by the

sum of the individual loads. The resulting distance is the load center length (L) for the total load (I) of the feeder.

*Example 1:*

The length of a 240V, three-wire panel feeder is 145'. The total panel load consists of 180A of non-continuous duty loads. No. 3/0 THHN copper conductors would normally be selected to supply this load. If they are used, will the voltage drop for this panel feeder exceed 2%?

Use the first voltage drop formula to determine the voltage drop for the feeder. Look up the resistance for No. 3/0 AWG copper in *NEC Chapter 9, Table 8*. The DC resistance is 0.0766Ω/ft. Using the voltage drop formula:

$$2 \times 145' \times 0.0766\Omega/\text{ft} \times 180A \div 1,000 = 4V$$
$$4V \div 240V = 0.0167V \times 100 = 1.67\%$$

Since this percentage does not exceed 2%, the answer to the question is no, the voltage drop for this feeder using No. 3/0 AWG conductors will not exceed the recommended value. Note that in

CALCULATION

| LOAD 1 = | 80' | × | 200A | = | 16,000 |
| LOAD 2 = | 100' | × | 200A | = | 20,000 |
| LOAD 3 = | 130' | × | 40A | = | 5,200 |
| TOTALS | | | 440A | | 41,200 = 93.64' (LOAD CENTER LENGTH) |

TOTAL LOAD (I) = 440A
LOAD CENTER LENGTH (L) = 93.64'

401F01.EPS

*Figure 1* ◆ Load center length calculation.

this example, the second formula could have been used, if desired. Either formula will yield similar results.

*Example 2:*

What size THHN copper conductors would be required for a continuous feeder load of 180A, 208V, 1Ø for fixed utilization equipment? The total length of the feeder is 318'.

Since this is a continuous load, the load is multiplied by 125% to determine the feeder ampacity.

$$180A \times 125\% = 225A$$

This feeder will require a No. 4/0 THHN copper conductor to supply the continuous load. The connected load, however, is 180A, and this is the amount of current that will be used in our voltage drop calculations.

Use the second voltage drop formula as an example to determine the voltage drop for this feeder. Look up the area in CM for a No. 4/0 THHN copper conductor in *NEC Chapter 9, Table 8.* Using the voltage drop formula:

$$2 \times 318' \times 12.9 \times 180A \div 211,600 = 6.98V$$
$$6.98V \div 208V = 0.0336 \times 100 = 3.36\%$$

This percentage exceeds 3%; therefore, No. 4/0 AWG copper would not meet the *NEC®* recommendations for voltage drop. Using the area in CM for 250 kcmil (250,000 CM) conductors, the formula becomes:

$$2 \times 318' \times 12.9 \times 180A \div 250,000 = 5.91V$$
$$5.91V \div 208V = 0.0284 \times 100 = 2.84\%$$

No. 250 kcmil conductors would meet the *NEC®* voltage drop recommendations for this feeder.

*Example 3:*

What size THHN copper conductors would be required for a tapped 240V, single-phase, three-wire feeder consisting of continuous fixed 240V utilization equipment loads of 180A at 30' and at the end, a noncontinuous fixed load of 100A at 450'?

Since there is one continuous load tap and one noncontinuous load tap, the minimum ampacity required for the feeder conductors is computed as follows:

$$Tap\ 1 = 180A \times 125\% = 225A$$
$$Tap\ 2 = 100A \times 100\% = 100A$$

The total computed load of the feeder = 225A + 100A = 325A. The minimum conductor size required for this feeder would be 400 kcmil copper per *NEC Table 310.16.*

To determine the conductor size that will prevent excessive voltage drop, use the load center length calculation. Multiply the loads by the distance from the feeder source, and then divide the sum of the two products by the sum of the two loads as follows:

$$Tap\ 1 = 30' \times 180A = 5,400$$
$$Tap\ 2 = 450' \times 100A = 45,000$$

Sum the products:

$$5,400 + 45,000 = 50,400$$

Divide by the sum of the loads:

$$180A + 100A = 280A$$
$$50,400 \div 280 = 180'\ for\ the\ load\ center$$

Using the second single-phase voltage drop formula, substitute values using the load center length, 280A, and 400 kcmil (400,000 circular mils to check the voltage drop:

$$2 \times 180' \times 12.9 \times 280A \div 400,000\ CM = 3.25V$$

The maximum recommended voltage drop 240V × 3% or 7.2V; therefore, 400 kcmil conductors are more than adequate. Note that if the full length of the feeder (450') had been used in this example instead of the load center length, the voltage drop would be 8.1V and 500 kcmil conductors would have to be selected, which is excessive for this application.

Voltage drop for balanced three-phase circuit (with negligible reactance and a power factor of 1.0) can be calculated using the two voltage drop formulas by substituting $\sqrt{3}$ (1.732) for the value of 2 in the first two formulas, which result in the following formulas:

Formula 3:

$$VD = \frac{\sqrt{3} \times L \times R \times I}{1,000}$$

Formula 4:

$$VD = \frac{\sqrt{3} \times L \times K \times I}{CM}$$

*Example 4:*

What is the voltage drop of a 208V, 3Ø feeder with a noncontinuous load of 230A, a distance from the circuit breaker to the load of 315', and using No. 4/0 copper conductors?

Use the third voltage drop formula to determine voltage drop for this 3Ø feeder. Look up the resistance for No. 4/0 copper conductor in *NEC Chapter 9, Table 8.* Using the voltage drop formula:

$$\sqrt{3} \times 315' \times 0.0608 \times 230A \div 1,000 = 7.63V$$

The maximum voltage drop permitted for a 208V circuit is:

$$208V \times 3\% = 6.24V$$

Since, in this problem, 7.63V is more than the maximum allowable voltage drop, this circuit will not meet the minimum *NEC*® recommendation for voltage drop, and the conductor size should be increased to compensate for the voltage drop.

*Example 5:*

What size THHN copper conductors would be required for a panelboard used to supply continuous nonlinear loads of 100A for a 208V, three-phase, four-wire feeder circuit with a length of 150' from the source to the panelboard?

Since the feeder is supplying nonlinear loads, the neutral wire becomes a current-carrying conductor per *NEC Section 310.15(B)(4)(c),* and therefore, there are four current-carrying conductors. This will require the ampacity of the wire to be adjusted by 80% per *NEC Table 310.15(B)(2)(a):*

Actual current = rated current × derating %

Since the actual current is known, solve the equation for the rated current:

Actual current ÷ derating % = rated current

Substituting values yields:

$$100A \div 80\% = 125A$$

With the computed value of 125A, the minimum size for the THHN copper conductor per the 90°C column of *NEC Table 310.16* is No. 2. However, because this is a feeder conductor, it must also meet the requirements of *NEC Section 215.2(A)(1).* This requires a minimum ampacity of 125% for continuous loads before the application of any adjustment factors. Multiply the actual load of 100A by 125% to obtain 125A for the required conductor ampacity. Since the actual load is 100A, we are limited to ampacity values of 60°C per *NEC Section 110.14(C).* Refer to *NEC Table 310.16* and select No. 1/0 copper based on the ampacity requirements of 125A.

Apply the fourth formula, substituting values (using the actual connected load in amps) to check that the voltage drop does not exceed the recommended 3% of 208V, or 6.24V.

$$\sqrt{3} \times 150' \times 12.9 \times 100A \div 105,600 \text{ CM} = 3.17V$$

The No. 1/0 AWG conductors will be adequate for this application.

### 2.2.3 Temperature Limitations for Terminating Conductors

*NEC Section 110.14(C)* includes temperature limitations for terminating conductors. The ampacity rating of conductors must be selected and coordinated so that the ampacity rating of the conductor does not exceed the temperature rating of any component in the feeder circuit. If the feeder size is smaller than 100A, the 60°C rating for the feeder conductor must be used unless all feeder components are rated and listed for use at a higher temperature. If the feeder size is larger than 100A, the 75°C rating for the feeder conductor must be used unless all feeder components are rated and listed for use at a higher temperature. For example, if the termination rating on a 125A fuse or circuit breaker is 75°C, type THHN conductors may be used for the feeder; however, the 75°C rating for the conductor size must be used. Conductors with higher temperature ratings may be used for ampacity adjustment, correction, or both. As you work through this module, please keep in mind that, although type THHN conductors are often used in example problems, the limitations of *NEC Section 110.14(C)* still apply.

*Example:*

A 200A feeder is required to serve a new panelboard. The terminals in the panelboard are rated at 75°C, and the terminals in the fusible switch protecting the feeder are rated at 60°C. What is the minimum size THHN copper conductor required to supply the panelboard?

Per *NEC Table 310.16,* No. 2/0 THHN is rated at 195A and *NEC Section 240.4(B)* would permit connection to the 200A fuse. However, because the fuse terminals are rated at 60°C, the rating must be taken from the 60°C column. The minimum allowable size taken from the 60°C column for the 200A load is No. 4/0. The answer is No. 4/0 THHN copper conductor.

### 2.3.0 Calculating Feeder Ampacity

Feeder ampacity for single-phase circuits (with negligible reactance and a power factor of 1.0) is calculated by dividing VA by the circuit voltage:

$$I = \frac{VA}{V}$$

For example, the ampacity of a single-phase 240V load rated at 21,600VA is determined by dividing 21,600VA by 240V.

$$21,600VA \div 240V = 90A$$

Feeder ampacity for balanced three-phase circuits (wye or delta with negligible reactance and a power factor of 1.0) is calculated by dividing VA by the line-to-line circuit voltage times $\sqrt{3}$.

$$I = \frac{VA}{V \times \sqrt{3}}$$

For example, the ampacity of a 208V, three-phase load rated at 15,200VA is determined by dividing 15,200VA by $(208V \times \sqrt{3})$.

$$15{,}200VA \div (208V \times \sqrt{3}) = 42.19A$$

The ampacity of a 144kVA three-phase load at 480V is 173.21A.

$$144{,}000VA \div (480V \times \sqrt{3}) = 173.21A$$

*Example 1:*

What is the ampacity of a single-phase load with a nameplate rating of 42.5kW, 240V?

Multiply 42.5kW by 1,000 to determine VA (watts = volt-amperes) and then divide the result by 240V.

$$42.5kW \times 1{,}000 = 42{,}500VA \div 240V = 177.08A$$

The ampacity of this load is 177.08A.

*Example 2:*

What is the ampacity of a three-phase panel feeder with a calculated load of 135kW, 208V?

Multiply 135kW by 1,000 and divide the result by $208V \times \sqrt{3}$.

$$135kW \times 1{,}000 = 135{,}000kW \div (208V \times \sqrt{3})$$
$$= 374.72A$$

*Example 3:*

What size THWN copper conductors are required to supply the primary of a 75kVA, 3Ø transformer? The primary line-to-line voltage is 480V.

Multiply 75kVA by 1,000 to determine total VA and divide the result by $480V \times \sqrt{3}$ to determine the transformer primary current. Using *NEC Table 310.16,* determine the conductor size:

$$75kVA \times 1{,}000 = 75{,}000VA \div (480V \times \sqrt{3})$$
$$= 90.21A$$

Per *NEC Table 310.16,* No. 3 THWN copper (rated at 100A) is required if both the transformer and the panel are marked for 75°C terminations. If not, then No. 1 AWG copper would be required.

*Example 4:*

What is the secondary current for a 1,500kVA three-phase transformer with a voltage rating of 480V/277Y?

Multiply 1,500kVA by 1,000 to determine total VA and divide the result by $480V \times \sqrt{3}$ to determine the secondary current.

$$1{,}500kVA \times 1{,}000 = 1{,}500{,}000VA \div (480V \times \sqrt{3})$$
$$= 1{,}804.22A$$

The secondary current for this transformer = 1,804.22A.

## 2.4.0 Tap Rules

When the overcurrent protection for a conductor is located at the load end instead of at the supply side of a conductor, the *NEC*® generally considers that to be a **tap conductor**. This means that almost all secondary sides of transformers are classified as taps, since there is no overcurrent device within the transformer itself. The most frequently used tap rules are the 10' tap rule and the 25' tap rule *(NEC Section 240.21)*.

### 2.4.1 The 10' Tap Rule

Generally, smaller conductors may be tapped from larger conductors, providing that the total length of the tap conductor does not exceed 10'. However, there are very specific *NEC*® requirements for each tap rule, including the 10' tap rule *[NEC Section 240.21(B)(1)]*. It is important to note that, when applying the 10' tap rule, the total length of the tap conductors (from their source of supply to their termination point in an overcurrent device) cannot exceed 10'. The *NEC*® requirements for the 10' tap rule state that, in order for this rule to be applied, all of the following conditions must be met:

- The total length of the tap conductors must not exceed 10'.
- The tap conductors must be rated at no less than the calculated load(s) to be served or the device to which the tap conductors are connected.
- The tap conductors cannot extend beyond the **switchboard**, panel, or control devices which they supply.
- The tap conductors must be enclosed in a raceway.
- The rating of the line side overcurrent device supplying the tap conductors shall not exceed 1,000% of the rating of the tap conductors.

### 2.4.2 The 25' Tap Rule

*NEC Section 240.21(B)(2)* lists specific conditions for the application of the 25' tap rule. It is important to note that, when applying the 25' tap rule, the total length of the tap conductors (from their source of supply to their termination point in an overcurrent device) cannot exceed 25'. The *NEC*® requirements for the 25' tap rule state that, in order for this rule to be applied, all of the following conditions must be met:

- The total length of the tap conductors must not exceed 25'.
- The tap conductors must be rated at no less than one-third the capacity of the overcurrent device protecting the feeder.

**Transformers**

*INSIDE TRACK*

Transformer secondary conductors are considered taps and as such are limited in length to no more than 10' or 25' (depending on the application) when located inside buildings. See *NEC Section 240.21(C).*

The tap conductors must terminate in a single circuit breaker or a single set of fuses that will limit the load to the conductor rating.

The tap conductors must be enclosed in a raceway or otherwise suitably protected from physical damage.

### .4.3 Taps Supplying a Transformer– Primary and Secondary Not Over 25'

*TEC Section 240.21(B)(3)* lists specific conditions or the application of the transformer 25' tap rule. is important to note that, when applying the 25' p rule, the total length of the tap conductors cluding one primary conductor and one secndary conductor (from their source of supply to ieir termination point in an overcurrent device) nnot exceed 25'. The requirements of this rule ply only when the primary conductors that pply a transformer are not protected by an overrrent device at their rated ampacity. The *NEC®* quirements for this transformer 25' tap rule state at, in order for this rule to be applied, all of the llowing conditions must be met:

The primary conductors must have an ampacity that is at least one-third the capacity of the overcurrent device protecting the primary conductors.

Use the ratio of the primary to the secondary voltage multiplied by one-third the size of the overcurrent device protecting the feeder conductors.

The total length of the primary and secondary conductors must not exceed 25'.

Both primary and secondary conductors must be protected from physical damage by being enclosed in an approved raceway or other approved means.

The secondary conductors must terminate in a single circuit breaker or set of fuses that limit the load per *NEC Section 310.15.*

### 2.4.4 The 100' Tap Rule

Use of the 100' tap rule is limited to installations in high-bay manufacturing **buildings** with wall heights over 35'. *NEC Section 240.21(B)(4)* lists specific conditions for the application of the 100' tap rule. This tap rule may be used in buildings where only qualified persons will service and maintain the systems. The length of this tap is limited to 25' horizontally, and the total length of the tap cannot exceed 100'. In addition, the *NEC®* requires that the following conditions be met:

- The ampacity of the tap conductors must be at least one-third the ampacity of the feeder overcurrent protection device.
- The tap conductors must terminate in a single circuit breaker or set of fuses that will limit the load to the conductor ratings.
- The tap conductors must be protected from physical damage.
- The tap conductors must not be spliced.
- The tap conductors must be a minimum size of No. 6 copper or No. 4 aluminum.
- The tap conductors must not penetrate walls, floors, or ceilings.
- The tap to the feeder must be made at least 30' above the floor.

### 2.4.5 Outside Taps of Unlimited Length

*NEC Section 240.21(B)(5)* states that where the conductors are located outside of a building, except at the point of load termination, there is no limit to the length of the tap conductors provided that all of the following conditions are met:

- The conductors are suitably protected from physical damage in an approved manner.
- The conductors terminate in a single circuit breaker or set of fuses that limit the load to the ampacity of the conductors. Additional loads may be supplied from the breaker or set of fuses.

- The overcurrent device for the conductors is an integral part of the disconnecting means or is located immediately adjacent to the disconnecting means.
- The disconnecting means is installed at a readily accessible location complying with one of the following:
  - Outside of a building or structure
  - Inside, nearest the point of entrance of the conductors
  - Where installed in accordance with *NEC Section 230.6,* nearest the point of entrance of the conductors

### 2.4.6 Transformer Secondary Conductors

*NEC Section 240.21(C)* provides the installation and length requirements for the secondary conductors of transformers. Although there are many similarities in these tap rules, there are a few differences. The 10' tap rule for a transformer secondary requires that the ampacity of the secondary conductors be at least 10% of the rating of the overcurrent device on the primary side multiplied by the primary to secondary transformer voltage ratio. The outside taps of unlimited length for transformers are similar to the tap rules previously discussed. To install secondary conductors longer than 10' inside buildings, the requirements in *NEC Section 240.21(C)(3)* or *NEC Section 240.21(C)(6)* must be met.

*NEC Section 240.21(C)(3)* will permit secondary conductors from a transformer in lengths up to 25' in industrial installations only, when the following conditions are met:

- The ampacity of the secondary conductors is not less than the secondary current rating of the transformer, and the sum of the ratings of the overcurrent devices does not exceed the ampacity of the secondary conductors.
- All overcurrent devices are grouped.
- The secondary conductors are protected from physical damage by approved means.

*NEC Section 240.21(C)(6)* will permit secondary conductors from a transformer in lengths up to 25' when these conditions are met:

- Use the ratio of the primary to the secondary voltage multiplied by one-third the size of the overcurrent device protecting the feeder conductors.
- The secondary conductors terminate in a single circuit breaker or set of fuses that limit the load

to not more than the conductor ampacity that i permitted by *NEC Section 310.15.*
- The conductors are protected from physica damage by approved means.

*Example 1:*

Using the 10' tap rule, what size THWN coppe conductors are required for a 40hp, 460V, three phase motor load tapped from a 400A feede when all terminations are marked as suitable fo 75°C connections?

According to *NEC Table 430.250,* the FLA fo that motor is 52A. All motor loads are calculate at 125%, so 52A × 1.25 = 65A.

Using *NEC Table 310.16,* determine th THWN copper conductor size needed to suppl 65A. No. 6 THWN copper is rated for 65A Assuming all conditions are met for applicatio of the 10' tap rule, No. 6 THWN copper conduc tors are required.

*Example 2:*

What size THWN copper conductors are require for a 25' tap supplying a load of 100A from feeder protected by a 600A overcurrent device?

To apply the 25' tap rule, the tap conductor must be rated at least one-third the capacity of th feeder overcurrent device.

$$600A \div 3 = 200A$$

The conductors must be rated for at least 200A even though the supplied load is substantiall lower. Using *NEC Table 310.16,* determine th THWN copper conductor size. No. 3/0 THWI copper is rated for 200A.

## 2.5.0 Applying Demand Factors

The total load placed upon certain feeders may b reduced by applying demand factors. The *NEC* permits the reduction of these loads by using th demand factors listed in the following *NEC®* table

- *NEC Table 220.42, Lighting Load Demand Facto*
- *NEC Table 220.44, Demand Factors for Nor dwelling Receptacle Loads*
- *NEC Table 220.54, Demand Factors for Househol Electric Clothes Dryers*
- *NEC Table 220.55, Demand Loads for Househol Cooking Appliances*
- *NEC Table 220.56, Demand Factors for Kitche Equipment – Other Than Dwelling Unit(s)*
- *NEC Section 220.82, Optional Calculation Dwelling Unit*

*NEC Section 220.83, Optional Calculation for Additional Loads in Existing Dwelling Unit*

*NEC Table 220.84, Optional Calculations – Demand Factors for Three or More Multi-Family Dwelling Units*

*NEC Table 220.86, Optional Method – Demand Factors for Feeders and Service-Entrance Conductors for Schools*

*NEC Section 220.87, Optional Method for Determining Existing Loads*

*NEC Table 220.88, Optional Method – Demand Factors for Service-Entrance and Feeder Conductors for New Restaurants*

*NEC Table 220.102, Method for Computing Farm Loads for Other Than Dwelling Unit(s)*

*NEC Table 220.103, Method for Computing Total Farm Load*

Calculations utilizing these demand factors will be applied throughout this module.

*Example:*

The total general-purpose receptacle load in an office building is 26,800VA. Calculate the demand load.

Per *NEC Table 220.44,* the first 10kVA is calculated at 100% and the remaining load is calculated at 50%. Subtract 10,000VA from the receptacle load in this example, and multiply the result by 50%. Add the result to the 10,000VA to determine the demand receptacle load.

$$26{,}800\text{VA} - 10{,}000\text{VA} = 16{,}800\text{VA}$$
$$16{,}800\text{VA} \times 50\% = 8{,}400\text{VA}$$
$$8{,}400\text{VA} + 10{,}000\text{VA} = 18{,}400\text{VA}$$

The total general-purpose receptacle load is calculated to be 18,400VA.

### 2.5.1 Demand Factors for Neutral Conductors

The neutral conductor of electrical systems generally carries only the current imbalance of the phase conductors. For example, in a single-phase feeder circuit with one phase conductor carrying 50A and the other carrying 40A, the neutral conductor would carry 10A. Since the neutral in many cases will not be required to carry as much current as the phase conductors, the *NEC®* allows us to apply a demand factor. Refer to *NEC Section 220.61* for specific information. Also, *NEC Section 310.15(B)(4)(a)* allows the exclusion of a neutral conductor carrying only unbalanced current when determining any adjustment factor for three or more conductors in a conduit.

**NOTE**

In certain circumstances such as electrical discharge lighting, data processing equipment, and other similar equipment, we cannot apply a demand factor on the neutral conductors because these types of equipment produce harmonic currents that increase the heating effect in the neutral conductor. Also see *NEC Section 220.61(C)(2).*

### 2.5.2 Service Conductor Considerations

You should be aware that the **overhead system service entrance, underground service entrance,** and primary feeder conductor sizing determined in the examples in the remainder of this module are based only on the calculated demand load for the premises served.

Except in a few instances, derating factors for temperature, number of conductors, or voltage drop due to conductor length have not been considered. In actual situations, these factors would have to be included when sizing the conductors.

Depending on the **service point** of the utility serving a particular location and, in some cases, the type of premises involved, sizing of a **service drop** or **service lateral** may also be required, and the same adjustment factors will apply to their conductors as well.

### 2.6.0 Lighting Loads

*NEC Section 220.12* provides specific information for determining lighting loads for occupancies. *NEC Table 220.12, General Lighting Load by Occupancy,* provides unit load per square foot according to the type of occupancy. For example, a **dwelling unit** has a unit lighting load of 3VA per square foot, and a storage warehouse has a unit lighting load of ¼VA per square foot.

To determine the lighting load, the square footage area of the occupancy is calculated using the outside dimensions of the occupancy area. For dwellings, this area does not include open porches, **garages,** or unused or unfinished spaces not adaptable for future use.

### 2.7.0 Basic Steps for Load Calculations

*Figure 2* is a block diagram that illustrates the basic steps in performing load calculations. This chart may be useful as a guide when calculating the loads of various types of electrical installations.

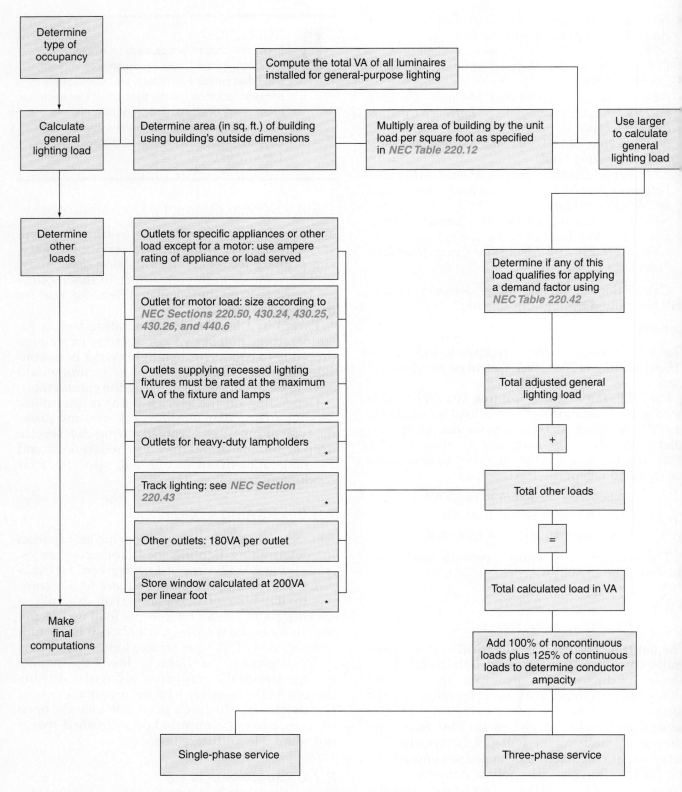

* Lighting not used for general illumination. Typical applications are task or display accent lighting.

401F02.EPS

*Figure 2* ◆ Basic steps in load calculation.

# 3.0.0 ◆ LOAD CALCULATIONS FOR A MINIMUM SIZE SERVICE

The steps below describe the method of determining the service load for a given type of occupancy. These are basic steps, and specific examples will be provided in later sections of this module.

**Step 1** Compute the floor area of the building using the outside dimensions of the building. The area arrived at is used to determine the general lighting load for the particular occupancy. *NEC Table 220.12* allows different general lighting loads based upon the use of the area. For example, an office in a warehouse building would require a multiplication factor of 3½VA per square foot, while another calculation of the general lighting load for a warehouse floor area requires a multiplication factor of ¼VA per square foot. If the use of the area is in question, the authority having jurisdiction (*NEC Section 90.4*) will make the determination of the use of the building as it relates to the *NEC®*.

**Step 2** Multiply the floor area determined in Step 1 by the unit load per square foot (volt-amperes), and calculate the general lighting load per *NEC Table 220.12*. Compare this value to the total installed lighting used for general illumination, and use the larger of the two loads.

**Step 3** Calculate the lighting loads used for other than general illumination, such as for task lighting, exterior lighting, or accent lighting. Refer to the applicable sections of the *NEC®*:
- Light fixtures, *NEC Section 220.14(D)*
- Heavy-duty lampholders, *NEC Section 220.14(E)*
- Sign or outline lighting, *NEC Section 220.14(F)*
- Show windows, *NEC Section 220.14(G) and 220.43*
- Track lighting, *NEC Section 220.43(B)*

**Step 4** Calculate the receptacle loads. Refer to the applicable sections of the *NEC®*:
- Specific-purpose receptacles, *NEC Section 220.14(A)*
- Fixed multi-outlet assemblies, *NEC Section 220.14(H)*
- General-purpose receptacles, *NEC Section 220.14(I)*

**Step 5** Apply applicable demand factors. For specific applications, refer to the following sections of the *NEC®*:
- General-purpose receptacles, *NEC Section 220.14(I)*
- Cranes, *NEC Article 610*
- Elevators, *NEC Article 620*
- Welders, *NEC Article 630*
- X-ray equipment, *NEC Article 660*
- Fire pumps, *NEC Article 695* (and other articles as needed for specific equipment or locations)

**Step 6** Calculate all the motor loads in accordance with *NEC Section 220.50*.
- Use *NEC Section 430.17* to determine the largest motor in the calculation.
- Add together 125% of the FLA of the largest motor plus 100% of the FLA for all other motors.

**Step 7** Calculate both the heating and air conditioning loads, and use only the largest of the two in the total load calculation (*NEC Section 220.60*).

**Step 8** Add all of the loads. The resultant load in volt-amps is divided by the system voltage for single-phase service or by the system voltage times the square root of three for three-phase services.

**Step 9** Add 100% of noncontinuous loads plus 125% of continuous loads to determine conductor ampacity.

## 3.1.0 Minimum Service Ratings

The total calculated load of an occupancy is determined by adding all the individual loads after any demand factors have been applied. Generally, the total calculated load determines the minimum size service for a particular occupancy (*NEC Section 230.42*).

### 3.1.1 Rural Pump House Sample Calculation

*Figure 3* shows the floor plan of a type of small rural pump house that may be used on some farms to supply water for livestock some distance from the farmhouse or other buildings containing electricity. Therefore, a separate service must be supplied for this pump house.

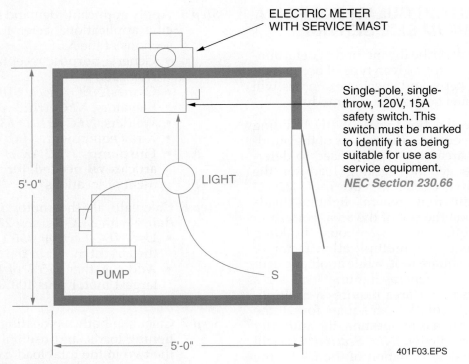

ELECTRIC METER
WITH SERVICE MAST

Single-pole, single-throw, 120V, 15A safety switch. This switch must be marked to identify it as being suitable for use as service equipment. *NEC Section 230.66*

5'-0"

LIGHT

PUMP

S

5'-0"

401F03.EPS

*Figure 3* ◆ Floor plan of a small pump house.

The total loads for this facility consist of the following:

• Shallow well pump with a ⅓hp, 115V single-phase motor
• One wall switch-controlled lighting fixture containing one 60W lamp

The load and service size are calculated as follows:

*Step 1* *NEC Table 220.12* does not list a small pump house. Therefore, we will use *NEC Section 220.14(A)* for our calculation.

*Step 2* *NEC Section 430.6(A)(1)* requires that where the current rating of a motor is used to determine the ampacity of conductors, the values given in *NEC Tables 430.247 through 430.250,* including notes, shall be used instead of the actual current rating marked on the motor nameplate. From *NEC Table 430.248,* we find that the listed ampacity for a ⅓hp single-phase 115VAC motor is 7.2A.

Also, according to *NEC Section 430.22(A),* a single motor shall have an ampacity of no less than 125% of the motor full-load current rating.

Therefore, the motor load is:

$$7.2A \times 1.25 = 9.0A$$
$$9.0A \times 120V = 1,080VA$$

This, added to the 60W lamp load (60VA gives a total connected load of 1,140VA.

*Step 3* Determine the size of the service-entranc conductors.

$$1,140VA \div 120V = 9.5A$$

*Step 4* Check *NEC Section 230.42(B)* for the min imum size of the service-entrance conduc tors. Check *NEC Section 230.79(A)* for th minimum rating of the service disconnect ing means. The service-entrance condu tors must have an ampacity that is not les than the load served and not less than th minimum required disconnecting means The disconnect in this case would be 15A

Since the total connected load for the pum house is less than 10A and the single branch ci cuit feeding the pump and light fixture need onl be No. 14 AWG copper (15A), a No. 14 AWG cop per or No. 12 aluminum conductor will qualify fo the service-entrance conductors.

*NEC Section 230.23* gives the minimum size of service drop conductors, and *NEC Section 230.31* gives the minimum size of service lateral conductors. In addition to being able to serve the load, service drops and service laterals must have a minimum mechanical strength.

**NOTE**

Many inspection jurisdictions and utility companies now require a fault current study prior to issuance of a permit. The fault current study may result in the use of a conductor size that is larger than the minimum *NEC*® requirement.

### 3.1.2 Roadside Vegetable Stand

Another practical application of *NEC Sections 230.42 and 230.79* is shown in *Figure 4*. This is a floor plan of a typical roadside vegetable stand. Again, *NEC Table 220.12* does not list this facility. Therefore, we will once again use *NEC Section 220.14* for our calculation.

*Step 1* Determine the lighting load. Two fluorescent fixtures are used to illuminate the 9 × 12 prime area. Since each fixture contains two 40W fluorescent lamps, and the ballast is rated at 0.83A (which translates to approximately 100VA), the total connected load for each fixture is 100VA, or a total of 200VA for both fixtures.

*Step 2* Determine the remaining loads. The only other electrical outlets in the stand consist of two receptacles: one furnishes power to

a refrigerator with a nameplate full-load rating of 12.2A (total VA = 120V × 12.2A = 1,464VA); the other furnishes power for an electric cash register rated at 300VA and an electronic calculator rated at 200VA (total VA for other loads is 300VA + 200VA = 500VA).

*Step 3* Determine the total connected load.

| | |
|---|---:|
| Fluorescent fixtures = | 200VA |
| Receptacle for refrigerator = | 1,464VA |
| Receptacle for other loads = | 500VA |
| Total calculated load = | 2,164VA |

*Step 4* Identify and total the continuous loads. In this example, the continuous loads are the fluorescent fixtures and the refrigerator.

$$200VA + 1,464VA = 1,664VA$$

*Step 5* Determine the size and rating of the service-entrance conductors. Add 100% of the noncontinuous loads plus 125% of the continuous loads.

$$500VA + (1,664VA \times 1.25) = 2,580VA \div 240 = 10.75A$$

*Step 6* Check *NEC Section 230.42(B)* for the minimum size of the service-entrance conductors. Check *NEC Section 230.79(B)* for the minimum rating of the service disconnecting means. No. 10 AWG copper or No. 8 aluminum is the minimum size allowed by the *NEC*® for the service-entrance conductors on this project. The disconnecting means in this instance would be 30A.

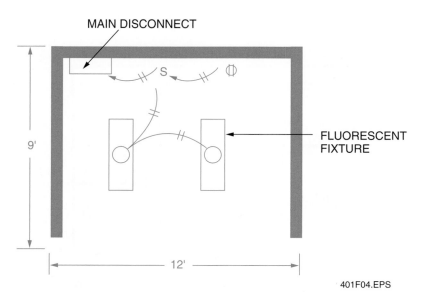

MAIN DISCONNECT

FLUORESCENT FIXTURE

9'

12'

401F04.EPS

*Figure 4* ◆ Roadside vegetable stand.

See *NEC Section 230.23* for the minimum size of service drop conductors or *NEC Section 230.31* for the minimum size of service lateral conductors when they are not under the jurisdiction of the serving utility.

### 3.1.3 Single-Family and Multi-Family Dwellings

A floor plan of a single-family dwelling is shown in *Figure 5*. This building is constructed on a concrete slab with no basement or crawlspace. There is an unfinished attic above the living area and an open carport just outside the kitchen entrance. Appliances include a 12kW electric range (12,000W = 12,000VA) and a 4.5kW water heater (4,500W = 4,500VA). There is also a washer and a 5.5kW dryer (5,500W = 5,500VA) in the utility room. Gas heaters are installed in each room with no electrical requirements. What size service entrance should be provided for this residence if no other information is specified?

*Figure 6* shows a typical form used for service load calculations. The steps necessary to perform these calculations are as follows:

**Step 1**   Compute the area of the occupancy *[NEC Section 220.12]*. The general lighting load (including general receptacle load) is determined by finding the area of the occupancy using the outside dimensions of the structure. Remember that this does not include open porches, garages, or unused or unfinished spaces that are not adaptable for future use. For example, an unfinished basement would be included in this area measurement because it might later be converted into living space. The area in square feet is used to calculate the general lighting load in Step 2.

Using the floor plan and an architect's scale, measure the longest width of the building using the outside dimensions. In this case, it is 33'. The longest length of the building is 48'. The product of these two measurements is:

$$33' \times 48' = 1,584 \text{ sq. ft.}$$

The area of the carport within this total area is:

$$12' \times 19.5' = 234 \text{ sq. ft.}$$

The net living area is then:

$$1,584 - 234 = 1,350 \text{ sq. ft.}$$

**Step 2**   Determine the general lighting load *[NEC Sections 220.10 and 220.12]*. Multiply the resulting area found in Step 1 by the unit load per square foot (volt-amperes) for dwelling units. In this example, it is 3VA per square foot. The lighting load is now:

$$1,350 \text{ sq. ft.} \times 3\text{VA/sq. ft.} = 4,050\text{VA}$$

**Step 3**   Multiply the number of small appliance branch circuits *[NEC Section 210.11(C)(1)]* by 1,500VA (minimum of two required).

The *NEC*® requires at least two 120V, 20A small appliance branch circuits to be installed in each kitchen, dining area, breakfast nook, and similar areas where toasters, coffee makers, and other small appliances will be used. *NEC Section 220.52* also requires small appliance branch circuits to be rated at 1,500VA for

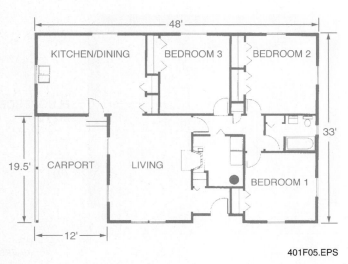

*Figure 5* ◆ Single-family dwelling.

401F05.EPS

| General Lighting Load | | | | | | Phase | | Neutral | |
|---|---|---|---|---|---|---|---|---|---|
| Square footage of the dwelling | [1] | 1,350 | × 3VA = | [2] | 4,050 | | | | |
| Kitchen small appliance circuits | [3] | 2 | × 1500 = | [4] | 3,000 | | | | |
| Laundry branch circuit | [5] | 1 | × 1500 = | [6] | 1,500 | | | | |
| Subtotal of general lighting loads per *NEC Section 220.52* | | | | [7] | 8,550 | | | | |
| Subtract 1st 3000VA per *NEC Table 220.42* | | | | [8] | 3,000 | × 100% = | [9] 3,000 | | |
| Remaining VA times 35% per *NEC Table 220.42* | | | | [10] | 5,550 | × 35% = | [11] 1,943 | | |
| Total demand for general lighting loads = | | | | | | | [12] 4,943 | [13] | 4,943 |

| Fixed Appliance Loads (nameplate or NEC FLA of motors) per *NEC Section 220.53* | | | | |
|---|---|---|---|---|
| Hot water tank, 4.5kVA, 240V | [14] 4,500 | | | |
| | [15] | | | |
| | [16] | | | |
| | [17] | | | |
| | [18] | | | |
| | [19] | | | |
| Subtotal of fixed appliances | [20] 4,500 | | | |
| If 3 or less fixed appliances take @ 100% = | [21] 4,500 | [22] 0 | | |
| If 4 or more fixed appliances take @ 75% = | [23] | [24] | | |

**Other Loads** per *NEC Section 220.14*

| | | Phase | Neutral |
|---|---|---|---|
| Electric range per *NEC Table 220.55* (neutral @ 70 % per *NEC Section 220.61*) | | [25] 8,000 | [26] 5,600 |
| Electric dryer per *NEC Table 220.54* (neutral @ 70% per *NEC Section 220.61*) | | [27] 5,500 | [28] 3,850 |
| Electric heat per *NEC Section 220.51* | | | |
| Air conditioning per *NEC Section 220.14(A)* | Omit smaller load per **NEC Section 220.60** | [29] | [30] |
| **Largest Motor =** 0 | × 25% per *NEC Section 430.24* = | [31] 0 | [32] 0 |
| Total VA Demand = | | [33] 22,943 | [34] 14,393 |
| VA/240V = Amps = | | [35] 96 | [36] 60 |
| Service OCD and Minimum Size Grounding Electrode Conductor = | | [37] 100 | [38] 8 AWG |
| AWG per *NEC Tables 310.15(B)(6)* and *310.16* for neutral | | [39] 4 AWG | [40] 6 AWG |

401F06.EPS

*Figure 6* ◆ Completed calculation form.

each kitchen area served. Since our sample residence has only one kitchen area, the load for these circuits would be:

2 × 1,500VA = 3,000VA

*Step 4* Multiply the laundry receptacle *[NEC Section 210.11(C)(2)]* circuit by 1,500VA *[NEC Section 220.52]*.

An additional 20A branch circuit must be provided for the exclusive use of each laundry area. This circuit must be an individual branch circuit and must not supply any other load except for the laundry receptacles.

1 × 1,500VA = 1,500VA

*Step 5* Calculate the lighting load demand. In *NEC Table 220.42*, note that the demand factor is 100% for the first 3,000VA, 35% for the next 117,000VA, and 25% for the remainder. Since all residential electrical

outlets are never used at the same time, the *NEC®* allows us to apply demand factors.

| First 3,000VA at 100% = | 3,000VA |
|---|---|
| The remainder (8,550 − 3,000) = 5,550 at 35% = | 1,942.5VA |
| Net general lighting and small appliance load = | 4,942.5VA |

*Step 6* Calculate the loads for other appliances *(NEC Section 220.53)*, such as a water heater, disposal, dishwasher, furnace blower motor, etc.

Water heater calculated at 100% = 4,500VA

*Step 7* Calculate the range load and other cooking appliances *(NEC Section 220.55 and Table 220.55)*.

Electric range (using demand factor) = 8,000VA

**Step 8**  Calculate the load for the clothes dryer *(NEC Section 220.54 and Table 220.54)*. Note that this load must be either 5,000VA or the nameplate rating of the dryer, whichever is larger. If a gas dryer is used, it will be part of the 1,000VA demand in Step 4.

Clothes dryer (nameplate rating) = 5,500VA

**NOTE**

Four or more other appliances may have a demand factor of 75% applied.

**Step 9**  Calculate the larger of the heating or air conditioning loads *(NEC Section 220.60)*. (Negligible in this example.)

**NOTE**

If a gas forced air furnace is used, the blower motor will have been included in Step 6. If some form of electric heat is used (baseboard, heat pump, or furnace), this load will be compared to the air conditioning load and the larger load then added to the calculations *(NEC Section 220.60)*.

**Step 10**  Calculate 25% of the largest motor load *(NEC Section 430.24)*. (None in this example.)

**Step 11**  Total all the loads.

| | |
|---|---:|
| General lighting and appliance load = | 4,942.5VA |
| Electric range (using demand factor) = | 8,000.0VA |
| Clothes dryer = | 5,500.0VA |
| Water heater = | 4,500.0VA |
| Total load = | 22,942.5VA |

**Step 12**  Convert the volt-amps to amperes. The total load amperage is derived by dividing the total volt-amps of the load by the circuit voltage. In this example, the system voltage is 240V.

22,942.5VA ÷ 240V = 95.6A

**Step 13**  Determine the required service size *[NEC Section 230.42(B)]*.

Typical electric service for residential use is 120/240V, three-wire, single-phase.

Services are sized in amperes after the to tal load in volt-amperes is determined.

For this ampere load, the minimum 100A service would be required *[NEC Section 230.79(C)]*.

## 3.2.0 Sizing Neutral Conductors

The neutral conductor in a three-wire, single phase service carries only the unbalanced load between the two hot legs. Since there are several 240V loads in our example residence, these 240V loads will be balanced and therefore reduce the load on the service neutral conductor. Conse quently, in most cases, the service neutral does not have to be as large as the ungrounded (hot conductors.

In this example, the water heater does not have to be included in the neutral conductor calcula tion since it is strictly 240V with no 120V loads The clothes dryer and electric range, however have 120V lights that will unbalance the current between phases. *NEC Section 220.61* allows demand factor of 70% for these two appliances Using this information, the neutral conductor may be sized accordingly:

| | |
|---|---:|
| General lighting and appliance load = | 4,942.5V |
| Electric range (8,000VA × 0.70) = | 5,600V |
| Clothes dryer (5,500VA × 0.70) = | 3,850V |
| Total = | 14,392.5V |

To find the total line-to-line amperes, divide th total volt-amperes by the voltage between lines.

14,392.5VA ÷ 240V = 59.97A or 60A

The service-entrance conductors have now been calculated and must be rated at 100A with neutral conductor rated for at least 60A.

In *NEC Table 310.15(B)(6)*, special considera tion is given to 120/240V, single-phase residentia services. This table shows that the NEC® allows No. 4 AWG copper or No. 2 AWG aluminum c copper-clad aluminum for a 100A service.

When sizing the grounded conductor for ser vices, all of the provisions stated in *NEC Section 215.2, 220.61, and 230.42* must be met, along wit other applicable sections.

### 3.2.1  Single-Family Dwelling Standard Calculation

We will take a single-family dwelling and calcu late the required service size. This dwelling cor sists of 1,624 square feet of living area. Th following loads are to be accounted for:

*Motor Sizes*

**THINK ABOUT IT**

Which is the largest motor, a 1hp, 240V single-phase motor or a ¾hp, 120V single-phase motor?

12kW range
5.5kW dryer
1,250VA dishwasher
¾hp, 120V disposal
1hp, 240V pump
⅓hp, 120V blower for gas furnace

**Step 1** Calculate the general lighting and small appliance loads.

General lighting:
1,624 sq. ft. × 3VA =                    4,872VA

Small appliance load:
1,500VA × 2 =                            3,000VA

Laundry load =                           1,500VA

Total general and small
appliance loads =                        9,372VA

**Step 2** Apply demand factors for general lighting and small appliances *(NEC Table 220.42)*.

First 3,000VA at 100% =                  3,000VA

9,372VA − 3,000VA =
6,372 at 35% =                           2,230VA

Total general and small
appliance loads =                        5,230VA

**Step 3** Range load *(NEC Table 220.55, Column C)*
                                       = 8,000VA

**Step 4** Dryer load *(NEC Table 220.54)* = 5,500VA

**Step 5** Calculate fixed appliance loads.

Dishwasher =                             1,250VA

Disposal *(NEC Table 430.248)*:
13.8A × 120V =                           1,656VA

Pump *(NEC Table 430.248)*:
8A × 240V =                              1,920VA

Blower *(NEC Table 430.248)*:
7.2A × 120V =                              864VA

Total fixed appliance loads =            5,690VA

**Step 6** Since four or more fixed appliances exist, apply the demand factor for fixed appliance loads *(NEC Section 220.53)*.

Total fixed appliance loads:
5,690VA × 75% =                          4,268VA

**Step 7** Use *NEC Section 430.17* to determine the largest motor.

25% of the largest motor load:
1,920VA × 25% =                            480VA

**Step 8** Combine the computed loads.

Total load: 5,230VA + 8,000VA + 5,500VA +
4,268VA + 480VA = 23,478VA

The minimum size service required for this dwelling is then determined by dividing the total calculated VA by the line-to-line service voltage. The line-to-line voltage is 240V, 1Ø.

23,478VA ÷ 240V = 97.83A

*NEC Section 230.79(C)* requires a minimum service size of 100A for a single-family dwelling.

### 3.2.2  Standard Calculation for Single-Family Dwelling Using Electric Heat

This section provides an example load calculation for a single-family residence using electric heat. In this example, the dwelling consists of 1,775 square feet of living area. The home has the following loads:

- 8.75kW range
- 5.5kW dryer
- 1,000VA dishwasher
- ¾hp, 120V disposal
- ½hp, 120V attic fan
- ⅓hp, 120V blower for electric furnace
- 20kW electric furnace
- Central air conditioning unit with a nameplate rating of 25A at 240V

**Step 1** Calculate the general lighting and small appliance loads.

| | |
|---|---|
| General lighting: 1,775 sq. ft. × 3VA = | 5,325VA |
| Small appliance load: 1500VA × 2 = | 3,000VA |
| Laundry load = | 1,500VA |
| Total general and small appliance loads = | 9,825VA |

**Step 2** Apply demand factors for general lighting and small appliances *(NEC Table 220.42)*.

| | |
|---|---|
| First 3,000VA at 100% = | 3,000VA |
| 9,825VA − 3,000VA = 6,825 at 35% = | 2,389VA |
| Total general and small appliance loads = | 5,389VA |

**Step 3** Range load *(NEC Table 220.55, Column B)*.

| | |
|---|---|
| 8,750VA × 80% = | 7,000VA |

**Step 4** Dryer load *(NEC Table 220.54)*.

| | |
|---|---|
| 5,500VA × 100% = | 5,500VA |

**Step 5** Calculate fixed appliance loads.

| | |
|---|---|
| Dishwasher = | 1,000VA |
| Disposal *(NEC Table 430.248)*: 13.8A × 120V = | 1,656VA |
| Furnace blower *(NEC Table 430.248)*: 7.2A × 120V = | 864VA |
| Attic fan *(NEC Table 430.248)*: 9.8A × 120V = | 1,176VA |
| Total fixed appliance loads = | 4,696VA |

**Step 6** Since four or more fixed appliances exist, apply the demand factor for fixed appliance loads *(NEC Section 220.53)*.

| | |
|---|---|
| Total fixed appliance loads: 4,696VA × 75% = | 3,522VA |

**Step 7** Calculate the larger of the heating and cooling loads (use *NEC Section 220.60* for noncoincidental loads to omit the smaller load).

| | |
|---|---|
| Heating load = | 20,000VA |
| Cooling load: 25A × 240V = | 6,000VA |
| Larger of the two loads = | 20,000VA |

**Step 8** Use *NEC Section 430.17* to determine the largest motor.

| | |
|---|---|
| 25% of the largest motor load: 1,656VA × 25% = | 414VA |

**Step 9** Combine the computed loads.

Total load: 5,389VA + 7,000VA + 5,500VA
+ 3,522VA + 20,000VA + 414VA
= 41,825VA

The minimum size service for this dwelling is determined by dividing the total calculated VA by the line-to-line service voltage. The line-to-line voltage is 240V, 1Ø.

$$41,825VA \div 240V = 174.27A$$

The next larger standard size overcurrent device is 175A. Although a 175A device would satisfy the *NEC*® requirements, it is more likely that a 200A service would be installed.

### 3.2.3 Optional Calculation for a Single-Family Dwelling

The *NEC*® provides an alternative method of computing the load for a dwelling unit in *NEC Section 220.82*. Using this method will almost always result in a calculation that is lower than the standard method when electric heat is used.

For our example calculation, we will use a single-family dwelling with 1,624 square feet of living area and the following loads:

**Optional Calculations**

*INSIDE TRACK*

When using the optional calculations, *NEC Section 220.82(B)* permits the use of motor nameplate values rather than the values listed in *NEC Tables 430.248 through 430.250*.

- 12kW range
- 5.5kW dryer
- 1,250VA dishwasher
- ½hp, 120V disposal at 1,176VA
- ¾hp, 120V attic fan at 1,656VA
- 14.4kW electric furnace
- ⅓hp, 120V (864VA) blower motor for electric furnace
- Air conditioning unit with a nameplate rating of 6,000VA

**Step 1**  Calculate the general lighting, small appliance, and fixed appliance loads. Use full nameplate values for each.

| | |
|---|---|
| General lighting: 1,624 sq. ft. × 3VA = | 4,872VA |
| Small kitchen appliance load: 1,500VA × 2 = | 3,000VA |
| Laundry load = | 1,500VA |
| Range = | 12,000VA |
| Dryer = | 5,500VA |
| Dishwasher = | 1,250VA |
| Disposal = | 1,176VA |
| Attic fan = | 1,656VA |
| Blower = | 864VA |
| Subtotal load = | 31,818VA |

**Step 2**  Apply the demand factor in *NEC Section 220.82(B)*.

| | |
|---|---|
| First 10kVA at 100% = | 10,000VA |
| Remaining load at 40%: 21,818VA × 40% = | 8,727VA |
| Subtotal for general loads = | 18,727VA |

**Step 3**  Compute the demands permitted for electric heating and air conditioning per *NEC Section 220.82(C)*. Use the largest of the computed demand loads.

| | |
|---|---|
| Air conditioner at 100% = 6,000VA × 100% = | 6,000VA |
| Central electric heating at 65%: 14,400 × 65% = | 9,360VA |

**Step 4**  Add together the demand for general loads and the largest of the heating or air conditioning load.

| | |
|---|---|
| Subtotal general loads = | 18,727VA |
| Heating load (larger than the air conditioning load) = | 9,360VA |
| Total load = | 28,087VA |

The minimum size service required for this dwelling is determined by dividing the total calculated VA by the line-to-line service voltage. The line-to-line voltage is 240V, 1Ø.

$$28,087VA \div 240V = 117A$$

The minimum service required for this dwelling would be 125A.

## 3.3.0 Multi-Family Calculations

The service load for multi-family dwellings is not simply the sum of the individual dwelling unit loads because of demand factors that may be applied when either the standard calculation or the optional calculation is used to compute the service load.

When the standard calculation is used to compute the service load, the total lighting, small appliance, and laundry loads as well as the total load from all electric ranges and clothes dryers are subject to the application of demand factors. Additional demand factors may be applied to the portion of the neutral load contributed by electric ranges and the portion of the total neutral load greater than 200A.

When the optional calculation is used, the total connected load is subject to the application of a demand factor that varies according to the number of individual units in the dwelling.

A summary of the calculation methods for designing wiring systems in multi-family dwellings and the applicable *NEC®* references are shown in *Figure 7*. The selection of a calculation method for computing the service load is not affected by the method used to design the feeders to the individual dwelling units.

The rules for computing the service load are also used for computing a main feeder load when the wiring system consists of a service that supplies main feeders that, in turn, supply a number of sub-feeders to individual dwelling units.

### 3.3.1   Multi-Family Dwelling Sample Calculation

A 30-unit apartment building consists of 18 one-bedroom units of 650 sq. ft. each, 6 two-bedroom units of 775 sq. ft. each, and 6 three-bedroom units of 950 sq. ft. each. The kitchen in each unit contains the following loads:

- 7.5kW electric range
- 1,250VA dishwasher
- ⅓hp, 120V garbage disposal at 864VA
- Air conditioning unit rated at 3,600VA

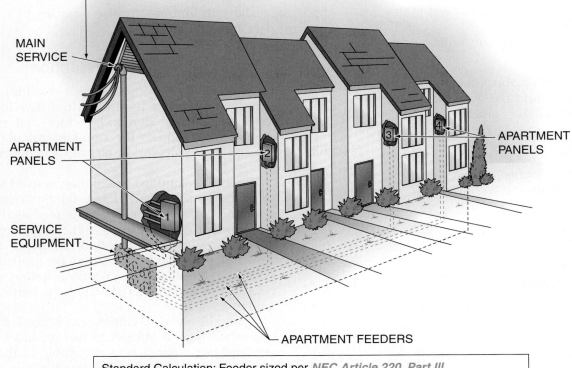

Standard Calculation: Feeder sized per *NEC Article 220, Part II*
Optional Calculation: Per *NEC Section 220.84*, if each dwelling unit has:
1. Single feeder
2. Electric cooking equipment
3. Electric space heating or air conditioning, or both

MAIN
SERVICE

APARTMENT
PANELS

SERVICE
EQUIPMENT

APARTMENT
PANELS

APARTMENT FEEDERS

Standard Calculation: Feeder sized per *NEC Article 220, Part III*
Optional Calculation: Use *NEC Section 220.84* if each dwelling unit has single
3-wire, 120/240V or 208Y/120V feeders with ampacity of 100A or greater.

401F07.EPS

*Figure 7* ◆ *NEC*® requirements for multi-family dwellings.

The entire building is heated by a boiler that uses three electric pump motors: a 2hp squirrel-cage motor and two ½hp squirrel-cage induction motors, all 240V single-phase, two-wire. There is a community laundry room in the building with four washers with a nameplate rating of 12.5A at 120V (1,500VA) and four clothes dryers, with the latter rated at 4,500VA each. The house lighting consists of 40 incandescent fixtures rated at 60W each. There are three general-purpose receptacle outlets for servicing of the boilers and laundry room. The building is furnished with a 120/240V, single-phase, three-wire service. What size service is required?

*Step 1*  Calculate the general lighting and small appliance loads in each apartment.

| | |
|---|---|
| General lighting: 650 sq. ft. × 3VA = 1,950VA × 18 units = | 35,100VA |
| General lighting: 775 sq. ft. × 3VA = 2,325VA × 6 units = | 13,950VA |
| General lighting: 950 sq. ft. × 3VA = 2,850VA × 6 units = | 17,100VA |
| Small appliance circuits: 1,500VA × 2 × 30 units = | 90,000VA |
| Total general lighting and small appliance load = | 156,150VA |

**Step 2** Apply the demand factors using *NEC Table 220.42*.

First 3,000VA (out of 120,000VA) at 100% = 3,000VA

Next 117,000VA (out of 120,000VA) at 35% = 40,950VA

Remaining 36,150VA at 25% = <u>9,038VA</u>

Net general lighting and small appliance load = 52,988VA

**Step 3** Calculate the appliance loads using *NEC Section 220.53*.

Dishwashers: 30 × 1,250VA × 75% = 28,125VA

Disposals: 30 × 864VA × 75% = 19,440VA

**Step 4** Calculate the range load using *NEC Table 220.55*.

Range load *(NEC Table 220.55, Column C)* = 45,000VA

**NOTE**

The range load could have been calculated using *NEC Table 220.55, Column B, Note 3*. However, the value obtained (54kVA) is higher, so Column C was used.

**Step 5** Calculate the air conditioning load *[NEC Sections 220.60 and 220.14(A)]*.

Air conditioners: 30 × 3,600VA × 100% = 108,000VA

**Step 6** Calculate the house load.

2hp boiler *(NEC Table 430.248)*: 12A × 240V = 2,880VA

Two ½hp boiler motors: 4.9A × 240V × 2 = 2,352VA

Laundry: 1,500VA × 4 = 6,000VA

Dryers *(NEC Table 220.54)*: 4,500 × 4 × 100% = 18,000VA

House lighting: 60W × 40 = 2,400VA

General-purpose receptacles: 180VA × 3 = <u>540VA</u>

Total house load = 32,172VA

**Step 7** Determine the largest motor load and multiply the FLA or VA by 25% *(NEC Section 430.24)*.

Boiler motor: 2,880VA × 25% = 720VA

**Step 8** Determine the total calculated load.

Net general lighting and small appliance loads = 52,988VA

Dishwasher loads = 28,125VA

Disposal loads = 19,440VA

Range loads = 45,000VA

Air conditioning loads = 108,000VA

House loads = 32,172VA

25% of largest motor load = <u>720VA</u>

Total load = 286,445VA

Add 25% of continuous loads (house lighting) = <u>600VA</u>

Total adjusted load = 287,045VA

**Step 9** Determine the total load in amperes in order to select service conductors, equipment, and overcurrent protective devices.

287,045VA ÷ 240V = 1,196A

**Step 10** Select the service-entrance conductors, **service equipment**, and overcurrent protection.

**NOTE**

Since the exact calculated load is not a standard size, the rating of the service for this apartment building would be 1,200A; this is the next largest standard size and is permitted by the *NEC®*. See *NEC Sections 240.4 and 240.6*.

### 3.3.2 Multi-Family Dwelling Calculation Using Optional Method

*NEC Section 220.84* permits an alternative method of computing the load for multi-family dwellings. The conditions that must be met to use this calculation are that each individual dwelling must be supplied by only one feeder, have electric cooking (or an assumed cooking load of 8kW), and have electric heating, air conditioning, or both. The demand factors of *NEC Table 220.84* are not permitted to be applied to the house loads. We will compute the same apartment building using this method.

For this example, we have a 30-unit apartment building consisting of 18 one-bedroom units of 650 sq. ft. each, six two-bedroom units of 775 sq. ft. each, and six three-bedroom units of 950 sq. ft. each. The kitchen in each unit contains one 7.5kW electric range, one 1,250VA dishwasher, and one ⅛hp, 120V garbage disposal at 864VA. Each unit has an air conditioning unit rated at 3,600VA.

The entire building is heated by a boiler that uses three electric pump motors: a 2hp squirrel-cage motor and two ½hp squirrel-cage induction motors, all 240V single-phase, two-wire. There is a community laundry room in the building with four washers and four clothes dryers, with the latter rated at 4,500VA each. The house lighting consists of 40 incandescent fixtures rated at 60W each. There are three general-purpose receptacle outlets for servicing of the boilers and laundry room. The building is to be furnished with a 120/240V, single-phase, three-wire service.

***Step 1*** Calculate the lighting and small appliance loads [*NEC Sections 220.84(C)(1) and (2)*].

| | |
|---|---|
| General lighting: 650 sq. ft. × 3VA = 1,950 × 18 units = | 35,100VA |
| General lighting: 775 sq. ft. × 3VA = 2,325 × 6 units = | 13,950VA |
| General lighting: 950 sq. ft. × 3VA = 2,850 × 6 units = | 17,100VA |
| Small appliance circuits: 1,500VA × 2 × 30 units = | 90,000VA |
| Total general lighting and small appliance loads = | 156,150VA |

***Step 2*** Calculate the appliance and motor loads [*NEC Sections 220.84(C)(3), (4), and (5)*].

| | |
|---|---|
| Dishwashers: 1,250VA × 30 units = | 37,500VA |
| Disposals: 864VA × 30 units = | 25,920VA |
| Ranges: 7,500VA × 30 units = | 225,000VA |
| Air conditioners = 3,600VA × 30 units = | 108,000VA |
| Total appliance and motor loads = | 396,420VA |

***Step 3*** Apartment unit loads:

| | |
|---|---|
| 156,150VA + 396,420VA = | 552,570VA |

***Step 4*** Apply the demand factor (*NEC Table 220.84*).

| | |
|---|---|
| 552,570VA × 33% = | 182,348VA |

***Step 5*** Calculate the total house load [*NEC Section 220.84(B)*].

| | |
|---|---|
| 2hp boiler (*NEC Table 430.248*): 12A × 240V = | 2,880VA |
| Two ½hp boiler motors: 4.9A × 240V × 2 = | 2,352VA |
| Laundry: 1,500VA × 4 = | 6,000VA |
| Dryers (*NEC Table 220.55*): 4,500VA × 4 × 100% = | 18,000VA |
| House lighting: 60W × 40 = | 2,400VA |
| General-purpose receptacles: 180VA × 3 = | 540VA |
| Total house load = | 32,172VA |

***Step 6*** Total load:

| | |
|---|---|
| 182,348VA + 32,172VA + 600VA (25% of continuous load) = | 215,120VA |

Using the optional method, the current would be:

$$215,120VA \div 240V = 896A$$

The next standard size of service equipment greater than 896A is 1,000A, so this apartment building would require 1,000A service. Note that this is less than the 1,200A required when using the standard method of calculation for the same building.

## 4.0.0 ◆ COMMERCIAL OCCUPANCY CALCULATIONS

Calculating load requirements for commercial occupancies is based on specific *NEC*® requirements that relate to the loads present. The basic approach is to separate the loads into the following:

- Lighting
- Receptacles
- Motors
- Appliances
- Other special loads

In general, all loads for commercial occupancies should be considered continuous unless specific information is available to the contrary. Smaller commercial establishments normally use single-phase, three-wire services; larger projects almost always use a three-phase, four-wire service. Many installations have secondary feeders supplying panelboards, which, in turn, supply branch circuits operating at different voltages. This requires separate calculations for the feeder nd branch circuit loads for each voltage. The rating of the main service is based on the total load with the load values transformed according to the various circuit voltages, if necessary.

Demand factors also apply to some commercial establishments. For example, the lighting loads in hospitals, hotels, motels, and warehouses are subject to the application of demand factors. In restaurants and similar establishments, the load of electric cooking equipment is subject to a demand factor if there are more than three cooking units. Optional calculation methods to determine feeder or service loads for schools and similar occupancies are also provided in the *NEC®*.

Special occupancies, such as mobile homes and recreational vehicles, require the feeder or service load to be calculated in accordance with specific *NEC®* requirements. The service for mobile home parks and recreational vehicle parks is also designed based on specific *NEC®* requirements that apply only to those locations. The feeder or service load for receptacles supplying shore power for boats in marinas and boatyards is also specified in the *NEC®*.

When transformers are not involved, a relatively simple calculation involving only one voltage results. If step-down transformers are used, the transformer itself must be protected by an overcurrent device that may also protect the circuit conductors in most cases.

Switches and panelboards used for the distribution of electricity within a commercial building are also subject to *NEC®* rules. In general, a **lighting panelboard** cannot have more than 42 overcurrent protective devices to protect the branch circuits originating at the panelboard. This requirement could affect the number of feeders required when a large number of lighting or appliance circuits are needed.

## 1.0 Commercial and Industrial Load Calculations

The type of occupancy determines the methods employed to calculate loads. Industrial and commercial buildings are two of these categories addressed in the *NEC®*. Buildings that fall into these categories are ones that manufacture, process, market, or distribute goods. Loads are calculated based on the type of occupancy and the electrical requirements of the installed equipment. Standard calculations used to compute the load and determine the service equipment requirement are arranged differently from those for dwelling units. There are specific types of loads that must be considered when making load

calculations of commercial and industrial occupancies. Demand factors may be required for certain types of loads.

The following are *NEC®* references for feeder and service loads:

- *NEC Section 220.42, General Lighting*
- *NEC Section 220.43, Show Window and Track Lighting*
- *NEC Section 220.44, Receptacle Loads – Nondwelling Units*
- *NEC Section 220.50, Motors*
- *NEC Section 220.51, Fixed Electric Space Heating*
- *NEC Section 220.56, Kitchen Equipment – Other Than Dwelling*
- *NEC Section 220.60, Noncoincident Loads*
- *NEC Section 220.61, Feeder or Service Neutral Load*

Each load must be designated as either continuous or noncontinuous. Most commercial loads are generally considered to be continuous. One exception would be a storage warehouse that is occupied on an infrequent basis. Demand factors may be applied to various noncontinuous loads according to the respective section of the *NEC®*. For example, *NEC Section 220.44* permits both general-purpose receptacles at 180VA per outlet and fixed multi-outlet assemblies to be adjusted for the demand factors given in *NEC Tables 220.42 and 220.44*.

### 4.1.1 Lighting Loads

Within this category, there are eight different categories to take into account:

- *NEC Section 215.2(A), General Lighting Loads*
- *NEC Table 220.12, General Lighting Loads*
- *NEC Section 220.14(D), Lighting Fixtures*
- *NEC Section 220.14(E), Heavy-Duty Lampholders*
- *NEC Section 220.14(F), Sign and Outline Lighting*
- *NEC Section 220.18(B), Inductive Lighting Loads*
- *NEC Section 220.14(G), Show Windows*
- *NEC Section 220.43(B), Track Lighting*

These lighting loads must be designated as either continuous or noncontinuous. Some of these lighting loads may have demand factors applied. The lighting loads should be calculated before any other loads are determined.

### 4.1.2 General Lighting Loads

This is the main lighting used for general illumination within the building and is in addition to any lighting installed for accent, display, task, show windows, or signs. It is computed based upon the type of occupancy and volt-amps per square foot given in *NEC Table 220.12*. For types of occupancies not listed in *NEC Table 220.12*, the general lighting load should be calculated according to the *NEC*® sections listed previously.

The minimum load for general lighting must be compared to the actual installed lighting used within a building, and the larger of the two computations must be used. In most cases, due to energy codes, the installed lighting will generally be lower than that required by *NEC Table 220.12*.

Any of these loads that are continuous duty are multiplied by 125% to determine the overcurrent protection device and conductor size. All others are calculated at 100%. Noncontinuous loads may have a demand factor applied in accordance with *NEC Section 220.42 and Table 220.42*.

*Example:*

Suppose a warehouse building has 57,600 square feet of floor area.

**Step 1** From *NEC Table 220.12:*

| | | |
|---|---|---|
| 57,600 sq. ft. × ¼ VA/sq. ft. = | | 14,400VA |

**Step 2** Apply demand factors per *NEC Table 220.42*.

| | |
|---|---|
| First 12,500VA at 100% = | 12,500VA |
| 14,400VA − 12,500VA = 1,900 at 50% | 950VA |
| Net lighting load = | 13,450VA |

### 4.1.3 Show Window Loads

*NEC Section 220.43(A)* requires that the lighting load for show window feeders be calculated at 200VA per linear foot of show window.

*Example:*

Suppose a show window is 55' in length. What is the feeder load?

Load = 55' × 200VA per linear ft. = 11,000VA

**NOTE**

Any loads that are continuous duty are multiplied by 125% to determine the overcurrent protection device and conductor size. All others are calculated at 100%.

### 4.1.4 Track Lighting Loads

Track lighting loads are calculated by allowing 150VA for every two feet of track or fraction thereof. Refer to *NEC Section 220.43(B)*.

*Example 1:*

Determine the lighting load for 140' of track lighting

140' ÷ 2 = 70'

70' × 150VA = 10,500VA

*Example 2:*

Determine the lighting load of 21' of track lighting

21' ÷ 2 = 10.5' (round fractions up) = 11'

11' × 150VA = 1,650VA

**NOTE**

Any loads that are continuous duty are multiplied by 125% to determine the overcurrent protection device and conductor size. All others are calculated at 100%.

### 4.1.5 Outside Lighting Loads

Outside lighting loads are calculated by multiplying the rating in VA by the number of fixtures Refer to *NEC Section 215.2(A)*.

*Example:*

Determine the load for 30 outside lighting fixtures, each rated at 250VA, including the ballast These lights are rated at 240V.

250VA × 30 = 7,500VA

**NOTE**

Any loads that are continuous duty are multiplied by 125% to determine the overcurrent protection device and conductor size. All others are calculated at 100%.

### 4.1.6 Sign and Outline Lighting Loads

*NEC Section 600.5(A)* requires that occupancies with a ground floor entry accessible to pedestrians have a 20A outlet installed for each tenant space in an accessible location. This must be a 20 branch circuit that supplies no other load.

*NEC Section 220.14(F)* states that the load for the branch circuit installed for the supply of exterior signs or outline lighting must be computed a minimum of 1,200VA. However, if the actual rating of the sign lighting is greater than 1,200VA, the actual load of the sign shall be used.

## 4.2.0 Retail Stores with Show Windows

*Figure 8* shows a small store building with a show window in front. Note that the storage area has four general-purpose duplex receptacles, while the retail area has 14 wall-mounted duplex receptacles and two floor-mounted receptacles for a

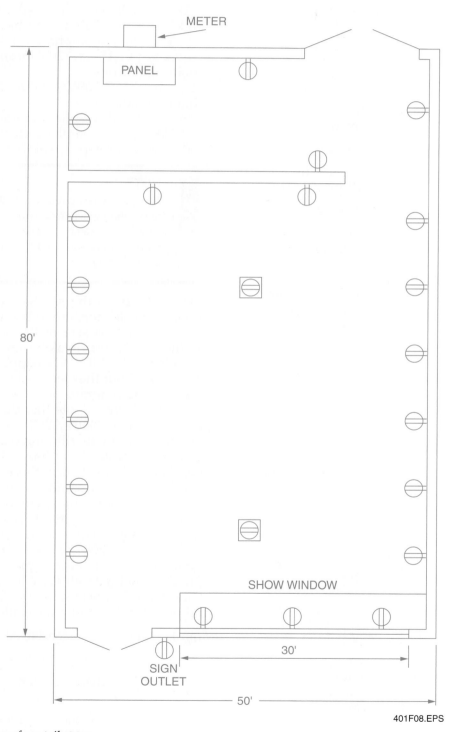

METER

PANEL

80'

SHOW WINDOW

30'

SIGN OUTLET

50'

401F08.EPS

*Figure 8* ◆ Floor plan of a retail store.

total of 16 in this area. These, combined with the storage area receptacles, bring the total to 20 general-purpose duplex receptacles that do not supply a continuous load. What are the conductor sizes for the service entrance if a 120/240V single-phase service will be used?

**Step 1** Determine the total area of the building by multiplying length by width.

$$50' \times 80' = 4,000 \text{ sq. ft.}$$

**Step 2** Calculate the lighting load using *NEC Table 220.12;* according to this table, the load is 3VA per square foot.

$$4,000 \text{ sq. ft.} \times 3\text{VA} = 12,000\text{VA}$$

**Step 3** Determine the total volt-amperes for the 20 general-purpose duplex receptacles.

$$20 \times 180\text{VA} = 3,600\text{VA}$$

**Step 4** Calculate the load for the 30' show window on the basis of 200VA per linear foot.

$$30' \times 200\text{VA} = 6,000\text{VA}$$

**Step 5** Allow one 20A outlet for sign or outline lighting if the store is on the ground floor *[NEC Section 600.5(A)]*.

If the actual load of the sign is not known, a 1,200VA load is used in the calculation per *NEC Section 220.14(F)*.

**Step 6** Calculate the total load in volt-amperes.

| | |
|---|---|
| Noncontinuous load | |
| Receptacle load = | 3,600VA |
| Continuous loads | |
| Lighting load = | 12,000VA |
| Show window = | 6,000VA |
| Sign = | 1,200VA |
| Total continuous load | 19,200VA |
| *Multiply × 125%* | |
| 19,200VA × 1.25 = | 24,000VA |
| Add noncontinuous load | 3,600VA |
| Total VA = | 27,600VA |

**Step 7** Calculate the service size in amperes.

$$27,600\text{VA} \div 240\text{V} = 115\text{A}$$

Consequently, the service-entrance conductors must be rated for no less than 115A. The next highest standard rating of an overcurrent device is 125A. The conductors would be No. 1 AWG copper or No. 2/0 AWG aluminum.

## 4.3.0 Office Building

A 20,000 sq. ft. office building is served by a 480Y/277V, three-phase service. The building contains the following loads:

- 10,000VA, 208V, three-phase sign
- 100 duplex receptacles supplying continuous loads rated at 180VA each
- 30' long show window
- 12kVA, 208Y/120V, three-phase electric range
- 10kVA, 208Y/120V, three-phase electric oven
- 20kVA, 480V, three-phase water heater
- Seventy-five 150W, 120V incandescent outdoor lighting fixtures
- Two hundred 200VA input, 277V fluorescent lighting fixtures
- 7.5hp, 480V, three-phase motor for fan coil unit
- 40kVA, 480V, three-phase electric heating unit
- 60A, 480V, three-phase air conditioning unit

**NOTE**

The 200VA listing represents the input rating rather than the sum of loads of the installed lamps. For example, these fixtures could represent four-lamp, 40W luminaires with a 200VA rating.

The ratings of the service equipment, transformers, and feeders are to be determined, along with the required size of the service grounding conductor. Circuit breakers are used to protect each circuit, and THWN copper conductors are used throughout the electrical system.

A one-line diagram of the electrical system is shown in *Figure 9*. Note that the incoming three-phase, four-wire, 480Y/277V main service terminates into a main distribution panel containing six overcurrent protective devices. Because there are only six circuit breakers in this enclosure, no main circuit breaker or disconnect is required (*NEC Section 230.71*). Five of these circuit breakers protect feeders and branch circuits to 480/277V equipment, while the sixth circuit breaker protects the feeder to a 480/208Y/120V transformer. The secondary side of this transformer feeds a 208/120V lighting panel with all 120V loads balanced. Start at the loads connected to the 208Y/120V panel and perform the required calculations.

**Step 1** Calculate the load for the 100 receptacles.

$$100 \times 180\text{VA} = 18,000\text{VA}$$

Apply demand factor from *NEC Table 220.44*:

First 10,000VA at 100% + remainder (8,000VA) at 50% = 14,000VA

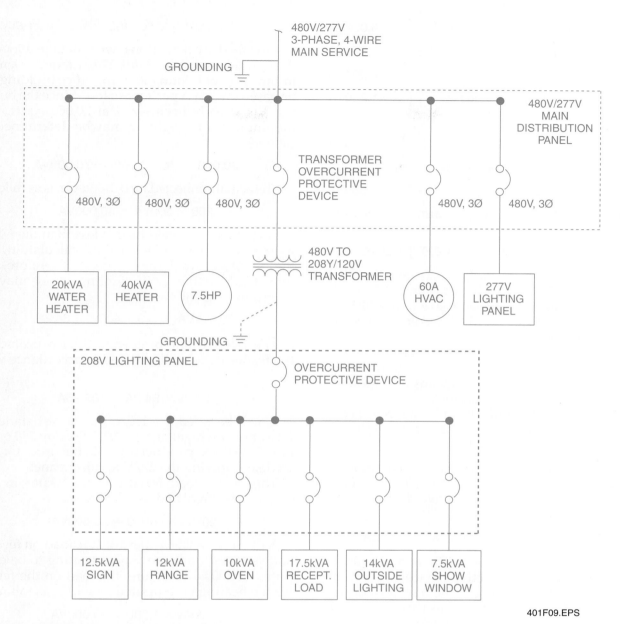

*Figure 9* ◆ One-line diagram of an office building.

*Step 2* Calculate the load for the show window using 200VA per linear foot.

$$200VA \times 30' = 6,000VA$$

*Step 3* Calculate the load for the incandescent outside lighting.

$$75 \times 150VA = 11,250VA$$

*Step 4* Calculate the load for the 10kVA sign.

$$10kVA \times 1,000 = 10,000VA$$

*Step 5* Calculate the load for the 12kVA range *(NEC Section 220.56)*.

$$12kVA \times 1,000 = 12,000VA$$

*Step 6* Calculate the load for the 10kVA oven *(NEC Section 220.56)*.

$$10kVA \times 1,000 = 10,000VA$$

*Step 7* Determine the sum of the loads on the 208/120V lighting panel.

Noncontinuous loads

| | |
|---|---|
| Range = | 12,000VA |
| Oven = | <u>10,000VA</u> |
| Total noncontinuous loads = | 22,000VA |

Continuous loads

| | |
|---|---|
| Receptacles = | 14,000VA |

| | |
|---|---|
| Show window = | 6,000VA |
| Outside lighting = | 11,250VA |
| Sign = | 10,000VA |
| Total continuous loads = | 41,250VA |
| Multiply × 125% | |
| 41,250VA × 1.25 = | 51,563VA |
| Add noncontinuous loads | 22,000VA |
| Total feeder load = | 73,563VA |

**Step 8** Determine the feeder rating for the sub-panel.

$$73{,}563VA \div (\sqrt{3} \times 208V) = 204A$$

**Step 9** Refer to *NEC Table 310.16* and find that 4/0 THWN conductor (rated at 230A) is the closest conductor size that will handle the load. A 225A breaker will protect this feeder.

The 208Y/120V feeder is a **separately derived system** from the transformer and is grounded by means of a grounding electrode conductor *(NEC Table 250.66)* that must be at least a No. 2 copper conductor based on the No. 4/0 copper feeder conductors.

**Step 10** The transformer is sized to accommodate the computed load of 73,563VA. Select the overcurrent protective device for the transformer.

$$73{,}563VA \div (\sqrt{3} \times 480V) = 88.5A$$

Per *NEC Table 450.3(B)* and because a secondary protective device is used, the maximum setting of the transformer primary overcurrent protective device can be up to 250% or 2.5 × 88.5 = 221A; that is, it may not exceed this rating. The secondary protective device maximum setting is 125% of the 208V load:

$$73{,}563VA \div (\sqrt{3} \times 208V) = 204A$$

204A × 125% = 255A, next highest standard overcurrent protective device is 300A

## 4.3.1 Calculations for the Primary Feeder

For the feeder calculations, we will take a look at the lighting first. *NEC Table 220.12* requires a minimum general lighting load for office buildings to be based on 3.5VA per square foot. Since the building has already been sized at 20,000 sq. ft., the minimum VA for lighting may be determined as follows:

20,000 sq. ft. × 3.5VA = 70,000VA

The actual connected load, however, is as follows:

200 × 200VA = 40,000VA

Since this connected load is less than the *NEC* requirement, it is neglected in the calculation, and the 3.5VA/sq. ft. figure is used. Therefore, the total load on the 277V lighting panel may be determined as follows:

$$70{,}000VA \div (\sqrt{3} \times 480V) = 84.2A$$

The overcurrent protective device protecting the feeder panel will be sized in accordance with *NEC Section 215.2(A)(1).*

125% × 84.2A = 105.25A

It will be rated for 110A, the closest standard fuse or circuit breaker size [*NEC Section 240.6(A)*]. No. 2 THWN conductors will be used for the feeder supplying the 277V lighting panel.

The feeder load for the water heater in this example is calculated as follows:

20kVA × 1,000 = 20,000VA

*NEC Section 220.51* permits the load on feeders and services for electric space heating to be computed at 100%. Therefore, the load on the feeder for the heating is computed at 40kVA as follows:

40kVA × 1,000 = 40,000VA

*NEC Section 220.50* requires that motor loads be computed in accordance with *NEC Section 430.24, 430.25, and 430.26.* Therefore, the FLA of this motor (11A) taken from *NEC Table 430.250* must be multiplied by 1.25 since this is the largest (only) motor.

$$11A \times (\sqrt{3} \times 480V) \times 1.25 = 11{,}431.5VA$$

## Receptacles

**INSIDE TRACK**

When the number of general-purpose receptacles is unknown, use 1VA per sq. ft. for office buildings.

*NEC Section 220.50* requires that hermetic refrigerant motor compressors be sized in accordance with *NEC Section 440.6.* Therefore, the load for the air conditioning unit is calculated as follows:

$$60A \times (\sqrt{3} \times 480V) = 49,883VA$$

### .3.2 Main Service Calculations

When performing the calculations for the main service, assume that all three-phase loads are balanced and may be computed in terms of volt-amperes or in terms of amperes. Calculation of the loads in amperes simplifies the selection of the main overcurrent protective device and service conductors. A summary of this calculation is shown below.

| Type of Load | Computed Load | Neutral |
|---|---|---|
| 208/120V system = | 88.5A | 0 |
| 277V lighting panel = | 105.25A | 105.25A |
| Water heater = | 24A | 0 |
| Electric heater (neglected) = | 0 | 0 |
| 5hp motor = | 11A | 0 |
| Air conditioner = | 60A | 0 |
| 25% of largest motor = | 15A | 0 |
| Service load = | 303.75A | 105.25A |

### .0.0 ◆ RESTAURANTS

The combined load of three or more cooking appliances and other equipment for a commercial kitchen may be reduced in accordance with *NEC®*

demand factors. This provision would apply to restaurants, bakeries, and similar locations. For example, a small restaurant is supplied by a 120/208V, four-wire, three-phase service. The restaurant has the following loads:

- 1,000 sq. ft. area lighted by 120V lamps
- Ten duplex receptacles
- 20A, 208V, three-phase motor compressor
- 5hp, 208V, three-phase roof ventilation fan, running continuously, protected by an inverse time circuit breaker
- More than six units of kitchen equipment with a total connected load of 80kVA (all units are 208V, three-phase equipment)
- Two 20A sign circuits

The main service uses type THHN copper conductors and is calculated as shown in *Figure 10.* Lighting and receptacle loads contribute 35.8A to either phase A or C and 35.8A to the neutral. The 80kVA kitchen equipment load is subject to the application of a 65% demand factor (per *NEC Section 220.56*), which reduces it to a demand load of 52kVA. This load requires a minimum ampacity of 144.3A per phase at 208V. The load of the three-phase motors and 25% of the largest motor load bring the service load total to 246.8A for phase A or C and 186A for phase B.

If the phase conductors are three 250 kcmil THHN copper conductors, the grounding electrode conductor and the neutral conductor must each be at least a No. 2 copper conductor.

The fuses are selected in accordance with the *NEC®* rules for motor feeder protection. The ungrounded conductors, therefore, are protected at 300A each.

| Service Loads | Line A, C | Neutral | Line B |
|---|---|---|---|
| **Note:** Unbalanced loads are calculated entirely on either phase A or C for a worst-case neutral (and conductor) load (*NEC Section 220.61*). | | | |
| A.  208/120V loads | 20.8 | 20.8 | 0 |
| Lighting = $\dfrac{1.25 \times 2\text{VA per sq. ft.} \times 1{,}000 \text{ sq. ft.}}{120\text{V}}$ = 20.8A | | | |
| Receptacles = $\dfrac{180\text{VA} \times 10}{120\text{V}}$ = 15.0A | 15.0 | 15.0 | 0 |
| B.  Three-phase loads<br>Kitchen equipment (6 or more units) = | 144.3 | 0 | 144.3 |
| $\dfrac{80{,}000\text{W} \times .65}{\sqrt{3} \times 208\text{V}}$ = 144.3A | | | |
| C.  20A three-phase motor compressor<br>Breaker rating = 1.75 × 20A = 35A<br>Use 35A (*NEC Table 430.52*) | 20 | 0 | 20 |
| D.  Three-phase 5hp fan (16.7A) (*NEC Table 430.250*)<br>Breaker rating = 2.5 × 16.7A = 41.75A<br>Use 45A inverse-trip breaker (*NEC Table 430.52*) | 16.7 | 0 | 16.7 |
| E.  25% of largest motor load = .25 × 20A = 5A | 5 | 0 | 5 |
| F.  Sign circuit = $\dfrac{1{,}200\text{VA}}{120\text{V}}$ = 10A each × 2 = 20A × 125% = 25A | 25 | 25 | 0 |
| | 246.8A | 60.8A | 186A |

Service Load
*NEC Table 310.16*
*NEC Table 250.66*
*NEC Section 310.15(B)(4)(a)*

*NEC Section 230.90*

*NEC Section 240.6(A)*

1. Conductors: Use No. 250 kcmil THHN copper at 75°C for ungrounded conductors; use No. 2 THHN copper conductor for neutral (neutral based on size of grounding electrode conductor).

2. Overcurrent protective device:
   Phases A and C = 45A (largest motor device) + 20.8A + 15.0A + 144.3A + 20A + 25A = 270.1A
   Use standard size 300A fuses.

3. Grounding electrode conductor required to be No. 2 copper.

401F10.EPS

*Figure 10* ◆ Restaurant service specifications.

1.32  ELECTRICAL LEVEL FOUR ◆ TRAINEE GUIDE

# 6.0.0 ◆ OPTIONAL CALCULATION FOR NEW RESTAURANTS

*NEC Section 220.88* allows an optional method for the service calculation of a new (or completely rewired) restaurant in lieu of the standard method.

According to *NEC Table 220.88,* add all electrical loads, including heating and cooling loads, to compute the total connected load. Then select a single demand factor from the column that applies to the total computed load, and multiply the load by that factor to obtain the total demand load used for sizing the primary feeder or service-entrance conductors.

# 7.0.0 ◆ SERVICES FOR HOTELS AND MOTELS

The portion of the feeder or service load contributed by general lighting in hotels and motels without provisions for cooking by tenants is subject to the application of demand factors. In addition, the receptacle load in the guest rooms is included in the general lighting load at 2VA per square foot. The demand factors, however, do not apply to any area where the entire lighting is likely to be used at one time, such as the dining room or a ballroom. All other loads for hotels or motels are calculated as shown previously.

*Example:*

Determine the 120/240V feeder load contributed by general lighting in a 100-unit motel. Each guest room is 240 sq. ft. in area. The general lighting load is:

2VA × 240 sq. ft. × 100 units = 48,000VA

The demand lighting load (per *NEC Table 220.42*) is:

| | |
|---|---|
| First 20,000 at 50% = | 10,000VA |
| 48,000 − 20,000 = 28,000 at 40% = | 11,200VA |
| Total = | 21,200VA |

This load would be added to any other loads on the feeder or service to compute the total capacity required.

# 8.0.0 ◆ OPTIONAL CALCULATIONS FOR SCHOOLS

*NEC Section 220.86* provides an optional method for determining the feeder or service load of a school equipped with electric space heating, air conditioning, or both. This optional method applies to the building load, not to feeders within the building.

The optional method for schools basically involves determining the total connected load in volt-amperes, converting the load to volt-amperes per square foot, and applying the demand factors from *NEC Table 220.86.* If both air conditioning and electric space heating loads are present, only the larger of the loads is to be included in the calculation.

A school building has 200,000 square feet of floor area and a 480Y/277V service. The electrical loads are as follows:

- Interior lighting at 3VA per square foot = 600,000VA
- 300kVA power load
- 100kVA water heating load
- 100kVA cooking load
- 100kVA miscellaneous loads
- 200kVA air conditioning load
- 300kVA heating load

The service load in volt-amperes is to be determined by the optional calculation method for schools.

The combined connected load is 1,500,000VA. (This excludes the 200kVA air conditioning load since the heating load is larger.) Based on the 200,000 square feet of floor area, the load per square foot is:

1,500,000VA ÷ 200,000 sq. ft. = 7.5VA per sq. ft.

The demand factor for the portion of the load up to and including 3VA per square foot is 100%. The remaining 4.5VA per square foot in the example is added at a 75% demand factor for a total load of 1,275,000VA.

(200,000 × 3VA/sq. ft.) + (200,000 × 4.5kVA/sq. ft. × 0.75) = 1,275,000VA

To size the service-entrance conductors, *NEC Section 230.42* must be applied to this demand.

1,275,000VA × 1.25 = 1,593,750VA

Assuming a relatively short, rigid conduit overhead service where voltage drop will be negligible, calculate the size of THHW service-entrance conductors as follows for the 480Y/277V, four-wire, three-phase load:

$$\text{Load current} = 1{,}593{,}750\text{VA} \div (480\text{V} \times \sqrt{3})$$
$$= 1{,}917\text{A}$$

*NEC Section 240.4(C)* requires that the conductors have an ampacity that is not less than the rating of the overcurrent device when the device is rated more than 800A. The nearest standard rating of a nonadjustable trip overcurrent device needed for a 1,917A load is 2,000A. The conductors for this service must have an ampacity of at least 2,000A.

Because no standard size copper conductor can carry this load, the service will be accomplished by a number of parallel, four-wire runs in separate conduit between the service equipment and the service drop. The desired result is to establish the minimum number of runs with the minimum sized conductors to accommodate the load. To accomplish this, divide the load by a number of different runs and select a wire size from *NEC Table 310.16* that is very close to or exceeds the resulting current load.

Option 1 = 2,000A ÷ 4 runs = 500A = 900 kcmil conductor

Option 2 = 2,000A ÷ 5 runs = 400A = 600 kcmil conductor

Option 3 = 2,000A ÷ 6 runs = 333A = 400 kcmil conductor

Option 4 = 2,000A ÷ 7 runs = 286A = 350 kcmil conductor

Evaluate the options:

- *Option 1* – Discarded because the size of the conductors makes them difficult to install and also because it provides more capacity than needed.
- *Option 2* – Discarded because of the handling problem due to conductor size.
- *Option 3* – Selected because it meets the load capacity desired with the minimum number of runs.
- *Option 4* – Although this option meets the load requirements, it is discarded because Option 3 meets the requirement and has one less run.

The overhead service entrance is therefore minimally sized as six paralleled four-wire runs of 400 kcmil XHHW-2 copper conductor. (Type XHHW-2 was selected because it can be used in either wet or dry locations. See *NEC Table 310.13, Note 4*.) At this point, if the length of the run had been known, the voltage drop could be checked using the appropriate formula to see if the drop exceeded 2%. If so, the next larger standard wire could be selected.

Note that Option 4 with 350 kcmil conductors could be installed to allow for future needs. Also note that an alternate solution is to bring the higher line voltage to a small high-voltage substation inside or adjacent to the building, where it would be stepped down to an intermediate voltage and/or then stepped down to 480V and busbarred directly to switchboard equipment. This is a fairly common practice, especially in medium to large industrial establishments.

## 9.0.0 ◆ SHORE POWER CIRCUITS FOR MARINAS AND BOATYARDS

The wiring systems for marinas and boatyards are designed using the same *NEC*® rules as for other commercial occupancies, except for the application of several special rules dealing primarily with the design of circuits supplying power to boats (*NEC Section 555.1*).

The smallest sized locking and grounding-type receptacle that may be used to provide shore power for boats is 30A. Each single receptacle that supplies power to boats must be supplied by an individual branch circuit with a rating corresponding to the rating of the receptacle [*NEC Section 555.19(A)(3)*].

The feeder or service ampacity required to supply the receptacles depends on the number of receptacles and their rating, but demand factors may be applied that will reduce the load of five or more receptacles (*NEC Section 555.12*).

For example, a feeder supplying ten 30A shore power receptacles in a marina requires a minimum ampacity of:

$$10 \times 30A \times 120V = 36,000VA$$
$$36,000VA \times 0.8 = 28,800VA$$
$$28,000VA \div 240V = 120A$$

This is the minimum required by the *NEC* unless individual watthour meters are provided for each shore power outlet.

## 10.0.0 ◆ FARM LOAD CALCULATIONS

*NEC Article 220, Part V* provides a separate method for computing farm loads (other than the dwelling). Tables of demand factors are provided for use in computing the feeder loads of individual buildings as well as the service load of the entire farm. See *NEC Sections 220.102 and 220.103*. See *NEC Article 547* for specific code requirements for agricultural buildings.

The demand factors may be applied to the 120/240V feeders for any building or load (other than the dwelling) that is supplied by two or more branch circuits. All loads that operate without diversity—that is, the entire load is on at one time—must be included in the calculation at 100% of the connected load. All other loads may be included at reduced demands. The load to be included at 100% demand, however, cannot be less than 125% of the largest motor and no less than the first 60A of the total load. In other words

If the nondiverse and largest motor load is less than 60A, a portion of the other loads will have to be included at 100% in order to reach the 60A minimum.

After the loads from individual buildings are computed, it may be possible to reduce the total farm load further by applying additional demand factors.

For example, a farm has a dwelling and two other buildings supplied by the same 120/240V service. The electrical loads are as follows:

- Dwelling = 100A load as computed by the calculation method for dwellings.
- Building No. 1 = 5kVA continuous lighting load operated by a single switch; 10hp, 240V motor; and 21kVA of other loads.
- Building No. 2 = 2kVA continuous load operated by a single switch and 15kVA of other loads.

Determine the individual building loads and the total farm load, as illustrated in *Figure 11*. The

| Building No. 1 Feeder Load | 240V Load | Neutral |
|---|---|---|
| Lighting (5kVA nondiverse load) = 5,000VA/240V | 20.8 | 20.8 |
| 10HP motor = 1.25 × 50A | 62.5 | -0- |
| Total motor and nondiverse load | 83.3 | 20.8 |
| Other loads = 21,000VA/240V | 87.5 | 87.5 |
| *Application of demand factors* | | |
| Motor and nondiverse loads @ 100% | 83.3 | 20.8 |
| Next 60A of other loads @ 50% | 30.0 | 30.0 |
| Remainder of other loads (87.5 − 60) @ 25% | 6.9 | 6.9 |
| **Feeder Load** | **120.2A** | **57.7A** |
| **Building No. 2 Feeder Load** | | |
| Lighting (2kVA nondiverse load) = 2,000VA/240V | 8.3 | 8.3 |
| Other loads = 15,000VA/240V | 62.5 | 62.5 |
| *Application of demand factors* | | |
| Nondiverse load @ 100% | 8.3 | 8.3 |
| Remainder of first 60 (60 − 8.3) @ 100% | 51.7 | 51.7 |
| Remainder of other loads (62.5 − 51.7) @ 50% | 5.4 | 5.4 |
| **Total Farm Load** | **65.4A** | **65.4A** |
| *Application of demand factors* | | |
| Largest load (Building No. 1) @ 100% | 120.2 | 57.7 |
| Next largest load (Building No. 2) @ 75% | 49.1 | 49.1 |
| Farm load (less dwelling) | 169.3 | 106.8 |
| Farm dwelling load | 100.0 | 100.0 |
| **Total Farm Load** | **269.3A** | **206.8A** |

401F11.EPS

*Figure 11* ◆ Summary of farm calculations.

nondiverse load for building No. 1 consists of the 5kVA lighting load and the 10hp motor for a total of 83.3A. This value is included in the calculation at the 100% demand factor. Since the requirement for adding at least the first 60A of load at the 100% demand factor has been satisfied, the next 60A of the 87.5A from all other loads are added at a 50% demand factor and the remainder of 27.5A (87.5 – 60) is added at a 25% demand factor.

In the case of building No. 2, the nondiverse load is only 8.3A; therefore, 51.7A of other loads must be added at the 100% demand factor in order to meet the 60A minimum.

Using the method given for computing the total farm load, we see that the service load is:

| | |
|---|---|
| Largest load at 100% (Building No. 1) | = 120.2A |
| Second largest at 75% (Building No. 2) | = 49.1A |
| Total for both buildings | = 169.3A |
| Dwelling | = 100.0A |
| Total load in amperes | = 269.3A |

The total service load of 269A requires the ungrounded service-entrance conductors to be at least 300 kcmil THHW copper conductors. The neutral load of the dwelling is assumed to be 100A, which brings the total farm neutral load to 207A.

# 11.0.0 ◆ MOTORS AND MOTOR CIRCUITS

Two or more motors may be connected to the same feeder circuit instead of routing an individual circuit to each motor. This saves money and is just as efficient if properly designed. *NEC Section 430.24* covers this type of installation. For two or more motors connected to the same feeder conductors, the rule is to compute the sum of all motors plus 25% of the largest motor. Note th exceptions in *NEC Section 430.24* regardin motors with duty cycle ratings.

Care must be taken when designing circuit such as this to prevent several motors connecte to the same circuit from starting at the same tim In most cases, this would result in a severe voltag dip that could affect the operation of other equip ment or prevent one or more of the motors fron starting. Many times, the solution may be t install time-delay devices on some of the mot starting circuits.

*Example:*

The following three-phase, 208V motors are su plied by the same feeder circuit:

- 20hp
- 5hp
- 10hp

Determine the total load and minimum si conductors to supply these motors.

*Step 1* Determine the FLA of each motor. Refer *NEC Table 430.250.*

$$20hp = 59.4A$$
$$5hp = 16.7A$$
$$10hp = 30.8A$$

*Step 2* Take 125% of the largest motor FLA.

$$59.4A \times 125\% = 74.25$$

*Step 3* Add all loads.

$$74.25A + 16.7A + 30.8A = 121.75A$$

*Step 4* Find the minimum size THWN copp conductor from *NEC Table 310.16.*

A No. 1 AWG, type THWN copper conductor rated at 130A.

1. What is the ampacity for each of eight No. 2 THWN copper current-carrying conductors installed in a single conduit?
   a. 57.5A
   b. 91A
   c. 80.5A
   d. 92A

2. What is the rating for a No. 250 kcmil THHN copper conductor in an ambient temperature of 101°F?
   a. 290A
   b. 232.05A
   c. 263.9A
   d. 278.4A

3. What is the rated ampacity per phase for six No. 3/0 THHN copper current-carrying conductors with two conductors per phase (parallel) and all conductors installed in the same conduit?
   a. 320A
   b. 360A
   c. 315A
   d. 280A

4. A feeder circuit supplying a lighting and appliance panelboard is sized by adding _____ % of the noncontinuous load and _____ % of the continuous load.
   a. 100; 100
   b. 80; 100
   c. 100; 125
   d. 100; 110

5. The voltage drop percentage for a panel feeder with a noncontinuous load of 180A, using 3/0 THWN copper conductors at 480V, 3Ø and a length of 248' is _____.
   a. 1.42%
   b. 1.23%
   c. 2.03%
   d. 1.28%

6. What is the minimum demand required for the portion of a feeder that supplies 30' of show windows?
   a. 2,700VA
   b. 3,000VA
   c. 5,400VA
   d. 6,000VA

7. What is the required size of THHN copper conductors for a tapped feeder serving two 208Y/120V, four-wire, three-phase, 75°C branch circuit panelboards, one with a continuous load of 150A and the other with a noncontinuous load of 180A?
   a. 250 kcmil
   b. 400 kcmil
   c. 600 kcmil
   d. 500 kcmil

8. What is the voltage drop, in volts and in percent, for a 208V, 3Ø feeder serving a load of 200A at a distance of 290' using 4/0 THWN copper conductors?
   a. 3.53V; 1.7%
   b. 7.07V; 3.39%
   c. 6.11V; 2.94%
   d. 10.05V; 4.83%

9. For a feeder rated at 225A, the _____ column from *NEC Table 310.16* must be used unless all components in the feeder circuit are rated for a higher temperature.
   a. 140°F
   b. 60°C
   c. 90°C
   d. 75°C

10. What size THWN copper conductors are required to supply a 120/208V, 3Ø panelboard with 20.5kVA of noncontinuous load and 25kVA of continuous load?
    a. 4/0
    b. 250 kcmil
    c. No. 1
    d. 1/0

11. What is the load, in amps, for a 1Ø, 240V feeder supplying a load calculated at 23,800VA?
    a. 99.17A
    b. 114.42A
    c. 57.25A
    d. 66.06A

12. What is the load, in amps, for a 3Ø, 208V feeder supplying a load calculated at 96.75kVA?
    a. 465.14A
    b. 403.13A
    c. 116.37A
    d. 268.55A

**13.** What is the load, in amps, for a 3Ø, 480V feeder supplying a load calculated at 112.5kVA?
a. 540.87A
b. 468.75A
c. 312.27A
d. 135.32A

**14.** Using the 10' tap rule, what size copper THWN conductor is required for a tap from a 400A, 480V, 3Ø feeder to serve a 150A load?
a. No. 2
b. No. 1
c. 1/0
d. 2/0

**15.** Using the 25' tap rule, what is the minimum size copper THWN conductor required for a tap from a 400A, 480V, 3Ø feeder?
a. No. 2
b. No. 1
c. 1/0
d. 2/0

**16.** What is the minimum general lighting load, in VA per square foot, required by the *NEC*® for a single-family dwelling?
a. 1
b. 2
c. 3
d. 3½

**17.** What is the minimum general lighting load, in VA per square foot, required by the *NEC*® for an office building?
a. 2
b. 3½
c. 4½
d. 3

**18.** What is the minimum general lighting load, in VA per square foot, required by the *NEC*® for a store?
a. 2
b. 2½
c. 3
d. 5

**19.** On what basis is the lighting load determined for dwellings and other *NEC*®-listed occupancies?
a. Total connected load for the entire building
b. Volt-amperes per linear foot
c. Volt-amperes per square foot
d. Anticipated connected load for the building

**20.** When determining the lighting load for dwellings and other *NEC*®-listed occupancies, building measurements are taken using the _____.
a. outside dimensions of the building
b. inside wall dimensions of the building
c. width and length of each individual room
d. property line perimeters

**21.** When both heating and cooling systems are used in a building, which of the following statements is true?
a. The total load for both systems must be combined and then multiplied by a factor of 125% (1.25).
b. The larger of the two loads is used in the calculation.
c. The smaller of the two loads is used in the calculation.
d. The total load for both systems must be multiplied by a factor of 150% (1.50).

**22.** When calculating the service size for a single-family dwelling using the standard calculation, what part of the total general lighting and small appliance loads must be calculated at 100%?
a. First 3,000VA
b. First 10,000VA
c. First 15,000VA
d. First 30,000VA

**23.** Using the standard calculation for a single-family dwelling, what is the demand factor for the general lighting and small appliance load that exceeds 120,000VA?
a. 10%
b. 15%
c. 25%
d. 30%

24. What is the total ampacity for a feeder serving two motors at 15hp, one motor at 25hp, and one motor at 40hp? All motors are rated at 480V, 3Ø.
    a. 100A
    b. 128A
    c. 141A
    d. 153A

25. When calculating the feeder size for a motor control center supplying several motors, which of the following statements is correct?
    a. Determine the sum of all motor loads.
    b. Determine the sum of all motor loads plus 30% of the largest motor.
    c. Determine the sum of all motor loads plus 25% of the largest motor.
    d. Determine the sum of all motor loads plus 125% of the largest motor.

## Summary

Load calculations are necessary for determining sizes and ratings of conductors, equipment, and overcurrent protection required by the *NEC®* to be included in each electrical installation, including the service, feeders, and branch circuit loads. These calculations are necessary in every electri-cal installation, from the smallest roadside vegetable stand to the largest industrial establishment. Therefore, every electrician must know how to calculate services, feeders, and branch circuits for any given installation and must also know what *NEC®* requirements apply.

## Notes

# Trade Terms
# Introduced in This Module

*Building:* A structure that stands alone or that is cut off from adjoining structures by fire walls with all openings therein protected by approved fire doors.

*Dwelling unit:* One or more rooms for the use of one or more persons as a housekeeping unit with space for eating, living, and sleeping, as well as permanent provisions for cooking and sanitation. A one-family dwelling consists solely of one dwelling unit. A two-family dwelling consists solely of two dwelling units. A multi-family dwelling is a building containing three or more dwelling units.

*Feeder:* All circuit conductors between the service equipment or the source of a separately derived system and the final branch circuit overcurrent device.

*Garage:* A building or portion of a building in which one or more self-propelled vehicles carrying volatile, flammable liquid for fuel or power are kept for use, sale, storage, rental, repair, exhibition, or demonstration purposes, and all that portion of a building that is on or below the floor or floors in which such vehicles are kept and that is not separated by suitable cutoffs.

*Lighting panelboard:* A branch circuit panelboard having more than 10% of its overcurrent devices rated at 30A or less, for which neutral connections are provided.

*Overhead system service entrance:* The service conductors between the terminals of the service equipment and a point usually outside the building, clear of building walls, where it is joined by a tap or splice to the service drop.

*Separately derived system:* A premises wiring system whose power is derived from a battery, a solar photovoltaic system, or from a generator, transformer, or converter windings, and that has no direct electrical connection, including a solidly-connected grounded circuit conductor, to supply conductors originating in another system.

*Service:* The conductors and equipment for delivering electric energy from the serving utility to the wiring system of the premises served.

*Service conductors:* The conductors from the service point to the service disconnecting means.

*Service drop:* The overhead service conductors from the last pole or other aerial support up to and including splices, if any, connecting to the service-entrance conductors to the building or other structure.

*Service equipment:* The necessary equipment, usually consisting of a circuit breaker or switch and fuses, and their accessories, located near the point of entrance of supply conductors to a building or other structure, or an otherwise defined area, and intended to constitute the main control and means of cutoff of the supply.

*Service lateral:* The underground service conductors between the street main, including any risers at a pole or other structure or from transformers, and the first point of connection to the service-entrance conductors in a terminal box or meter or other enclosure with adequate space, inside or outside the building wall. Where there is no terminal box, meter, or other enclosure with adequate space, the point of connection shall be considered to be the point of entrance of the service conductors into the building.

*Service point:* The point of connection between the facilities of the serving utility and the premises wiring.

*Switchboard:* A large single panel, frame, or assembly of panels on which are mounted, on the face, back, or both, switches, overcurrent and other protective devices, buses, and instruments. Switchboards are generally accessible from the rear as well as from the front and are not intended to be installed in cabinets.

*Tap conductors:* As defined in *NEC Article 240,* a tap conductor is a conductor, other than a service conductor, that has overcurrent protection ahead of its point of supply that exceeds the value permitted for similar conductors that are protected as described in *NEC Section 240.4.*

*Underground service entrance:* The service conductors between the terminals of the service equipment and the point of connection to the service lateral.

his module is intended to present thorough esources for task training. The following refer-nce works are suggested for further study. These re optional materials for continuing education ather than for task training.

*American Electrician's Handbook,* Terrell Croft and Wilfred I. Summers. New York, NY: McGraw-Hill, 1996.

*National Electrical Code® Handbook,* Latest Edition. Quincy, MA: National Fire Protection Association.

The NCCER makes every effort to keep these textbooks up-to-date and free of technical errors. We appreciate your help in this process. If you have an idea for improving this textbook, or if you find an error, a typographical mistake, or an inaccuracy in NCCER's *Contren*® textbooks, please write us, using this form or a photocopy. Be sure to include the exact module number, page number, a detailed description, and the correction, if applicable. Your input will be brought to the attention of the Technical Review Committee. Thank you for your assistance.

*Instructors* – If you found that additional materials were necessary in order to teach this module effectively, please let us know so that we may include them in the Equipment/Materials list in the Annotated Instructor's Guide.

**Write:** Product Development
National Center for Construction Education and Research
P.O. Box 141104, Gainesville, FL 32614-1104

**Fax:** 352-334-0932

**E-mail:** curriculum@nccer.org

Craft                                   Module Name
_____

Copyright Date          Module Number              Page Number(s)
_____

Description
_____

_____

_____

(Optional) Correction
_____

_____

_____

(Optional) Your Name and Address
_____

_____

_____

# Motor Maintenance, Part One

## 26310-05

**St. Vincent's North Tower**
Birmingham, Alabama
Health Care $25–99 Million Award Winner
Brasfield & Gorrie, LLC

# 26310-05
# *Motor Maintenance, Part One*

### *Topics to be presented in this module include:*

## Overview

Motors require a comprehensive maintenance program in order to provide uninterrupted service. Unfortunately, it is far too common to see motors put into operation and never touched again until the motor fails to operate. Premature motor failures can be attributed to a number of problems, including lack of cleaning, lack of lubrication, and excessive loads.

DC motors require much more maintenance than AC motors because most are equipped with some type of contact brush assembly on the commutator of the motor. Only qualified persons should attempt to maintain DC motors and motor drives. Mishandling or misalignment of brushes can damage the motor or prevent it from operating.

Always use the proper tools and techniques when troubleshooting any motor. If a motor does not start, do not assume the problem is in the motor. Many operational motors have been changed out only to find that the supply voltage is absent. If the motor control circuitry proves to be operational but the motor still won't run, follow the manufacturer's procedures for testing the motor before replacing it.

## Objectives

When you have completed this module, you will be able to do the following:

1. Properly store motors and generators.
2. Test motors and generators.
3. Make connections for specific types of motors and generators.
4. Clean open-frame motors.
5. Lubricate motors that require this type of maintenance.
6. Collect and record motor data.
7. Select tools for motor maintenance.
8. Select instruments for motor testing.

## Trade Terms

Armature
Brush
Brush holders
Commutator
Commutator pole
Generator
Slip rings
Starting winding

## Required Trainee Materials

1. Pencil and paper
2. Appropriate personal protective equipment
3. Copy of the latest edition of the *National Electrical Code®*

## Prerequisites

Before you begin this module, it is recommended that you successfully complete *Core Curriculum; Electrical Level One; Electrical Level Two; Electrical Level Three*, Modules 26301-05 through 26308-05.

This course map shows all of the modules in Electrical Level Three. The suggested training order begins at the bottom and proceeds up. Skill levels increase as you advance on the course map. The local Training Program Sponsor may adjust the training order.

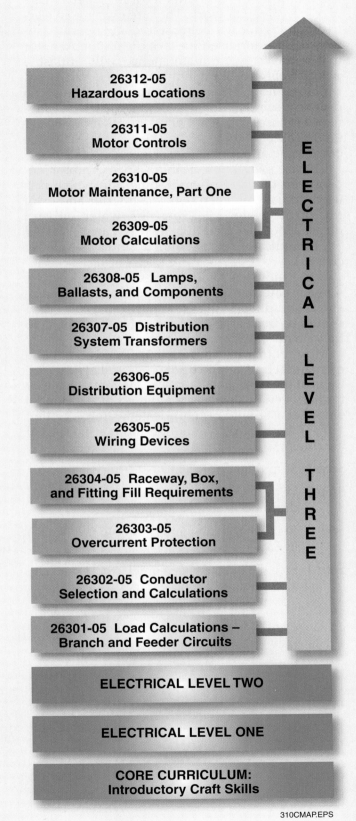

26312-05
Hazardous Locations

26311-05
Motor Controls

26310-05
Motor Maintenance, Part One

26309-05
Motor Calculations

26308-05   Lamps, Ballasts, and Components

26307-05  Distribution System Transformers

26306-05
Distribution Equipment

26305-05
Wiring Devices

26304-05  Raceway, Box, and Fitting Fill Requirements

26303-05
Overcurrent Protection

26302-05  Conductor Selection and Calculations

26301-05  Load Calculations – Branch and Feeder Circuits

ELECTRICAL LEVEL TWO

ELECTRICAL LEVEL ONE

CORE CURRICULUM: Introductory Craft Skills

ELECTRICAL LEVEL THREE

310CMAP.EPS

# 1.0.0 ◆ INTRODUCTION

AC motor failure accounts for a high percentage of electrical repair work. The care given to an electric motor while it is being stored and operated affects the life and usefulness of the motor. A motor that receives good maintenance will outlast a poorly treated motor many times over. Actually, if a motor is initially installed correctly and has been properly selected for the job, very little maintenance is necessary—provided it does receive a little care at regular intervals. The basic care consists of cleaning and lubrication.

The frequency for cleaning an AC motor depends on the type of environment in which it is used. In general, keep both the interior and exterior of the motor free from dirt, water, oil, and grease. Motors operating in dirty areas should be periodically disassembled and thoroughly cleaned.

If the motor is totally enclosed (fan-cooled or nonventilated), such as the one shown in *Figure 1*, and is equipped with automatic drain plugs, they should be free of oil, grease, paint, grit, and dirt so they do not clog up.

Most motors are properly lubricated at the time of manufacture, and it is not necessary to lubricate them at the time of installation. However, if a motor has been in storage for a period of six months or longer, it should be relubricated before starting.

To lubricate conventional motors with ball bearings:

**Step 1** Stop the motor.

**Step 2** Wipe clean all grease fittings (filler and drain).

**Step 3** Remove the filler and drain plugs (A and B in *Figure 2*).

**Step 4** Free the drain hole of any hard grease (use a piece of wire if necessary).

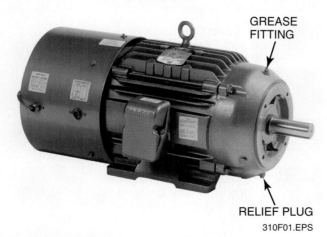

GREASE FITTING

RELIEF PLUG

310F01.EPS

*Figure 1* ◆ Totally enclosed, fan-cooled motor.

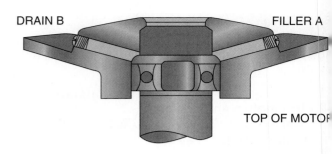

DRAIN B                                    FILLER A

TOP OF MOTOR

310F02.EPS

*Figure 2* ◆ Location of motor filler and drain plugs.

**Step 5** Add grease using a low-pressure grease gun.

**Step 6** Start the motor and let it run for approximately 30 minutes.

**Step 7** Stop the motor, wipe off any drained grease and replace the filler and drain plugs.

**Step 8** The motor is now ready for operation.

Every four years (every year in the case of severe duty), motors with open bearings should be thoroughly cleaned, washed, and repacked with grease. *Table 1* shows the relubrication periods for various motors. Standard conditions mean operation of 8 hrs./day, normal or light loading, and a 100°F maximum ambient temperature. Severe conditions represent operation of 24 hrs./day, shock loadings, vibration, dirty or dusty areas, or areas at 100°F to 150°F ambient temperature. Extreme conditions are defined as heavy shock or vibration, large amounts of dirt or dust, or high ambient temperatures (above 150°F).

Bearings provide minimum resistance and align the motor rotor during operation. Therefore, the quantity of grease is important for proper bearing operation. The grease cavity should be filled one-third to one-half full. Always remember that too much grease is as detrimental as insufficient grease. *Table 2* shows the amount of grease required and *Table 3* gives the recommended grease for a Class B or F motor. However, always check with the motor manufacturers for their recommendations and specifications for greasing motors.

> **CAUTION**
>
> The amount of grease added to motor bearings is very important. Only enough grease should be added to replace the grease used by the bearings. Too much grease can be as harmful as insufficient grease.

**Table 1** Relubrication Periods for Various Sizes and Types of Motors

| Frame Size | Relubrication Period | | |
|---|---|---|---|
| **900 rpm, 1,200 rpm, and Variable Speed** | **Standard Conditions** | **Severe Conditions** | **Extreme Conditions** |
| 140–180 | 4.5 years | 18 months | 9 months |
| 210–280 | 4 years | 16 months | 8 months |
| 320–400 | 3.5 years | 14 months | 7 months |
| 440–508 | 3 years | 12 months | 6 months |
| 510 | 2.5 years | 11.5 months | 6 months |
| **1,800 rpm** | **Standard Conditions** | **Severe Conditions** | **Extreme Conditions** |
| 140–180 | 3 years | 1 year | 6 months |
| 210–280 | 2.5 years | 10.5 months | 5.5 months |
| 320–400 | 2 years | 9 months | 4.5 months |
| 440–508 | 1.5 years | 8 months | 4 months |
| 510 | 1 year | 6 months | 3.5 months |
| **Over 1,800 rpm** | 6 months | 3 months | 3 months |

**Table 2** Typical Amount of Grease Required When Regreasing Electric Motors

| Bearing Number | Amount in Cubic Inches | Approximate Equivalent Teaspoons |
|---|---|---|
| 203 | 0.15 | 0.5 |
| 205 | 0.27 | 0.9 |
| 206 | 0.34 | 1.1 |
| 207 | 0.43 | 1.4 |
| 208 | 0.52 | 1.7 |
| 209 | 0.61 | 2.0 |
| 210 | 0.72 | 2.4 |
| 212 | 0.95 | 3.1 |
| 213 | 1.07 | 3.6 |
| 216 | 1.49 | 4.9 |
| 219 | 2.8 | 7.2 |
| 222 | 3.0 | 10.0 |
| 307 | 0.53 | 1.8 |
| 308 | 0.66 | 2.2 |
| 309 | 0.81 | 2.7 |
| 310 | 0.97 | 3.2 |
| 311 | 1.14 | 3.8 |
| 312 | 1.33 | 4.4 |
| 313 | 1.54 | 5.1 |
| 314 | 1.76 | 5.9 |
| 316 | 2.24 | 7.4 |
| 318 | 2.78 | 9.2 |

## 2.0.0 ◆ PRACTICAL MAINTENANCE TECHNIQUES

Once the motor has been sized and installed properly, the key to long, trouble-free motor life is proper maintenance. Maintaining a motor in good operating condition requires periodic inspection to determine if any faults exist, and then promptly correcting these faults. The frequency and thoroughness of these inspections depend on such factors as:

- Number of hours and days the motor operates
- Importance of the motor in the production scheme
- Nature of service
- Environmental conditions

Each week, every motor in operation should be inspected to see if the windings are exposed to any dripping water, acid, or alcohol fumes as well as excessive dust, chips, or lint on or about the motor. Make certain that objects that will cause problems with the motor's ventilation system are not placed too near the motor and do not come into direct contact with the motor's moving parts.

In sleeve-bearing motors, check the oil level frequently (at least once a week) and fill the oil cups

**Table 3** Recommended Grease for Motor Lubrication

| Insulation Class Shown on Nameplate | Grease Designation | Grease Supplier |
|---|---|---|
| B or F | Chevron SRI-2 | Standard Oil of California or equivalent |

## Ventilation and Temperature Control

to the specified line with the recommended lubricant. If the journal or motor shaft diameter is less than 2", always stop the motor before checking the oil level. For special lubricating systems such as forced, flood-and-disc, and wool-packed lubrication, follow the manufacturer's recommendations. Oil should be added to the bearing housing only when the motor is stopped, and then a check should be made to ensure that no oil creeps along the shaft toward the windings where it may harm the insulation.

Always be alert to any unusual noise, which may be caused by metal-to-metal contact (bad bearings, etc.), and also learn to detect any abnormal odor, which might indicate scorching insulation varnish.

Feel the bearing housing each week for evidence of excess heat and vibration. Listen for any unusual noise. Also inspect the bearing housing for the possibility of creeping grease on the inside of the motor, which might harm the insulation.

**WARNING!**
Before performing any motor maintenance procedures, other than external visual inspection or noise monitoring, always lock out and tag out the equipment according to approved procedures.

**Commutators** and **brushes** should be checked for sparking and should be observed through several cycles if the motor is on cycle duty. A stable copper oxide carbon film—as distinguished from a pure copper surface—on the commutator is an essential requirement for good commutation. Such a film, however, may vary in color from copper to straw or from chocolate brown to black. The commutator should be clean and smooth and have a high polish. All brushes should be checked for wear and connections should be checked for looseness. The commutator surface may be cleaned

using a piece of dry canvas or other durable, lint free material that is tightly wound and securely fastened to a wooden dowel and held against the commutator while manually rotating it.

The air gap on sleeve-bearing motors should be checked frequently, especially if the motor has recently been rewound or otherwise repaired. After new bearings have been installed, for example, make sure that the average reading is within specified tolerances. Check the air passages through punchings and make sure they are free of all foreign matter.

Low-pressure compressed air (with working pressures within safety standards) may be used to blow motor windings clean. Industrial-grade vacuum cleaners may also be used to remove dirt and other debris from the motor windings. The windings may be wiped clean with a dry, lint-free cloth while checking for moisture in the bottom of the motor frame. Also check to see if any oil or grease has worked its way up to the rotor or armature windings. If so, clean away the oil or grease with an approved cleaning solution.

**WARNING!**
When using compressed air, exercise caution by wearing appropriate personal protective equipment and using an airflow tip or pulse nozzle. Excess air pressure can result in personnel injury and cause damage to the motor windings.

As mentioned previously, always disconnect the power, and lock out/tag out the equipment per proper procedures prior to performing any motor maintenance tasks. Check other motor parts and accessories such as belts, gears, couplings, chains, and sprockets for excessive wear or misalignment. Inspect the motor starter and verify that the motor reaches proper speed each time it is started.

At least once a month, check the shunt, series, and commutator field windings for tightness in their mountings, as drying may sometimes cause these windings to loosen. Check for tightness by attempting to move the field spools on the poles. If movement is present, the motor should be removed from service and repaired immediately. Also check the motor cable connections for looseness and tighten as needed.

Also on a monthly or more frequent basis, inspect the brushes in their holders for proper fit and free play, as well as brush spring pressure. If required, tighten the brush studs in the holders to remove slack caused by washers drying out, making sure the studs are not displaced. Look carefully for chipped or cracked brushes during the inspection and replace as necessary.

During this monthly inspection, also examine the commutator surface for high bars, high mica, and evidence of scratches or roughness. See that the risers are clean and have not been damaged in any way.

Where motors having ball or roller bearings are exposed to extreme conditions or constant usage, bearings should be serviced at least monthly by purging out the old grease through the drain hole and applying new grease. After changing the grease in these bearings, inspect the bearing housing for leaking grease. If present, correct the leakage prior to starting the motor.

On motors with sleeve bearings, check the sleeve bearings for wear at least once every two months. Clean out the oil wells if there is evidence of dirt or sludge. Flush with lighter oil before refilling with the specified bearing lubricant.

On motors with gears, open the drain plug and check the oil for the presence of metal scale, sand, grit, or water. If any of these conditions are present, drain, flush, and refill as recommended by the motor manufacturer. Check the rotor for slack or backlash by carefully rocking the rotor.

Loads being driven by motors have a tendency to change from time to time due to wear on the machine or the product being processed through the machine. Therefore, all loads should be checked from time to time for a changed condition, bad adjustment, and poor handling or control.

During the monthly inspection, check the tightness of all belts and adjust as necessary. Check the belts to verify that they are running steadily and near the inside edge of the pulley. On chain-driven machines, check the chain for evidence of wear and stretch, and clean the chain thoroughly. Check the chain lubricating system and note the incline of the slanting base to make sure it does not cause oil rings to rub on the housing.

Once or twice each year, all motors in operation should be given a thorough inspection consisting of the following:

- *Windings* – Check the insulation resistance using the proper instruments and techniques, which are described in detail later in this module. The windings should also be given a visual inspection; look for cracks and other evidence of insulation deterioration or damage. Clean all surfaces thoroughly, especially ventilating passages. Examine the frame for evidence of moisture or the presence of water in the bottom of the frame. The presence of either moisture or water may require the windings to be dried, varnished, and baked.
- *Air gap and bearings* – Check the air gap to make sure that average readings are within the tolerances specified by the manufacturer. All bearings (ball, roller, and sleeve) should be thoroughly checked and defective ones replaced. Waste-packed and wick-oiled bearings should have waste or wicks renewed if they have become glazed or filled with metal, grit, or dirt, making sure that the new material bears well against the shaft.
- *Squirrel cage rotors* – Check for broken parts or loose bars as well as evidence of local heating. If the fan blades are not cast in place, check for loose blades. Also look for marks on the rotor surface, which may indicate the presence of foreign matter in the air gap or a worn bearing or bearings.
- *Wound rotors* – Wound rotors should be cleaned thoroughly, especially around collector rings, washers, and connections. Tighten all connections. If the ring surfaces appear rough in finish, spotted, or out-of-round, they should be refinished by qualified personnel familiar with machine shop equipment. Make certain all components that make up the rotor are firmly secured in place; tighten any component that appears loose.
- *Armatures* – Clean all armature air passages thoroughly. Look for oil or grease seeping along the shaft and running back to the bearing. Check the commutator surface condition, looking for high bars, high mica, or eccentricity (out-of-round) conditions. If necessary, the commutator should be turned by a qualified machinist to secure a smooth, fresh surface, as illustrated in *Figure 3*.

The following procedures should only be performed by qualified personnel. For armatures with drilled center holes, a securing device called a lathe dog is installed on the shaft opposite the commutator and tightened. If it is necessary to put

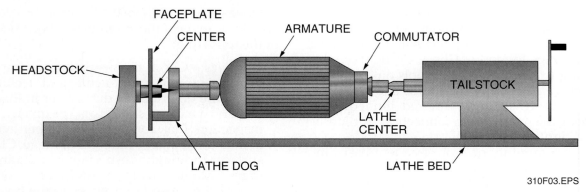

*Figure 3* ◆ Motor armature secured in lathe between centers.

the lathe dog on a bearing surface, a thin piece of copper sheeting is first placed around the shaft to protect it. A faceplate is installed on the spindle end of the lathe, along with centering tools in both the headstock and tailstock. White lead or oil is applied on the tailstock centering tool and the commutator is placed between the centering tools as the tailstock is tightened firmly, but not so tight that it distorts the end of the shaft.

A sharp-pointed, lathe cutting tool is used in the tool holder to turn the commutator down, with the lathe speed set at medium speed (approximately 700 rpm). The process is finished using a fine file, followed by polishing paper.

Armatures without drilled center holes necessitate the use of chucks. This is accomplished by securing the armature shaft end opposite the commutator in a three-jaw universal chuck in the headstock. A bearing of proper shaft size is then installed in a drill-type chuck and secured in the tailstock of the lathe. The bearing is oiled and the commutator end of the shaft is placed in the bearing (see *Figure 4*). The commutator is then turned in the same manner as described previously.

When turning down any armature, a pointed tool with a sharp, smooth edge should always be used to obtain the cleanest cut possible, taking only a fine cut each time to prevent tearing the

commutator. The job is finished by first smoothing down the commutator surface with a fine file while the armature is turning in the lathe, then finally polishing it with a fine polishing abrasive paper.

After the armature has been turned, clean between the bars if necessary and test the armature for shorts using a growler or other appropriate test instruments. The vibration of a hacksaw blade on any coil means that the coil is shorted at the leads or commutator. Clean between the **commutator poles** and test again. As soon as the armature tests okay, it is ready to put back into service.

Motor loads should be re-evaluated from time to time, as they can vary for several reasons. Using an ammeter, take an ampere reading on the motor, first with no load, second at full load, and finally through a full cycle of no load to full load. This test should provide information concerning the mechanical condition of the driven machine (load).

Without proper maintenance, no motor can be expected to perform well for any length of time or to remain in service as long as it should. Although motor maintenance is costly, it is far less expensive than continually replacing or overhauling motors.

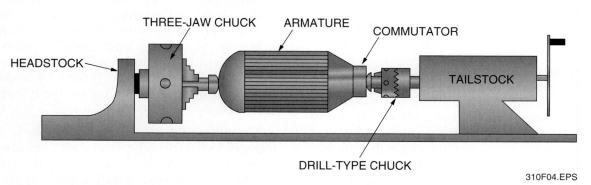

*Figure 4* ◆ Motor armature secured in lathe with lathe chucks.

# 3.0.0 ◆ MOTOR BEARING MAINTENANCE

AC motors account for a large percentage of industrial maintenance and repair, with many motor failures caused by faulty bearings. Consequently, most industrial facilities place a great amount of emphasis on proper care of motor bearings. Electric motors last much longer and perform better when a carefully planned motor lubrication schedule is followed.

If an AC motor failure does occur, the first step is to find out why the motor failed. There are various causes of motor failures, including excessive load, binding or misalignment of motor drives, wet or dirty environments, and bearing failures. Bearing failures can occur in newer motors with high-quality bearings as often as in older motors with less reliable bearings if the bearings are not maintained properly. A notable exception in bearing failures may be found in motors equipped with sealed bearings, which are much less prone to failure.

## 3.1.0 Types of Bearings

Ball bearings are the most common type of bearings used in the construction of electric motors. This type of bearing is found on various sizes of motors, with bearing design types including:

- Open
- Single-shielded
- Double-shielded
- Sealed
- Double-row and other special types

Open bearings, as the name implies, are open construction and must be installed in a sealed housing. These bearings are less apt to cause churning of grease and are therefore used mostly on large motors.

The single-shield bearing has a shield on one side to keep grease from the motor windings. Double-shielded bearings have a shield on both sides of the bearing. This type of bearing is less susceptible to contamination and, because of its design, reduces the possibility of over-greasing. Sealed bearings have a double shield on each side

of the bearing, which forms an excellent seal. This bearing requires no maintenance, affords protection from contamination at all times, and does not require regreasing. It is normally used on small or medium motor sizes.

Many large motors are furnished with oil-ring sleeve bearings, while some of the smaller fractional-horsepower motors are equipped with simple sleeve bearings without oil rings.

Each bearing type has characteristics that are suited for a particular application. Replacement of bearings should be made using the same type of bearing originally installed in the motor or equipment. *Figure 5* shows several types of bearings used in electric motors. The following list provides a basic overview of bearing applications and a guide to analyzing bearing failures.

- *Self-aligning ball bearing* – The self-aligning ball bearing has two rows of balls rolling on the spherical surface of the outer ring, and this design compensates for angular misalignment due to errors in mounting, shaft deflection, or distortion of the foundation. This design also prevents any exertion of bending influence on the motor shaft—a most important consideration in applications requiring extreme accuracy at high speeds. Self-aligning ball bearings are used for radial loads and moderate thrust loads in either direction.
- *Single-row, deep-groove ball bearing* – The single-row, deep-groove ball bearing will sustain, in addition to radial load, a substantial thrust load in either direction, even at very high speeds. The ability to sustain these loads is made possible by the close-tolerance contact that exists between the roller balls and the continuous groove in each ring. Accurate alignment between the motor shaft and housing is essential in the application of this type of bearing. The single-row, deep-groove bearing is also available with seals and shield, which provide protection from contamination and retain lubricant.
- *Angular-contact ball bearings* – The angular-contact ball bearing can support a substantial thrust load in one direction, combined with a moderate radial load. A steep contact angle

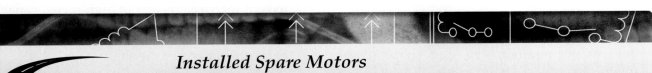

### Installed Spare Motors

*INSIDE TRACK*

Installed spare motors should be operated on a regularly established time schedule. This prevents the spare motor from deteriorating while the primary motor is in use.

SELF-ALIGNING
BALL BEARING

SPHERICAL-ROLLER
BEARING

SINGLE-ROW,
DEEP-GROOVE
BALL BEARING

CYLINDRICAL-
ROLLER BEARING

ANGULAR-CONTACT
BALL BEARING

BALL-THRUST
BEARING

SPHERICAL-
ROLLER THRUST
BEARING

DOUBLE-ROW,
DEEP-GROOVE
BALL BEARING

TAPERED-ROLLER
BEARING

310F05.EPS

*Figure 5* ◆ Various types of bearings.

## Establishing a Rotor's Magnetic Center

Before large-frame motors are put into service, the motor should be run uncoupled in order to locate the electrical (magnetic) center of the rotor. While it is running, mark or etch the established reference on the shaft next to the bearing. This will ensure efficient motor operation when the load is mechanically coupled to the motor.

assures the highest thrust capacity and axial rigidity. This characteristic is obtained through the addition of a thrust-supporting shoulder on the inner ring, with a similar high shoulder on the opposite side of the ring. These bearings can be mounted singly, or in special applications in tandem, to allow constant thrust in one direction. They can also be mounted in pairs if the sides of the bearings have been ground to a flush finish. This installation provides for a combined load, either face-to-face or back-to-back.

- *Double-row, deep-groove ball bearing* – The double-row, deep-groove ball bearing embodies the same principle of design as the single-row bearing. However, this bearing has a lower axial displacement than occurs in the single-row design, substantial thrust capacity in either direction, and high radial capacity due to the two rows of balls.

- *Spherical-roller bearing* – The exceptional capacity of the spherical-roller bearing can be attributed to the number, size, and shape of the rollers, as well as the accuracy by which they are guided. Since the bearing is inherently self-aligning, angular misalignment between the shaft and housing has no detrimental effect on

the application of the bearing. The design and proportion of the bearing are such that both thrust loads and radial loads may be carried in either direction.

- *Cylindrical-roller bearing* – This type of bearing has a high radial capacity, which provides accurate guiding of the rollers, and a close approach to true rolling. The low friction permits operation at high speeds. Cylindrical-roller bearings having flanges on one ring also allow a limited free axial movement of the shaft in relation to the housing, and are easy to dismount even when both rings are mounted within a close tolerance to one another. The double-row type is particularly suitable for machine-tool spindles.

- *Ball-thrust bearing* – The ball-thrust bearing is designed for thrust load in one direction only. The load line through the balls in parallel to the axis of the shaft results in high thrust capacity and minimum axial deflection. Flat bearing seats are essential for heavy loads or for close axial positioning of the shaft.

- *Spherical-roller thrust bearing* – The spherical-roller thrust bearing is designed to carry heavy thrust loads or combined loads that are predominantly thrust. This bearing has a single row of rollers, which roll on a spherical outer race with full self-alignment. The cage, centered by an inner ring sleeve, is constructed so that lubricant is pumped directly against the inner ring's unusually high guide flange. This bearing operates best with relatively heavy oil lubrication.

*Tapered-roller bearings* – Since the axes of the rollers and raceways of a tapered-roller bearing form an angle with the shaft angle, the tapered-roller bearing is especially suitable for carrying coordinated radial and axial loads. This type of bearing is typically installed adjacent to another bearing capable of carrying thrust loads in the opposite direction. Tapered roller bearings are designed so that their cone (inner ring) and roller/cup assembly (outer ring) are mounted separately.

Recommendations for ball bearing assembly, maintenance, inspection, and lubrication are shown in *Table 4*. Refer to this list often when working with electric motors.

## 3.2.0 Frequency of Lubrication

The frequency of motor lubrication depends not only on the type of bearing, but also on the motor application. Small to medium-size motors equipped with ball bearings (except sealed bearings) should be greased every three to six years if the motor duty is normal. On severe applications (high temperature, wet or dirty locations, or corrosive atmospheres), lubrication may be required more often. In severe applications, past experience and condition of the grease are the best guides to the frequency of lubrication.

The lubrication in sleeve bearings should be changed at least once a year or more often when the motor duty is severe or the oil appears dirty.

### 3.2.1 Lubrication Procedure

Before lubricating a ball bearing motor, the bearing housing, grease gun, and fittings should be cleaned. Care must be exercised in keeping out dirt and debris during lubrication. The relief plug

**Table 4** Ball Bearing Assembly, Maintenance, and Lubrication Recommendations

| DO | DO NOT |
|---|---|
| DO work with clean tools in clean surroundings. | DO NOT work with poor tools, a cluttered workbench, or dirty surroundings. |
| DO remove all outside dirt from the housing before exposing the bearing. | DO NOT handle bearings with dirty or moist hands. |
| DO treat a used bearing as carefully as a new one. | DO NOT spin uncleaned bearings. |
| DO use clean solvents and flushing oils. | DO NOT spin any bearings using compressed air. |
| DO lay bearings out on clean paper or cloth. | DO NOT use the same container to clean and rinse the bearings. |
| DO protect disassembled bearings from dirt and moisture. | DO NOT scratch or nick the bearing surfaces. |
| DO use clean, lint-free rags to wipe bearings. | DO NOT remove grease or oil from new bearings. |
| DO keep bearings wrapped in oil-proof paper when not in use. | DO NOT use the incorrect type or amount of lubricant. |
| DO clean the outside of the housing before replacing the bearings. | DO NOT use a bearing as a measuring tool to check the housing bore or shaft fit. |
| DO keep bearing lubricants clean when applying and cover containers when not in use. | DO NOT install a bearing on a shaft that shows excessive wear. |
| DO be sure the shaft size is within the specified tolerances recommended for the bearing. | DO NOT open the bearing carton until the bearing is ready to be installed. |
| DO store bearings in their original unopened cartons in a dry place. | DO NOT determine the condition of a bearing until it has been properly cleaned. |
| DO use a clean, short-bristle brush with firmly embedded bristles to remove dirt, scale, or chips. | DO NOT tap directly on a bearing or ring during installation. |
| DO be certain that, when installed, the bearing is square with and held firmly against the shaft shoulder. | DO NOT overfill during lubrication. Excess oil or grease may enter the motor housing. Too much lubricant will also cause overheating, particularly where bearings operate at high speeds. |
| DO follow lubricating instructions supplied with the machinery. Use only grease where grease is specified; use only oil where oil is specified. Be sure to use the exact kind of lubricant called for. | DO NOT allow motors to remain idle for long periods of time without rotating their shafts periodically. |
| DO handle grease with clean paddles or grease guns. Store grease in clean containers. Keep grease containers covered. | |

should be removed from the bottom of the bearing housing. This is done to prevent excessive pressure from building up inside the bearing housing during lubrication. If possible, run the motor and add grease until it begins to flow from the relief hole. The motor should be allowed to run for approximately 5 or 10 minutes to expel any excess grease. The relief plug should then be reinstalled and the bearing housing cleaned.

It is important to avoid over-lubrication. When excessive grease is forced into a bearing, a churning of the grease may occur, resulting in high bearing temperatures and eventual bearing failure.

On motors that do not have a relief plug, grease should be applied slowly and sparingly. If possible, disassemble the motor and repack the bearing with the proper amount of grease. Always maintain cleanliness during lubrication.

When lubricating sleeve-type bearings, use only the recommended type and amount of lubrication as recommended by the manufacturer of the motor or bearing.

### 3.3.0 Testing Bearings

Two simple methods commonly used to check bearings during motor operation are touching and listening. If the bearing housing feels unusually hot, or if a growling or grinding sound is being emitted from the area of the bearings, one of the bearings is probably nearing failure. Special stethoscopes are also available for listening to bearings while the motor is running.

**NOTE**

Keep in mind that some bearings may safely operate in a higher temperature range than other bearings, even in ranges exceeding 85°C. Check the motor manufacturer's specifications.

Using a feeler gauge, periodically check the air gap on sleeve-bearing motors for bearing wear. Four separate measurements should be taken approximately 90° apart around the diameter of the rotor. These measurements should be recorded and compared with previous measurements to determine if any deviations are present, which may indicate bearing wear since the last measurements were recorded.

Motors should also be checked for end play, which is the backward and forward movement in the shaft. Ball bearing motors typically will have ¹⁄₃₂" to ¹⁄₁₆" of end movement. Sleeve-bearing motors may have up to ½" of end movement.

On larger sleeve bearings, the oil level shoul be checked periodically and the oil visually in spected for contamination. If safely possible, th oil rings should be checked while the motor i running.

Other inspections may include periodicall checking for misalignment or bent shafts, and fo excessive belt tension.

### 4.0.0 ◆ TROUBLESHOOTING MOTORS

To detect defects in electric motors, the winding are typically tested for ground faults, open: shorts, and reverses. The methods used in per forming these tests may depend on the type c motor being tested.

**WARNING!**

Before testing or troubleshooting a motor beyond a simple visual/auditory inspection, disconnect the power and follow the proper lockout/tagout procedures.

Before we can begin our study of troubleshooting, it is important to clarify some basic terms These include the following:

- *Grounded winding* – A winding become grounded when it makes electrical contact witl the metal frame of the motor. Causes may in clude end plate bolts contacting conductors o windings, winding wires pressing against th laminations at the corners of slots damaged during rewinding, or conductive parts of th centrifugal switch contacting the end plate.
- *Open circuits* – Loose connections or broke wires can cause an open circuit in an electri motor.
- *Shorts* – Two or more windings of separate phases that contact each other at a point creat ing a path other than the one intended cause short circuit. This condition may develop in relatively new winding if the winding is wound too tight at the factory and excessive force wa used to place the wires in position. Shorts ma also be caused by excessive heat caused b overloads, which can degrade the insulation.
- *Shorted turns* – Loose or broken turns within winding, which contact each other in a manne that effectively causes the turns within th winding to be reduced, can cause high curren in the winding. This can cause excessive heat causing degradation of insulation.

## Three-Phase Motor Windings

The windings of motor A are good. Motor B has been run with one open phase, which caused overheating in the other two windings.

(A)

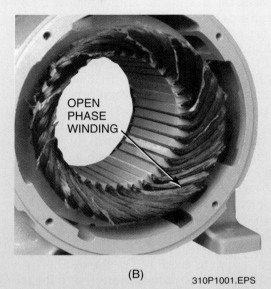

OPEN PHASE WINDING

(B)

310P1001.EPS

## What's wrong with this picture?

310P1002.EPS

## 4.1.0 Tools for Troubleshooting

This section describes some of the tools used in troubleshooting electric motors.

In addition to typical equipment such as voltmeters, ammeters, brush-spring tension testers, and sound amplifiers used for checking motor bearings, motor maintenance equipment should also include an insulation resistance tester such as a 500V megger, an oil dielectric tester, and a portable oil filtering unit.

Some of these tools have been covered in previous modules, and only those not covered will be presented in this subsection.

- *Transistorized stethoscope* – A transistorized stethoscope is equipped with a transistor-type amplifier and is used to determine the condition of motor bearings. A little practice in interpreting its usage may be required, but in general, it is relatively simple to use. When the stethoscope is applied to a motor bearing housing, a smooth purring sound should be heard if the bearing is operating normally. However, if a thumping, grinding, or growling sound is detected, it could be an indication of a failing bearing.
- *Insulation resistance tests* – High-voltage cables rated at 2,300V or above should be tested according to specified standards. Conductors and equipment carrying 480V should have their insulation tested at least annually. This includes transformers, motors, motor starters, generators, and switches.
- *Winding resistance and surge (resonance) tests* – A winding resistance or surge test provides baseline values for comparison to other phases to detect shorts or opens between the windings.

Before performing an insulation resistance test, first perform a safety check to ensure that the circuits and equipment to be tested are rated at or above the output voltage of the megger, and that all equipment scheduled for testing is disconnected and locked out according to procedure.

Also, check the megger and other testing equipment for proper operation. A megger may be checked for an infinity reading by cranking the megger handle with the test leads disconnected from the meter. The megger may also be zeroed by cranking the megger handle with the test leads connected to the meter and to each other. A reading of zero should be indicated, and if not, the zero adjustment should be adjusted until $0\Omega$ is indicated on the meter scale while cranking the handle with the test leads shorted together.

Once the megger has been checked and zeroed, insulation resistance readings should be taken by testing between a conductor and ground, or between two conductors, or both. Insulation readings from conductor to ground are obtained by connecting the line test lead to the conductor and the earth test lead to ground. For the test between conductors, the test leads are connected to the two conductors to be tested.

After the proper connections have been made to the test leads, the megger handle should be turned at a uniform rate for approximately one minute, at which time the insulation resistance value should be recorded. This is considered a short time or spot megger test.

Because temperature and humidity have profound effects on insulation resistance readings, the temperature and humidity at the apparatus should be recorded immediately after the test. In addition, pertinent information such as the condition of the environment and the running or idle time of the equipment should be noted.

After the readings have been recorded, they should be corrected for temperature using a temperature chart (supplied with most meggers). Typically, maintenance departments follow a standard referred to as the One Megohm Rule of Thumb, which states that an insulation resistance rated at 600V is acceptable if the corrected resistance value is one megohm or greater. Insulation resistance values that are within these tolerances, yet show a downward trend, usually indicate insulation deterioration and demand close monitoring.

*Table 5* provides a list of practical tools and equipment for effective electrical maintenance both for motors and other electrical apparatus.

Elaborate motor insulation tests such as time resistance and step voltage tests use various megger

**Table 5** Tools for Electrical Maintenance

| Tools or Equipment | Application |
|---|---|
| Multimeters, voltmeters, ohmmeters, clamp-on ammeters, wattmeters, clamp-on power factor meter | Measure circuit voltage, resistance, current, and power. Useful for circuit tracing and troubleshooting. |
| Potential and current transformers, meter shunts | Increase range of test instruments to permit the reading of high-voltage and high-current circuits. |
| Tachometer | Checks rotating machinery speeds. |
| Recording meters | Provide a permanent record of voltage, current, power, temperature, etc., on charts for analytic study. |
| Insulation resistance tester, thermometer, psychrometer | Test and monitor insulation resistance; use a thermometer and psychrometer for temperature and humidity correction. |
| Portable oil dielectric tester, portable oil filter | Test OCB, transformer oil, or other insulating oils. Recondition used oil. |
| Transistorized stethoscope | Detects faulty rotating machinery bearings and leaky valves. |
| Air gap feeler gauges | Check motor or generator air gap between rotor and stator. |
| Cleaning solvent | Removes grease or dirt from motor windings or other electrical parts. |
| Hand stones (rough, medium, fine), grinding rig, canvas strip | Used for grinding, smoothing, and finishing commutators or slip rings. |
| Spring tension scale | Checks brush pressure on DC motor commutators or on AC motor skip rings; tests electrical contact pressure on relays, starters, or contacts. |
| Surge comparison tester or bridge resistance tester | Checks detailed resistance of windings/coils. |

eading ratios and indexes (i.e., absorption ratio and polarization index) to determine the effects of temperature and humidity on insulation breakdown.

## 4.2.0 Grounded Coils

The usual effect of one grounded coil in a winding is the repeated blowing of a fuse or tripping of the circuit breaker when the line switch is closed, provided that the machine frame and the line are both grounded. Two or more grounds will give the same result and will also short out part of the winding in that phase in which the grounds occur. A quick and simple test to determine whether or not a ground exists in the winding can be made with a conventional continuity tester. Before testing with this instrument, first make certain that the line switch is open and locked out, causing the motor leads to be de-energized. Place one test lead on the frame of the motor and the other in turn on each of the line wires leading from the motor. If there is a grounded coil at any point in the winding, the lamp of the continuity tester will light, or in the case of a meter, the reading will show low or zero resistance.

To locate the phase that is grounded, test each phase separately. In a three-phase winding, it will be necessary to disconnect the star or delta connections, if accessible. After the grounded phase is located, the pole group connections in that phase can be disconnected and each group tested separately. When the test leads are connected (one on the frame and the other on the grounded coil group), a glowing lamp will indicate a ground in this group when using a lamp-indicating continuity tester, or near-zero ohms when using a meter. The stub connections between the coils and this group may then be disconnected and each coil tested separately until the exact coil that is grounded is located.

Sometimes moisture in old and deteriorating insulation around the coils will cause a high-resistance leakage to ground that is difficult to detect with a test lamp continuity tester. A megger can be used to detect such faults, but in many cases, a megger may not be available. If not, a homemade tester may be constructed using a headphone set (telephone receiver) and several dry cell batteries connected in series, as shown in *Figure 6*. This test set is capable of detecting grounds of relatively high resistance by producing an audible clicking sound through the receiver when one is detected, and often is more effective than an ordinary test lamp in locating grounds or leakage.

### The One Megohm Rule of Thumb

*INSIDE TRACK*

The minimal acceptable reading is one megohm per kilovolt rating (with a minimum of one megohm). This only works at 68°F. To correct for the ambient temperature, the reading must be adjusted up for temperatures above 68°F and down for temperatures below 68°F. The reasoning is that equipment insulation resistance decreases at higher temperatures and increases at lower temperatures. The readings are adjusted as follows:

- For every 17° above 68°F, double the megohm reading.
- For every 17° below 68°F, halve the megohm reading.

For example, a 2,300V, 600hp motor has a megohm reading of 2.3 megohms. The motor heaters are on to keep the motor dry, and the conductor/motor temperature (ambient) is 105°F. The minimum acceptable reading is 2.3 megohms at 68°F. The temperature-corrected reading is as follows:

$$105°F - 68°F = 37°F$$

$$37 \div 17 = 2 \text{ (rounded off)}$$

Therefore, the reading must be doubled twice, as follows:

$$2.3 \times 2 = 4.6$$

$$4.6 \times 2 = 9 \text{ (rounded off)}$$

The temperature-corrected reading is 9 megohms. It is acceptable because it is greater than the 2.3 megohm minimum requirement.

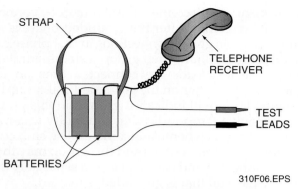

**Figure 6** ◆ When used for testing, a clicking sound indicates a fault.

Armature windings and the commutator of a motor may be tested for grounds in a similar manner. On some motors, the **brush holders** are grounded to the end plate. Consequently, before the armature is tested for grounds, the brushes must be lifted away from the commutator.

When a grounded coil is located, it should be either removed and reinsulated or cut out of the circuit. At times, however, it may be inconvenient to stop a motor long enough for a complete rewinding or permanent repairs. In such cases, when trouble develops, it is often necessary to make a temporary repair until a later time when the motor may be taken out of service.

To temporarily repair a defective coil, a jumper wire of the same size as that used in the coil is connected to the bottom lead of the coil immediately adjacent to the defective coil and run across to the top lead of the coil on the other side of the defective coil, leaving the defective coil entirely out of the circuit. The defective coil should then be cut at the back of the winding and the leads taped so that they cannot function when the motor is started again. If the defective coil is grounded, it should also be disconnected from the other coils.

## 4.3.0 Shorted Coils

Shorted turns within coils are usually the result of failure of the insulation on the wires. This is frequently caused by the wires being crossed and having excessive pressure applied on the crossed conductors when the coils are being inserted in the slot. Quite often it is caused by using too much force when driving the coils down in the slots. In the case of windings that have been in service for several years, failure of the insulation may be caused by oil or moisture, as well as other factors. If a shorted coil is left in a winding, it will usually burn out in a short time, and if it is not located and repaired promptly, it will probably cause a ground and the burning out of a number of other coils.

One inexpensive way of locating a shorted co[il] when the motor is in the shop is by the use of [a] growler and a thin piece of steel. *Figure 7* shows [a] growler being used on a stator. Note that the pole[s] are shaped to fit the curvature of the teeth insid[e] the stator core. The growler should be placed i[n] the core as shown, and the thin piece of ste[el] should be placed the distance of one coil spa[n] away from the center of the growler. Then, b[y] moving the growler around the bore of the stato[r] and always keeping the steel strip the same dis[-] tance away from it, all of the coils can be tested.

If any of the coils has one or more shorted turns[,] the piece of steel will vibrate very rapidly an[d] cause a loud humming noise. By locating the tw[o] slots over which the steel vibrates, both sides o[f] the shorted coil can be found. If more than tw[o] slots cause the steel to vibrate, they should all b[e] marked, and all shorted coils should be remove[d] and replaced with new ones or cut out of the cir[-] cuit, as previously described.

Sometimes one coil or a complete coil group be[-] comes short circuited at the end connections. Th[e] test for this fault is the same as that for a shorte[d] coil. If all the coils in one group are shorted, it wi[ll] generally be indicated by the vibration of the stee[l] strip over several consecutive slots, correspon[-] ding to the number of coils in the group.

The end connections should be carefully exam[-] ined, and those that appear to have poor insula[-] tion should be moved during the time that th[e] test is being made. It will often be found tha[t] when the shorted end connections are move[d] during the test, the vibration of the steel will sto[p.] If these ends are reinsulated, the trouble shoul[d] be eliminated.

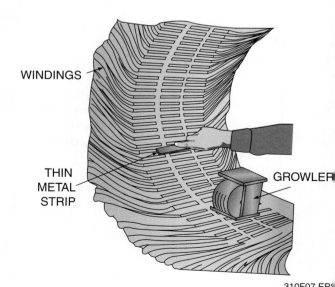

**Figure 7** ◆ Growler used to test a stator of an AC motor.

## 4.4.0 Open Coils

When one or more coils become open due to a break in the turns or a poor connection at the end, they can be tested with a continuity tester, as previously explained. If this test is made at the ends of each winding, an open can be detected by the lamp failing to light. The insulation should be removed from the pole group connections, and each group should be tested separately.

An open circuit in the **starting winding** may be difficult to locate, since the problem may be in the centrifugal switch or in the winding itself. (The starting winding is only in the circuit when the motor is starting.) In fact, the centrifugal switch is probably more apt to cause trouble than the winding since parts become worn, defective, and most likely dirty. Insufficient pressure of the rotating part of centrifugal switches against the stationary part will prevent the contacts from closing and thereby produce an open circuit.

If the trouble is a loose connection at the coil ends, it can be repaired by resoldering the splices, but if it is within the coil, the coil should either be replaced or a jumper should be connected around it until a better repair can be made.

## 4.5.0 Reversed Connections

Reversed coils cause the current to flow through them in the wrong direction. This fault usually manifests itself, as do most irregularities in winding connections, by a disturbance of the magnetic circuit, which results in excessive noise and vibration. The fault can be located by the use of a magnetic compass and some source of low-voltage direct current. This voltage should be adjusted so it will send about one-fourth to one-sixth of the full-load current through the winding, and the DC leads should be placed on the start and finish of one phase. If the winding is three-phase, star-connected, this would be at the start of one phase and the star point. If the winding is delta-connected, the delta must be disconnected and each phase tested separately.

Place a compass on the inside of the stator and test each of the coil groups in that phase. If the phase is connected correctly, the needle of the compass will reverse as it is moved from one coil group to another. However, if any one of the coils is reversed, the reversed coil will build up a field in the direction opposite to the others, thus causing a neutralizing effect, which will be indicated by the compass needle refusing to point definitely to that group. If there are only two coils per group, there will be no indication if one of them is reversed, as that group will be completely neutralized.

When an entire coil group is reversed, it causes the current to flow in the wrong direction in the whole group. The test for this fault is the same as that for reversed coils. The winding should be magnetized with direct current, and when the compass needle is passed around the coil groups, they should indicate alternately north/south, north/south, etc. If one of the groups is reversed, three consecutive groups will be of the same polarity. The remedy for either reversed coil groups or reversed coils is to make a visual check of the connections at that part of the winding, locate the wrong connection, and reconnect it properly.

When the wrong number of coils are connected in two or more groups, the trouble can be located by counting the number of ends on each group. If any mistakes are found, they should be remedied by reconnecting properly.

## 4.6.0 Reversed Phase

Sometimes in a three-phase winding, a complete phase is reversed, caused by either taking the starts from the wrong coils or by connecting one of the windings incorrectly in relation to the others when making a star or delta connection. If the winding is connected in a delta configuration, disconnect any one of the points where the phases are connected together and pass current through the three windings in series. Place a compass on the inside of the stator and test each coil group by slowly moving the compass one complete revolution around the stator.

The reversals of the needle in moving the compass one revolution around the stator should be three times the number of poles in the winding.

When testing a star-connected or wye-connected winding, connect the three starts together and place them on one DC lead. Then connect the other DC lead to the star point, causing the current to pass through all three windings in parallel. Test with a compass as explained for the delta winding. The result should then be the same, or the reversals of the needle in making one revolution around the stator should again be three times the number of poles in the winding.

These tests for reversed phases apply to full-pitch windings only. If the winding is fractional pitch, a careful visual check should be made to determine whether there is a reversed phase or mistake in connecting the star or delta connections.

*Table 6* is a troubleshooting chart for AC motors that may be used by qualified personnel who have access to the proper tools and test equipment. This table does not cover all details and variations associated with troubleshooting motors, nor does it provide a solution for every possible condition that may be encountered. Always refer to the manufacturer's instructions before testing any motor.

**Table 6** General Troubleshooting Chart for AC Motors

| Malfunction | Probable Cause | Corrective Action |
|---|---|---|
| Slow to accelerate | Excess loading | Reduce load |
| | Poor circuit | Check for high resistance |
| | Defective squirrel-cage rotor | Replace |
| | Applied voltage too low | Get power company to increase voltage tap |
| Wrong rotation | Wrong sequence of phases | Reverse connections at motor or at switchboard |
| Motor overheats | Overloaded motor | Reduce load |
| | Clogged blowers or air shields | Clean to restore proper ventilation of motor |
| | Motor may have one phase open | Check to make sure that all leads are well connected |
| | Grounded coil | Locate and repair |
| | Unbalanced terminal voltage | Check to make sure that all leads are well connected |
| | Unbalanced terminal voltage | Check for faulty leads |
| | Shorted stator coil | Repair and then check wattmeter reading |
| | Faulty connection | Indicated by high resistance; locate and repair |
| | High voltage | Check terminals of motor with voltmeter |
| | Low voltage | Same as above |
| Motor stalls | Wrong application | Change type or size (consult manufacturer) |
| | Overloaded motor | Reduce load |
| | Low motor voltage | See that nameplate voltage is maintained |
| | Open circuit | Fuses blown |
| | Incorrect control resistance of wound rotor | Check control sequence; replace broken resistors; repair open circuits |
| Motor does not start | One phase open | See that no phase is open; reduce load |
| | Defective rotor | Look for broken bars or rings; repair or replace |
| | Poor stator coil connection | Remove end bells |
| Motor runs, then quits | Power failure | Check for loose connections to line, fuses, and control |
| Slow running speed | Not applied properly | Consult supplier for proper type |
| | Voltage too low at motor terminals because of line drop | Use higher voltage on transformer terminals or reduce load |
| | If wound rotor, improper control operation of secondary | Correct secondary control |
| | Starting load too high | Check load that the motor is supposed to carry upon starting |
| | Low pull-in torque of synchronous motor | Change rotor starting resistance or change rotor design |
| | Brushes riding on rings | Check secondary connections; leave no leads poorly connected |
| | Broken rotor bars | Look for cracks near the rings; a new rotor may be required |
| Motor vibrates | Motor misaligned | Realign |
| | Weak foundation | Strengthen base |
| | Coupling out of balance | Balance coupling |
| | Driven equipment unbalanced | Rebalance driven equipment |
| | Defective ball bearing | Replace bearing |
| | Bearing not in line | Line up properly |
| | Balancing weights shifted | Rebalance rotor |
| | Wound rotor coils replaced | Rebalance rotor |
| | Polyphase motor running single phase | Check for open circuit |
| | Excessive end play | Adjust bearing or add washer |
| Unbalanced line current | Unequal terminal volts | Check leads and connections |
| | Single-phase operation | Check for open circuit |
| | Poor rotor contacts in wound rotor control | Check control devices |
| | Brushes not in proper position in wound rotor | See that brushes are properly seated and shunts are in good condition |
| | Fan rubbing air shield | Remove interference |
| | Fan striking insulation | Clear fan |
| | Loose on bedplate | Tighten holding bolts |
| Magnetic noise | Air gap not uniform | Check and correct bracket fits or bearing |

## Verifying Rotation

Which end of the motor should be observed when verifying rotation?

---

## .0.0 ◆ TROUBLESHOOTING SPLIT-PHASE MOTORS

a split-phase motor fails to start, the trouble may e due to one or more of the following faults:

- Tight or frozen bearings
- Worn bearings, allowing the rotor to drag on the stator
- Bent rotor shaft
- One or both bearings out of alignment
- Open circuit in either the starting or running windings
- Defective centrifugal switch
- Improper connections in either winding
- Grounds in either winding or both
- Shorts between the two windings
- Shorted or open starting capacitor

Tight or worn bearings may be caused by a failng bearing lubricating system. In the case of new earings, they sometimes fail if the motor shaft is ot kept properly lubricated.

The rotor may not start if the bearings are worn such an extent that they allow the rotor to drag n the stator. When this condition exists, it can enerally be detected by noticeable bright spots n the inside of the stator laminations where they ave been rubbed by the dragging rotor.

A bent rotor shaft will usually cause the rotor to ind in a certain position and then run freely unl it returns to that position. An accurate test for a ent shaft can be made by placing the rotor beween centers on a lathe and turning the rotor lowly while a tool or marker is held in the tool ost close to the surface of the rotor. If the rotor vobbles, it is an indication of a bent shaft.

Bearings getting out of alignment can be caused y uneven tightening of the end shield plates. Vhen placing end shields or brackets on a motor, e bolts should be tightened alternately, first rawing up two bolts that are directly opposite ne another. These two should be drawn up only a few turns and then the others tightened an equal amount all the way around. When the end shields are drawn up as far as possible with the bolts, they should be tapped tightly against the frame with a mallet and the bolts tightened again. Many motor manufacturers specify a bolt-tightening sequence to be applied when reassembling a motor.

Open circuits in either the starting or running winding will prevent the motor from starting. This fault can be detected by testing the windings using a test lamp or an ohmmeter.

A defective centrifugal switch may cause symptoms that are difficult to identify unless previously encountered while diagnosing motor failures caused by centrifugal switches. If the switch fails to close when the rotor stops, the motor will not start when the line switch is closed. Failure of the centrifugal switch to close can be caused by dirt, grit, or some other foreign matter getting into the switch, as well as a defective or broken switch. The switch should be thoroughly cleaned with a degreasing solution such as AWA 1,1,1 and then inspected for weak or broken springs.

If the winding is on the rotor, the brushes sometimes stick in the holders and fail to make good contact with the **slip rings.** This causes sparking at the brushes. Likewise, there may be a certain spot where the rotor will not start until it is moved far enough for the brush to make contact on the ring. The brush holders should be cleaned and the brushes carefully fitted so they move more freely with a minimum of friction between the brush and the holders. If a centrifugal switch fails to open when the motor is started, the motor may growl and continue to run slowly, causing the starting winding to heat up and possibly burn out if it is not promptly disconnected from the line. In most cases, however, the heaters in the motor control will take care of this before any serious damage occurs.

Reversed connections are typically caused by incorrectly connecting a coil or a group of coils.

Reversed connections can be identified by applying a DC voltage with a compass to indicate direction of flow, as previously described for three-phase motors. The starting and running windings should be tested separately, exciting only one winding at a time with the DC voltage. The compass should indicate alternate poles around the winding.

The symptoms demonstrated by a motor that has a grounded winding depend on the location of the ground. If the frame is grounded, a grounded winding will typically blow a line fuse or trip the overcurrent protective device.

Identifying grounded windings can be accomplished using either a test lamp or an ohmmeter. One test lead should be placed on the motor frame, while the other test lead is touched to each of the motor leads. If a grounded winding is present, the test lamp will glow, or the meter will indicate a ground by reading approximately zero ohms.

Short circuits between the starting winding and the running windings can be detected by using a test lamp or continuity tester, as with testing for grounds. One of the test leads should be placed on the wire of the starting winding and the other test lead should be placed on the wire of one of the running windings. If these windings are properly insulated from each other, the lamp will not light or the meter will not indicate continuity. However, if the lamp does light or continuity is indicated, a short probably exists between the two windings. A short between the windings will usually cause part of the starting winding to burn out. The starting winding is normally wound over the running winding, and can be replaced without disturbing the running winding.

## 6.0.0 ◆ STORING MOTORS

Reasons for storing motors include:

- The project on which they are to be used is not complete.
- Spare motors are often kept as backups on most industrial installations.

The first consideration when storing motors for any length of time is the location in which they are to be stored. A dry location (one that does not undergo severe changes in temperature over a 24-hour period) should be selected whenever possible. When ambient temperature changes frequently, condensation is likely to form on the stored motor or motors. Moisture in motor insulation can cause motors to fail upon startup; therefore, guarding against moisture is vital when storing motors of any type.

A means for transporting the motor from the place of storage to the place where it will be used or else shifted around in the storage area, is also important. Motors should not be lifted by their rotating shafts. Doing so can damage the alignment of the rotor in relationship to the stator. Even picking up the smaller fractional horsepower motor by the shaft is not recommended. Many workers have received bad cuts from the sharp keyway on motor shafts when picked up with bare hands.

 **WARNING!**
Never handle a motor by its shaft without proper hand protection. Motor shaft keyways have sharp edges that can cause severe cuts.

When an electric motor is received on a job site, always follow the manufacturer's recommendations for unloading, uncrating, and installing the motor. Failure to follow these recommendations can cause injury to personnel and possible damage to the motor.

Once the motor has been uncrated, check for damage that might have occurred during shipment. Check the motor shaft to verify that it turns freely. This is also an appropriate time to clean the motor of any debris, dust, moisture, or any foreign matter that might have accumulated during shipment.

 **NOTE**
Motors in storage should have their shafts turned by hand at least once a month to redistribute the grease in the bearings.

Clean the motor of any debris, dust, moisture, or any foreign matter before putting it into service.

 **WARNING!**
Never start a wet or damp motor.

Eyebolts on motors are intended for lifting the motor and any factory motor-mounted accessory. These lifting devices should never be used when lifting or handling the motor when the motor is attached to other equipment.

### Oil Reservoirs

Empty the motor oil reservoirs to prevent oil from being spilled into the windings during shipping or when moving a motor from storage to the point of use.

### Stored Motor Maintenance

To prevent shaft bowing, large horizontal motors in storage should have their rotors rotated 180° at least once a month.

### Motor Storage

Motors should be stored in a humidity-controlled environment. Moisture is a major cause of insulation deterioration in motor windings.

---

The eyebolt lifting capacity is based on a lifting alignment that corresponds to the eyebolt centerline. The eyebolt capacity lessens as deviation from this alignment increases.

The following is a list of procedures that should be followed when storing motors for any length of time:

Make sure motors are kept clean.

Make sure motors are kept dry.

Supply supplemental heating in the storage area, if necessary.

Motors should be stored in an orderly fashion (i.e., grouped by horsepower, etc.).

Motor shafts should be rotated periodically.

Lubrication should be checked periodically.

Protect shafts and keyways during storage and also while transporting motors from one location to another.

Test motor winding resistance upon receiving; test again after placing in storage.

## .0.0 ◆ IDENTIFYING MOTORS

Electricians will sometimes encounter motors with no identification (nameplate or motor lead tags) that must be put back into service or repaired. There are methods that may be applied to help identify the motor leads on motors without tags.

The NEMA standard method of motor identification can be applied to motors without tags by drawing the coils to form a wye connection. First identify one outside coil end with the number 1, then draw a decreasing spiral, numbering each coil end in sequence, as shown in *Figure 8*.

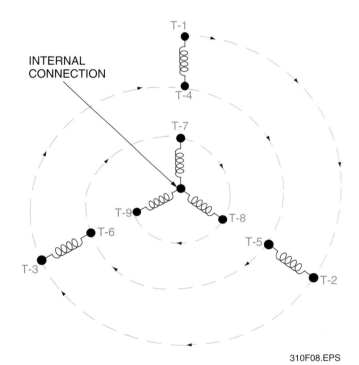

310F08.EPS

*Figure 8* ◆ Identify one outside coil and then draw a decreasing spiral and number each coil.

By using an ohmmeter or other continuity tester, the individual circuits can be located as follows:

*Step 1*   Connect one probe of the tester to any lead, and check for continuity to each of the other eight leads. A reading from only one other lead indicates one of the two-wire circuits. A reading to two other leads indicates the three-wire circuit that makes up the internal wye connection.

***Step 2*** Continue checking and isolating leads until all four circuits have been located. Tag the wires of the three lead circuits T-7, T-8, and T-9 in any order. The other leads should be temporarily marked T-1 and T-4 for the circuit, T-2 and T-5 for the second circuit, and T-3 and T-6 for the third and final circuit.

**NOTE**

The following test voltages are for the most common dual voltage range of 230/460V. For other motor ranges, the voltages listed should be changed in proportion to the motor rating.

As all the coils are physically mounted in slots on the same motor frame, the coils will act almost like the primary and secondary coils of a transformer. *Figure 9* shows a simplified electrical arrangement of the coils. Depending on which coil group power is applied to, the resulting voltage readings will be additive, subtractive, balanced, or unbalanced, depending on their physical location with regard to the coils themselves.

***Step 3*** The motor may be started on 230V by connecting leads T-7, T-8, and T-9 to the three-phase source. If the motor is too large to be connected directly to the line, the voltage should be reduced by using a reduced voltage starter or other suitable means.

***Step 4*** Start the motor with no load connected and bring it up to normal speed.

***Step 5*** With the motor running, a voltage will be induced in each of the open two-wire circuits that were tagged T-1 and T-4, T-2 and

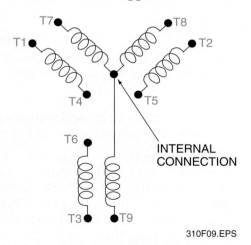

310F09.EPS

***Figure 9*** ◆ Simplified electrical arrangement of wye-wound motor coils.

T-5, and T-3 and T-6. With a voltmeter check the voltage reading of each circuit. The voltage should be approximately 125V to 130V and should be the same on each circuit.

**NOTE**

The voltages referred to in this section are for reference only and will vary greatly from motor to motor, depending on size, design, and manufacturer. If the test calls for equal voltages of 125V to 130V and the reading is only 80V to 90V, that is acceptable as long as the voltage readings are nearly equal.

***Step 6*** With the motor still running, carefully connect the lead that was temporarily marked T-4 with the T-7 and line lead. Read the voltage between T-1 and T-8 and also between T-1 and T-9. If both readings are of the same value and are approximately 330V to 340V, leads T-1 and T-4 may be disconnected and permanently marked T-1 and T-4.

***Step 7*** If the two voltage readings are of the same value and are approximately 125V to 130V, disconnect and interchange leads T-1 and T-4 and mark them permanently (original T-1 changed to T-4 and original T-4 changed to T-1).

***Step 8*** If the readings between T-1 and T-8 and also between T-1 and T-9 are of unequal values, disconnect T-4 from T-7 and reconnect T-4 to the junction of T-8 and the line.

***Step 9*** Measure the voltage between T-1 and T-7 and also between T-1 and T-9. If the voltages are equal and approximately 330V to 340V, tag T-1 is permanently marked T-2 and T-4 is marked T-5 and disconnected. If the readings taken are equal but are approximately 125V to 130V, leads T-1 and T-4 are disconnected, interchanged, and marked T-2 and T-5 (T-1 changed to T-5, and T-4 changed to T-2). If both voltage readings are different, the T-4 lead is disconnected from T-7 and moved to T-9. Voltage readings are taken again (between T-1 and T-7, and T-1 and T-8) and the leads permanently marked T-3 and T-6 when equal readings of approximately 330V to 340V are obtained.

**Step 10** The same procedure is followed for the other two circuits that were temporarily marked T-2 and T-5, and T-3 and T-6 until a position is found where both voltage readings are equal and approximately 330V to 340V and the tags change to correspond to the standard lead markings, as shown in *Figure 10*.

**Step 11** Once all leads have been properly and permanently tagged, leads T-4, T-5, and T-6 are connected together and voltage readings are taken between T-1, T-2, and T-3. The voltages should be equal and approximately 230V.

**Step 12** As an additional check, the motor is shut down and leads T-7, T-8, and T-9 are disconnected, and leads T-1, T-2, and T-3 are connected to the line. Connect T-1 to the line lead T-7 was connected to, T-2 to the same line that T-8 was connected to, and T-3 to the same lead to which T-9 was connected. With T-4, T-5, and T-6 still connected together to form a wye connection, the motor can again be started without a load. If all lead markings are correct, the motor rotation with leads T-1, T-2, and T-3 connected will be the same as when T-7, T-8, and T-9 were connected.

The motor is now ready for service and is connected in series for high voltage or parallel for low, as indicated by the NEMA connections shown in *Figure 10*.

> **NOTE**
> This procedure may not work on some wye-wound motors with concentric coils.

## 7.1.0 Three-Phase, Delta-Wound Motors

Most dual-voltage, delta-wound motors have nine leads, as illustrated in *Figure 11*, with three circuits of three leads each.

Continuity tests are used to find the three coil groups as was done for the wye-wound motor. Once the coil groups are located and isolated, further resistance checks must be made to locate the common wire in each coil group. As the resistance of some delta wound motors is very low, a digital ohmmeter, Wheatstone bridge, or other sensitive device may be needed.

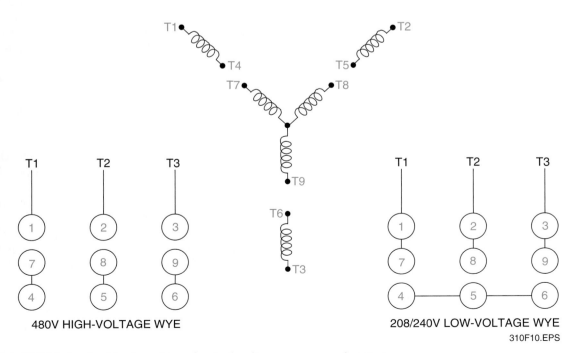

480V HIGH-VOLTAGE WYE

208/240V LOW-VOLTAGE WYE

310F10.EPS

*Figure 10* ◆ NEMA standard lead markings for dual-voltage, wye-wound motors.

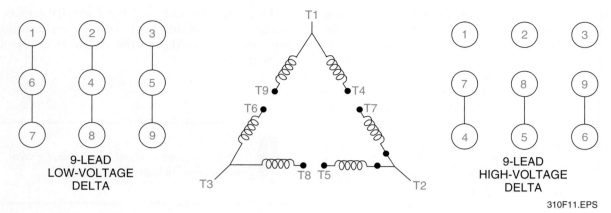

*Figure 11* ◆ NEMA standard lead markings for dual-voltage, delta-wound motors.

Each coil group consists of two coils tied together with three leads brought out to the motor junction or terminal box. Reading the resistances carefully between each of the three leads shows that the readings from one of the leads to each of the other two leads will be the same (equal), but the resistance reading between those two leads will be double the previous readings. *Figure 12* may help to clarify this technique.

The common lead found in the first coil group is permanently marked T-1, and the other two leads are temporarily marked T-4 and T-9. The common lead of the next coil group is found and permanently marked T-2, and the other leads are temporarily marked T-5 and T-7. The common lead of the last coil group is located and marked T-3, with the other leads temporarily marked T-6 and T-8.

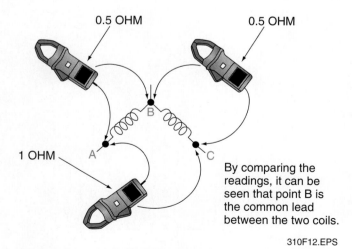

By comparing the readings, it can be seen that point B is the common lead between the two coils.

310F12.EPS

*Figure 12* ◆ Using an ohmmeter to test motor leads.

After the leads have been marked, the motor may be connected to a 230V, three-phase line using leads T-1, T-4, and T-9. Lead T-7 is connected to the line and T-4, and the motor is started with no load connected. Voltage readings are taken between T-1 and T-2. If the voltage is approximately 460V, the markings are correct and may be permanently marked.

If the voltage reading is 400V or less, interchange T-5 and T-7 or interchange T-4 and T-9 and read the voltage again. If the voltage is approximately 230V, interchange both T-5 with T-7 and T-4 with T-9. The readings should now be approximately 460V between leads T-1 and T-2. The leads connected together now are actually T-4 and T-7 and are marked permanently. The remaining lead in each group can now be marked T-9 and T-5.

Connect one of the leads of the last coil group (not T-3) to T-9. If the reading is approximately 460V between T-1 and T-3, the lead may be permanently marked T-6. If the reading is 400V or less, interchange T-6 and T-8. A reading of 460V should exist between T-1 and T-3. T-6 is changed to T-8 and marked permanently and temporary T-8 is changed to T-6.

If all leads are now correctly marked, equal readings of approximately 460V can be obtained between leads T-1, T-2, and T-3.

To double-check the markings, the motor is shut off and reconnected using T-2, T-5, and T-7. T-2 is connected to the same line lead as T-1, lead T-5 is connected where T-4 was, and T-7 is hooked where T-9 was previously connected. When started, the motor should rotate in the same direction as before.

Stop the motor and connect leads T-3, T-6, and T-8 to the line leads previously connected to T-2

-5, and T-7, respectively, and when the motor is started, it should still rotate in the same direction.

The motor is now ready for service and is connected in series for high or parallel for low voltage, as indicated by the NEMA standard connections.

## .2.0 Recordkeeping

One of the first steps in establishing a reliable maintenance program is preparing accurate records. As a minimum, records on each motor should include:

- A complete description, including age and nameplate data
- Location and application, keeping such notations up-to-date if motors are transferred to different areas or used for different purposes
- Notations of scheduled preventive maintenance and previous repair work performed
- Location of duplicate or interchangeable motors
- An estimate of the motor's importance in the production process to which it relates

1. Which of the following provides minimum resistance and aligns the motor rotor while turning?
   a. Compensator
   b. Brushes
   c. End bells
   d. Bearings

2. Which of the following is true concerning lubricating motor bearings?
   a. Always add a little more grease than is needed.
   b. Too much grease can be as harmful as insufficient grease.
   c. No grease is better than too much grease.
   d. Too much grease is better than insufficient grease.

3. Which of the following may be eliminated as a concern in good motor maintenance?
   a. Number of hours and days the motor operates
   b. Manufacturer of the motor
   c. Environmental conditions
   d. Importance of the motor in the production scheme

4. Which of the following is usually an indication of a bad motor bearing?
   a. Hot bearing housing
   b. Low current draw
   c. Low pull-in torque
   d. Sparking at the brushes

5. When using compressed air to clean motors, which of the following precautions should be taken?
   a. Make sure the air is warmer than the ambient motor temperature.
   b. Use air pressure within safety standards.
   c. Avoid using a pulse nozzle.
   d. Use only a high-velocity nozzle.

6. Which of the following parts of a wound rotor motor requires special attention to proper cleaning?
   a. Lifting eyebolt
   b. End bells
   c. Collector rings
   d. Motor terminal enclosure

7. The _____ is/are used only during the brief period when the motor is starting.
   a. motor leads
   b. drum armature
   c. starting winding
   d. shunt-field winding

8. If a split-phase motor fails to start, which of the following may be eliminated as the cause?
   a. Tight or frozen bearings
   b. Bent rotor shaft
   c. Defective centrifugal switch
   d. Improper air gap

9. Which of the following statements is true concerning motors in storage?
   a. Rotors should not be moved or turned until the motor is put in use.
   b. Rotors should be turned once a month to distribute bearing grease.
   c. Rotors should be turned once a year to distribute bearing grease.
   d. Rotors should be turned once every three years to keep them from rusting.

10. The best attachment point for lifting heavy motors is/are the _____.
   a. eyebolt
   b. shaft
   c. base
   d. end bells

## Summary

his module covered various motor maintenance ·chniques, including lubrication, storage, and elnentary troubleshooting.

In determining which motors are likely to fail rst, it is important to remember that motor failures are generally caused by loading, age, vibration, contamination, or commutation problems.

Advanced motor maintenance techniques will be presented in your Level Four training.

## Notes

# Trade Terms
# Introduced in This Module

*Armature:* (1) Rotating machine: the member in which alternating voltage is generated. (2) Electromagnetic: the member that is moved by magnetic force.

*Brush:* A conductor between the stationary and rotating parts of a machine; usually made of carbon.

*Brush holders:* Adjustable arms for holding the commutator brushes of a generator against the commutator, feeding them forward to maintain proper contact as they wear, and permitting them to be lifted from the contact when necessary.

*Commutator:* A device used on electric motors or generators to maintain a unidirectional current.

*Commutator pole:* An electromagnetic bar inserted between the pole pieces of a generator to offset the cross-magnetization of the armature currents.

*Generator:* (1) A rotating machine that is used to convert mechanical energy to electrical energy. (2) General apparatus, equipment, etc. that is used to convert or change energy from one form to another.

*Slip rings:* The means by which the current is conducted to a revolving electrical circuit.

*Starting winding:* A winding in an electric motor used only during the brief period when the motor is starting.

# Additional Resources

This module is intended to present thorough resources for task training. The following reference works are suggested for further study. These are optional materials for continued education rather than for task training.

*American Electrician's Handbook.* Terrell Croft and Wilfred I. Summers. New York, NY: McGraw-Hill, 1996.

*National Electrical Code® Handbook,* Latest Edition. Quincy, MA: National Fire Protection Association.

The NCCER makes every effort to keep these textbooks up-to-date and free of technical errors. We appreciate your help in this process. If you have an idea for improving this textbook, or if you find an error, a typographical mistake, or an inaccuracy in NCCER's *Contren®* textbooks, please write us, using this form or a photocopy. Be sure to include the exact module number, page number, a detailed description, and the correction, if applicable. Your input will be brought to the attention of the Technical Review Committee. Thank you for your assistance.

*Instructors* – If you found that additional materials were necessary in order to teach this module effectively, please let us know so that we may include them in the Equipment/Materials list in the Annotated Instructor's Guide.

**Write:**  Product Development
National Center for Construction Education and Research
P.O. Box 141104, Gainesville, FL 32614-1104

**Fax:**  352-334-0932

**E-mail:**  curriculum@nccer.org

Craft _____   Module Name _____

Copyright Date _____   Module Number _____   Page Number(s) _____

Description _____

_____

_____

_____

(Optional) Correction _____

_____

_____

(Optional) Your Name and Address _____

_____

_____

# Motor Maintenance, Part Two
## 26410-05

**St. Vincent's North Tower**
Birmingham, Alabama
Health Care $25–99 Million Award Winner
Brasfield & Gorrie, LLC

# 26410-05
# *Motor Maintenance, Part Two*

*Topics to be presented in this module include:*

## Overview

In large industrial locations, it is common to replace minimal horsepower motors instead of repairing them when it is known that the motor is at fault. The minimal horsepower cutoff point at which motors are repaired instead of replaced is usually determined by the budget or standard practice of a plant maintenance department. When it is feasible to repair instead of replace electric motors, motors are usually sent out to motor repair shops that specialize in this type of work. However, someone must first make the determination whether the motor should go out for repair or not.

Even though plant electricians are not expected to know how to rewind or repair internal problems with a motor, they must know how to troubleshoot and diagnose motor problems in order to determine how to resolve the problem. Many motors may indicate a potential problem when the internal motor windings become wet or damp. Corrective drying procedures can be applied to dry the motor to a point of proper operation without sending the motor out for contract repair. Visual inspection of the motor windings will often provide conclusive evidence in the form of burned or discolored windings to indicate a motor winding problem that requires rewinding.

## Objectives

When you have completed this module, you will be able to do the following:

1. Test motor winding resistance.
2. Select and use motor testing equipment.
3. Clean and test open frame motors.
4. Clean, dry, and test motors that have been subjected to water damage.
5. Troubleshoot and repair electric motors.

## Trade Terms

Breakdown
Dielectric
Insulation class

Leakage
Megohmmeter
Totally enclosed motor

## Required Trainee Materials

1. Pencil and paper
2. Appropriate personal protective equipment
3. Copy of the latest edition of the *National Electrical Code*®

## Prerequisites

Before you begin this module, it is recommended that you successfully complete *Core Curriculum; Electrical Level One; Electrical Level Two; Electrical Level Three; Electrical Level Four*, Modules 26401-05 through 26409-05.

This course map shows all of the modules in *Electrical Level Four*. The suggested training order begins at the bottom and proceeds up. Skill levels increase as you advance on the course map. The Local Training Program Sponsor may adjust the training order.

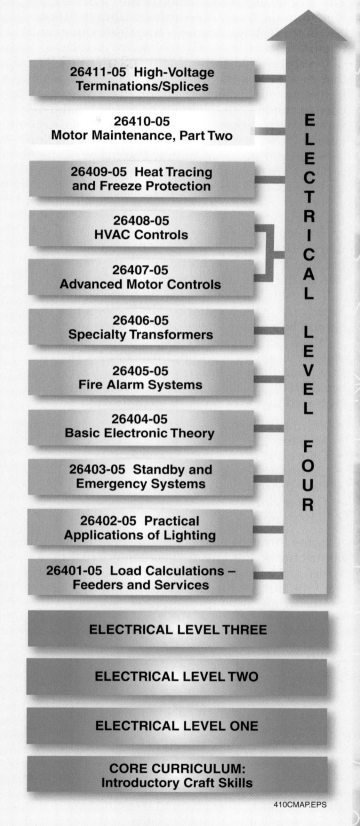

410CMAP.EPS

# 1.0.0 ◆ INTRODUCTION

This module is a continuation of the *Electrical Level Three* module *Motor Maintenance, Part One*. It covers motor testing, cleaning, troubleshooting, and repair.

Induction motors get their name from the fact that they utilize the principle of electromagnetic induction. An induction motor has a stationary part, or stator, with windings connected to the AC supply, and a rotating part, or rotor, which contains coils or bars. There is no electrical connection between the stator and rotor. The magnetic field produced in the stator windings induces a voltage in the rotor coils or bars.

Since the stator windings act in the same way as the primary winding of a transformer, the stator of an induction motor is sometimes called the primary. Similarly, the rotor is called the secondary because it carries the induced voltage in the same way as the secondary of a transformer.

The useful life of an induction motor depends largely upon the condition of its insulation, which should be suitable for the operating requirements.

When an induction motor malfunctions, the stator (stationary) windings will usually be defective, and these windings will then have to be repaired or replaced. Stator problems can usually be traced to one or more of the following causes:

- Worn bearings
- Moisture
- Overloading
- Operating single phase
- Poor insulation
- Dust and dirt
- Vibration

Some forms of dust are highly conductive and contribute materially to insulation breakdown, which is the failure of insulation to effectively prevent the flow of current. The effect of dust on the motor temperature through restriction of ventilation is another reason for keeping the machine clean, either by periodically blowing it out with compressed air or by dismantling and cleaning it. The compressed air must be dry and throttled down to a low pressure that will not endanger the insulation.

One of the worst enemies of motor insulation is moisture. Therefore, motor insulation must be kept reasonably dry, although many applications make this practically impossible unless a totally enclosed motor is used. If a motor must be operated in a damp location, special moisture-resisting treatment should be given to the windings.

The life of a winding depends upon keeping it in its original condition as long as possible. In a new machine, the winding is snug in the slots, and the insulation is fresh and flexible. This condition is best maintained by periodic cleaning, followed by varnish and oven treatments, described later in this module.

One condition that frequently contributes to winding failure is movement of the coils due to vibration during operation. After insulation dries out, it loses its flexibility. The mechanical stresses caused by starting, plugging, and operating under load may cause short circuits in the coil and possibly failures from the coil to ground, usually at the point where the coil leaves the slot. Periodic maintenance is required to fill all air space caused by drying and shrinkage of the insulation. This helps to maintain a solid winding and also provides an effective seal against moisture.

## 1.1.0 Rotor Windings

The rotors of wound-rotor motors have many characteristics in common with the stators; therefore, the same guidelines apply to the care of rotor windings as to the care of stator windings. However, the rotor introduces some additional problems because it is a rotating element.

Most wound rotors have a three-phase winding and are, therefore, susceptible to trouble from single-phase operation. The first symptom of an open rotor circuit is lack of torque, with failure to start the load or a decrease in speed accompanied by a growling noise. The first place to look for an open secondary circuit is in the resistance bank of the control circuit external to the rotor. Short circuiting the rotor circuit at the slip rings and then operating the motor will usually determine whether the trouble is in the control circuit or the rotor itself. It may also be one of the stud connections to the slip rings.

If the rotor is wave wound with the winding made up of copper strap coils with clips connecting the top and bottom half of the coil, inspect these end connections for possible signs of heating, which would be an indication of a partially open circuit. Faulty or improperly made end connections are a common source of open circuits in rotor windings.

A ground in a rotor circuit does not affect the performance of the motor unless another ground also develops, which could cause the equivalent of a short circuit, in which case it has the effect of unbalancing the rotor electrically. In addition to reduced torque, another symptom of this condition might be excessive vibration of the motor. There might also be sparking and uneven wear on the collector rings.

Another method of checking for short circuiting in the rotor windings is to raise the brushes off the slip rings and energize the stator. If the rotor winding is free from short circuits, it should have little or no tendency to rotate, even when disconnected from the load. If it does show considerable torque or tendency to come up to speed, the rotor should be removed and the winding opened and examined for faults. In completing this test, note that some rotors having a wide tooth design may show a tendency to rotate even though the windings are in good condition.

Another test that can be conducted with the rotor in place, the stator energized, and the brushes raised is to check the voltage across the rings to see if they are balanced. Use judgment in completing this check to make sure that any inequality in voltage measurements is not due to the relative positions of the rotor and stator phases. In other words, move the rotor to several positions when taking these voltage measurements.

## 2.0 Squirrel Cage Rotors

Squirrel cage rotors are more rugged and usually require less maintenance than wound rotors, but may also cause trouble due to open circuits or high resistance points in the rotor circuit. The symptoms of such conditions are generally the same as with wound-rotor motors; that is, slowing down under load and reduced starting torque. Such conditions can usually be detected by looking for evidence of heating at the end ring connections, which is particularly noticeable when shutting down after operating under load.

In brazed rotors, any fractures in the rotor bars will usually be found either at the point of connection to the end ring or at the point where the bar leaves the laminations. Discolored rotor bars are also evidence of excessive heating.

With die cast rotors, look for cracks or other imperfections that may have developed in the end rings. A faulty die cast rotor can rarely be effectively repaired and should be replaced.

## 3.0 Air Gap

A small air gap is characteristic of the induction motor. The size of this gap has an important bearing on the power factor of the motor. Grinding the rotor laminations or filing the stator teeth results in increased magnetizing current, with a resultant lower power factor.

Good maintenance procedures call for periodically checking the air gap with a feeler gauge to guard against a worn sleeve bearing that might permit the rotor to rub the laminations. These measurements should be made on the shaft end of the motor.

On large machines, it is desirable to keep a record of these checks. Four measurements should be taken approximately 90° apart, with one of these points being the load side (that is, the point on the rotor periphery that corresponds to the load side of the bearing).

A comparison of the new measurements to those previously recorded permits the early detection of bearing wear. A very slight rub generates enough heat to destroy the coil insulation.

## 1.4.0 Eddy Currents

The rotating magnetic field of any motor, in addition to inducing voltages in the rotor bars, induces voltages in the stator and rotor cores. The voltages in these cores cause currents to flow. These currents, called eddy currents, serve no useful purpose and only result in wasted power. To keep these currents to a minimum, the stator and rotor cores are made of thin steel plates called laminations. These laminations are coated with an organic (varnish) or inorganic (phosphate or oxide) coating and then connected to form the core. The organic or inorganic lamination coating is called interlaminar insulation or coreplate. This type of core substantially reduces eddy current losses, but it does not entirely eliminate them. Shorts between laminations in the stator or rotor due to arcing, wear, or damage inflicted during winding replacement will increase core losses.

## 1.5.0 Effects of Overloading and Single-Phase Operation

Many times a motor that was originally of adequate capacity for a given load is later found to be overloaded or otherwise unsuited for the task. The following are some reasons for this problem:

- More severe duty imposed on the machine tool, such as a different die job in a punch press
- Heavier material or material of different machining characteristics
- Changed machine operations

Connecting measuring instruments in the motor circuit quickly discloses the reason for motor overheating, failure to start the load, or other abnormal symptoms. It is frequently desirable to connect recording instruments in the motor circuit for other purposes, such as analyzing the output of the machine, as a check on the operator, or to gauge processing operations. With enclosed wiring, this is usually rather difficult.

## Core Losses

Core losses occur in motors with damaged stator or rotor cores. These losses result in higher operating temperatures and increased power consumption. An increase in motor operating temperature of as little as 10°C can reduce the life of the winding insulation by half. Core loss tests are used to identify damaged stator, rotor, or armature cores and are performed before and after winding replacement.

Damage to a core can occur when windings are stripped. Windings are normally heated (pyrolyzed) to break down the winding insulation and chemical bonds binding the coils together. The temperature must be rigidly controlled so that it is hot enough to break down the winding materials but not so hot that it damages the coreplate. If the temperature is not hot enough, the winding will be difficult to remove and the core slots will be hard to clean, which can lead to lamination damage. If the temperature is too hot, it can cause shorts in the core laminations. Either situation will result in additional core losses and reduced efficiency of the rewound motor.

Both automatic and manual core test sets are available. A typical automatic core test set is shown here.

410P1001.EPS

However, standard sockets for electrical instruments provide a ready means of plugging either recording or indicating instruments into a circuit without necessitating the usual shutdown. Installation of the standard socket in a motor circuit provides a ready means of obtaining either continuous or periodic checks by plugging in any one of a complete line of plug-type meters or instruments.

Control circuits for many of the older induction motor installations were not provided with relay protection, and single-phase operation of polyphase induction motors on such circuits has frequently been responsible for motor burnout. Usually, this has resulted from the blowing of one of the fuses while the motor is up to speed and under load. Under such conditions, the portion of the winding remaining in the circuit will carry the load until it fails due to overheating.

The effect of increasing the load on the motor beyond its rated capacity is simply to increase the operating temperature, which shortens the life of the insulation. Momentary overloads usually cause no damage; consequently, there is a tendency to use the thermal type of overload protection in modern control systems. Obviously, the ideal place to measure the thermal effect of overload is on the motor itself. This is readily accomplished through the use of various measuring devices and overload protective devices.

The polyphase induction motor is the simplest and most foolproof piece of rotating electrical equipment. The largest single cause of winding failures is probably due to the rotor rubbing the stator iron, usually because of a worn bearing or complete bearing failure. The subject of bearings and lubrication is a large one, and because it applies to all types of rotating electrical apparatus, it was treated in considerable detail in *Electrical Level Three*.

# 2.0.0 ◆ SQUIRREL CAGE MOTORS

Three-phase squirrel cage induction motors are the most common motors in commercial and industrial use. The following sections briefly describe starting methods, insulation, usual and unusual service conditions, and common electrical failures for these motors. *Figure 1* shows the basic elements of a squirrel cage motor.

## 2.1.0 Starting Configurations

Squirrel cage motors are usually designed for cross-the-line starting, which means that they can be connected directly to the power source by means of a suitable contactor.

In large squirrel cage motors and in some other types of motors, the starting currents are very high. Usually, the motor is built to stand these high currents, but since these currents are almost six times the rated-load current, there may be a large voltage drop in the power system. Some method of reducing the starting current must therefore be employed to limit the voltage drop to a tolerable value.

Reducing the starting current may be accomplished by the use of a solid-state programmable motor controller or by any one of the following starting methods:

- *Primary resistor or reactance* – Primary resistor or reactance starting employs series reactance or resistance to reduce the current on the first step and then after a preset time interval, the motor is connected directly across the line. It can be used with any standard motor.
- *Autotransformer* – Autotransformer starting employs autotransformers to directly reduce the voltage and current on the first step and then after a preset time interval, the motor is connected directly across the line. It can be used with any standard motor.
- *Wye-delta* – Wye-delta starting impresses the voltage across the Y connection to reduce the current on the first step and then after a preset time interval, the motor is connected in delta, permitting full-load operation. The motor must have a winding capable of wye-delta connection.
- *Part-winding* – Part-winding starting employs motors with two separate winding circuits. Upon starting, only one winding circuit is engaged, and current is reduced. After a preset time interval, the full winding of the motor is put directly across the line. It must have a motor with two separate winding circuits. To avoid possible overheating and subsequent damage to the winding, the time between the connection of the first and second windings is limited to a four-second maximum.

All of these starting methods are commonly referred to as reduced-voltage starting. They all require special starters designed for the particular method and are controlled between the start and run functions by an adjustable timer.

Reduced-voltage starting significantly reduces the load acceleration characteristic of any motor. It is, therefore, necessary to have the motor unloaded or nearly so at the start.

## 2.2.0 Insulation Systems

An insulation system is an assembly of insulating materials in association with conductors and the supporting structural parts of a motor. Insulation systems are divided into classes according to the thermal endurance of the system for temperature rating purposes. Four classes of insulation systems are used in motors: A, B, F, and H. Do not confuse these insulation classes with motor designs, which are also designated by letter.

- *Class A* – Class A insulation systems are those which by experience or accepted test can be shown to have a suitable thermal endurance when operated at the limiting Class A temperature of 105°C. Typical materials used include

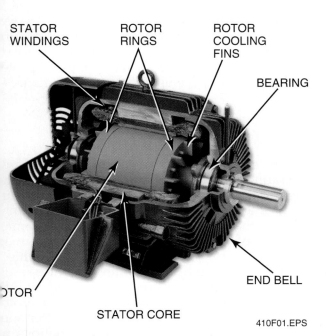

STATOR WINDINGS | ROTOR RINGS | ROTOR COOLING FINS

BEARING

END BELL

ROTOR

STATOR CORE

410F01.EPS

*Figure 1* ◆ Squirrel cage motor construction.

cotton, paper, cellulose acetate films, enamel-coated wire, and similar organic materials impregnated with suitable substances.

- *Class B* – Class B insulation systems are those which by experience or accepted tests can be shown to have suitable thermal endurance when operated at the limiting Class B temperature of 130°C. Typical materials include mica, glass fiber, and other materials, not necessarily inorganic, with compatible bonding substances having suitable thermal stability.
- *Class F* – Class F insulation systems are those which by experience or accepted test can be shown to have suitable thermal endurance when operated at the limiting Class F temperature of 155°C. Typical materials include mica, glass fiber, and other materials, not necessarily inorganic, with compatible bonding substances having suitable thermal stability.
- *Class H* – Class H insulation systems are those which by experience or accepted test can be shown to have suitable thermal endurance when operated at the limiting Class H temperature of 180°C. Typical materials used include mica, glass fiber, silicone elastomer, and other materials, not necessarily inorganic, with compatible bonding substances (for example, silicone resins) having suitable thermal stability.

## 2.3.0 Usual Service Conditions

When operated within the limits of the following NEMA usual service conditions, standard motors will perform in accordance with their ratings:

- *Ambient or room temperature not over 40°C* – If the ambient temperature is over 40°C (104°F), the motor service factor must be reduced or a higher horsepower motor used. The larger motor will be loaded below full capacity, so the temperature rise will be less and overheating will be reduced.
- *Altitude does not exceed 3,300' (1,000 meters)* – Motors having Class A or B insulation systems and temperature rises according to NEMA will operate satisfactorily at altitudes above 3,300' in these locations where the decrease in ambient temperature compensates for the increase in temperature rise, as shown in *Table 1*. Motors having a service factor of 1.15 or higher will operate satisfactorily at unity service factor and an ambient temperature of 40°C at altitudes above 3,300' up to 9,000'.
- *Voltage variation of not more than 10% of nameplate voltage* – Operation outside these limits or a voltage imbalance can result in overheating or loss of torque and may require using a larger hp motor.

**Table 1** Ambient Temperature at Various Altitudes

| Ambient Temperature | Maximum Altitude |
|---|---|
| 40°C | 3,300' |
| 30°C | 6,600' |
| 20°C | 9,900' |

- *Frequency variation of not more than 5% of nameplate frequency* – Operation outside of these limits results in a substantial speed variation and causes overheating and reduced torque.

In addition to the above-listed conditions, the following installation guidelines must be observed:

- The mounting surface must be rigid, and the drive must be in accordance with NEMA specifications.
- The location of supplementary enclosures must not seriously interfere with the ventilation of the motor.

## 2.4.0 Unusual Service Conditions

Motors are often exposed to damaging atmospheres such as excessive moisture, steam, salt air, abrasive or conductive dust, lint, chemical fumes, and combustible or explosive dust or gases. To protect such motors, a special enclosure or encapsulated windings and special bearing protection may be required.

Motors exposed to damaging mechanical or electrical loading such as unbalanced voltage conditions, abnormal shock or vibration, torsional impact loads, or excessive thrust or overhang loads may require special mountings or protection designed by the user for the installation.

## 2.5.0 Typical Squirrel Cage Motor Winding Failures

Severe electrical, mechanical, or environmental operating conditions can damage the stator winding of a three-phase squirrel cage motor. Winding failures and their causes are shown in *Figure*. Motors that have suffered severe core damage because of overheating or mechanical damage from the rotor are usually discarded. This is because severe core damage almost always results in abnormal core losses or loss of efficiency if the motor is rewound. In an emergency, some motors with severe damage can be rewound after some or most of the damaged core laminations are restacked. Such a motor has a shortened operating life and should be replaced as soon as possible.

Single-phased undamaged winding (caused by a missing voltage phase in a wye-connected motor)

Single-phased damaged winding (caused by a missing voltage phase in a delta-connected motor)

Phase-to-phase short (caused by contamination, abrasion, vibration, or voltage surge)

Turn-to-turn short (caused by contamination, abrasion, vibration, or voltage surge)

Shorted coil (caused by contamination, abrasion, vibration, or voltage surge)

Winding grounded at edge of slot (caused by contamination, abrasion, vibration, or voltage surge)

410F02A.EPS

*Figure 2* ◆ Stator winding failures and causes. (1 of 2)

Winding grounded in slot (caused by contamination, abrasion, vibration, or voltage surge)

Shorted connection (caused by contamination, abrasion, vibration, or voltage surge)

Unbalanced voltage damage (severe for one phase, slight for another phase, and caused by unbalanced power source loads or poor connections)

Overload damage to all windings
**Note:** Under-voltage and over-voltage (exceeding NEMA standards) will result in the same type of insulation deterioration.

Locked rotor overload damage to all windings (may also be caused by excessive starts or reversals)

Voltage surge damage (caused by lightning, capacitor discharges, voltage kickbacks caused by de-energizing large inductive loads, or voltage disturbances caused by solid-state devices)

410F02B.EPS

*Figure 2* ◆ Stator winding failures and causes. (2 of 2)

Normally, motors below 20hp or 30hp are not salaged when they fail, nor are they included in eriodic maintenance and testing programs. However, the cause of failure for any motor should be investigated and corrected to prevent rapid failures of any replacement/rewound motors.

## .0.0 ◆ MOTOR INSULATION TESTING

After installation, periodic tests are usually performed on large motors (over 20hp or 30hp) to determine the condition of the motor's insulation. Such tests, usually conventional resistance tests, indicate the presence of moisture, dirt, or other conductive material. An insulation resistance test indicates the condition of motor insulation, with particular regard to moisture and dirt. However, chemical tests, physical tests, or other laboratory tests may be required to determine the cause of some unusual insulation failure.

## .1.0 Insulation Resistance Tests

Insulation resistance tests give an indication of the condition of insulation, particularly with regard to moisture and dirt. The actual value of the resistance varies greatly in different types of machines, depending on the type, size, voltage rating, etc. The principal worth of such measurements, therefore, is in the relative values of insulation resistance of the same apparatus taken under similar conditions at various times. Such tests usually reveal how well the machine has been maintained.

Measuring insulation resistance is rather straightforward. Identify any two points between which there is insulation, and make a connection with a *megohmmeter*. Take a measurement; the measured value represents the equivalent resistance of all the insulation that exists between the two points and any component resistance that might also be connected between the two points.

Megohmmeters are available in several varieties. Some are powered by a hand-cranked generator; others are battery powered. Some use power supply voltages as low as 50V, but the most common is 500V, with some going as high as 10,000V. The power supply, in all cases, is DC.

The insulation between the two connection points can be thought of as a *dielectric*, thus forming a capacitance. A phenomenon known as dielectric absorption occurs whereby the dielectric soaks up current and then releases it when the potential is removed. This is in addition to the current that charges and discharges the capacitance, and it occurs much more slowly. It is dependent on the nature of the dielectric. Two types of items where this is of concern are capacitors and motors. Such current is referred to as dielectric absorption current, or $I_A$ in *Figure 3(A)*. The phenomenon may be demonstrated by taking a large capacitor, charging it to its rated voltage, and allowing it to remain at that voltage for some length of time. Then discharge the capacitor

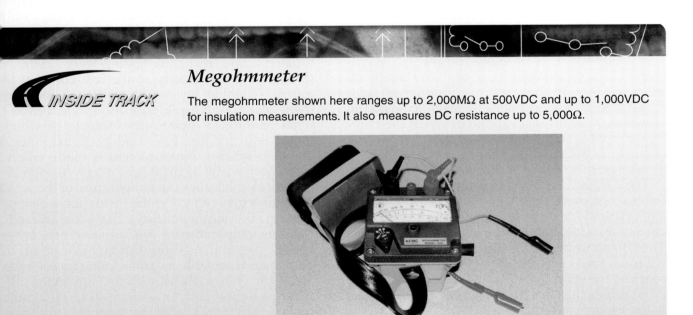

**INSIDE TRACK**

### *Megohmmeter*

The megohmmeter shown here ranges up to 2,000MΩ at 500VDC and up to 1,000VDC for insulation measurements. It also measures DC resistance up to 5,000Ω.

410P1002.EPS

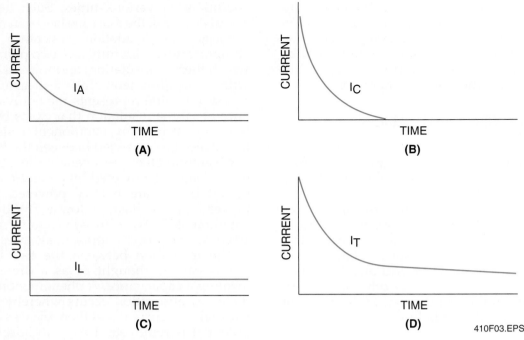

*Figure 3* ◆ Current curves related to insulation testing.

quickly and completely until a voltmeter placed across it reads zero. Remove the voltmeter and again allow the capacitor to sit for some length of time with its leads open circuited. When you again put the voltmeter across the capacitor, any voltage you find there is due to the dielectric absorption phenomenon. Some types of capacitors exhibit this more than others. The larger the capacitor, the more apparent it will be.

The current required to charge whatever capacitance is present is known as charging current, or $I_C$ in *Figure 3(B)*. Like the dielectric absorption current, it decays exponentially to zero, but much more quickly. It is this current which in most cases determines how long it takes to make an accurate megohm measurement. When the reading appears to stabilize, it means that the charging current has decayed to a point where it is negligible with respect to the **leakage** current.

The current that flows through the insulation is the leakage current, or $I_L$ in *Figure 3(C)*. The voltage across the insulation divided by the leakage current through it equals the insulation resistance. Thus, to accurately measure insulation resistance, we must wait until the dielectric absorption current and the charging current have decayed to the point where they are truly negligible with respect to the leakage current.

The total current that flows is the sum of the three components just mentioned, or $I_T$ in *Figure 3(D)*. It decays exponentially from an initial maximum and approaches a constant value, which is the leakage current alone. The megohm reading is dependent on the voltage across the insulation and the total current. It increases exponentially from an initial minimum and approaches a constant value, which is the true insulation resistance. Note that the residual dielectric absorption current and charging current cause the reading to be less than the actual insulation resistance. It will never be greater.

Motor manufacturers, installers, users, and repairers find megohm testing very useful in determining the quality of the insulation in the motor. A single insulation resistance measurement, along with experience and guidelines as to what reading to expect, can indicate whether a motor is fit for use. Information of real value is obtained when a measurement is made when a motor is new and again at least every year while it is in service. Because the temperature of the windings has a great effect on the insulation resistance reading, the motor industry has standardized a winding temperature of 40°C as a reference when specific recommendations can be made about the minimum acceptable megohm value for each type of motor. When measurements are made at a winding temperature other than 40°C, they can be corrected to reflect what the reading would have been at 40°C by using a temperature coefficient Kt, obtained from a chart such as the one shown in *Figure 4*.

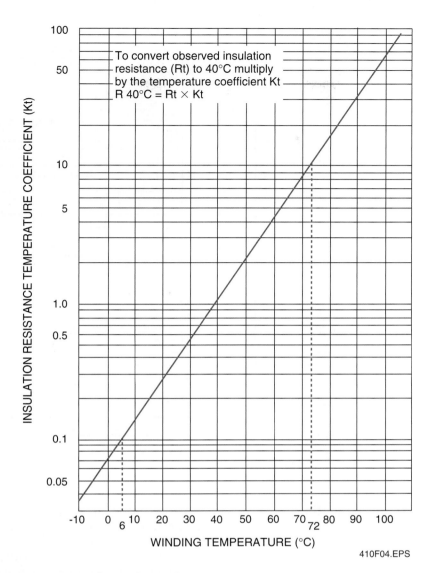

**To convert observed insulation resistance (Rt) to 40°C multiply by the temperature coefficient Kt**

$$R\ 40°C = Rt \times Kt$$

INSULATION RESISTANCE TEMPERATURE COEFFICIENT (Kt)

WINDING TEMPERATURE (°C)

410F04.EPS

*Figure 4* ◆ Approximate temperature coefficient for insulation resistance.

*Figure 5* shows the actual readings obtained on motor over several years (the dashed lines) and he same readings corrected to a common 40°C eference (the solid lines). Note the very gradual ecline characteristic of the motor's normal aging rocess until, in late 1997, a sharp drop occurred. hat drop signaled a problem with the insulation at would probably lead to an insulation failure, hich would be costly in terms of repair and own time. Therefore, at the earliest practical pportunity, the motor was sent out for rewind-g. The rewinding restored the high megohm adings, and the steady, very gradual decline sumed.

*Figure 6* shows the type of records employing mperature compensation that are normally kept n large motors.

Another factor that affects megohm readings is moisture. Motors may have excessive moisture in and around the insulation from either high humidity or having been submerged. This is a temporary effect, and by letting the motor dry out naturally or accelerating the process by baking, the readings will increase. It is important not to start the motor until a satisfactory megohm reading can be obtained, because to do so might cause an insulation failure.

The phenomenon of dielectric absorption is also present in large motors. A dielectric absorption test is often made, which involves leaving a megohmmeter connected to the motor for 10 minutes and taking one reading per minute. The readings will gradually rise due to dielectric absorption. Again, it is essential to record a

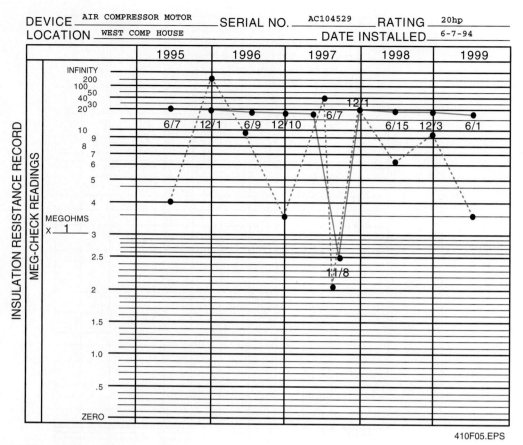

DEVICE ___AIR COMPRESSOR MOTOR___ SERIAL NO. ___AC104529___ RATING ___20hp___
LOCATION ___WEST COMP HOUSE___ DATE INSTALLED___6-7-94___

410F05.EPS

**Figure 5** ◆ Chart of insulation resistance readings.

history of the motor from the time it is first installed. See *Figure 7*.

A gradual decline in the amount of dielectric absorption is normal. If a significant drop occurs, it signals a potential problem. A calculation that is sometimes applied when there is no prior history on a motor is called a polarization index. This is the 10-minute megohm reading divided by the one-minute megohm reading. A rule of thumb used only for large motors is that the polarization index should be at least two.

### 3.1.1 Determining the Polarization Index

Knowing the polarization index of a motor or generator can be useful in appraising the fitness of the machine for service. The index is calculated from measurements of the winding insulation resistance.

Before measuring the insulation resistance, remove all external connections to the machine and completely discharge the windings to the grounded machine frame.

Proceed by applying either 500VDC or 1,000VDC between the winding and ground using

a direct-indicating, power-driven megohmmeter. For machines rated 500V and over, the higher value is used. The voltage is applied for 10 minutes and kept constant for the duration of the test.

The polarization index is calculated as the ratio of the 10-minute value to the one-minute value of the insulation resistances measured consecutively.

$$\text{Polarization index} = \frac{\text{resistance after 10 minutes}}{\text{resistance after one minute}}$$

The recommended minimum value of polarization index for AC and DC motors and generators is 2.0. Machines having windings with a lower index are less likely to be suited for operation.

The polarization index is useful in evaluating windings for:

- Buildup of dirt or moisture
- Gradual deterioration of the insulation (by comparing results of tests made earlier on the same machine)
- Fitness for overpotential tests
- Suitability for operation

The procedure for determining the polarization index is covered in detail in *IEEE Standard No. 43*.

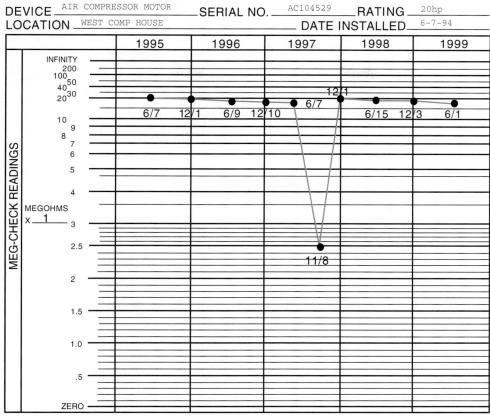

## INSULATION RESISTANCE RECORD

DEVICE __AIR COMPRESSOR MOTOR__ SERIAL NO. __AC104529__ RATING __20hp__
LOCATION __WEST COMP HOUSE__ DATE INSTALLED __6-7-94__

410F06.EPS

*Figure 6* ◆ Temperature compensation record for a large motor.

In testing components before they are installed in a product, it is sometimes necessary or desirable to verify that the components meet their insulation resistance specifications. Wire and cable, connectors, switches, transformers, resistors, capacitors, and other components are specified to have a certain minimum insulation resistance. The megohmmeter is the proper instrument to use. Remember, the part may have a limitation on the voltage that may be applied, or the insulation resistance may be specified at a particular voltage. Pay careful attention to these restrictions to avoid improper comparisons and damage to the part.

Use caution when selecting the test voltage. The voltage rating of the part or motor across the points where the measurement is made should not be exceeded. Many users prefer to use the highest available voltage that does not exceed the rating. In other cases, the customary test voltage is 00V, regardless of a higher rating. The megohm test is a valuable tool, but it does not substitute for the dielectric voltage withstand test, as described next.

### 3.2.0 Dielectric Voltage Withstand Tests

The dielectric voltage withstand test, or hi-pot test, is designed to stress insulation far beyond what it will encounter in normal use. If the insulation can withstand the much higher voltage for a given period of time, it is assumed that it will be able to adequately function at its normal voltage level.

This is the origin of the term voltage withstand. In addition to overstressing the insulation, the test also has the ability to uncover material and workmanship defects that result in conductor spacings that are too close. The addition of humidity, dirt, vibration, shock, or contaminants in normal use tend to close these small gaps and allow current to flow, creating a shock hazard later if the defects are not found and corrected in the factory. No other test can find this type of defect as well as the dielectric voltage withstand test.

| DATE | MEG-CHECK READING | DEVICE | | AIR TEMP. | HUMIDITY | REMARKS |
|---|---|---|---|---|---|---|
| | | HOT | COLD | | | |
| 6/7/95 | 20 | X | | 70°F | 72% | Temp. Corrected |
| 12/1/95 | 19 | | X | 80°F | 50% | Temp. Corrected |
| 6/9/96 | 18 | | X | 80°F | 78% | Temp. Corrected |
| 12/10/96 | 17 | X | | 76°F | 60% | Temp. Corrected |
| 6/7/97 | 16 | | X | 82°F | 82% | Temp. Corrected |
| 11/8/97 | 2.5 | X | | 80°F | 60% | Temp. Corrected |
| 12/1/97 | 20 | | X | 78°F | 60% | Temp. Corrected |
| 6/15/98 | 19 | | X | 80°F | 80% | Temp. Corrected |
| 12/3/98 | 18 | | X | 80°F | 50% | Temp. Corrected |
| 6/1/99 | 17 | X | | 82°F | 82% | Temp. Corrected |
| | | | | | | |
| | | | | | | |
| | | | | | | |
| | | | | | | |
| | | | | | | |
| | | | | | | |
| | | | | | | |
| | | | | | | |
| | | | | | | |
| | | | | | | |
| | | | | | | |

410F07.EPS

*Figure 7* ◆ Motor history chart.

## 3.3.0 AC Voltage Withstand Tests

Several varieties of AC voltage withstand equipment are available. One type employs a high-reactance transformer, which is inherently current limiting.

This is good from the standpoint of operator safety because the current is often limited to less than a lethal value. Many such testers do not have push-to-test switches; when they are switched on and the voltage brought up, it is continuously available. Many do not automatically switch off the high voltage; in case of failure, the current is limited to a value that does no harm whatsoever to the transformer. Such testers are simple and attractively priced, but they cannot be used for tests required by an agency if there is a requirement that the failure indication remain active and conspicuous until reset manually. They also cannot be used to test products with significant capacitance because of their low current output.

Testers with conventional transformers must have a high-voltage shutoff mechanism to protect the output transformer. This mechanism also turns on a failure indication that remains activ and conspicuous until reset manually. These ar clearly go/no-go testers. If a tester has a hig enough current capability to test highly capacitiv products, then it has a high enough current capa bility to kill. The test connections and produc under test must be handled with extreme care b competent operators, and unauthorized person must not be allowed in the area.

Some testers are equipped with current meter rather than shutoff mechanisms. Unlike the nor metered models, they can indicate how good how bad a product is. They are often used f design tests and other lab work.

Once the proper tester for the job has been cho sen, a plan for testing is developed. Componen are tested by identifying the placement of th insulation to be tested and arranging the test s that only that insulation is stressed. A commo practice is to tie connections of circuits that shoul not be stressed together. As one example, suppos a potentiometer is to be tested. Its dielectric with stand rating is 900VAC for one minute betwee

## Preliminary Motor Circuit Insulation Testing

Some manufacturers suggest that the wiring, motor starter, and motor insulation be checked with a megohmmeter before testing the motor alone. The instruction manual accompanying the megohmmeter contains detailed instructions about preparing for the tests, as well as connections for various types of equipment. The megohmmeter connections for an AC motor and starting equipment are shown here. One lead is connected to the motor side of the main switch, and the second lead is connected to a slip on the motor housing. If insulation weakness is indicated by this test, the motor and starter should be checked separately.

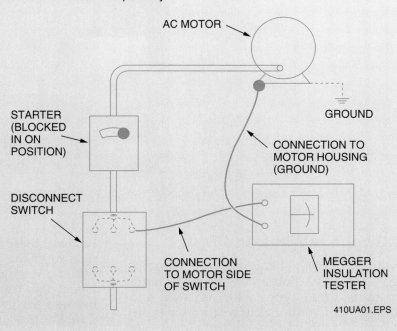

410UA01.EPS

he resistance element and the metal shell or etween the wiper and the metal shell. One would e all three terminals (each end of the element and he wiper) together. The low (ground) side of the ester would be connected to the metal shell and he hot side to the three terminals. Then the test vould be performed at 900V for one minute. You vill not pass any current through the potentiome- er because it is not being tested; you are only test- ng the insulation between the potentiometer and s shell. AC tests include the following:

*Breakdown* – In the product itself, breakdown may be (but is not always) evidenced by arcing at the location of the breakdown. It may be heard if it is allowed to continue or seen if the area is dark enough. In the high-reactance transformer type of tester, breakdown may be indicated by a separate breakdown light and is also indicated by erratic readings observed on the voltmeter. In the type of tester that has failure and high-voltage shutoff circuitry, it will trigger the failure

system. Such systems do not always distinguish between breakdown and leakage in their display of failures. However, although there may be an adjustable leakage threshold, the breakdown detector will respond to any amount of arcing, because it is sensitive to the wide range of frequencies associated with arcing, as opposed to the power line frequency only of leakage. On models with current meters, erratic voltage readings and high, erratic current readings signal breakdown.

- *Excessive leakage* – Most testers have adjustable thresholds for leakage, below which they will not indicate leakage failures. In the high-reactance type of tester, excessive leakage will often be indicated by a separate leakage light, and the voltmeter reading will fall to near zero. In the type of tester that has failure and high-voltage shutoff circuitry, it will trigger the failure system. On models with current meters, excessive current will be indicated.

## INSIDE TRACK

### DC Hi-pot Test Set

The DC hi-pot test set shown here can conduct high-voltage insulation tests up to 60kV. It incorporates a guard circuit for stray leakage current bypass and an interlock plug that can be used for an external cage interlock. Some units are also available with a high-voltage test pot for testing small components. Other DC hi-pot test sets are available that range up to 170kV.

410P1003.EPS

### 3.4.0 DC Voltage Withstand Tests

Several varieties of DC voltage withstand equipment are available. Some are simply high-reactance transformer types with rectifiers and filters added. Conventional transformer types with failure and high-voltage shutoff circuits are available, and there are some AC/DC switchable models. Models with current meters are available, and current metering is somewhat more popular in DC testing than in AC because of the ability to monitor the decay of the charging current.

The connections for DC tests are generally the same as for AC tests. The same insulation is being stressed. The most important difference, as mentioned previously, is that the voltage must be applied gradually so that the charging current will not exceed the leakage threshold. If a very capacitive item is being tested or in situations with tight time constraints, as on a production line, the waiting time for charging current to diminish is intolerable, and either an unmetered model should be used or a fixed time should be established after the full test voltage is reached. At the conclusion of this fixed time, the current reading should be taken and used to judge whether the item passed the test. It is also important that the last step of voltage (up to the full test voltage) always be uniform in terms of the amount of voltage raised and the time over which it is raised

because these factors can also affect the curren reading if the charging current is not allowed t become negligible. For items with little capac tance, the test is quite similar to the AC tes because the gradual application is not as impor tant. DC tests include the following:

- *Breakdown* – The indications of breakdown ar the same in DC testing as in AC. Arcing may b present. Erratic voltmeter indications an lighting of the separate breakdown lights sig nal breakdown in high-reactance, transforme type equipment. Failure indication due t frequency-sensitive circuitry will be given i conventional transformer types. Again, o models with current meters, erratic voltag readings and high, erratic current reading indicate breakdown.
- *Excessive leakage* – The current read on the cu rent meter or sensed by the failure circuit is th total current drawn by the item being tested. consists of the leakage current, which depend on the present voltage level, and the chargin current, which depends on the rate and amoun of the last voltage increase and the time elapse since it occurred. The current always shoots u during a voltage increase.

When using equipment with a failure detecto it is necessary to limit the size and speed o

## Nondestructive Motor Circuit Analysis

Some manufacturers offer handheld, low-voltage AC/DC test instruments that perform motor circuit analysis using automated measurements, calculations, and comparisons to pinpoint winding and rotor faults in three-phase induction motors, synchronous motors, DC motors, traction motors, and machine tool servos. The tests reveal shorted stator windings, shorted rotor fields, air gap eccentricity, rotor and stator winding contamination, and ground insulation faults. Results of the tests are used along with U.S. Department of Energy Motormaster+ as part of an energy- and reliability-based predictive maintenance program.

voltage increases so that the current does not reach the leakage threshold. Until enough experience is gained with the tester and the product, when failures are indicated, the test should be repeated more slowly to be certain that the failures are from excessive leakage or breakdown, and not due to charging current. When using models with separate breakdown and leakage lights and no failure circuitry, expect the leakage light to stay on after a voltage increase for some amount of time. Again, experience will tell how long to expect it to stay on. If it stays on indefinitely, or much longer than expected, suspect excessive leakage.

On metered models, set the current range switch to the highest range, and after the full test voltage has been reached, observe the current meter. As the reading falls below the full-scale value for each lower range, the range may be changed to one step lower. Finally, the reading should stabilize. It may then be compared to the normal reading for the type of product being tested. Of course, if it is desired to monitor the current as the voltage is raised in steps, then the meter should not be ignored until the full voltage is reached, but rather, a reading should be noted after each step. Remember to select the highest current range before raising the voltage each time. If you do not wait for the reading to stabilize after each step, then there must be a uniform amount of time between raising the voltage and taking the current reading for each step.

## 3.5.0 Safety

Before any tests are made, the safety of the test operator must be assured. Certain insulation tests, such as dielectric withstand tests, can shock, burn, or cause death if improperly conducted.

An area out of the mainstream of activity should be selected for the test station. Preferably, it should not be a room that employees must walk through in their normal course of duties. If this is

not practical because of production line flow, the area should be marked or roped off and employees other than the ones who perform tests not allowed inside. If benches are placed back to back, be especially careful about the use of the bench opposite the test station. Signs should be posted: *DANGER—HIGH-VOLTAGE TEST IN PROGRESS—UNAUTHORIZED PERSONNEL KEEP AWAY.*

Power to the test station should be so arranged that all power except to lights can be cut off by a single, prominently located and marked switch at the perimeter of the test area. In the event of an emergency, any responsible employee may then cut off the power before entering the area to offer assistance.

Use a nonconductive table or workbench for performing tests. Any metal that is in the area should not be between the operator and the area where products being tested will be placed, and the metal should be connected to a good ground, never left floating.

If the product or component being tested is small, it may be possible to construct guards or an enclosure made of a nonconductive material such as clear acrylic so that the item being tested is within the guards or enclosure during the test. Fit the guards with switches so that the tester will not operate unless the guards are in place or the enclosure sealed.

Keep the area clean and uncluttered. All test leads not absolutely necessary for the test should be put away, not left on the test bench. The same applies to extra equipment. It should be clear not only to the operator, but also to any observer, which product is being tested and which ones are waiting to be tested or have already been tested. Provide considerable clear bench space around the product being tested. The tester should be placed off to the side in such a way that the operator does not have to reach over the product being tested to activate or adjust the meter.

If the tester can be operated by remote switches, consider the type that requires two switches spaced far apart to be actuated simultaneously in order to test. This may require the use of a separate relay or control. Never allow any connection to be made to the tester that could energize the high voltage without the control of the operator.

Dielectric voltage withstand equipment must be connected to a good ground. Be certain that the power wiring to the test bench is properly polarized and that the proper low-resistance bonding to ground is in place. Some testers incorporate monitor circuits that check the connections to the power line and ground. The lights on these line monitors show at a glance if the wiring is proper or if polarity is wrong, the ground is missing, etc. Turn off and unplug the equipment, and do not use it until the wiring is repaired if anything other than an OK signal is given.

Operators should understand the electrical fundamentals of voltage, resistance, and current. They should recognize that the tester is a variable voltage power supply with one side connected directly to an earth ground; therefore, the current will flow to any available ground path.

The range of output voltage should be emphasized, as well as the correct voltage to use for the products being tested. The amount of current that the tester can supply should be stressed, along with the idea that current, not voltage, injures or kills.

Overriding or tampering with any safety systems should be treated as a serious offense and should result in severe penalties, such as removal from the job. Allowing unauthorized personnel in the area during testing should also be dealt with seriously. Operators should understand these rules before they begin testing.

Operators should not wear jewelry, especially items such as hanging bracelets, which could accidentally complete a circuit.

## 3.6.0 Suggestions for Test Procedures

Test procedures should include the following basic tasks:

- Verify that the high voltage is off before making connections.
- Connect the low (grounded) side of the tester first. The clip lead should be connected securely to the exposed metal parts designated to be tested.
- If using a clip lead to connect the high-voltage side of the tester, handle the clip only by its insulator; do not touch the clip directly.

- If using a tester with a receptacle, after first connecting the ground clip lead, plug the product's cordset into the tester. There must be no confusion about which product belongs to which cordset.
- If using a test fixture, be certain that it is properly closed and that all guards are in place. I should be interlocked with switches so that the test cannot begin otherwise.
- Double-check the connections before testing and especially look for enough clear space around the product being tested. Follow the high-voltage lead from the tester to the product which should stay on the bench as it goes as directly as possible to the product. Coil any excess neatly halfway between the tester and the product. Avoid crossing test leads, if possible.
- Check the settings of the equipment before beginning the test. Perform the test according to a standard test procedure developed in advance.
- Never touch any of the cables or connections during the test. Never touch the product under test.
- When performing DC testing, have on hand a hot stick, which is a nonconductive rod with a metal probe at the end connected to a grounded wire. In case a connection comes loose during the test, it is not sufficient to turn off the power anything the tester's hot lead contacted must be discharged using the hot stick.
- If a connection comes loose during the test immediately turn off the high voltage. Discharge the item if DC was used. Restore the connection and then repeat the test.
- After the test, turn off the high voltage. Discharge items tested with DC for the proper length of time. Items tested with AC need not be discharged.

High-voltage testing need not be inherently unsafe, if handled properly. The key points to remember are:

- Keep unqualified and unauthorized persons away.
- Arrange the test station in a safe manner.
- Never touch the product or connections during the test.
- In case of any problem, turn off the high voltage first.
- Properly discharge any item tested with DC before touching connections.

# 4.0.0 ◆ INSULATION CLEANING AND DRYING

Operating instructions for electric motors emphasize the importance of keeping them clean and dry. Favorable locations, suitable enclosures, adequate ventilation, drip-proof covers, splash-proof protection, and heaters to prevent condensation of moisture on the apparatus when out of service all serve to reduce the number of interruptions and to lower maintenance costs.

When electrical apparatus does get dirty, the insulation must be cleaned. Various methods for cleaning are available; the method used will depend on the kind of dirt to be removed and whether the apparatus is to be returned to use immediately or the coils are to be removed and the apparatus rewound.

Drying after cleaning is necessary. This is illustrated by the experiences in floods, when great numbers of motors and generators become submerged and have to be rehabilitated.

Testing is necessary after cleaning and drying to determine whether the insulation has been properly reconditioned.

Electric motors should be kept reasonably free from accumulations of dirt so that ventilating ducts may function and low-resistance paths are not formed between live parts.

Cleaning may include wiping, removing dirt by suction, and/or blowing using compressed air.

If a solvent is necessary to remove oil or grease, it is recommended that a petroleum solvent of the safety type be used exclusively. The flash point of the solvent should be greater than 100°F (37.8°C) as measured by the Tagliobue Closed Cup Method (a method used for such testing), or as stated in the MSDS for the solvent.

Insulating varnishes, unless well cured, are attacked by solvents. Petroleum solvents are less likely to attack varnishes than stronger solvents, such as chlorinated solvents or coal tar solvents. Synthetic varnish films are more resistant to solvents than oleoresinous varnish films, but they may be softened or lifted by strong solvents, especially if not fully cured. Solvents should be used to clean silicone-treated windings only as a last resort.

 **WARNING!**

- When solvents are used, adequate ventilation must be provided to avoid fire, explosion, and health hazards.
- Avoid breathing solvent vapors. Vapors of chlorinated and coal tar solvents are especially toxic.

 **WARNING!**

- When working with solvents in confined spaces where ventilation is poor, as in tanks, pits, or holds of ships, an air line respirator, breathing equipment with a self-contained air supply, or hose masks must be worn.
- Petroleum distillates, coal tar solvents, alcohol, and many other materials are flammable, and their vapors may form explosive mixtures with air.
- The metal nozzle on a hose used for spraying flammable solvents should be grounded.
- Personal protective equipment, such as goggles, neoprene gloves, and aprons should be provided when working with solvents to prevent irritation due to continuous or repeated contact with the skin.
- Avoid wetting clothing with solvent. If clothing becomes saturated with solvent, it should be changed.
- Appropriate personal protective equipment should be worn when blowing out dust with compressed air.
- Use a reduced-capacity nozzle or a pulse nozzle.

The methods of cleaning electrical insulation include:

- Wiping off dirt with a clean, dry cloth
- Blowing out dirt with compressed air
- Drawing off dirt by suction
- Air blasting with ground nutshells or ground corncobs
- Removing the soil with solvents
- Washing off with water, hot alkali, and emulsion cleaners

The method selected will depend on the type of apparatus, insulation, soil, and other conditions involved. Descriptions of appropriate uses for each method follow.

- *Cloths* – Cleaning with a dry cloth may be satisfactory when the motor is small, the surfaces to be cleaned are accessible, and only dry dirt is to be removed. However, use only lint-free cloths because lint will adhere to the insulation and increase the collecting of dirt, moisture, and oil. This is particularly objectionable on high-voltage insulation, because it tends to cause a concentration of corona.

- *Compressed air* – Blowing out dirt with a jet of air is usually effective, particularly when the dirt has collected in places which cannot be reached with a cloth. Cleaning can be done more quickly with compressed air than with a cloth, especially on large machines. However, if blowing with compressed air simply transfers dirt from one place to another in the machine, little or no good has been accomplished. The following conditions should be emphasized:
  - Do not blow the compressed air against insulation until it is certain that the air is dry and does not carry water that may have condensed and accumulated in the air line.
  - Do not use air pressures greater than 30 pounds per square inch. Excess pressure may damage the insulation and blow dirt under loosened tape.
  - Do not direct the stream of compressed air in such a way that the dirt will be blown into some inner recess from which it would be difficult to remove and where it might close ventilating ducts.
- *Brushing and suction cleaning* – Dry dust and dirt may be removed by brushing with bristle brushes followed by vacuum cleaning. Do not use wire brushes. A vacuum system is an effective and desirable method of removing dry and loose dirt, since it does not scatter the dirt and thereby avoids any dust settling on other apparatus.
- *Shell blasting* – Air blasting with ground nutshells may be satisfactory for removal of hard dirt deposits from insulation. Use mild abrasives such as 12-20 mesh ground walnut shells. If a softer abrasive is required, use ground corncobs. The cleaning may be done in a cabinet-type air blasting machine or by an operator directing the jet of abrasive at a small area long enough to remove the dirt without damaging the insulation. Canopies or other shields should be erected to prevent unnecessary contamination of other equipment or areas.
- *Solvents* – If the accumulated soil contains oil or grease, a solvent is usually required to remove it. A rag dampened with solvent may be used for wiping the apparatus, it may be sprayed with solvent, or it may be dipped into solvent. Solvents include:
  - Petroleum distillates
  - Other solvents including chlorinated solvents, mixtures of chlorinated and petroleum solvents, aromatic or coal tar solvents, alcohols, and lacquer thinners
  - Water, hot alkali, or emulsion cleaners
  - Vapor degreasers

It is recommended that only petroleum distillates be used where a solvent is required for cleaning electric motors. Petroleum distillates that are classified as safety solvents and have a flash point above 100°F are supplied by practically all oil companies under various trade names.

## 4.1.0 Drying Electrical Insulation

After cleaning, storing, or shipping, electric motors must be dried before being placed in operation if tests indicate that the insulation resistance is below a safe minimum value. Moisture may be derived from the following:

- Exposure to rain, snow, or fog during shipment or storage
- Exposure to a humid atmosphere
- Cleaning with water or other aqueous solutions

It is sometimes assumed that insulation is moisture-free when the electric motor is shipped by the manufacturer. However, air always contains a considerable amount of moisture, except in arid desert regions, and electrical insulation exposed to the atmosphere at ordinary temperatures will always contain some moisture, with the amount depending on the humidity of the atmosphere. Attention to this item is particularly important during periods of continuous high humidity, such as during summer rains in temperate regions or in the continuous high humidity of tropical regions.

Special packing in sealed cases with a drying agent such as silica gel will protect the apparatus from moisture during shipment, but suitable steps will have to be taken to protect the motor after unpacking and during subsequent storage and installation.

Experience indicates that apparatus may safely be placed in service without special drying if a careful inspection of the windings discloses no defects, dirt, or visible moisture, and if insulation resistance tests are satisfactory. It is a good practice to operate the motor at a lower voltage for a short time, if practical.

The motor apparatus should be dried if the insulation resistance test shows a value below a safe minimum, which is usually accepted to be one megohm for each 1,000V of operating or rated voltage (corrected to 68°F) and a minimum of one megohm for operating voltages less than 1,000V.

Since the insulation of an electric motor standing idle in a high-humidity atmosphere absorbs moisture, provision should be made for drying the coils before returning the motor to operation. This applies particularly to such items as motors on ships, motors on pumps of flood control projects, and similar applications where operation is irregular and intermittent.

## Automatic Drying of Idle Motors

*INSIDE TRACK*

If a motor will be left idle in an area with high humidity, small electric heaters can be mounted inside the motor housing and automatically activated when the motor is off to keep the windings above the dew point. In other cases, a small DC current is automatically routed through the windings to keep them warm when the motor is off.

It is important that the insulation of all new motors be protected against moisture during shipment and also after the apparatus has arrived at its destination. One satisfactory procedure is to maintain the insulated parts and the air surrounding them at a temperature that is 15°C to 25°C higher than the general air temperature of the room in which the motor is located, but the actual temperature of the motor should not be less than 40°C and a continuous change of air should be provided. This procedure will dry off moisture that may have accumulated during shipment and previous storage and will maintain the insulation in a satisfactory condition with regard to dryness. If these conditions are continued during the time usually required for the erection of a large apparatus, the insulation will generally be raised from a value indicating extreme dampness to one that will be satisfactory for other potential tests or for placing the motor into service.

The method of producing and applying the heat will depend on a number of conditions. Ideal conditions will seldom be found and consequently, the drying may often require a great deal of ingenuity and resourcefulness on the part of the operator. Since much damage can be done by improper heating of the windings of electric motors, it is very important that this type of work be done only by competent persons. The manufacturer's nearest district sales office should be consulted for instructions if there is any doubt as to the proper procedure.

When heat is applied to the motor windings, it should be regulated in such a way that the insulation is not damaged by overheating. The heating rate should not be so rapid that internal vapor pressures develop that are great enough to cause the formation of pockets or blisters or that rupture the insulation.

It is essential that adequate provision be made for circulating the hot air within the motor that is being dried so as to remove the vapors; if the motor is enclosed, openings must be provided for the escape of moisture-laden air and gases.

The temperature of the insulation should not exceed 85°C during drying.

## 4.2.0 Methods of Drying

Drying with external heat and with internal heat are the two general methods of drying the insulation of motor windings. A combination of these two methods may be desirable under certain conditions.

### 4.2.1 Drying with External Heat

The methods of drying with external heat include the following:

- *Drying with an oven* – A permanent drying oven is a good investment for a large industrial or power company that operates motors in damp locations. Sump pumps and some steam auxiliary motor drives are examples of such applications. Oven drying is particularly desirable for small transformers, DC armatures, control apparatus, etc. Ovens have also been used extensively for salvaging motors that have been in floods.

  Ovens should be ventilated to provide for air circulation and to permit the removal of moisture.

  Electric heaters or steam coils may be placed inside the ovens, or air may be preheated by passing over electric heaters or steam coils before being blown into the oven. Some form of temperature-indicating device should be provided to permit proper heat regulation.

  Temporary ovens may be constructed of asbestos board, sheet iron, brick, or concrete block and lined with noncombustible heat-insulating material. Various types of heating may be used, but smoke and soot should not be permitted to enter the oven and proper precautions should be taken to eliminate fire risk. Fire extinguishers (e.g., dry chemical or carbon dioxide types) should always be available.

- *Drying with steam heat* – Where low-pressure steam is available, radiators or steam pipes placed below the end windings of a stator will provide safe and easily controlled steam heat. The enclosing parts should be set up against the frame, or a temporary enclosure should be used. There should always be ventilating openings at the top of the motor to provide for the escape of moisture. Where motors are equipped with water-coil air coolers, low-pressure steam may be circulated through these coolers to keep the insulation dry or to dry it.

- *Drying with forced air* – Hot air may be forced or blown through electrical apparatus to dry its insulation. The air may be heated by steam coils, hot air furnaces, electric heaters, or open fires. Although it removes surface moisture quickly, this method is generally inefficient and costly unless a blower and air duct have been provided for permanent installation and there is ample space to locate a heating unit in the duct.

- *Drying with electric heat* – External drying of the insulation of electrical rotating apparatus by electric heaters distributed under the end windings is strongly recommended. Space heaters are most convenient for this purpose. Typical heaters are ³⁄₁₆" thick, 1½" wide, and from 12" to 43" long, depending upon their capacity. The cost of the heaters is low, and their installation costs very little. These heaters are so sturdy and have so many applications that their salvage value is high.

- *Heater capacity requirements* – The radiation factor of apparatus to be dried varies to such an extent with the type of apparatus and the conditions under which the heaters are applied that it is impractical to give definitive data for use in calculating the heat required for a satisfactory drying temperature. The approximate kW capacity of heaters required for drying the insulation of an enclosed horizontal machine, such as a turbine generator or synchronous condenser, may be obtained by multiplying the total outside area of the end bells in square feet by the desired temperature rise (in °C) and dividing the result by 1,000. This assumes that space heaters will be suspended under the end windings and that there will be small vents at the top of the frame.

The insulation resistance of high-voltage armature windings depends almost entirely on the condition of the end winding insulation. This insulation is not dried efficiently with internal heat and when dried externally, the punching and other metal parts absorb a considerable part of the heat, making it still more difficult to calculate the heat required.

When drying the insulation of a large vertical machine that has not been subjected to unusual dampness, the temperature of the stator end winding insulation will rise much more rapidly than the temperature of the stator punching. Record both temperatures.

With space heaters suspended under the end windings and the exhaust ventilation at the top of the machine, the temperature of the end winding insulation should be slowly brought up to 85°C and then maintained at that temperature until the insulation resistance has dipped to the minimum and then increased to a satisfactory value. This may be obtained before a temperature of 55°C is indicated on the armature punching.

The required heater capacity for drying the insulation of vertical machines is difficult to determine by a general formula, because such machines, particularly large, vertical water wheel generators, differ greatly in design and construction. Experience indicates that the insulation of large vertical machines may generally be dried satisfactorily by using a total capacity of space heaters equivalent to three watts per square foot of the outside cylindrical area of the stator punching assembly per degree Centigrade of rise required.

- *Drying with infrared lamps* – Heating by infrared lamps may be found to be desirable in some cases. A group of these lamps may be used depending on the size of the apparatus and the heat from the lamps focused on the parts to be dried. Care should be taken not to overheat the insulation.

### 4.2.2 Drying with Internal Heat

The coil insulation of wound motors may be dried by circulating current through the windings. Internal heat can be developed in this way without subjecting the insulation to voltages that might damage it during the drying operation. The procedure will depend upon the type of apparatus to be dried and on the facilities available for producing or applying the current.

There is always a danger of serious injury to the windings when drying the insulation with current because the heat generated in the inner parts is not readily dissipated; furthermore, coils containing moisture are much more susceptible to injury from overheating than they are when thoroughly dry. Gases and vapor generated within the insulation by high temperatures may develop such pressure that they are forced through the insulation, breaking the continuity of the layers or actually rupturing the material. This method should be followed only under competent supervision.

The drying should be continued until the insulation resistance has dropped to a minimum and has then increased until at least one megohm for each 1,000V operating voltage (corrected to 68°F) is indicated, but in no case less than one megohm, regardless of voltage. It may then be desirable to maintain the temperature from 15°F to 25°F above ambient until ready for operation.

### 4.2.3 Emergency Methods

Conditions may arise that make it necessary to devise emergency methods for heating and drying. Among these methods are open fires of various kinds. However, open fires are objectionable in many ways and should be used only when no other source of heat is available.

Open fires are dangerous to workers because of carbon monoxide fumes and fire risk. The property damage may be high. Even if no fire occurs, the building walls may require scrubbing to remove smoke and sludge resulting from their use. Heat from open fires should not be directed against the electrical apparatus unless the products of combustion are prevented from being deposited on or coming into contact with the insulation. More harm may be done by gases, ashes, and soot or lamp black than would be done by moisture. Rather elaborate duct baffles may be required if heat from open fires is used.

### 4.3.0 Synchronous Motors and Condensers

The short circuit method is generally impractical for drying synchronous motors and condensers. Low voltage from an external source may be applied with satisfactory results under certain conditions, but external heat from electric heaters will be found to be more satisfactory.

### 4.4.0 Synchronous Converters

If the converter can be driven from some external source, such as a separately belted motor, it may be dried by the short circuit method using the following procedure:

*Step 1* Raise the collector brushes, then short-circuit the armature on the DC side. Use a very weak field excitation. If the converter is shunt wound, low-voltage separate excitation must be used; if it is compound wound, the armature may be short-circuited through the series field coils.

*Step 2* Synchronous converters are very sensitive when operated as series machines, and there is danger of generating an excessive current that may result in damage to the machine and personal injury. Consequently, this method of drying should not be undertaken except by the most experienced operators.

*Step 3* When drying synchronous converters with current from a separate AC source, block the rotor so that it cannot turn. Raise the DC brushes. Short-circuit the shunt field. Apply approximately 10% of normal AC voltage to the collector rings.

> **NOTE**
>
> Commutators that are so wet that the insulation does not dry out when the winding insulation is dried will require special treatment.

*Step 4* If the front V-ring is secured by bolts or studs, remove two that are diametrically opposed, if possible, and drain out any trapped water. In some constructions, the bolts cannot be removed, and it may be necessary to take off several nuts in order to get the water out and admit hot air inside the assembly. When the front V-ring is held in place by a nut or a threaded ring, the commutator should be securely banded before the V-ring is loosened or removed.

*Step 5* The hot vacuum process is most satisfactory for drying commutators. Oven drying may be effective, but it is slow. When conditions necessitate drying the commutator of a large machine without removing the armature from the field frame, this may be done by forcing hot air inside the commutator assembly or by applying low-temperature electric heaters to the surface of the commutator. Extreme care and very close attention will be required for such operations. Commutators that were hot when submerged are likely to have water in the segment mica as well as in the brush and V-rings.

## 4.5.0 Industrial Motors

Small and medium size AC or DC motors may be disassembled and dried satisfactorily in an oven. Large individual motors are often dried in an improvised oven or hot box built around the motor and heated by electric grids or space heaters.

## 4.6.0 Troubleshooting and Repair

The troubleshooting charts in *Tables 2* and *3* list many of the motor problems found in the industry, along with their causes and remedies. You may want to keep these charts as a reference.

### INSIDE TRACK

### *Vacuum Pressure-Impregnated Windings*

Instead of using a varnish on the windings of stators or rotors, some motor rewinding facilities use a technique called vacuum pressure impregnation or VPI to seal the windings. This technique is similar to the one used for transformer coils. The windings are encased with a mixture of epoxy resin and quartz powder under a high vacuum, which removes any moisture. Then the windings are cured with heat. This seals the windings against moisture and allows the operating heat to be rapidly transmitted away from the windings to the rotor core and stator where it can be effectively removed by air cooling or radiation.

**Table 2** AC/DC Motor Troubleshooting Chart

| Malfunction | Cause | Corrective Action |
|---|---|---|
| Hot bearings– general | Bent or sprung shaft<br>Excessive belt pull<br>Pulley too far away<br>Pulley diameter too small<br>Misalignment | Straighten or replace shaft.<br>Decrease belt tension.<br>Move pulley closer to bearing.<br>Use larger pulleys.<br>Correct by realignment of drive. |
| Hot bearings– sleeve | Oil grooving in bearing obstructed by dirt<br>Bent or damaged oil rings<br>Oil too heavy<br>Oil too light<br>Insufficient oil<br><br>Too much end thrust<br><br>Badly worn bearing | Remove bracket or pedestal with bearing and clean oil grooves and bearing housing; renew oil.<br>Repair or replace oil rings.<br>Use a recommended lighter oil.<br>Use a recommended heavier oil.<br>Fill reservoir to proper level in overflow plug with motor at rest.<br>Reduce thrust induced by driven machine or supply external means to carry thrust.<br>Replace bearing. |
| Hot bearings– ball | Insufficient grease<br>Deterioration of grease or lubricant contaminated<br>Excess lubricant<br><br>Heat from hot motor or external source<br>Overloaded bearing<br>Broken or rough races | Replace bearing and provide sufficient grease.<br>Remove old grease, wash bearings thoroughly in kerosene, and replace with new grease.<br>Reduce quantity of grease. Bearing should not be more than half filled.<br>Protect bearing by reducing motor temperature.<br>Check alignment, side thrust, and end thrust.<br>Clean housing thoroughly and replace bearing. |
| Oil leakage from overflow plugs | Stem of overflow plug not tight<br>Cracked or broken overflow plug<br>Plug cover not tight | Remove, re-cement threads, replace, and tighten.<br>Replace the plug.<br>Add a cork gasket, or, if screw type, may be tightened. |
| Dirty motor | Ventilation blocked, end windings filled with fine dust or lint<br><br><br>Rotor winding clogged<br><br>Bearing and brackets coated inside<br>Subject to dripping<br><br><br>Drenched condition<br><br>Submerged in flood waters | A clean motor will run 10° to 30°C cooler. The dust may be cement, sawdust, rock dust, grain dust, coal dust, or the like. Dismantle entire motor and clean all windings and parts.<br>Clean, grind, and undercut commutator. Clean and treat windings with good insulating varnish.<br>Dust and wash with cleaning solvent.<br>Wipe motor and dry by circulating heated air through motor. Install a drip or canopy-type cover over motor for protection.<br>Motor should be covered to retain heat and the rotor position shifted frequently.<br>Dismantle and clean parts. Bake windings in oven at 105°C for 24 hours or until resistance to ground is sufficient. First make sure commutator bushing is drained of water. |

**Table 3** DC Motor Troubleshooting Chart (1 of 4)

| Malfunction | Cause | Corrective Action |
|---|---|---|
| Fails to start | Circuit not complete | Switch is open or leads broken. |
| | Brushes not down on commutator | Brushes are worn out or held up by brush springs and need replacement. Replace brushes. |
| | Brushes stuck in holders | Remove and sand, clean up brush boxes. |
| | Armature locked by frozen bearings in motor or main drive | Remove brackets and replace bearings or recondition old bearings if inspection makes this possible. |
| | Power off | Check line connections to starter with light. Check contacts in starter. |
| Motor starts, then stops and reverses direction of rotation | Reversed polarity in generator that supplies power | Check generating unit for cause of changing polarity. |
| | Shunt and series fields bucking each other | Reconnect either shunt or series field so as to correct polarity. Then connect armature leads for desired direction of rotation. The fields can be tried separately to determine direction of rotation individually and connected so both give the same rotation. |
| Motor does not come up to rated speed | Overload | Check bearings to see if they are in good condition with correct lubrication. Check driven load for excessive load or friction. |
| | Starting resistance not all out | Check starter to see if mechanically and electrically in correct condition. |
| | Voltage low | Measure voltage with meter and check with motor nameplate. |
| | Short circuit in armature windings or between bars | For shorted armature, inspect commutator for blackened bars and burned adjacent bars. Inspect windings for burned coils or wedges. |
| | Starting heavy load with very weak field | Check full field relay and possibilities of full field setting of field rheostat. |
| | Motor off neutral | Check for factory setting of brush rigging or test motor for true neutral setting. |
| | Motor cold | Increase load on motor so as to increase temperature or add field rheostat to set speed. |
| Motor runs too fast | Voltage above rated level | Correct voltage or get recommended change in air gap from manufacturer. |
| | Load too light | Increase load or install fixed resistance in armature circuit. |
| | Shunt field coil shorted | Install new coil. |
| | Shunt field coil reversed | Reconnect coil leads in reverse. |
| | Series coil reversed | Reconnect coil leads in reverse. |
| | Series field coil shorted | Install new or repaired coil. |
| | Neutral setting shifted off neutral | Reset neutral by checking factory setting mark or testing for neutral. |
| | Part of shunt field rheostat or unnecessary resistance in field circuit | Measure voltage across field and check with nameplate rating. |
| | Motor ventilation restricted causing hot shunt field | Restore proper ventilation. |
| Motor gaining speed and increasing load does not slow it down | Unstable speed load regulation | Inspect motor to see if off neutral. If series field has a shunt around series circuit that can be removed, check series field to determine shorted turns. |
| | Reversed field coil shunt or series | Test with compass and reconnect coil. |
| | Too strong a commutating pole or commutating pole air gap too small | Check with factory for recommended change in coils or air gap. |
| | Voltage below rated level | Measure voltage and try to correct to value on motor nameplate. |
| | Overload | Check bearings of motors and drive to see if in good condition. Check for excessive friction in drive. |
| | Motor operates cold | Motor may run 20% slow due to light load. Install smaller motor. |
| | Neutral setting shifted | Check for factory setting of brush rigging or test for true neutral setting. |
| | Armature has shorted coils or commutator bars | Remove armature to repair shop and return to good condition. |

**Table 3**  DC Motor Troubleshooting Chart (2 of 4)

| Malfunction | Cause | Corrective Action |
|---|---|---|
| Motor overheats or runs hot | Overloaded and draws 25% to 50% more current than rated | Reduce load by reducing speed, gearing, or loading in the drive. |
| | Voltage above rated level | Motor runs drive above rated speed, requiring excessive hp. Reduce voltage to nameplate rating. |
| | Inadequately ventilated | Location of motor should be changed. |
| | Draws excessive current due to shorted coil | Repair armature coils or install new coil. |
| | Grounds in armature such as two grounds that constitute a short | Locate grounds and repair or rewind with new set of coils. |
| | Armature rubs pole faces due to off-center rotor causing friction and excessive current | Check brackets or pedestals to center rotor and determine condition of bearing wear for bearing replacement. |
| Hot armature | Core hot in one spot indicating shorted punching and high iron loss | Sometimes full-slot metal wedges have been used for balancing. These should be removed and other means of balancing investigated. |
| | Punching uninsulated; punching has been turned or band grooves machined in the core; machined slots | No-load running of motor will indicate hot core and draw high no-load armature current. Replace core and rewind armature. Check temperature on core with thermometer (not to exceed 90°C). |
| | Brush tension too high | Limit pressure to 2 to 2½ psi. Check brush density and limit to density recommended by brush manufacturer. |
| Hot commutator | Brushes off neutral | Reset neutral. |
| | Brush grade too abrasive | Get recommendation from manufacturer. |
| | Shorted bars | Investigate commutator mica and undercutting; repair if necessary. |
| | Hot core and coils that transmit heat to commutator | Check temperature of commutator with thermometer to see that total temperature does not exceed ambient plus 55°C rise (total not to exceed 105°C). |
| | Inadequate ventilation | Check as for hot motor. |
| Hot fields | Voltage too high | Check with meter and thermometer and correct voltage to nameplate value. |
| | Shorted turns or grounded turns | Repair or replace with new coil. |
| | Resistance of each coil not the same | Check each individual coil for equal resistance within 10% and if one coil is too low, replace coil. |
| | Inadequate ventilation | Check as for hot motor. |
| | Coil not large enough to radiate its loss wattage | New coils should replace all coils if room is available in motor. |
| Motor vibrates and indicates imbalance | Armature out of balance | Remove and statically balance or balance in dynamic balancing machine. |
| | Misalignment | Realign. |
| | Loose or eccentric pulley | Tighten pulley on shaft or correct eccentric pulley. |
| | Belt or chain whip | Adjust belt tension. |
| | Mismating of gear and pinion | Recut, realign, or replace parts. |
| | Imbalance in coupling | Rebalance coupling. |
| | Bent shaft | Replace or straighten shaft. |
| | Foundation inadequate | Stiffen mounting plate members. |
| | Motor loosely mounted | Tighten hold-down bolts. |
| | Motor feet uneven | Add shims under foot pads to mount each foot tight. |
| Motor sparks at brushes or does not commutate | Neutral setting not true neutral | Check and set on factory setting or test for true neutral. |
| | Commutator rough | Grind and roll edge of each bar. |
| | Commutator eccentric | Turn, grind, and roll commutator. |
| | Mica high—not undercut | Undercut mica. |
| | Commutating pole strength too great, causing overcompensation or strength too weak, indicating undercompensation | Check with manufacturer for correct change in air gap or new coils for the commutating coils. |
| | Shorted commutating pole turns | Repair coils or install new coils. |
| | Shorted armature coils on commutator bars | Repair armature. |

**Table 3** DC Motor Troubleshooting Chart (3 of 4)

| Malfunction | Cause | Corrective Action |
|---|---|---|
| Motor sparks at brushes or does not commutate (continued) | Open circuited coils | Repair coils or install new coils. |
| | Poor soldered connection to commutator bars | Resolder with proper alloy of tin solder. |
| | High bar or loose bar in commutator at high speeds | Inspect commutator nut or bolts and retighten and grind commutator face. |
| | Brush grade wrong type; brush pressure too light, current density excessive, brushes stuck in holders; brush shunts loose | See corrections for brushes. |
| | Brushes chatter due to dirty film on commutator | Resurface commutator face and check for change in brushes. |
| | Vibration | Eliminate cause of vibration by checking mounting and balance of rotor. |
| Brush wear excessive | Brushes too soft | Blow dust from motor and replace brushes with a changed grade as recommended by manufacturer. |
| | Commutator rough | Grind commutator face. |
| | Abrasive dust in ventilating air | Replace brushes and correct condition to protect motor. |
| | Off neutral setting | Recheck factory neutral or test for true neutral. |
| | Bad commutation | See corrections for commutation. |
| | High, low, or loose bar | Retighten commutator motor bolts and resurface commutator. |
| | Brush tension excessive | Adjust spring pressure (not to exceed 2 to 2½ psi). |
| | Electrical wear due to loss of film on commutator face | Resurface brush faces and commutator face. Check for change in brush grade. |
| | Threading and grooving | Same as above. |
| | Oil or grease from atmosphere or bearings | Correct oil condition and surface brush faces and commutator. |
| | Weak acid and moisture-laden atmosphere | Protect motor by changing ventilating air or change to enclosed motor. |
| Motor noisy | Brush singing | Check brush angle and commutator coating; resurface commutator. |
| | Brush chatter | Resurface commutator and brush face. |
| | Motor loosely mounted | Tighten foundation bolts. |
| | Foundation hollow and acts as sounding board | Coat underside with soundproofing material. |
| | Strained frame | Shim motor feet for equal mounting. |
| | Armature punching loose | Replace core on armature. |
| | Armature rubs pole faces | Recenter by replacing bearings or relocating brackets or pedestals. |
| | Magnetic hum | Refer to manufacturer. |
| | Belt slap or pounding | Check condition of belt and change belt tension. |
| | Excessive current load | May not cause overheating, but check chart for correction of shorted or grounded coils. |
| | Mechanical vibration | Check chart for causes of vibration. |
| | Noisy bearings | Check alignment, loading of bearings, and lubrication; get recommendations from manufacturer. |
| Motor stalls | Wrong application | Change type or size. Consult manufacturer. |
| | Overloaded motor | Reduce load. |
| | Low motor voltage | See that nameplate voltage is maintained. |
| | Open circuit | Fuses blown; check overload relay, starter, and pushbuttons. |
| | Incorrect control resistance of wound rotor | Check control sequence. Replace broken resistors. Repair open circuits. |
| Motor connected but does not start | One phase open | See that no phase is open. |
| | Motor may be overloaded | Reduce load. |
| | Rotor defective | Look for broken bars or rings. |
| | Poor stator coil connection | Remove end bells. |

**Table 3** DC Motor Troubleshooting Chart (4 of 4)

| Malfunction | Cause | Corrective Action |
|---|---|---|
| Motor runs and then slows down | Power failure | Check for loose connections to line, fuses, and control. |
| Motor does not come up to speed | Not applied properly | Consult supplier for proper type. |
| | Voltage too low at motor terminals because of line drop | Use higher voltage on transformer terminals or reduce load. |
| | If wound rotor, improper control operation of secondary resistance | Correct secondary control. |
| | Starting load too high | Check load motor is supposed to carry at start. |
| | Low pull-in torque of synchronous motor | Change rotor starting resistance or change rotor design. |
| | Check that all brushes are riding on rings | Check secondary connections. |
| | Broken rotor bars | Look for cracks near rings. A new rotor may be required as repairs are usually temporary. |
| | Open primary circuit | Locate fault with testing device and repair. |
| Motor takes too long to accelerate | Excess loading | Reduce load. |
| | Poor circuit | Check for high resistance. |
| | Defective squirrel cage rotor | Replace with new rotor. |
| | Applied voltage too low | Get power company to increase voltage tap. |
| Wrong rotation | Wrong sequence of phase | Reverse connections at motor or switchboard. |
| Motor overheats while running under load | Check for overload | Reduce load. |
| | Wrong blowers or air shields; may be clogged with dirt and prevent proper ventilation of motor | Good ventilation is manifest when a continuous stream of air leaves the motor. If not, check with manufacturer. |
| | Motor may have one phase open | Check to make sure that all leads are well connected. |
| | Grounded coil | Locate and repair. |
| | Unbalanced terminal voltage | Check for faulty leads, connections, and transformers. |
| | Shorted stator coil | Repair and then check wattmeter reading. |
| | Faulty connection | Indicated by high resistance; check all connections. |
| | High voltage | Check terminals of motor with voltmeter. |
| | Low voltage | Same as for high voltage. |
| | Rotor rubs stator bore | If not poor machining, replace worn bearings. |
| Motor vibrates after corrections have been made | Motor misaligned | Realign. |
| | Weak foundation | Strengthen base. |
| | Coupling out of balance | Balance coupling. |
| | Driven equipment unbalanced | Rebalance driven equipment. |
| | Defective ball bearing | Replace bearing. |
| | Bearings not in line | Line up properly. |
| | Balancing weights shifted | Rebalance rotor. |
| | Wound rotor coils replaced | Rebalance rotor. |
| | Polyphase motor running single phase | Check for open circuit. |
| | Excessive end play | Adjust bearing or add washer. |
| Unbalanced line current on polyphase motors during normal operation | Unequal terminal volts | Check leads and connections. |
| | Single-phase operation | Check for open contacts. |
| | Poor rotor contacts in control wound-rotor resistance | Check control devices. |
| | Brushes not in proper position in wound-rotor motor | See that brushes are properly seated and shunts in good condition. |
| Scraping noise | Fan rubbing air shield | Remove interference. |
| | Fan striking insulation | Clear fan. |
| | Loose on bedplate | Tighten holding bolts. |
| Magnetic noise | Air gap not uniform | Check and correct bracket fits or bearings. |
| | Loose bearings | Correct or renew. |
| | Rotor imbalance | Rebalance. |

INSIDE TRACK

## *Online Motor Monitoring*

Some manufacturers offer comprehensive motor analysis instruments that can be used for the operational monitoring of large motors. These instruments can monitor online motor power circuit quality, overall motor condition, load conditions, and performance efficiency during motor operation. Most instruments provide data collection and trending information for periodic maintenance purposes. Some instruments can also monitor and provide data for variable frequency drive (VFD) motor systems. Depending on the complexity of a particular instrument, the following tests may be performed:

- Over/undervoltage
- Voltage unbalance
- Harmonic distortion
- Effective service factor for thermal overloading
- Single-phase overcurrent
- Amplitude of rotor bar sideband and rotor cage signature related to stored thresholds
- Torque, frequency, and average stator current value comparison and alert for deviating values
- Torque ripple
- Load history
- Vibration signature monitoring of a motor-load system and alert for signature deviation

The instrument shown here can be directly connected to terminals in motor control centers for up to 600V motors or, for safety purposes, to an external interface port that is permanently installed at the motor control center. This particular instrument uses the U.S. Department of Energy Motormaster+ software to aid in providing periodic maintenance trending information, energy efficiency of comparable motors, and motor replacement recommendations with payback estimates.

MOTOR ANALYSIS INSTRUMENT

EXTERNAL INTERFACE PORT

410P1004.EPS

# Review Questions

1. When an induction motor fails, the most likely cause of the problem is the _____.
   a. rotor
   b. stator
   c. shaft
   d. end bells

2. One of the first symptoms of an open rotor circuit in a wound-rotor motor is _____.
   a. lack of torque
   b. low voltage
   c. low current
   d. increased torque

3. If a squirrel cage induction motor slows down under load and shows reduced starting torque, look for _____.
   a. low resistance points in the rotor circuit
   b. excess current
   c. excess voltage
   d. open circuits or high resistance points in the rotor circuit

4. If the load connected to a motor is increased beyond the motor's rated amount, which of the following is most likely to occur?
   a. Contact between the rotor and stator
   b. Decreased operating temperature
   c. Increased operating temperature and decreased motor life
   d. Loss of bearing lubrication

5. Grinding the rotor laminations in an induction motor _____ the power factor.
   a. does not change
   b. slightly increases
   c. maximizes
   d. lowers

6. The purpose of using laminated steel plates in constructing the stator and rotor of a motor is to _____.
   a. reduce eddy currents
   b. reduce the weight of the motor
   c. increase horsepower
   d. increase power consumption

7. _____ starting employs motors with two separate winding circuits.
   a. Primary resistor
   b. Autotransformer
   c. Wye-delta
   d. Part-winding

8. An insulation system that, by experience or accepted test, can be shown to have a suitable thermal endurance when operated at a limiting temperature of 105°C is a Class _____ insulation system.
   a. A
   b. B
   c. F
   d. H

9. An insulation system that, by experience or accepted test, can be shown to have a suitable thermal endurance when operated at a limiting temperature of 130°C is a Class _____ insulation system.
   a. A
   b. B
   c. F
   d. H

10. The maximum compressed air pressure that may be used to clean motor insulation is _____ psi.
    a. 10
    b. 20
    c. 30
    d. 40

11. Filing the stator teeth in an induction motor _____ the power factor.
    a. does not change
    b. increases
    c. maximizes
    d. lowers

12. An insulation system that, by experience or accepted test, can be shown to have a suitable thermal endurance when operated at a limiting temperature of 155°C is a Class _____ insulation system.
    a. A
    b. B
    c. F
    d. H

**13.** An insulation system that, by experience or accepted test, can be shown to have a suitable thermal endurance when operated at a limiting temperature of 180°C is a Class _____ insulation system.
   a. A
   b. B
   c. F
   d. H

**14.** Typical materials used in a Class H insulation system include _____.
   a. cotton
   b. paper
   c. cellulose acetate films
   d. silicone elastomer

**15.** Typical materials used in a Class F insulation system include _____.
   a. cotton
   b. paper
   c. cellulose acetate films
   d. mica

# Summary

To ensure long life and trouble-free operation, motors must be carefully maintained. The best approach to good motor maintenance is to use a systematic program of inspection. In general, these inspections should be made frequently enough to prevent serious trouble. The exact interval between inspections will depend, to a certain extent, on the conditions of the application involved. However, experience will soon indicate the approximate time interval required.

Electricians who maintain motor starting equipment must be thoroughly trained for the job and know how to correct common faults. Good maintenance personnel, coupled with a good preventive maintenance program, will almost certainly keep motors operating in good condition for the majority of the time. In general, this program will consist of continuing inspection of equipment, the reporting and recording of the condition of the equipment, and motor repair. Motor controls, overcurrent protection, and motor overload protective devices should also receive the same amount of care.

# Notes

# Trade Terms
# Introduced in This Module

*Breakdown:* The failure of insulation to effectively prevent the flow of current, sometimes evidenced by arcing. If the voltage is gradually raised, breakdown will begin suddenly at a certain voltage level. Current flow is not directly proportional to voltage. Once a breakdown current has flowed, especially for a period of time, the next gradual application of voltage will often show breakdown beginning at a lower voltage than initially.

*Dielectric:* An insulating material positioned between two conductive materials in such a way that a charge or voltage may appear across the two conductive materials.

*Insulation class:* Category of insulation based on the thermal endurance of the insulation system used in a motor. The insulation system is chosen to ensure that the motor will perform at the rated horsepower and service factor load.

*Leakage:* AC or DC current flow through insulation and over its surfaces, and AC current flow through a capacitance. Current flow is directly proportional to voltage. The insulation and/or capacitance is thought of as a constant impedance unless breakdown occurs.

*Megohmmeter:* An instrument or meter capable of measuring resistances in excess of 200 megohms. It usually employs a higher voltage power supply than that used in ohmmeters, which measure up to 200 megohms.

*Totally enclosed motor:* A motor that is encased to prevent the free exchange of air between the inside and outside of the case.

This module is intended to present thorough resources for task training. The following reference works are suggested for further study. These are optional materials for continuing education rather than for task training.

*American Electrician's Handbook.* Terrell Croft and Wilfred I. Summers. New York, NY: McGraw-Hill, 1996.

*National Electrical Code® Handbook,* Latest Edition. Quincy, MA: National Fire Protection Association.

The NCCER makes every effort to keep these textbooks up-to-date and free of technical errors. We appreciate your help in this process. If you have an idea for improving this textbook, or if you find an error, a typographical mistake, or an inaccuracy in NCCER's *Contren®* textbooks, please write us, using this form or a photocopy. Be sure to include the exact module number, page number, a detailed description, and the correction, if applicable. Your input will be brought to the attention of the Technical Review Committee. Thank you for your assistance.

*Instructors* – If you found that additional materials were necessary in order to teach this module effectively, please let us know so that we may include them in the Equipment/Materials list in the Annotated Instructor's Guide.

**Write:**    Product Development
National Center for Construction Education and Research
P.O. Box 141104, Gainesville, FL 32614-1104

**Fax:**    352-334-0932

**E-mail:**    curriculum@nccer.org

Craft _____ Module Name _____

Copyright Date _____ Module Number _____ Page Number(s) _____

Description _____

_____

_____

_____

(Optional) Correction _____

_____

_____

(Optional) Your Name and Address _____

_____

_____

# Motors: Theory and Application

## 26202-05

**Lake House Spa & Pool Barn
at Lake Austin Spa Resort**
Austin, Texas
Commercial $5–10 Million Award Winner
Spaw Glass Contractors, Inc.

# 26202-05
# *Motors: Theory and Application*

*Topics to be presented in this module include:*

## Overview

Motor windings are electromagnets in which like polarities repel one another and unlike polarities attract each other. The rotor in any motor is the part that turns and is used to drive the load. The stationary windings are typically mounted in a doughnut-like arrangement into which the rotor is installed.

    Windings are built into the rotor, and current flows through these windings. Likewise, a current flow is created through the stationary windings. Any time current flows through a conductor, a magnetic field is created around that conductor. Since both windings have current flowing through them at the same time, magnetic fields are generated around both windings. As these magnetic fields interact, they either repel or attract each other. Manipulating the current flow through the rotor and the secondary windings enables the rotor to turn at controlled speeds or in different directions. This is the basic operation of any motor. Motors can be designed to supply high speed, high torque, or both, depending on the demands of the load.

## Objectives

Upon completion of this module, you will be able to do the following:

1. Define the following terms:
   - Ampacity
   - Branch circuit
   - Circuit breaker
   - Controller
   - Duty
   - Equipment
   - Full-load amps
   - Ground fault circuit interrupter
   - Interrupting rating
   - Motor circuit switch
   - Thermal protector
   - NEMA design letter
   - Nonautomatic
   - Overcurrent
   - Overload
   - Power factor
   - Rated full-load speed
   - Rated horsepower
   - Remote control circuit
   - Service factor
   - Thermal cutout
2. Describe the various types of motor enclosures.
3. Describe how the rated voltage of a motor differs from the system voltage.
4. Describe the basic construction and components of a three-phase squirrel cage induction motor.
5. Explain the relationships among speed, frequency, and the number of poles in a three-phase induction motor.
6. Describe how torque is developed in an induction motor.
7. Explain how and why torque varies with rotor reactance and slip.
8. Define percent slip and speed regulation.
9. Explain how the direction of a three-phase motor is reversed.
10. Describe the component parts and operating characteristics of a three-phase wound-rotor induction motor.
11. Describe the component parts and operating characteristics of a three-phase synchronous motor.
12. Define torque, starting current, and armature reaction as they apply to DC motors.
13. Explain how the direction of rotation of a DC motor is changed.
14. Describe the design and characteristics of a DC shunt, series, and compound motor.
15. Describe dual-voltage motors and their applications.
16. Describe the methods for determining various motor connections.
17. Describe general motor protection requirements as delineated in the *NEC®*.

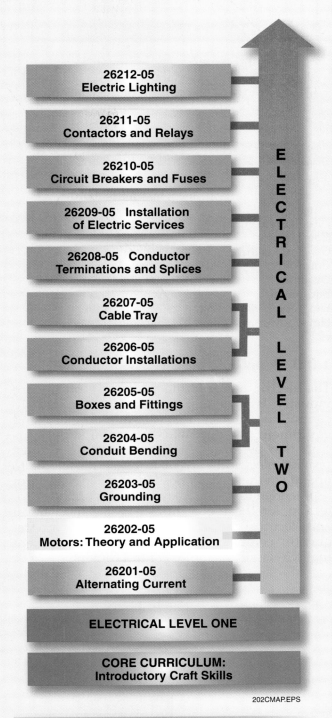

202CMAP.EPS

## Prerequisites

Before you begin this module, it is recommended that you successfully complete *Core Curriculum; Electrical Level One;* and *Electrical Level Two,* Module 26201-05.

This course map shows all of the modules in *Electrical Level Two.* The suggested training order begins at the bottom and proceeds up. Skill levels increase as you advance on the course map. The local Training Program Sponsor may adjust the training order.

1. Pencil and paper
2. Appropriate personal protective equipment
3. Copy of the latest edition of the *National Electrical Code*®

### Trade Terms

| | |
|---|---|
| Armature | Hours |
| Branch circuit | Intermittent duty |
| Brush | Overcurrent |
| Circuit breaker | Overload |
| Commutator | Periodic duty |
| Continuous duty | Revolutions per minute |
| Controller | (rpm) |
| Duty | Rotation |
| Equipment | Synchronous speed |
| Field poles | Thermal protector |
| Horsepower | Varying duty |

## 1.0.0 ◆ INTRODUCTION

The electric motor is the workhorse of modern industry. Its functions are almost unlimited. To control the motors that drive machinery and **equipment**, we must have electrical supply circuits that perform certain functions. They must provide electrical current to cause the motor to operate in the manner needed to make it perform its intended function. They must also provide protection for the motor from adverse mechanical and electrical conditions. These functions are frequently combined within electrical equipment that we classify as motor control centers.

A thorough understanding of the functions of the various components of a motor control center is desirable from both a maintenance and a troubleshooting standpoint. Properly-maintained motor control centers ensure a minimum of downtime for unscheduled repairs, increase productivity, and contribute to a safer working environment.

## 2.0.0 ◆ DC MOTOR PRINCIPLES

When a bar of magnetic material is given an induced magnetic charge, a field of magnetic force is developed around the bar. We picture this field as consisting of lines of force that exist in the space surrounding the bar. These lines of force appear to leave one end of the bar and extend outside the bar to the opposite end.

The end of the bar magnet where magnetic lines appear to start is called the north pole of the magnet, while the end where these lines reenter the magnet is called the south pole. Actually, the lines extend inside the magnet from the south pole to the north pole, completing a closed loop. This principle is shown in *Figure 1*.

There are several characteristics of these magnetic lines of force that must be remembered when dealing with electric motors. They are:

- Magnetic lines of force are continuous and always form closed loops.
- Magnetic lines of force do not cross.
- Magnetic lines of force with polarities in the same direction repel each other. In other words, a north pole will repel a north pole and a south pole will repel a south pole.

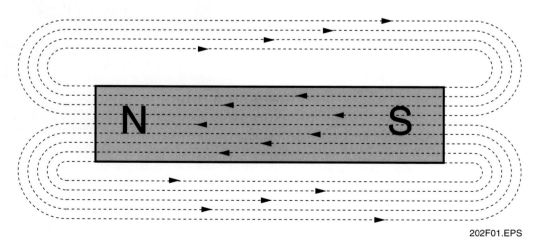

202F01.EPS

*Figure 1* ◆ Magnetic field.

- Magnetic lines of force having polarities in opposite directions tend to attract each other and combine. In other words, a south pole will be attracted by a north pole and vice versa.
- Magnetic lines of force tend to shorten themselves. Therefore, the magnetic lines of force existing between two unlike poles cause the poles to tend to pull together.
- Magnetic lines of force pass through all known materials, magnetic or nonmagnetic. Some materials provide a much easier path for these lines than others. These materials have high permeability and low reluctance. (Reluctance is discussed later in this module.)

## 2.1.0 Hand Rules

When a current is passed through the wire, circular lines of force are produced around the wire. These flux lines go in a direction described by the left-hand rule. This rule is shown in *Figure 2*.

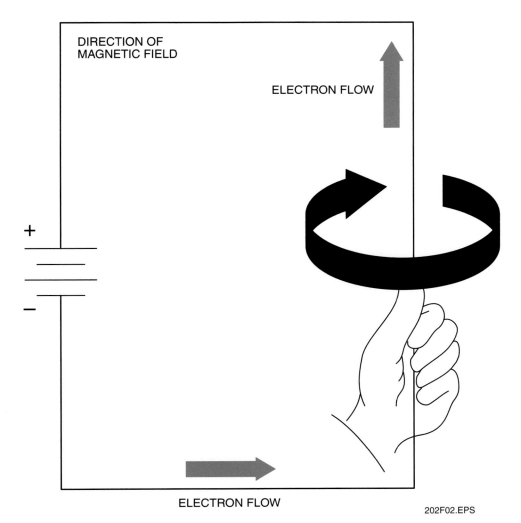

*Figure 2* ◆ Left-hand rule for conductors.

The left-hand rule shows the direction of the flux lines around a wire that is carrying current. When the thumb points in the direction of the electron current, the fingers will point in the direction of the magnetic lines of force.

The right-hand rule for motors shows the direction that a current-carrying wire will be moved in a magnetic field (see *Figure 3*). When the forefinger is pointed in the direction of the magnetic field lines, and the center finger is pointed in the direction of the current in the wire, the thumb will point in the direction that the wire will be moved.

## 2.2.0 DC Motor Components

A DC motor consists of a few major components, each with a specific purpose in the motor's operation.

The armature is a movable electromagnet located between the poles of another fixed permanent (field) magnet, as shown in *Figure 4*.

The magnetic field from the armature conductors interacts with the magnetic field from the field magnet. The result of the field interaction is motor action.

Current in a conductor also has its associated magnetic field. When a conductor is placed in another magnetic field from a separate source, the two fields can react to produce motor action. The conductor must be perpendicular to the magnetic field, as illustrated in *Figure 5*. This way, the perpendicular magnetic field of the current is in the same plane as the external magnetic field.

Unless the two fields are in the same plane, they cannot affect each other. In the same plane, however, lines of force in the same direction reinforce to make a stronger field, while lines in the opposite direction cancel and result in a weaker field. The stronger field tends to move the conductor toward the weaker field, as illustrated in *Figure 5*.

These directions are summarized as follows:

- With the conductor at 90°, or perpendicular to the external field, the reaction between the two magnetic fields is at its maximum.
- With the conductor at 0°, or parallel to the external field, there is no effect between them.
- When the conductor rise is at an angle between 0° and 90°, only the perpendicular component is effective.

In motor action, the wire only moves in a straight line, and it stops moving once out of the field, even though current still exists. A practical motor must develop continuous rotary motion. To produce this, a twisting force called torque must be developed.

Torque is produced by mounting a loop in a fixed magnetic field. Current is applied and the flux lines along both sides of the loop interact, causing the loop to act like a lever with a force pushing on its two sides in opposite directions. This is shown in *Figure 6*.

The combined forces result in a turning force or torque, because the rotor or armature is arranged to pivot on its axis. The overall turning force on the armature depends on several factors, including field strength, armature current strength, and the physical construction of the armature, especially the distance from the loop sides to the axis lines.

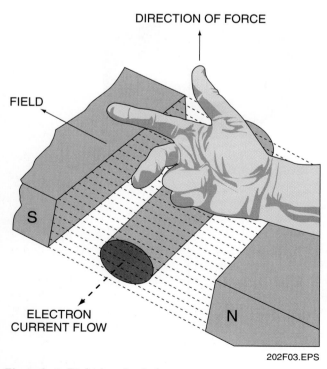

202F03.EPS

*Figure 3* ◆ Right-hand rule for motors.

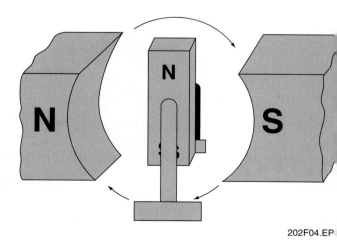

202F04.EP

*Figure 4* ◆ Basic motor action.

## Hand Rules for Motors

**THINK ABOUT IT**

Use the left-hand conductor rule and the right-hand motor rule to explain the motor action pictured in *Figure 5*.

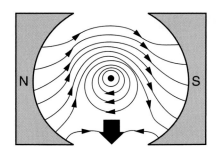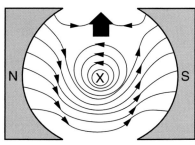

202F05.EPS

*Figure 5* ◆ Motor action.

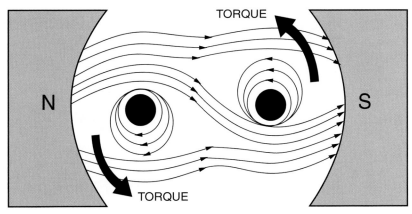

202F06.EPS

*Figure 6* ◆ Torque.

Because of the lever action, the forces on the sides of the armature loop will increase as the loop sides are farther from the axis; therefore, larger armatures will produce greater torques.

In the practical motor, the torque determines the energy available for doing useful work. The greater the torque, the greater the energy. If a motor does not develop enough torque to turn its load, it stalls.

To get continuous **rotation,** the armature must be kept moving in the same direction. This requires reversing the direction of current through the armature for every 180° of revolution. A **commutator** is used to provide this switching action. This is shown in *Figure 7*.

The commutator on a DC motor is a conducting ring that is split into two segments, with each segment connected to an end of the armature loop. Current enters the side of the armature closest to the south pole of the field and leaves the side closest to the north pole of the field. The interaction of the two fields produces a torque, and the armature rotates in that direction.

A **brush** makes contact with each segment of the commutator, providing a connection between the movable commutator and the stationary DC power source. *Figure 8* shows various brushes and commutator connections used in DC motors.

The problem of switching commutator segments in a simple single-loop motor is that when

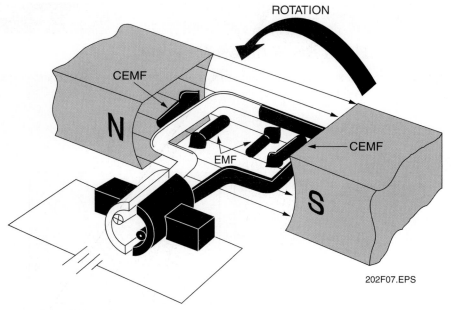

202F07.EPS

*Figure 7* ◆ Single-loop armature DC motor.

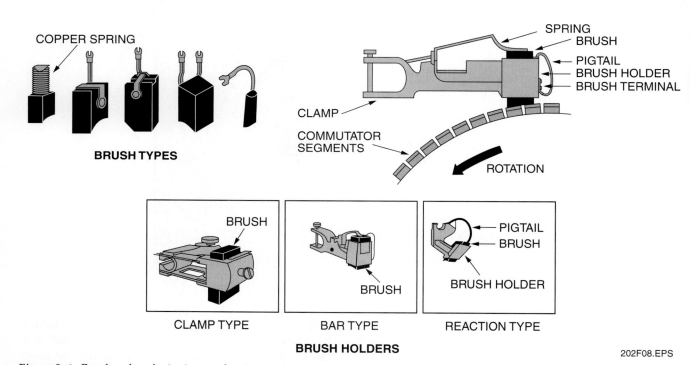

202F08.EPS

*Figure 8* ◆ Brushes, brush rigging, and commutator connections.

the motor stops, there is no way of predicting the position of the armature at rest. If the armature stops in a position where the commutator is in the middle of switching, the motor will not start unless you physically turn the armature.

This problem can be overcome by winding more coils on the armature and by using more commutator segments. This will produce a self-starting motor. The motor shown in *Figure 9* uses three armature coils and three commutator segments. Regardless of where the armature comes to rest, there is always a path for current that will produce torque to rotate the armature.

## 2.3.0 The Neutral Plane

The armature turns when torque is produced, and torque is produced as long as the fields of the

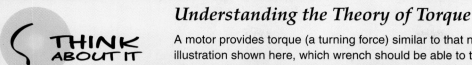

## *Understanding the Theory of Torque*

A motor provides torque (a turning force) similar to that needed to turn a nut. In the illustration shown here, which wrench should be able to turn the nut easier?

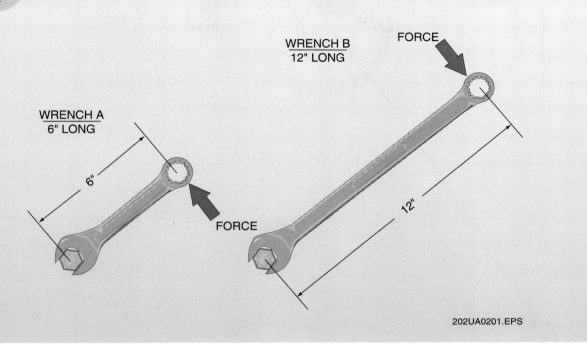

202UA0201.EPS

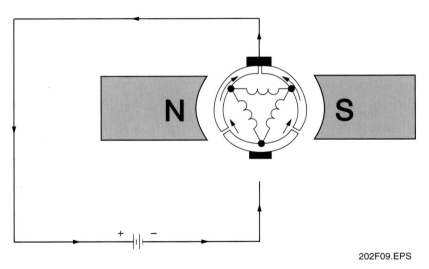

202F09.EPS

*Figure 9* ◆ Self-starting motor.

magnet and armature interact. When the loop reaches a position perpendicular to the field, the interaction of the magnetic fields stops. This position is the neutral plane, shown in *Figure 10*.

In the neutral plane, no torque is produced and the rotation of the armature should stop. However, inertia tends to keep the armature in motion even after the prime moving force is removed; thus the armature tends to rotate past the neutral plane. At the neutral position, the commutator disconnects from the brushes, and once the armature goes past neutral, the sides of the loop reverse positions. The switching action of the commutator maintains the direction of current through the

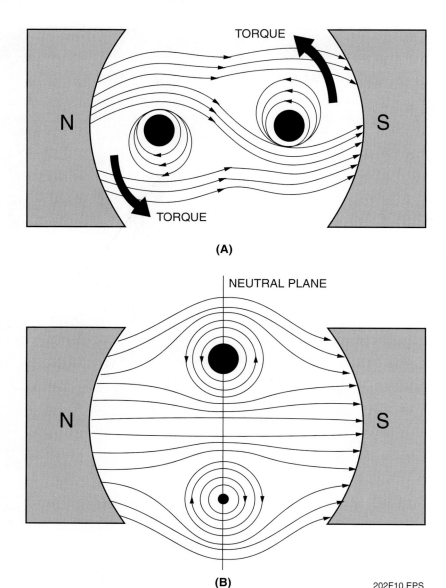

**Figure 10** ◆ Neutral plane.

armature. Current still enters the armature side that is closest to the south pole.

Since the magnet's field direction remains the same throughout, the interaction of fields after commutation keeps the torque going in the original direction; thus, continuous rotation is maintained. See *Figure 11*.

Although such an elementary DC motor can be built and operated, it has two serious shortcomings that prevent it from being useful: first, such a motor cannot always start by itself; and second, once started, it operates very irregularly.

When the elementary DC motor runs, its operation is erratic because it produces torque irregularly. Maximum torque is produced only when the plane of the single-loop armature is parallel with the plane of the field. This is the

position at right angles to the neutral plane. Once the armature passes this plane of maximum torque, less and less torque is developed until it arrives at the neutral plane again. Inertia carries the armature past the neutral plane and so the motor continues to turn. Its irregularity in producing torque, however, prevents the single-loop elementary DC motor from being used for practical jobs.

## 2.4.0 Two-Loop DC Motors

The basic DC motor is improved by building the armature with two or more loops. The loops are placed at right angles to each other; when one loop lies in the neutral plane, the other is in the plane of maximum torque. See *Figure 12*.

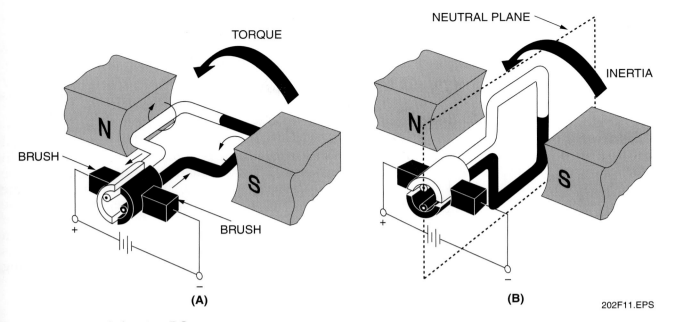

*Figure 11* ◆ Neutral plane in a DC motor.

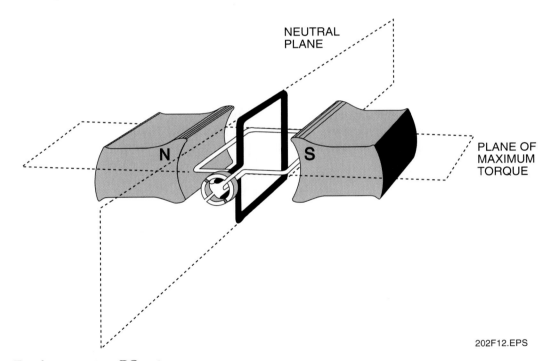

*Figure 12* ◆ Two-loop armature DC motor.

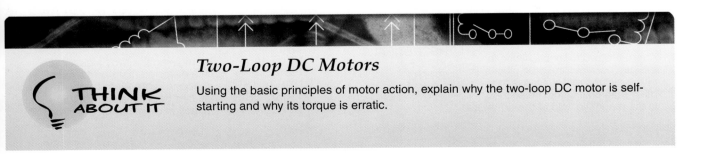

## *Two-Loop DC Motors*

Using the basic principles of motor action, explain why the two-loop DC motor is self-starting and why its torque is erratic.

In this case, the commutator is split into two pairs or four segments, with one segment associated with each end of each armature loop. This sets up two parallel loop circuits. Only one loop at a time is ever connected if power is supplied through one pair of fixed brushes to one set of ring segments.

In this multi-loop armature, the commutator serves two functions: it maintains current through the armature in the same direction at all times, and it switches power to the armature loop nearing the maximum torque position.

This motor is self-starting because at least one winding will have interaction with the main field. With this two-loop system, the torque developed is steadier and stronger but still somewhat erratic, because only one loop at a time provides the torque that drives the motor.

## 2.5.0 Armature Reaction

When a motor armature is supplied with current, a magnetic flux is built up around the conductors of the armature windings. Armature reaction is caused by two magnetic fields: the main magnetic field from the field magnets and the magnetic field produced by the armature. These two fields combine to produce a new resultant magnetic field.

The resultant field is distorted and shifts opposite the main field and opposite the direction of armature rotation. This distortion shifts the neutral plane of the motor. See *Figure 13* for an illustration of armature reaction.

The amount of armature reaction determines how far the neutral plane is shifted. The amount of armature reaction depends on the amount and direction of the armature current. The concern over the neutral plane shift occurs because of the need for commutation.

Commutation, or the switching of the armature polarity, must take place at the neutral plane in order to allow the output current from the machine to remain in the same direction without arcing. When commutation takes place anywhere other than the neutral plane, it is like a switch that is opened during high current—it will draw an arc.

This armature reaction can be overcome by installing interpole windings. Interpoles are special electromagnetic pole pieces that are connected in series with the armature winding. The armature current causes a magnetic field to form around the windings. Their action is self-regulating, and the interpole field will apply the proper amount of cancellation field for any set of conditions. For a high armature reaction, the canceling field is strong. For a low armature reaction, the canceling field is weaker. See *Figure 14*.

## 2.6.0 Counter-Electromotive Force (CEMF)

When a DC motor is in operation, it acts much like a DC generator. A magnetic field is produced by the **field poles,** and a loop of wire in the armature turns and cuts this magnetic field. To understand counter-electromotive force (CEMF), first disregard the fact that external current is being applied to the rotor via the carbon brushes on the commutator segments. As the armature wires rotate and cut the magnetic field of the field poles, a voltage is induced in them similar to that which was discussed in induction motors. This induced voltage (EMF) causes a current to flow in them and a resulting magnetic field is created.

Before analyzing the relative direction between the current induced in the armature windings and the current that caused it in the field poles, first

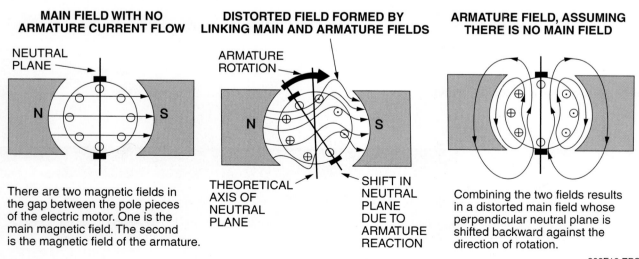

MAIN FIELD WITH NO ARMATURE CURRENT FLOW

NEUTRAL PLANE

There are two magnetic fields in the gap between the pole pieces of the electric motor. One is the main magnetic field. The second is the magnetic field of the armature.

DISTORTED FIELD FORMED BY LINKING MAIN AND ARMATURE FIELDS

ARMATURE ROTATION

THEORETICAL AXIS OF NEUTRAL PLANE

SHIFT IN NEUTRAL PLANE DUE TO ARMATURE REACTION

ARMATURE FIELD, ASSUMING THERE IS NO MAIN FIELD

Combining the two fields results in a distorted main field whose perpendicular neutral plane is shifted backward against the direction of rotation.

202F13.EPS

*Figure 13* ◆ Armature reaction.

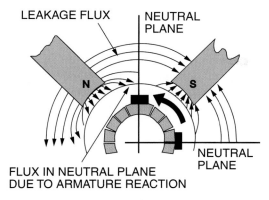

LEAKAGE FLUX

NEUTRAL PLANE

FLUX IN NEUTRAL PLANE
DUE TO ARMATURE REACTION

NEUTRAL PLANE

Interpoles produce a local field at the neutral plane that opposes the flux produced by armature reaction to restore the original neutral plane.

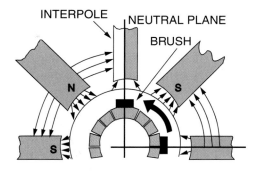

Interpoles are used on practical DC motors to counteract armature reaction.

INTERPOLE  NEUTRAL PLANE

BRUSH

202F14.EPS

*Figure 14* ◆ Interpoles.

remember the left-hand rule. Using your left hand, hold it such that your index finger points in the direction of the magnetic field (north to south) and your thumb points in the direction of rotational force on a given conductor. Your middle finger will now point in the direction of current flow for that conductor. This current would be in opposition to the current that is flowing from the battery. Since this induced voltage and induced current are opposite to those of the battery, they are called CEMF. The two currents are flowing in opposite directions. This would mean that the battery voltage and the CEMF are opposite in polarity. See *Figure 15*.

When first discussing CEMF, we disregarded the fact that external DC was being applied to the armature via the brushes. The induced voltage and resulting current flow was then shown to flow opposite to the externally applied current. This was an oversimplification, since only one current flows. Since the CEMF can never become as large as the external applied voltage, and since they are opposite in polarity, the CEMF works to cancel only a part of the applied voltage. The single current that flows is smaller due to the CEMF.

Since the CEMF of a motor is generated by the action of the armature windings cutting the lines of force set up by the field poles, the value of it will

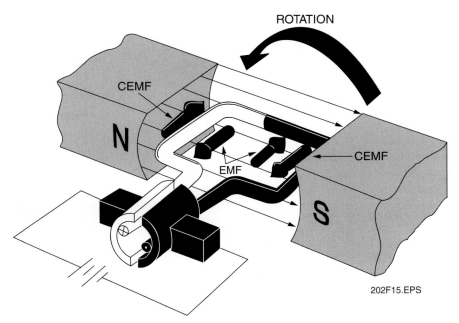

ROTATION

CEMF

N

EMF

CEMF

S

202F15.EPS

*Figure 15* ◆ Counter-electromotive force (CEMF).

depend on the field strength and the armature speed. The effective voltage acting in the armature is the terminal voltage minus the CEMF. Ohm's law gives the value of armature current by:

$$\text{Armature } (I_A) = \frac{\text{terminal voltage} - \text{CEMF}}{\text{armature resistance } (R_A)}$$

$$\text{Where CEMF} = \text{terminal voltage} - (I_A \times R_A)$$

*Example:*

Find the value of CEMF of a DC motor when the terminal voltage is 240V and the armature current is 60 amps. The armature resistance has been measured at 0.08 ohm.

$$\text{CEMF} = \text{terminal voltage} - (I_A \times R_A)$$

$$\text{CEMF} = 240 - (60 \times 0.08) = 240 - 4.8 = 235.2\text{V}$$

CEMF acts as an automatic current limiter that reduces armature current to a level adequate to drive the motor but not great enough to heat the armature to where it is in danger of burning out. CEMF acts as a load for the DC power supply feeding the motor, so that the low-resistance motor windings do not draw excessive amounts of current.

If we stalled the armature so that no CEMF was produced, we would find that the motor draws so much current it heats up. This reaction is shown in *Figure 16*. CEMF is present in all motors and is necessary for a motor's operation.

We have now covered the basic principles and major components of the DC motor. However, there are many types of DC motors, and several of them will be covered later in this module.

## 2.7.0 Starting Resistance

Large DC motors require that a starting resistance be inserted in series with the motor armature. The current drawn by the armature is governed by CEMF and the armature resistance. When starting, CEMF will be zero because the rotor is at a standstill. There is also no inductive reactance, as in AC induction motors. This means that the starting current will be abnormally high unless limited by external starting resistance.

*Figure 17* shows a shunt motor that is connected directly across a 250V line. The armature resistance is known to be 0.5 ohm. The full-load current of the motor is known to be 25 amps and the shunt field current is one amp. The resulting armature current under full-load conditions would therefore be 24 amps.

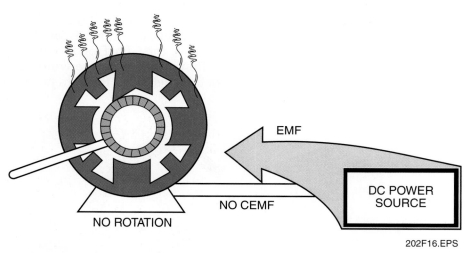

*Figure 16* ◆ No CEMF.

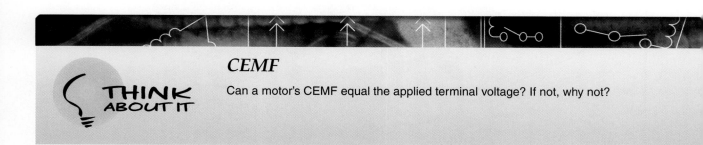

*CEMF*

Can a motor's CEMF equal the applied terminal voltage? If not, why not?

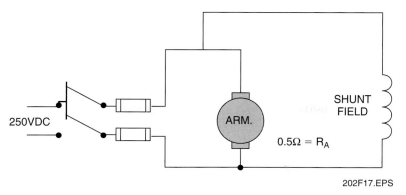

*Figure 17* ◆ Shunt motor.

If starting resistance is not used, the value of the armature current ($I_A$) can be found using the following equation:

$$I_A = \frac{\text{terminal voltage} - \text{CEMF}}{R_A}$$

$$I_A = \frac{250V - 0V}{0.5 \text{ ohm}}$$

$$I_A = 500 \text{ amps}$$

This amount of starting current is too high and may result in excessive torque and heat that may cause damage to the motor. When starting resistance is added in series with the armature, the starting current can be limited to 1.5 times the full-load current value. After starting, this external resistance can be removed from service.

If we want to limit the starting armature current to 1.5 times the full-load value, we can solve for the size of resistance that would be required using the previous equations.

$$R_{starting} = \frac{(\text{terminal voltage} - \text{CEMF}) - (I_A \times R_A)}{I_A}$$

*Where:*

Starting $I_A$ = 1.5 × steady state

= 1.5 × 24 amps

= 36 amps

At the moment of motor start, when the rotor is at a standstill and the CEMF is zero, the series resistance will be:

$$R_{starting} = \frac{(250V - 0V) - (36A)(0.5\Omega)}{36A} = 6.44\Omega$$

To find the wattage required in the starting resistance, take the square of the current multiplied by the resistance, where watt loss is calculated by the $I^2R$ method.

*Example:*

Find the power developed in both watts and **horsepower** in a DC motor that has a terminal voltage of 240V and an armature current of 60A. The armature resistance is known to be 0.08Ω.

$$CEMF = V_T - (I_A \times R_A)$$

$$CEMF = 240 - (60 \times 0.08) = 235.2V$$

$$Power = EI$$

$$Power = 235.2V \times 60A = 14{,}112 \text{ watts}$$

$$Horsepower = \frac{\text{watts}}{746}$$

$$= \frac{14{,}112 \text{ watts}}{746}$$

$$= 18.92hp$$

## 3.0.0 ◆ TYPES OF DC MOTORS

There are two basic types of motor connections that are in common use. They are the series motor and the shunt motor. The series motor is so called because the field is connected in series with the armature winding. The shunt motor has the field coils connected in parallel with the armature (rotor) winding. One additional type of motor is a compound motor. This motor has both a series- and a shunt-connected field. *Figure 18* shows a typical DC motor.

### 3.1.0 Shunt Motors

The field circuit of a shunt motor is connected across the supply line and is in parallel with the armature. A shunt motor connection is shown in *Figure 19*.

When an external load is applied to the shunt motor, it tends to slow down. The slight decrease in

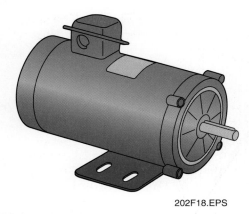

**Figure 18** ◆ Typical DC motor.

202F18.EPS

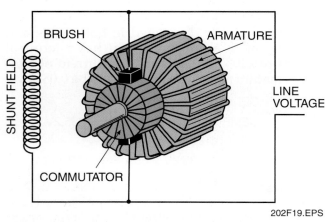

**Figure 19** ◆ Shunt DC motor.

202F19.EPS

Thus, it may be seen that the amount of current through the armature of a shunt motor depends largely upon the load on the motor. The larger the load, the larger the armature current; the smaller the load, the smaller the armature current. The change in speed causes a change in CEMF and armature current in each case.

The main advantage of a shunt-wound motor is that its speed is fairly constant, changing only a few **revolutions per minute (rpm)** when the amount of load changes. The main disadvantage of this connection is that the motor does not develop much torque when it is first started. If a motor is to be started with a large load, it is generally series connected.

It is important to note that the shunt field circuit of a DC motor should never be opened when the motor is operating, especially when unloaded. This is because an open field may cause the motor to rotate at dangerously high speeds. Large DC shunt motors have a field rheostat with a no-field release feature that disconnects the motor from the power source if the field circuit opens.

### 3.1.1 Torque

A DC shunt motor has high torque at any rated speed. At startup, a DC shunt motor can develop up to 150% of its normal running torque as long as the resistors in the starting circuit can withstand the heating effect of the current.

### 3.1.2 Speed Control

DC motors have excellent speed control. To operate the motor above rated speed, a field rheostat is used to reduce the field current and field flux. To operate below rated speed, resistors are used to reduce the armature voltage.

### 3.1.3 Speed Regulation

The speed regulation of a shunt motor drops from 5% to 10% from no-load to full-load. As a result, a shunt motor is superior to the series DC motor but is inferior to a differential compound-wound DC motor.

speed causes a corresponding decrease in CEMF. Since the armature resistance is low, the resulting increases in armature current and torque are relatively large. Therefore, the torque is increased until it matches the opposing torque of the load. The speed of the motor then remains constant at the new value as long as the load is constant.

If the load on the shunt motor is reduced, the motor tends to speed up. The increased speed causes a corresponding increase in CEMF and a relatively large decrease in armature current and torque.

### DC Motor Applications

*INSIDE TRACK*

DC motors were developed before AC motors and one of their first uses was in electric trolleys. The DC motor is still widely used in applications that require accurate speed control or high starting torque. For example, in an elevator, the motor must start under a heavy load and accelerate smoothly. It must also stop precisely and reverse direction easily. A DC motor is a good choice for this application.

## 3.2.0 Series Motors

The field coils of a series motor are connected in series with the armature (*Figure 20*). The value of current through the armature and the field is the same. Hence, if the armature current changes, the field current must also change.

As the motor speeds up, the armature current and field current decrease. With a weaker field, the armature speed will increase still more. The limiting factor on the speed is the load.

If there is no load on the motor, the armature will speed up to such an extent that the windings might be thrown from the slots and the commutator destroyed by the excessive centrifugal forces. For this reason, series motors are seldom belt-connected to their loads. The belt might break, allowing the motor to overspeed and destroy itself. Series motors are usually connected to their loads directly or through gears.

The series motor is used where there is a wide variation in both torque and speed requirements, such as traction equipment, blowers, hoists, cranes, and so forth.

### 3.2.1  Torque

The DC series motor develops 500% of its full-load torque at starting. Therefore, this type of motor is used in applications where large amounts of starting torque are needed, such as cranes, railway applications, and other equipment with high starting torque demands. With a series motor, any increase in load causes an increase in both the armature current and the field current. Since torque depends on the interaction of these two flux fields, the torque increases as the square of the value of the current increases. Therefore, series motors produce greater torque than shunt motors

for the same increase in current. The series motor shows a greater reduction in speed for an equal change in load.

### 3.2.2  Speed Control and Speed Regulation

The speed control of a series motor is poorer than that of a shunt motor because if the load is reduced, a simultaneous reduction of current occurs in both the armature and field windings, and therefore, there is a greater increase in speed than there would be in a shunt-wound motor.

If the mechanical load were to be disconnected completely from a series motor, the motor would continue to accelerate until the motor armature self-destructed. For this reason, series-wound motors are always permanently connected to their loads.

The speed of a series DC motor is controlled by varying the applied voltage. A series motor **controller** is usually designed to start, stop, reverse, and regulate speed. The direction of rotation of a series motor is changed by reversing either the armature or field winding current flow.

## 3.3.0  Compound Motors

Compound DC motors are used whenever it is necessary to obtain speed regulation characteristics not obtainable with either the shunt- or series-wound motor. Because many applications require high starting torque and constant speed under load, the compound motor is used. Some industrial applications include drives for elevators, stamping presses, rolling mills, and metal shears. The compound motor has a normal shunt winding and a series winding on each field pole. They may be connected as a long shunt, as shown in *Figure 21(A)*, or a short shunt, as shown in *Figure 21(B)*. When the series winding is connected to aid the shunt winding, the machine is known as a cumulative compound motor. When the series field opposes the shunt field, the machine is known as a differential compound motor.

### 3.3.1  Torque

The operating characteristics of a cumulative compound-wound motor are a combination of the series motor and the shunt motor. A cumulative compound-wound motor develops high torque for sudden increases in load.

### 3.3.2  Speed

Unlike the series motor, the cumulative compound-wound motor has definite no-load speeds and will not build up self-destructive speeds if the

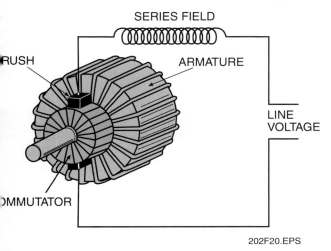

SERIES FIELD

BRUSH

ARMATURE

LINE VOLTAGE

COMMUTATOR

202F20.EPS

*Figure 20* ◆ Series DC motor.

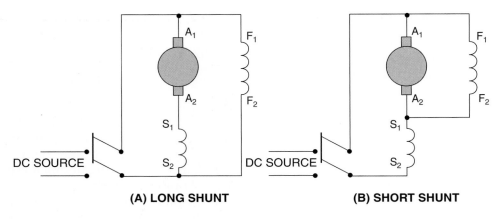

**(A) LONG SHUNT**          **(B) SHORT SHUNT**

202F21.EPS

*Figure 21* ◆ Long and short shunts.

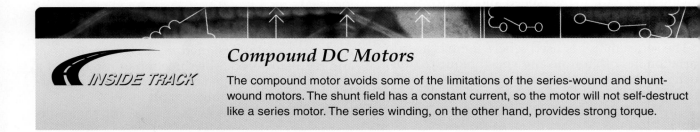

## Compound DC Motors

The compound motor avoids some of the limitations of the series-wound and shunt-wound motors. The shunt field has a constant current, so the motor will not self-destruct like a series motor. The series winding, on the other hand, provides strong torque.

load is removed. Speed control of a cumulative compound-wound motor can be controlled by inserting resistors in the armature circuit to reduce the applied voltage. When the motor is to be used for installations where the rotation must be reversed frequently, such as in elevators, hoists, and railways, the controller should have voltage dropping resistors and switching arrangements to accomplish reversal.

### 3.3.3   Speed Regulation

The speed regulation of a cumulative compound-wound motor is inferior to that of a shunt motor and superior to that of a series motor.

### 3.4.0  Operating Characteristics

Different types of motors have different operating characteristics. Therefore, the proper type of DC motor should be selected when the load to be driven is known. *Figure 22* shows the operating characteristics of a typical DC shunt motor.

Notice that the motor speed is relatively independent of the torque (load applied) from 0 to 150% of the rated capacity of the motor. Such motors find application where relatively constant speed over a wide load range is required. *Figure 2* shows the operating characteristics of a typical DC series motor.

Notice that the motor speed varies greatly with respect to the torque (load applied). With less than half of its rated load applied, the motor operates at more than 150% of its rated speed. When 150%

## Permanent Magnet DC Motors

Many ¼hp to 3hp variable-speed DC motors available for constant or diminishing torque applications use permanent magnets for the field poles instead of shunt or series windings. They employ variable DC armature voltages up to 90V or 180V for speed control. However, they are inefficient if they use only rheostat control of the armature voltage.

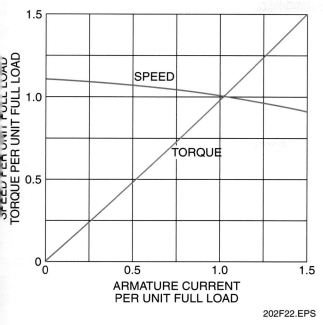

Figure 22 ◆ Operating characteristics of a typical DC shunt motor.

202F22.EPS

*Figure 23* ◆ Operating characteristics of a typical series motor.

202F23.EPS

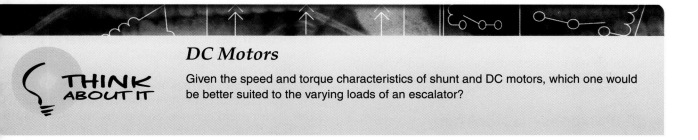

## DC Motors

Given the speed and torque characteristics of shunt and DC motors, which one would be better suited to the varying loads of an escalator?

THINK ABOUT IT

f the rated load is applied to the motor, it drops o 75% of its rated speed. Such motors find appliation where a constant heavy load exists or vhere great speed variations are tolerable.

*Figure 24* shows the operating characteristics of DC compound motor. Notice that the motor peed is relatively constant over the operating ange. Its speed does vary with the torque somevhat more than the shunt motor, but will not run way or markedly decrease, as with the series moor. Such motors find application where the load is ot known exactly or where some speed variation s tolerable with load variation.

## 3.5.0 Brushless DC Motors

he brushless DC motor was developed to elimiate commutator problems in missiles and spaceraft operating above the Earth's atmosphere. wo general types of brushless motors are in use: he inverter-induction motor and a DC motor vith an electronic commutator.

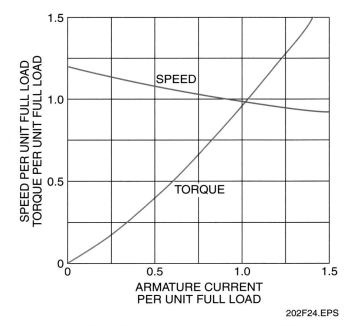

*Figure 24* ◆ Operating characteristics of a typical DC compound motor.

202F24.EPS

# 4.0.0 ◆ ALTERNATING CURRENT MOTORS

Alternating current motors can be divided into two major types: single-phase motors and polyphase motors. The single-phase motor is normally limited to fractional horsepower ratings up to about five horsepower. They are commonly used to power such things as fans, small pumps, appliances, and other devices not requiring a great amount of power. Single-phase motors are not likely to be connected to complicated motor control circuitry.

Polyphase motors make up the majority of motors needed to drive large machinery such as pumps, large fans, and compressors. These motors have several advantages over single-phase motors in that they do not require a separate winding or other device to start the motor. They have relatively high starting torque and good speed regulation for most applications.

There are two classes of polyphase motors: induction and synchronous. The rotor of a synchronous motor revolves at **synchronous speed,** or the speed of the revolving magnetic field in the stator. The rotor of an induction motor revolves at a speed somewhat less than synchronous speed. The differences in rotor speed are due to differences in construction and operation. Both will be discussed in depth after a review of motor theory.

## 4.1.0 Polyphase Motor Theory

AC motors consist of two parts: the stator, or stationary part; and the rotor, or revolving part. The stator is connected to the incoming three-phase AC power. The rotor in an induction motor is not connected to the power supply, whereas the rotor of a synchronous motor is connected to external power. Both induction and synchronous motors operate on the principle of a rotating magnetic field.

### 4.1.1 Rotating Fields

This section shows how the stator windings can be connected to a three-phase AC input to create a magnetic field that rotates. Another magnetic field in the rotor can be made to chase it by being attracted and repelled by the stator field. Because the rotor is free to turn, it follows the rotating magnetic field in the stator.

Polyphase AC is brought into the stator and connected to windings that are physically displaced 120° apart. These windings are connected to form north and south magnetic poles, as shown in *Figure 25*. An analysis of the electromagnetic polarity of the poles at points 1 through 7 in *Figure 25* shows how the three-phase AC creates magnetic fields that rotate.

At point 1, the magnetic field in coil (pole) 1–1A is at its maximum. Negative voltages are shown in 1–2A and 3–3A. The negative voltages in these windings create smaller magnetic fields that will tend to aid the field set up in 1–1A.

At point 2, phase 3 creates a maximum negative flux in 3–3A windings. This strong negative field is aided by the weaker magnetic fields in 1–1A and 1–2A.

The three-phase AC input rises and falls with each cycle. Analyzing each point on the voltage graph shows that the resultant magnetic field rotates clockwise. When the three-phase input completes a full cycle at point 7, the magnetic field has completed an entire revolution of 360°.

### 4.1.2 Rotor Behavior in a Rotating Field

An oversimplification of rotor behavior shows how the magnetic field of the stator influences the rotor. Assume that a simple bar magnet is placed in the center of the stator diagrams shown in *Figure 25*. Also assume that the bar magnet is free to rotate. It has been aligned such that at point 1 its south pole is opposite the large north of the stator field.

Unlike poles attract and like poles repel. As the AC completes a cycle, going from point 1 to point 7, the stator field rotates and pulls the bar magnet with it because of the attraction of unlike poles and the repulsion of like poles. The bar magnet is rotating at the same speed as the revolving flux of the stator. This speed is known as synchronous speed. The synchronous speed of a motor is given by the equation:

$$N = \frac{120f}{P}$$

*Where:*

N = speed in rpm
f = frequency in cycles per second
P = number of magnetic poles

### 4.1.3 Induction

Current flowing through a conductor sets up a magnetic field around the length of the conductor. Conversely, a conductor in a magnetic field will produce a current when the magnetic lines of flux cut across the conductor. This action is called induction because there is no physical connection between the magnetic field and the conductor. Current is induced in the conductor.

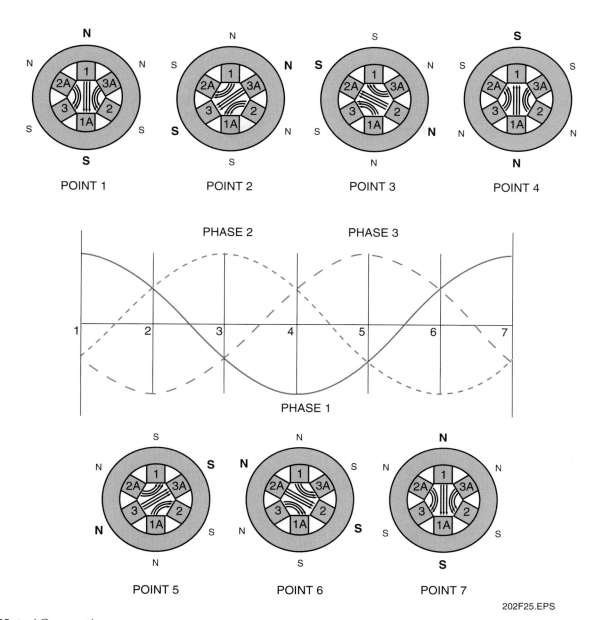

**POINT 1**  **POINT 2**  **POINT 3**  **POINT 4**

PHASE 2  PHASE 3

PHASE 1

**POINT 5**  **POINT 6**  **POINT 7**

202F25.EPS

*Figure 25* ◆ AC generation.

## .2.0 Three-Phase Induction Motors

ı a three-phase induction motor, the driving orque is caused by the reaction of a current-arrying conductor in a magnetic field. In induc-on motors, the rotor currents are supplied by lectromagnetic induction. The stator windings re supplied with three-phase power and produce rotating magnetic field.

The rotor is not electrically connected to the ower supply. The induction motor derives its ame from the mutual inductance taking place be-veen the stator and the rotor under operating onditions. The rotating field produced by the sta-or cuts the rotor conductors, inducing a voltage ιto the conductors. The induced voltage causes

rotor current. This develops motor torque due to the reaction of a current-carrying conductor in a magnetic field. This torque causes the rotor to rotate. This principle is shown in *Figure 26*.

The three-phase (3ϕ) induction motor has a frame, or stationary part, which is the stator. The stator is made of laminated steel rings with slots on the inside circumference. The motor stator windings are the phase windings. They are symmetrically placed on the stator and may be either wye- or delta-connected. Depending on how the stator is wound, it may have two, four, or any even number of poles.

There are two varieties of three-phase induction motors: the squirrel cage rotor motor and the wound rotor motor.

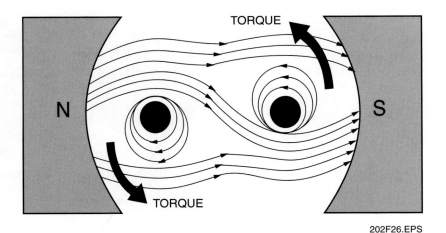

**Figure 26** ◆ Producing torque.

### 4.2.1 Squirrel Cage Induction Motor

The squirrel cage is probably the most popular rotor in use. Three-phase squirrel cage induction motors consist of a stator, a rotor, and two end shields that house the bearings that support the rotor shaft. The frame is usually made of cast steel. The stator core is pressed into the frame. In this rotor, the bars are connected together at the ends by shorting rings made of similar material. The conductor bars carry large currents at low voltages. The bearings can be either sleeve or ball bearings. *Figure 27* shows the main components of an induction motor.

It is not necessary to insulate the bars from the core because the current will follow the path of least resistance and is confined to the cage windings. *Figure 28* shows how a squirrel cage rotor is constructed.

The squirrel cage rotor induction motor has a fixed rotor circuit. The resistance and reactance of the windings are determined when the motor is designed. The standard cage rotor motor is a general-purpose motor. It is used to drive loads that require variable torque at relatively constant speed with high full-load efficiency. Some examples are blowers, centrifugal pumps, and fans.

**Figure 27** ◆ Main components of an induction motor.

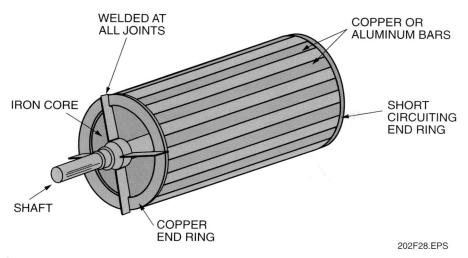

WELDED AT
ALL JOINTS

COPPER OR
ALUMINUM BARS

IRON CORE

SHORT
CIRCUITING
END RING

SHAFT

COPPER
END RING

202F28.EPS

*Figure 28* ◆ Squirrel cage rotor.

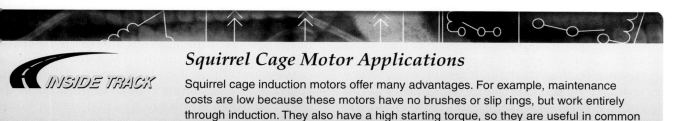

## Squirrel Cage Motor Applications

Squirrel cage induction motors offer many advantages. For example, maintenance costs are low because these motors have no brushes or slip rings, but work entirely through induction. They also have a high starting torque, so they are useful in common applications such as overhead doors, large compressors, fans, and printing presses.

Due to the absence of any moving electrical contacts, they are suitable for use where they are exposed to flammable dust or gas.

If the load requires special operating characteristics, such as high starting torque, the squirrel cage rotor can be designed to have high resistance bars for a starting circuit and low resistance bars for running operation. A rotor of this type is called a double squirrel cage rotor.

### 4.2.2 Wound Rotor Induction Motor

A wound rotor (*Figure 29*) has a winding that is similar to the three-phase stator windings. The rotor windings are usually wye-connected with the free ends of the windings connected to three slip rings mounted on the rotor shaft. The slip rings are shown physically mounted on the end of the rotor shaft in *Figure 29*. They are used with brushes to form an electromechanical connection to the rotor.

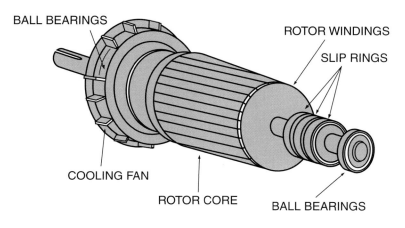

BALL BEARINGS

ROTOR WINDINGS

SLIP RINGS

COOLING FAN

ROTOR CORE

BALL BEARINGS

202F29.EPS

*Figure 29* ◆ Wound rotor.

## *Wound Rotor Motors*

**THINK ABOUT IT**

When might you want a wound rotor motor to run like a squirrel cage motor at full speed?

Slip rings are contact surfaces mounted on the shaft of a motor or generator to which the rotor windings are connected and against which the brushes ride. The brushes are sliding contacts, usually made of carbon, that make continuous electrical connection to the rotating part of a motor or generator.

The wound rotor motor often uses an external wye-connected resistor connected to the rotor through slip rings. The resistor provides a means of varying the rotor resistance. This can be used when the motor is started to produce a high starting torque. As the motor accelerates, the resistance is reduced. When the motor has reached full speed, the slip rings are short circuited, and the operation is similar to that of a squirrel cage rotor induction motor. A schematic representation of this is shown in *Figure 30*.

The wound rotor induction motor is used when it is necessary to vary the rotor resistance, to limit starting current, or to vary the motor speed. Speed can be varied by as much as 50% to 75%; the greater the resistance inserted in the rotor circuit, the lower the speed will be below synchronous speed. When the motor is operating below full speed, the percent slip is increased and the motor is operating at reduced efficiency and horsepower. When all resistance is cut completely out, the speed is somewhat less than that obtained with squirrel cage rotors. Because the rotor circuit heat generation is largely external to the rotor windings, the wound rotor motor is used for applications that require frequent starts without overheating the motor.

### 4.2.3  Wound Rotor Speed Control

The insertion of resistance in the rotor circuit not only limits the starting surge of current, but also produces a high starting torque and provides a means of adjusting the speed. If the full resistance of the speed controller is cut into the rotor circuit when the motor is running, the rotor current decreases and the motor slows down. As the rotor speed decreases, more voltage is induced in the rotor windings and more rotor current is developed to create the necessary torque at the reduced rotor speed.

If all the resistance is removed from the rotor circuit, both the current and motor speed will increase. However, the rotor speed will always be less than the synchronous speed of the field developed by the stator windings. Recall that this is also true of the squirrel cage induction motor. The speed of a wound rotor motor can be controlled manually or automatically with timing relays, contactors, and pushbutton speed selection.

The advantages of the wound rotor motor are high starting torque with moderate starting current, smooth acceleration under heavy load, no excessive heating during starting, good running characteristics, and adjustable speed control. Th

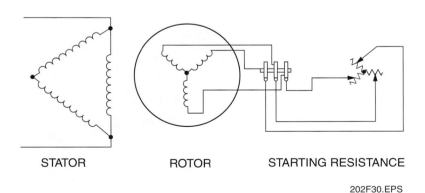

STATOR          ROTOR          STARTING RESISTANCE

202F30.EPS

*Figure 30* ◆ Wound rotor motor circuit.

## *Wound Rotor Motor Applications*

*INSIDE TRACK*

Like DC motors, wound rotor motors are used where high inertia loads must be started easily or often. Wound rotor motors have starting torques in the range of 225% of full-load torque. They are used for hoists, hydraulic gates, yard locomotives, and cranes.

hief disadvantage is that both initial and mainte-ance costs are greater than those of the squirrel age rotor motor.

### .2.4 Torque

he torque on the rotor of an induction motor ends to turn the rotor in the same direction as the otating field. If the motor is not driving a load, it vill accelerate to nearly the same speed as the roating field. As the rotor accelerates, the magni-ude of the induced voltage in the rotor decreases. his is because the relative motion between the roating field and the rotor conductors is reduced. It s impossible for an induction motor to operate at ynchronous speed because there would be no elative motion between the rotating field and the otor. Thus, there would be no induced voltage, o rotor current, no rotor magnetic field, and no orque.

### .2.5 Slip

n an induction motor, the rotor always rotates at speed less than the synchronous speed. The ro-or speed is such that sufficient torque is produced o balance the restraining torque caused by motor riction and mechanical load. The difference be-veen the synchronous speed and the rotor speed s known as slip. Slip is expressed mathematically s follows:

$$S = \frac{N - N_R}{N} \times 100\%$$

*Vhere:*

$S$ = slip

$N$ = synchronous speed

$N_R$ = rotor speed

To express the quantity as a percent, multiply y 100.

*xample:*

A four-pole, 208V, 2hp, 60Hz, three-phase in-uction motor has a no-load speed of 1,790 rpm nd a full-load speed of 1,650 rpm.

Find the percent slip for each case below:

- No-load condition
- Full-load condition
- Locked-rotor condition (standstill)

Before any calculations can be made, we must first calculate synchronous speed.

$$N = \frac{120f}{P}$$

$$N = \frac{120 \times 60}{4}$$

$$N = 1,800 \text{rpm}$$

- At no-load condition:

$$S = \frac{N - N_R}{N} \times 100\%$$

$$S = \frac{1,800 - 1,790}{1,800} \times 100\%$$

$$S = 0.556\%$$

- At full-load condition:

$$S = \frac{N - N_R}{N} \times 100\%$$

$$S = \frac{1,800 - 1,650}{1,800} \times 100\%$$

$$S = 8.33\%$$

- At locked-rotor condition:

$$S = \frac{N - N_R}{N} \times 100\%$$

$$S = \frac{1,800 - 0}{1,800} \times 100\%$$

$$S = 100\%$$

*Figure 31* shows how torque relates to speed over the operating range of a motor. Note that speed is proportional to torque on the left side up to pullout torque. Beyond this point, however, torque decreases as speed increases.

Slip is the difference between the synchronous speed and the actual speed of the rotor in an in-duction motor. Slip is necessary to permit motor action to occur. Under increasing load, the rotor torque increases. Since percent slip is proportional

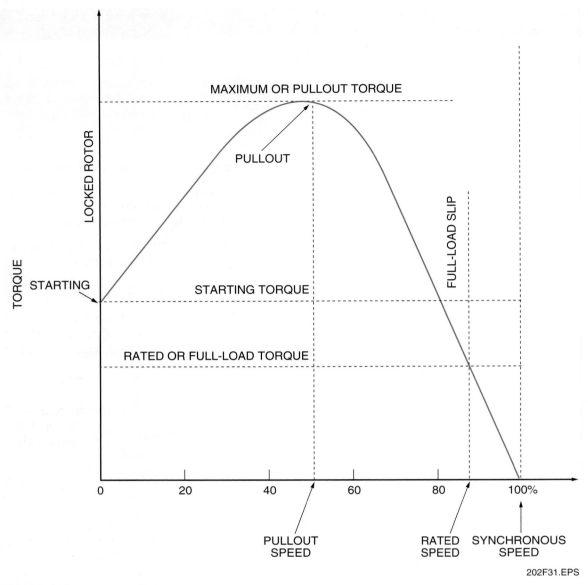

*Figure 31* ◆ Typical torque-speed curve.

to torque, the amount of slip will increase. This increase means a higher current draw by the motor due to the greater difference between the rotor and the magnetic field. Motor supply voltages, current, torque, speed, and rotor impedance are closely related. By changing the resistance and reactance of the rotor, the characteristics of the motor can be changed; however, for any one rotor design these characteristics are fixed.

### 4.2.6  Starting Current

At the moment a three-phase induction motor is started, the current supplied to the motor stator terminals may be as high as six times the motor full-load current. This is because at starting, the rotor is at rest; therefore, the rotating magnetic field of the stator cuts the squirrel cage rotor at the maximum rate, inducing large amounts of EMF in the rotor.

This results in proportionally high currents at the input terminals of the motor as was previously discussed. Because of this high inrush, current starting protection as high as 300% of full-load current must be provided to allow the motor to start and come up to speed.

Because 100% slip exists at the instant the motor is energized (see *Figure 31*), the rotor current lags the rotor EMF by a large angle. This means that the maximum current flow occurs in a rotor conductor at a time after the maximum amount of stator flux has passed by. This results in a high starting current at a low power factor, which results in a low value of starting torque.

As the rotor speeds up, the rotor frequency and reactance decrease, causing the torque to increase up to its maximum value, then decrease to the value needed to carry the load.

## 4.2.7 Loaded Torque

If a load is now placed on the shaft, the rotor will tend to slow down. As it slows down, more flux lines are cut until enough torque is developed to overcome the load placed on the shaft.

The motor now runs under load at a slower speed than before the load was placed on the shaft. This normal range of operation is shown in the lower right corner of *Figure 31* as the rated or full-load torque.

In this range, the slip will vary from 2% to 10%, depending on the load applied and the motor. Rated slip will occur at the point where 100% rated load is applied. Increased load means increased slip, which means the rotor is now rotating slower. An induction motor is considered to be a constant speed motor. We will now examine how much speed fluctuates from no-load speed to full-load speed.

*Example:*

A two-pole induction motor has a no-load slip of 2% and a full-load slip of 8%. What are the no-load speed, full-load speed, and percent speed change?

$$\text{Nominal} = \frac{120 \times 60}{2} = 3,600 \text{ rpm}$$

$$\begin{aligned}\text{No-load}\\\text{speed}\end{aligned} = \frac{100\% - 2\%}{100\%} \times 3,600 \text{ rpm} = 3,528 \text{ rpm}$$

$$\begin{aligned}\text{Full-load}\\\text{speed}\end{aligned} = \frac{100\% - 8\%}{100\%} \times 3,600 \text{ rpm} = 3,312 \text{ rpm}$$

Percent speed change

$$= \frac{\text{no-load speed} - \text{full-load speed}}{\text{no-load speed}} \times 100\%$$

$$= \frac{3,528 - 3,312}{3,528} \times 100\%$$

$$= 6.12\%$$

## 4.2.8 Overload Condition

If the load is increased above full-rated load, everything happens as stated before to increase torque up to a certain point. *Figure 32* shows typical torque and current curves.

In *Figure 32*, note how the torque climbs as the load is increased.

This will continue as load is increased until the pullout torque point is reached. Beyond this point, the torque decreases and the motor will quickly

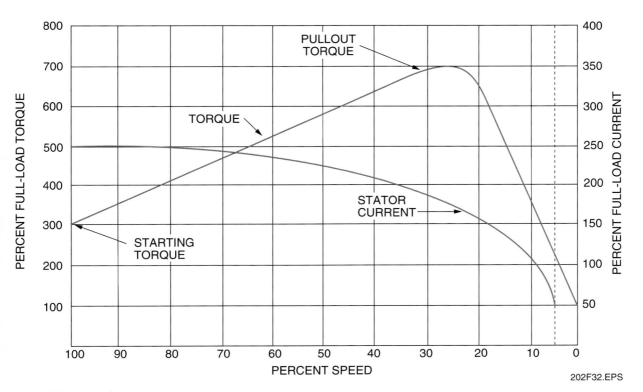

*Figure 32* ◆ Torque and current curves.

stall. A typical situation is when a bench circular saw or a lathe stalls on a heavy cut. The machine will slow down as its cutting load is increased until it suddenly stalls and hums or growls loudly. The condition will persist until the load is relieved or a fuse blows or a breaker trips. The motor has simply reached a point where it cannot continue to increase its torque. Any further increase in load will cause a stall.

### 4.2.9 Power Factor

The power factor of a squirrel cage induction motor is poor at no-load and low-load conditions. At no-load conditions, the power factor can be as low as 15% lagging. However, as load is increased, the power factor increases. At high-rated load, the power factor may be as high as 85% to 90% lagging.

The power factor at no-load speed is low because the magnetizing component of input current is a large part of the total input current of the motor. When the load on the motor is increased, the in-phase current supplied to the motor increases, but the magnetizing component of current remains practically the same. This means that the resultant line current is more nearly in phase with the voltage, and the power factor is improved when the motor is loaded compared with an unloaded motor, which chiefly draws its magnetizing current.

*Figure 33* shows the increase in power factor from no-load conditions to full-load conditions. In the no-load diagram, the in-phase current ($I_{ENERGY}$) is small when compared to the magnetizing current ($I_M$); thus, the power factor is poor at no-load conditions. In the full-load diagram, the in-phase current has increased, while the magnetizing current remains the same. As a result, the angle of lag of the line current decreases, and the power factor increases.

### 4.2.10 Speed Control

The speed of a three-phase squirrel cage induction motor depends on the frequency of the applied voltage and the number of poles. As a result, these motors are used in applications where speed remains constant or where it can be controlled by other means such as variable frequency drives.

### 4.2.11 Reversing Rotation

The direction of rotation of a three-phase induction motor can be readily reversed. The motor will

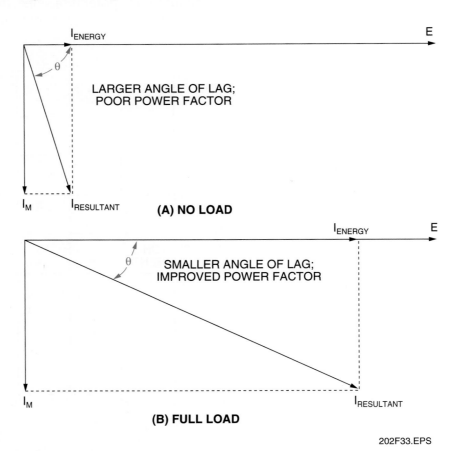

*Figure 33* ◆ Power factor versus load for an induction motor.

---

## Variable-Speed Drives

Variable-speed drives, known as VSDs or ASDs (adjustable-speed drives), are powerful electronic devices that are available for virtually any size motor in all types of applications. Of the various types of VSDs available, the most efficient versions for AC motors are VFDs (variable-frequency drives), which control both the frequency and the voltage applied to the motor. By changing the frequency of the rotating stator field, you change the speed of the rotor, thus changing the speed of the motor. VSDs are often used in energy management systems to conserve energy by supporting variable loads such as those that occur in heating, ventilating, and air conditioning systems. In addition to controlling the speed of a motor, VSDs are available to control both motor starting and stopping functions, as well as to provide controlled acceleration and deceleration.

rotate in the opposite direction if any two of the three incoming leads are reversed, as shown in *Figure 34*.

## 4.3.0 Synchronous Motors

The synchronous motor is a three-phase motor that operates at synchronous speed from no-load conditions to full-load conditions.

### 4.3.1 Characteristics

This type of motor has a revolving field that is energized from a source separate from the stator winding. The rotor is excited by a DC source. The magnetic field set up by the direct current on the rotor then locks in with the rotating magnetic field of the stator and causes the rotor to revolve at synchronous speed. By changing the magnitude of DC excitation, the power factor of the motor can be changed over a wide variety of power factors from leading to lagging. Because of the unique ability of synchronous motors to change power factors, they are often used as power-factor correctors. They are most often used in applications that require constant speed from no-load conditions to full-load conditions.

### 4.3.2 Construction

The construction of synchronous motors is essentially the same as the construction of three-phase

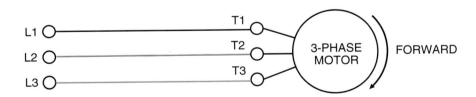

**(A) ROTATION BEFORE CONNECTIONS ARE CHANGED**

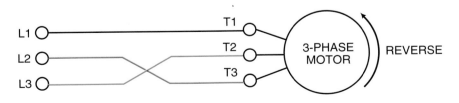

**(B) ROTATION AFTER CONNECTIONS ARE CHANGED**

202F34.EPS

*Figure 34* ◆ Three-phase induction motor rotational direction change.

## Synchronous Motors

Three-phase synchronous motors can be used in industrial applications to correct the low power factor of a number of induction motors or other inductive devices that are operating at less than their rated load levels. Synchronous motors can accomplish power factor correction while driving their own mechanical loads. Correcting a low power factor created by inductive loads through the use of synchronous motors reduces energy costs by making efficient use of the power supplied to the industrial facility. The use of synchronous motors can eliminate the need for dedicated capacitor banks or switched capacitor banks and the surges caused by them.

generators. They have three stator windings that are 120° apart and a wound rotor that is connected to slip rings where the rotor excitation current is applied.

When three-phase AC is applied to the stator, a revolving magnetic field is created just as it is in induction motors. The rotor is energized with DC, which creates a magnetic field around the rotor. The strong rotating magnetic field of the stator attracts the rotor field. This results in a strong turning force on the rotor shaft.

This is how the synchronous motor works once it is started. However, one of the disadvantages of this type of motor is that it cannot be started just by applying AC to the stator. When AC is applied to the stator, the high-speed rotating magnetic field rushes past the rotor poles so quickly that the rotor does not have a chance to get started. The rotor is locked; it is repelled in one direction and then in another direction. In its purest form, the synchronous motor has no starting torque.

This is more easily understood using *Figure 35*. When the stator and rotor fields are energized, the poles of the rotating field approach the rotor poles of opposite polarity. The attracting force will tend to turn the rotor in a direction opposite the rotating field. As the rotor starts to move in that direction, the rotating field moves past the rotor poles and tends to pull the rotor in the same direction as the rotating field. The result is no starting torque.

To allow this type of motor to start, a squirrel cage winding is added to the rotor to cause it to start like an induction motor. This winding is called an amortisseur winding. The rotor windings are constructed so that definite north and south poles are created and these poles, when excited by DC, will lock in with the revolving field. The rotor windings are wound about the salient field poles, which are connected in series for opposite polarity.

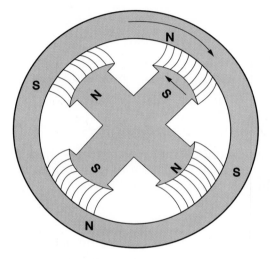

TENDENCY OF ROTOR TO
TURN COUNTERCLOCKWISE

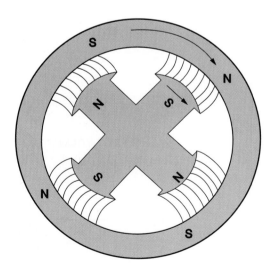

TENDENCY OF ROTOR TO
TURN CLOCKWISE

202F35.EPS

*Figure 35* ◆ Synchronous motor operation at start.

The number of field poles must equal the number of stator poles. The rotor field windings are brought out to slip rings that are mounted on the rotor shaft. The field current is supplied through carbon brushes to the field windings. *Figure 36* shows a simplification of a synchronous motor. *Figure 37* shows the construction of the rotor pole assembly.

### 4.3.3  Principles of Operation

When a synchronous motor is started, current is first applied to the stator windings. Current is induced in the amortisseur winding and the motor starts as an induction motor. The motor then comes up to near-synchronous speed (about 5% to 10% slip). At that point, the field is excited, and the motor, turning at high speed, pulls into synchronism. When this occurs, the rotor is turning at synchronous speed, and the squirrel cage winding will not be generating any current, and therefore will not affect the synchronous motor's operation. The amortisseur windings serve an additional purpose. When the load changes frequently, the motor speed is not steady because the torque angle (discussed later) oscillates (or hunts) back and forth, trying to settle at its required value. This momentary change in speed creates a current due to induction, and there will be torque in the amortisseur winding. This momentary torque serves to dampen or stabilize the oscillating torque angle. That is why amortisseur windings are sometimes referred to as damper windings.

### 4.3.4  Rotor Field Excitation

The rotor must be excited from an external DC source. *Figure 38* shows a simplified synchronous motor excitation circuit. Notice that the DC field current can be varied by the rheostat; however, this does not change the speed of the motor. It only changes the power factor of the motor stator circuit. If full resistance is applied to the rotor field circuit, then the field strength of the rotor is at its minimum and the power factor is extremely lagging. As the DC field strength is increased, the power factor improves. If current is increased sufficiently, the power factor can be increased to near unity or 100%. This value of field current is referred to as normal excitation. By increasing the rotor field strength further, the power factor decreases but in a leading direction; that is, the stator circuit becomes capacitive and the motor is said to be overexcited. The synchronous motor can be used to counteract the lagging power factor in circuits by adding capacitive reactance to the circuit, thereby bringing the overall power factor closer to unity.

If the rotor DC field windings of a synchronous motor are open when the stator is energized, a high AC voltage will be induced in it because the

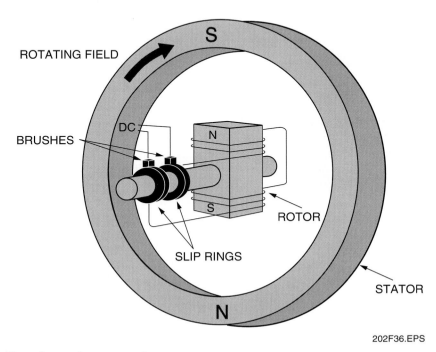

202F36.EPS

*Figure 36* ◆ Simplification of a synchronous motor.

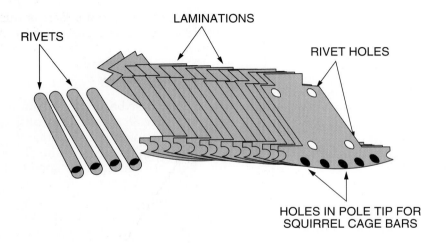

RIVETS

LAMINATIONS

RIVET HOLES

HOLES IN POLE TIP FOR
SQUIRREL CAGE BARS

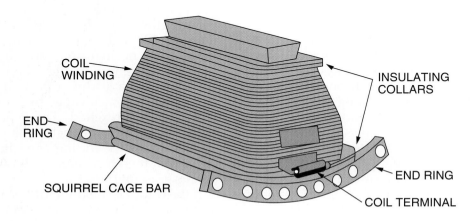

COIL
WINDING

INSULATING
COLLARS

END
RING

END RING

SQUIRREL CAGE BAR

COIL TERMINAL

202F37.EPS

*Figure 37* ◆ Pole assembly.

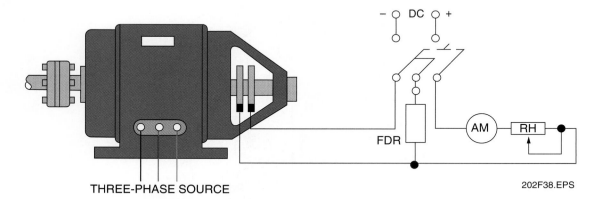

THREE-PHASE SOURCE

DC

FDR

AM

RH

202F38.EPS

*Figure 38* ◆ Simplified synchronous motor excitation circuit.

rotating field sweeps through the large number of turns at synchronous speed.

It is therefore necessary to connect a resistor of low resistance across the rotor DC field winding during the starting period. During the starting period, the DC field winding is disconnected from the source, and the resistor is connected across the field terminals. This permits alternating current to flow in the DC field winding. Because the impedance of the winding is high compared with the inserted external resistance, the internal voltage drop limits the terminal voltage to a safe value.

### 4.3.5 Synchronous Motor Pullout

When a synchronous motor loses synchronism with the system to which it is connected, it is said to be out of step. This occurs when the following take place singly or in combination:

- Excessive load applied to the shaft
- Supply voltage reduced excessively
- Motor excitation lost or too low

Torque pulsations applied to the shaft of a synchronous motor are also a possible cause of loss of synchronism if the pulsations occur at an unfavorable period relative to the natural frequency of the rotor with respect to the power system.

A prevalent cause of loss of synchronism is a fault occurring on the supply system. Underexcitation of the rotor is also a distinct possibility.

Synchronous motor pullout is significant in that the squirrel cage or amortisseur winding is designed for starting only. They are not as hardy as those found in induction motors. The amortisseur winding will not overheat if the motor starts, accelerates, and reaches synchronous speed within a time interval determined to be normal for the motor. However, the motor must continue to operate at synchronous speed. If the motor operates at a speed less than synchronous, the amortisseur winding may overheat and suffer damage.

Protection against a synchronous motor losing synchronism can be provided by polarized field frequency relays and out-of-step relays as well as various digital methods.

### 4.3.6 Synchronous Motor Torque Angle

Once the rotor is brought up to high speed (close to synchronous speed) it will lock on to the rotating magnetic field. Under these conditions, a running torque will be developed. The rotor will rotate at synchronous speed in a direction and at a speed determined by synchronous speed.

While the motor is running, the two rotating fields will line up perfectly. The rotor pole will always lag behind the stator pole by some angle. This angle is called the torque angle and is shown in *Figure 39*.

As the load on the shaft increases, the torque angle increases even though the rotor continues to turn at synchronous speed. This behavior continues until the torque angle is approximately 90°. At that point, the motor is developing a maximum torque. Any further increase in load will cause either of the following to occur:

- If the increase in load is momentary or very small, the rotor will slip a pole. In other words, the stator field will lose hold of the rotor and grab onto it again the next time around.

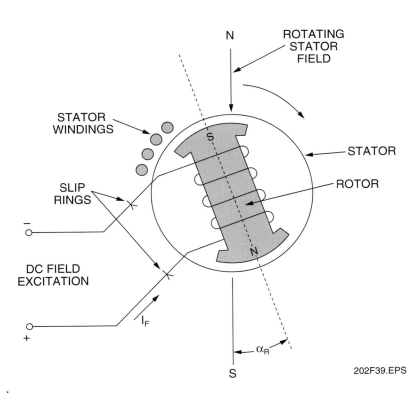

*Figure 39* ◆ Torque angle.

- If the increase in load is large enough and is not momentary, the motor will lose synchronism and will either stall or cause the rotor to suffer thermal damage.

In both cases, a noticeable straining sound will be heard.

The synchronous motor should not be used where fluctuations in torque are violent. As a rule, it is also not used in small sizes (under 50hp), because it requires DC excitation. It is more difficult to start than induction motors and falls out of step quite readily when system disturbances occur. Its common applications are in motor generator sets, air compressors, and compressors in refrigerating plants.

## 4.4.0 Single-Phase AC Motors

Single-phase motors operate on a single-phase power supply. This is important because in the typical home or office and many areas of industrial plants, the only power source available is single-phase AC. Not only do single-phase AC motors eliminate the need for three-phase AC lines, but they are also easier to manufacture in small sizes and are, therefore, less expensive.

Examples of the many applications of single-phase AC motors today are the following: refrigerators, freezers, washers, dryers, power tools, typewriters, copying machines, heating systems, water pumps, computer peripherals, and various small appliances.

There are two basic types of single-phase motors. First, there is the single-phase induction motor. Its theory of operation is similar to that of the three-phase induction motor; hence, it runs at a speed slightly lower than synchronous speed. Second, there is the single-phase synchronous motor.

### 4.4.1 Single-Phase Induction Motors

Single-phase AC induction motors are extremely popular. Unlike polyphase induction motors, the stator field in the single-phase motor does not rotate. Instead, it simply alternates polarity between poles as the AC voltage changes polarity.

Voltage is induced in the rotor, and a magnetic field is produced around the rotor. This field will always be in opposition to the stator field. However, the interaction between the rotor and stator fields will not produce rotation (see *Figure 40*). Because this force is across the rotor and through the pole pieces, there is no rotary motion, just a push and/or pull along this line.

If the rotor is rotated by some outside force (a twist of your hand, for example), the push-pull

$N_R$, $S_R$ = ROTOR FIELD
$N_S$, $S_S$ = STATOR FIELD

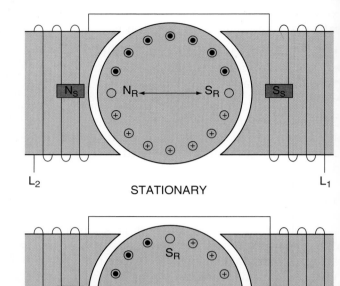

*Figure 40* ◆ AC induction motor.

along the line is disturbed. Look at the fields shown in *Figure 40* as the motor begins to rotate. At this instant, the south pole on the rotor is being attracted to the left-hand pole. The north rotor pole is being attracted to the right-hand pole. All of this is a result of the rotor being rotated 90° by the outside force.

The pull that now exists between the two fields becomes a rotary force, turning the rotor toward magnetic correspondence with the stator. Because the two fields continuously alternate, they will never actually line up and the rotor will continue to turn once started.

Since a single-phase rotor will rotate if it has a rotating magnetic field present, all that remains is to find a means of generating a rotating field at the start. There are a number of practical means for generating a rotating field. All the methods used for single-phase induction motors involve the simulation of a second phase for a starting circuit. In this module, we will discuss the following types of motors: split-phase, capacitor-start, capacitor-run, shaded-pole, and repulsion-start.

## Single-Phase Induction Motors

Outside of large industrial and commercial facilities, single-phase induction motors are the most common type of motor used. While they are initially less expensive than polyphase motors, they are also less efficient and more costly to maintain. They are typically available in small sizes from ⅛hp to 1hp (previously referred to as fractional horsepower sizes) and in sizes up to 10hp.

202P0201.EPS

### 4.4.2 Split-Phase Induction Motor

The split-phase motor, shown schematically in *Figure 41*, has a stator composed of slotted laminations that contain an auxiliary (starting) winding and a running (main) winding. The axes of these two windings are displaced by an angle of 90 electrical degrees. The starting winding has fewer turns and smaller wire than the running winding and, therefore, has different electrical characteristics. The main winding occupies the lower half of the slots and the starting winding occupies the upper half. The two windings are connected in parallel across the single-phase line supplying the motor. The motor derives its name from the action of the stator during the starting period.

When energized with single-phase AC, the two windings are physically different enough in position and construction to produce a magnetic revolving field that rotates around the stator air gap at synchronous speed. As the rotating field moves around the air gap, it cuts across the rotor conductors and induces a voltage in them. The interaction between the rotor and stator causes the rotor to accelerate in the direction in which the stator field is rotating.

When the rotor has come up to about 75% of synchronous speed, a centrifugally operated switch disconnects the starting winding from the line supply, and the motor continues to run on the main winding alone. As the motor ages, the centrifugal switch contacts pit and corrode. When this happens, they may get stuck in the closed position. To safeguard against the winding burning up, a thermal relay is also used. If the motor draws the high starting current for more than 5 or 10 seconds, the relay will de-energize.

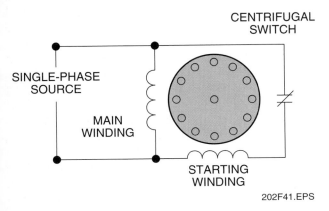

*Figure 41* ◆ Split-phase motor.

202F41.EPS

## Modern Split-Phase Induction Motor

Photo (A) shows a centrifugally-actuated start winding switch that is closed when the motor is at rest. The start winding switch is opened and closed by the movement of an actuator disk against a contact lever. The actuator disk is moved back and forth on the rotor shaft by a centrifugal weight assembly. When the motor is at rest, springs retract the weights and cause the actuator disk to move toward the bearing at the end of the shaft. This pushes on the contact lever, closing the switch contacts. After the motor starts and reaches about 75% of its rated speed, the weights swing out against the spring tension and retract the contact disk from the contact lever. This opens the switch contacts, removing the starting winding from the circuit. If the switch does not open after starting, the motor will operate at a reduced speed until it overheats the starting winding and activates the thermal relay. Photo (B) shows the starting winding (green) and the running winding (copper).

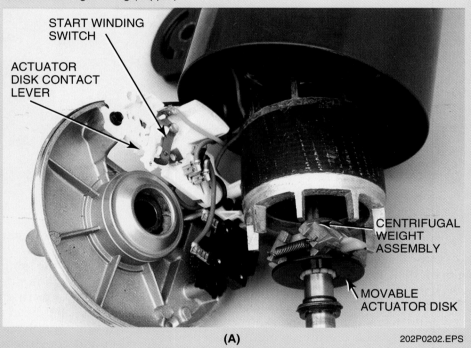

**(A)**

202P0202.EPS

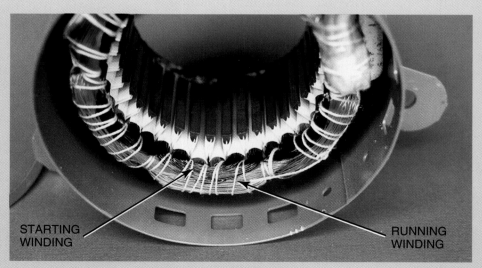

**(B)**

202P0203.EPS

In a split-phase motor, the starting torque is 50% to 200% of the full-load torque, and the starting current is six to eight times the full-load current. Fractional-horsepower split-phase motors are used in a variety of devices such as washers, oil burners, and ventilating fans. The direction of rotation of the split-phase motor can be reversed by interchanging the starting winding leads.

### 4.4.3 Capacitor-Type Induction Motor

The capacitor-type motor is a modified form of split-phase motor. A typical capacitor-type motor is shown in *Figure 42*. The capacitor is located on top of the motor.

To develop a larger starting torque than that available with a standard split-phase motor, a capacitor is placed in series with the auxiliary winding of a split-phase motor, as shown in *Figure 43*. This is called a capacitor-start motor. The capacitor tends to create a greater electrical phase separation of the two windings. Also, because the reactance of a capacitor is 180° out of phase with the inductive reactance of the motor windings when they are combined, they yield a lower total impedance. This allows a larger current to produce a greater magnetic field.

The net effect of the capacitor is to give its motor a starting torque of about four times its rated torque. The split-phase motor, on the other hand, produces a starting torque of about one to two times its rated torque. Once the capacitor motor has come up to speed and the starting winding has been disconnected, it will have the same running characteristics as the split-phase motor.

To reverse the direction of rotation of the capacitor-start motor and split-phase motor, the connection of either winding would have to be reversed. Since the starting winding is disconnected at a high speed, this reversal can be accomplished only at standstill or at low speeds when the centrifugal switch is still closed.

The capacitor-start motor is made in sizes from ¼ to 10hp (150W to 7.5kW). The starting capacitor is the dry-type electrolytic capacitor made for AC use. Typical values are from 200 to 600 microfarads (µF). *Figure 44* shows a comparison of torque slip curves for a split-phase and capacitor-start motor. It also shows the typical effect of the starting capacitor.

A variation of the capacitor-start motor is one in which the capacitor and auxiliary winding are not disconnected. The centrifugal switch in *Figure 43* is eliminated, and the auxiliary winding is left in all the time. This motor is called a capacitor-run motor.

202F42.EPS

*Figure 42* ◆ Capacitor motor.

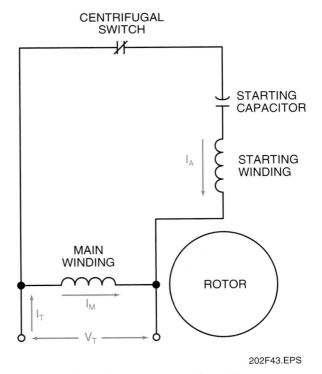

202F43.EPS

*Figure 43* ◆ Capacitor-start motor schematic.

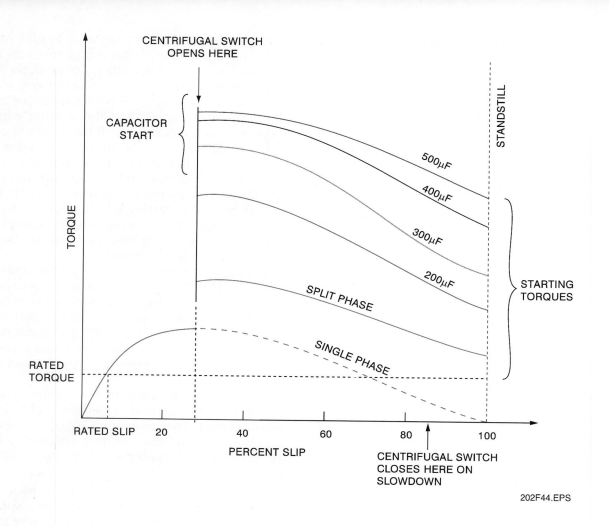

**Figure 44** ◆ Torque-slip curves.

The capacity used for running under load is not the same as that needed for starting. Furthermore, the capacitors used for starting cannot be used for continuous operation. Since the capacitor used in this motor is in all the time, it must be of a different type; that is, one capable of operating continuously. The net result is that the motor has improved running characteristics; however, it does not provide a starting torque as large as that of the capacitor-start motor.

Among the improvements are higher efficiency and power factor at rated load, lower line current, and very quiet operation. It should also be pointed out that the start winding must be designed for continuous operation. This makes the motor somewhat more costly.

Another variation is the capacitor-start, capacitor-run motor. This motor combines the useful features of the capacitor-start and the capacitor-run motors by using two different capacitors, as shown in *Figure 45*.

### 4.4.4   Shaded-Pole Induction Motor

The shaded-pole motor employs a salient-pole stator and a cage rotor. The projecting poles on the stator resemble those of DC machines, except that the entire magnetic circuit is laminated and a portion of each pole is split to accommodate a short circuited copper strap called a shading coil. This motor is generally manufactured in very small sizes and runs up to ⅟₂₀hp. A four-pole motor of this type is illustrated in *Figure 46*.

The shading coils are placed around the leading pole tip, and the main pole winding is concentrated and wound around the entire pole. The four coils that make up the main winding are connected in series across the motor terminals. An inexpensive type of two-pole motor that uses shading coils is illustrated in *Figure 47*.

Referring to *Figure 47*, we see that during part of the cycle when the main pole flux ($\phi_1$) is increasing, the shading coil is cut by the flux, and the resulting induced EMF and current in the

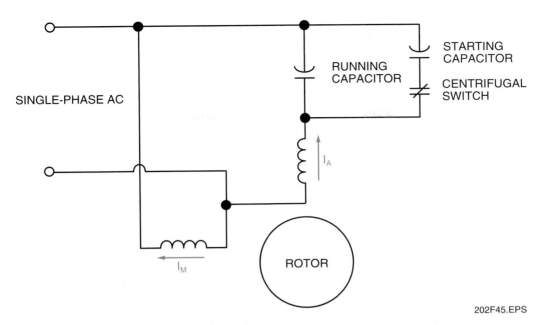

*Figure 45* ◆ Capacitor-start, capacitor-run motor schematic.

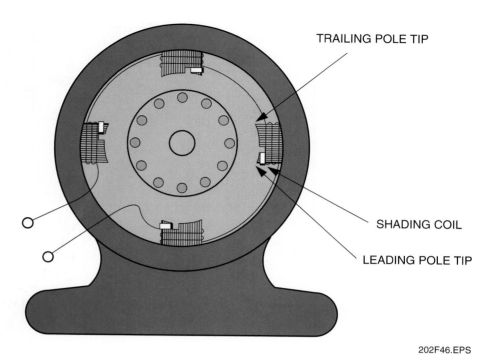

TRAILING POLE TIP

SHADING COIL

LEADING POLE TIP

202F46.EPS

*Figure 46* ◆ Four-pole shaded-pole motor.

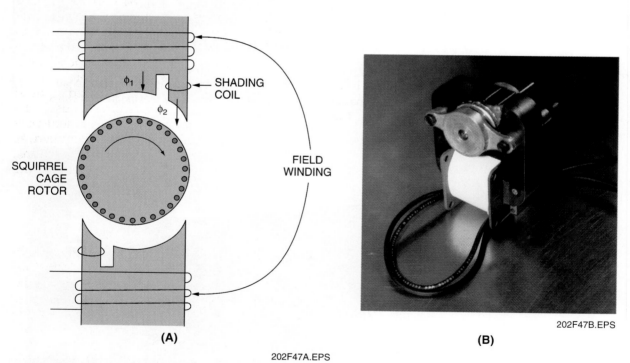

SHADING COIL

$\phi_1$

$\phi_2$

SQUIRREL CAGE ROTOR

FIELD WINDING

**(A)**

202F47A.EPS

**(B)**

202F47B.EPS

*Figure 47* ◆ Two-pole shaded-pole motor.

## Shaded-Pole Motors

**INSIDE TRACK**

The efficiency of this type of motor can be as low as 5%, but this low efficiency is rarely significant because these motors use very little power to begin with (1/20hp or less).

shading coil tend to prevent the flux from rising readily through it. Thus, the greater portion of the flux rises in that portion of the pole that is not in the vicinity of the shading coil ($\phi_1 > \phi_2$). When the flux reaches its maximum value, the rate of change of flux is zero, and the voltage and current in the shading coil are also at zero. At this time, the flux is distributed more uniformly over the entire pole face ($\phi_1 = \phi_2$).

As the main flux decreases toward zero, the induced voltage and current in the shading coil reverse their polarity, and the resulting force tends to prevent the flux from collapsing through the iron in the region of the shading coil ($\phi_2 > \phi_1$). The result is that the main flux rises first in the unshaded portion of the pole and later in the shaded portion. This action is equivalent to a sweeping movement of the field across the pole face in the direction of the shaded pole. The cage rotor conductors are cut by this moving field, and the force exerted on them causes the rotor to turn in the direction of the sweeping field.

Most shaded-pole motors have only one edge of the pole split, and therefore, the direction of rotation is not reversible. However, some shaded-pole motors have both leading and trailing pole tips split to accommodate shading coils. The leading pole tip shading coils form one series group, and the trailing pole tip shading coils form another series group. Only the shading coils in one group are simultaneously active, while those in the other group are on an open circuit.

The shaded-pole motor is similar in operating characteristics to the split-phase motor. It has the advantages of simple construction and low cost. It has no sliding electrical contacts and is reliable in operation. However, it has low starting torque, low efficiency, and a high noise level. It is normally used to operate small fans. The shading coil and split pole are also used in timers to make them self-starting.

### 4.4.5 Single-Phase Synchronous Motor

The single-phase synchronous motor, as its name implies, runs at synchronous speed. It finds use where a constant speed is needed, such as in turntables and clocks. It is started in the same way as any of the single-phase induction motors and therefore has a rotating field. By having a modified rotor, the motor pulls into synchronism and runs at synchronous speed.

## 5.0.0 ◆ MULTIPLE-SPEED INDUCTION MOTORS

The speed of an induction motor depends on the power supply frequency and the number of pairs of poles used in the motor. Obviously, to alter motor speed it is merely necessary to change one of these two factors. By far the most common method used involves changing the number of poles, generally at some type of external controller.

There are two types of multiple-speed squirrel cage induction motors in common use: the multiple-winding motor and the consequent-pole motor. Both feature poles that may be changed, as required, by shifting key external connections, and in this way they provide for operating the motor at a limited number of different speeds.

### 5.1.0 Multiple-Winding Motor

In the multiple-winding motor, two or more separate windings are placed in the stator core slots, one over the other, as shown in *Figure 48*. For example, a four-pole winding can be positioned in the core slots and have a two-pole winding placed on top of it. The windings are insulated from each other and arranged so that only one winding at a time can be energized. Switching speeds is normally accomplished by switching contacts that are in the motor controller external to the motor itself.

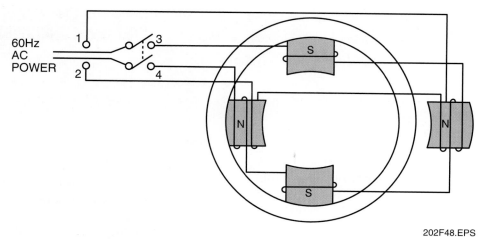

202F48.EPS

*Figure 48* ◆ Two-winding, two-speed motor.

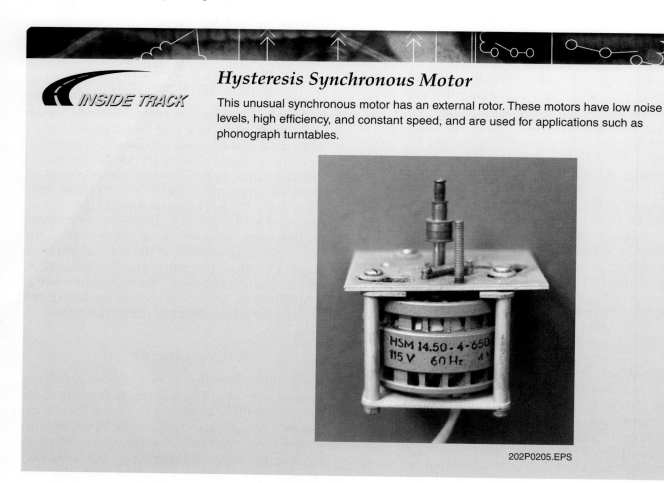

## *Hysteresis Synchronous Motor*

This unusual synchronous motor has an external rotor. These motors have low noise levels, high efficiency, and constant speed, and are used for applications such as phonograph turntables.

202P0205.EPS

## 5.2.0 Consequent-Pole Motor

In the consequent-pole motor, there are two speeds. The motor is constructed to have a certain number of poles for high-speed operation and then, by a switching action, double this number of poles to give low-speed operation. The switching action is illustrated by the use of the two-phase motor in *Figure 49*. If you trace the wiring in *Figure 49*, you can see how the system is phased so that both magnetic north and south poles are produced at the winding projections. With two-phase power applied to the two-pole motor (two poles per phase), a rotating magnetic field of 3,600 rpm is produced.

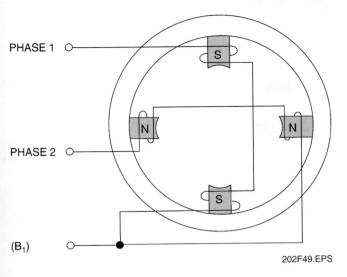

PHASE 1

PHASE 2

(B₁)

202F49.EPS

*Figure 49* ◆ High-speed consequent-pole motor.

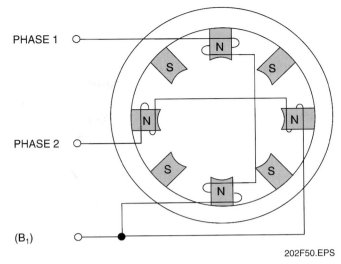

PHASE 1

PHASE 2

(B₁)

202F50.EPS

*Figure 50* ◆ Low-speed consequent-pole motor.

In *Figure 50*, the connections are changed so that the system is phased to produce four magnetic north poles at the winding projections. Since every north pole must have a south pole, consequent south poles are produced between the projecting north poles as a consequence of having formed north poles. Accordingly, in *Figure 50*, there are twice as many pole groups as in *Figure 49*. Therefore, a four-pole rotating magnetic field of 1,800 rpm is produced.

*Figure 51* shows the short-jumpering arrangement of the consequent-pole motor. In this, all windings are in series, and alternate north and south poles are produced. To produce consequent poles, the series connection is replaced with a parallel connection accomplished by the long-jumpering arrangement. By connecting the motor

in this manner, four salient monopoles are produced and, as a result, create four opposite consequent poles. In the practical consequent-pole motor, all necessary internal connection rearrangements are accomplished at an external control panel.

Consequent-pole motor characteristics depend on the intended application. In a constant-horsepower motor, torque varies inversely with speed. It is used for driving machine tools.

In a constant-torque motor, horsepower varies directly with speed. It is used to drive pumps and air compressors, as well as in constant-pressure blowers. In a variable-torque, variable-horsepower motor, both torque and horsepower change with changes in speed. This is the type of motor found in household fans and air conditioners.

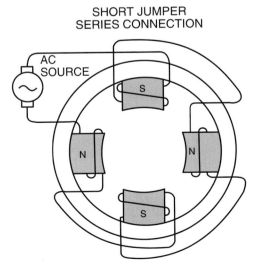

SHORT JUMPER
SERIES CONNECTION

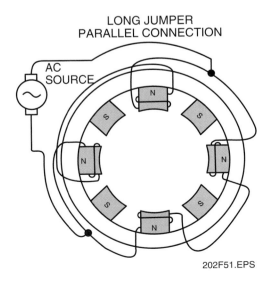

LONG JUMPER
PARALLEL CONNECTION

202F51.EPS

*Figure 51* ◆ Single-phase consequent-pole motor.

# 6.0.0 ◆ VARIABLE-SPEED DRIVES

The use of adjustable speed in industrial equipment is increasing due to the need for better equipment control and for energy savings where partial power is required. AC drives compete with DC drives, eddy current drives, and mechanical and hydraulic systems as methods to control speed. Reliability, cost, and control capabilities are the major factors in system selection.

A drive system includes both the drive controller and the motor being driven. This module focuses specifically on the electronic drive components and covers various types of control for both DC and AC drives. This section provides a basic review of some fundamental principles that are important to understand when starting up, operating, or troubleshooting a variable-speed drive system.

## 6.1.0 Types of Adjustable Speed Loads

Most drive controllers can be adjusted or modified to optimize performance and provide the most efficient and cost-effective drive, depending on the load characteristics of the application.

It is important to understand the speed and torque characteristics as well as the maximum horsepower requirements for the type of load to be considered. Based on this, either a constant-torque controller or a variable-torque controller is selected. The most common types of loads are shown in *Figure 52*. Note that a load requires the same amount of torque at low speed as at high speed.

For a constant-torque load, the torque remains constant throughout the speed range, and the

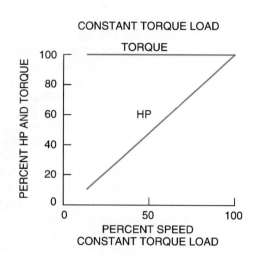

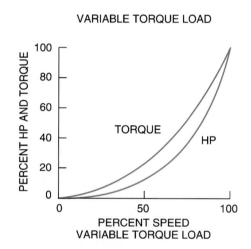

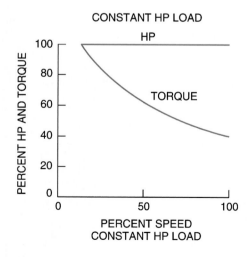

202F52.EPS

*Figure 52* ◆ Types of adjustable speed loads.

---

horsepower increases and decreases in direct proportion to the speed. This applies to applications such as conveyors, as well as applications in which shock loads, overloads, or high inertia loads are encountered.

A variable-torque load requires much lower torque at low speeds than at high speeds. Horsepower varies approximately as the cube of the speed, and the torque varies approximately as the square of the speed. This applies to applications such as centrifugal fans, pumps, and blowers.

A constant-horsepower load requires high torque at low speeds, low torque at high speeds, and thus constant horsepower at any speed. It applies to applications such as lathes requiring low speeds for deep cuts and high speeds for finishing. Usually, very high starting torques are required.

## 6.2.0 Motor Considerations

For industrial applications, motors are required to function at varying torques and speeds, and in forward and reverse directions. Besides operating as a motor, the machine may also function as a brake or a generator for short periods.

The various operating modes for industrial drives are shown in *Figure 53*. Positive and negative speed (rotation) are plotted on the horizontal axis and the torques are plotted on the vertical axis. The four quadrants of operation are labeled 1, 2, 3, and 4.

A machine operating in quadrant 1 has positive torque and speed, which means that they both act in the same direction (in this case, clockwise). A machine in this quadrant is functioning as a motor. It delivers mechanical power to a load. The machine will also act as a motor in quadrant 3, but torque and speed are reversed from quadrant 1 (counterclockwise).

While operating in quadrant 2, a machine will develop a positive torque and a negative speed. The torque is acting clockwise, and the speed is counterclockwise. In this quadrant, the machine is absorbing mechanical power from the load and functions as a generator. This mechanical power is converted into electric power and is generally transmitted back into the line. The electric power may also be dissipated in an external resistor, which is known as dynamic braking.

Depending on its connections, a machine may also be used as a brake while operating in quadrant 2. Absorbed mechanical power is converted to electric power, then converted into heat. If the machine absorbs electric line power as it is converting mechanical power into electric power, it functions as a brake. Both power inputs are dissipated as heat. Large power drives seldom use the brake mode of operation as it is very inefficient. The circuitry is generally chosen so that the machine will function as a generator when it is operating in quadrant 2. Quadrant 4 operation is identical to quadrant 2 except that speed and torque are reversed.

### 6.2.1 Typical Torque-Speed Curves

A three-phase motor has a torque-speed curve that is a good example of an electrical machine's behavior as a generator brake. The solid curve in *Figure 54* is the torque-speed curve for a machine acting as a motor in quadrant 1, a brake in quadrant 2, and a generator in quadrant 4.

If the stator leads are reversed, the torque-speed curve is shown by the dotted curve. Now the motor operates as a motor in quadrant 3, a generator in quadrant 2, and a brake in quadrant 4. The machine functions as a brake or a generator in quadrants 2 and 4, but it always runs as a motor in quadrants 1 and 3.

*Figure 55* shows the torque-speed curve of a DC shunt motor. Motor, generator, and brake modes are apparent. The dotted curve represents reversed armature leads.

Variable-speed electric drives are designed to vary speed and torque in a smooth and continuous manner so as to satisfy load requirements. Typically, this is accomplished by shifting the torque-speed characteristic back and forth along the horizontal axis. The torque-speed characteristic of the motor is shifted by varying the armature

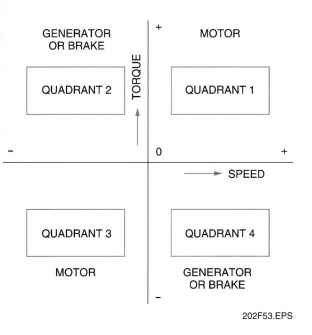

202F53.EPS

*Figure 53* ◆ Electric drive operation in four quadrants.

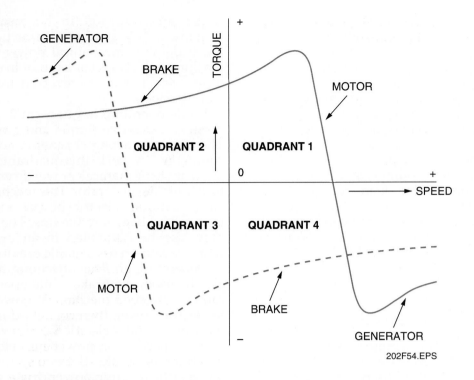

202F54.EPS

*Figure 54* ◆ Four-quadrant operation for a squirrel cage motor.

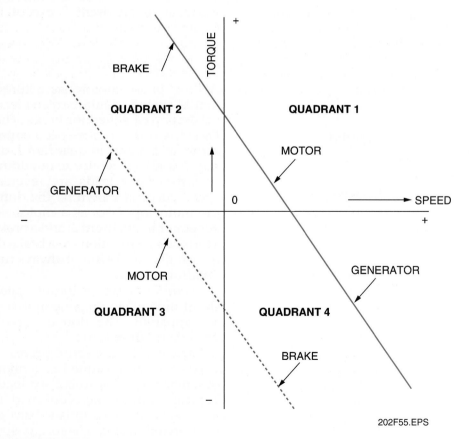

202F55.EPS

*Figure 55* ◆ Four-quadrant operation for a DC motor.

voltage. Also, the curve of an induction motor can be shifted by varying the voltage and frequency applied to the stator.

In describing the various methods of motor control, only the behavior of power circuits will be discussed. The many ways of shaping and controlling triggering pulses will not be covered. They constitute a complex subject that involves sophisticated electronics, logic circuits, integrated circuits, and microprocessors.

### 6.2.2  Motor Heating

Since a variable-speed drive system includes both the drive controller and the motor, the design engineer should always consider the capabilities of the motor to perform acceptably under the desired operating conditions. One of the factors that you should be aware of is motor heating. When operating a motor at reduced speeds, the ability to dissipate heat is also reduced due to the slower cooling fan speed. This factor should be considered when maintaining the motor, modifying its enclosure or surrounding area, or troubleshooting the drive system.

## 6.3.0  Motor Speed Control

It is important to understand how DC or AC motor speed can be varied in order to understand how a drive controller accomplishes that task. This section reviews the fundamentals of DC and AC motor speed control.

### 6.3.1  Varying the Speed of a DC Shunt Motor

A DC shunt motor is shown in *Figure 56(A)*. Basically, there are two ways of varying the running speed of a DC shunt motor:

- Adjusting the voltage (and current) applied to the field winding. As the field voltage is increased, the motor slows down. This method is suggested by *Figure 56(B)*.

- Adjusting the voltage (and current) applied to the armature. As the armature voltage is increased, the motor speeds up. This method is suggested by *Figure 56(C)*.

### 6.3.2  Field Control

Here is how method 1, adjusting the field voltage, works. As the field voltage is increased, by reducing $R_V$ in *Figure 56(B)*, for example, the field current is increased. This results in a stronger magnetic field, which induces a greater CEMF in the armature winding. The greater CEMF tends to oppose the applied DC voltage and thus reduces the armature current, $I_A$. Therefore, an increased field current causes the motor to slow down until the induced CEMF has returned to near its normal value.

Going in the other direction, if the field current is reduced, the magnetic field gets weaker. This causes a reduction in CEMF created by the rotating armature winding. The armature current increases, forcing the motor to spin faster, until the CEMF is once again approximately equal to what it was before. The reduction in magnetic field strength is compensated for by an increase in armature speed.

This method of speed control has certain positive features. It can be accomplished by a small, inexpensive rheostat, since the current in the field winding is fairly low. Also, because of the low value of the field current, $I_F$, the rheostat $R_V$ does not dissipate very much energy. Therefore, this method is energy efficient.

However, there is one major drawback to speed control from the field winding: to increase the speed, you must reduce $I_F$ and weaken the magnetic field, thereby lessening the motor's torque-producing ability. The ability of a motor to create torque depends on two things: the current in the armature conductors and the strength of the magnetic field. As $I_F$ is reduced, the magnetic field is weakened, and the motor's torque-producing ability declines. Unfortunately, it is at this point

### *Using a Motor as Both a Generator and a Brake*

**INSIDE TRACK**

DC motors that power subway cars are also used for regenerative braking. When driven by the train's momentum, such as when slowing down upon approaching a station, the motor acts as a generator and puts current back into the system. Thus, while the train's motors are creating a significant amount of power from the train's movement, the train makes use of the resistive torque created by the power generation to slow down the train.

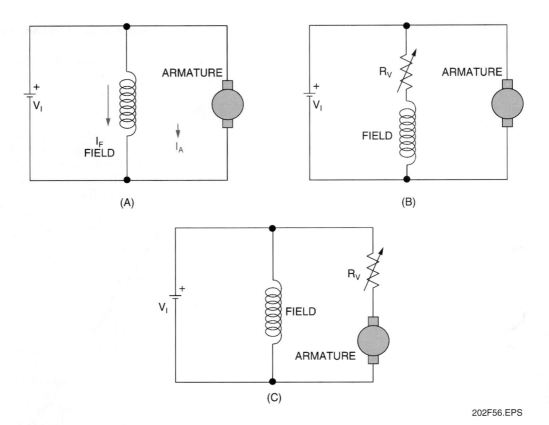

**Figure 56** ◆ DC shunt motor schematic.

202F56.EPS

that the motor needs all the torque-producing ability it can get, since it probably requires greater torque to drive the load at a faster speed.

### 6.3.3  Armature Control

From the torque-producing point of view, method 2, armature control, is much better. As the armature voltage and current are increased by reducing $R_V$, the motor starts running faster, which normally requires more torque. The reason for the rise in speed is that the increased armature voltage demands an increased CEMF to limit the increase in armature current to a reasonable amount. The only way the CEMF can increase is for the armature winding to spin faster, since the magnetic field strength is fixed. In this instance, the ingredients are all present for increased torque production, since the magnetic field strength is kept constant and $I_A$ is increased.

The problem with the armature control method of *Figure 56(C)* is that $R_V$, the rheostat, must handle the armature current, which is relatively large. Therefore, the rheostat must be physically large and expensive, and it will waste a considerable amount of energy.

### 6.3.4  Varying the Speed of an AC Motor

The principle of speed control for adjustable frequency drives is based on the following fundamental formula for a standard AC motor:

$$N_s = \frac{120f}{P}$$

*Where:*

$N_s$ = synchronous speed (rpm)
$f$ = frequency
$P$ = number of poles

The number of poles of a particular motor is set in its design and manufacture.

The adjustable-frequency system controls the frequency (f) applied to the motor. The speed ($N_s$) of the motor is then proportional to this applied frequency. Control frequency is adjusted by means of a potentiometer or external signal, depending on the application.

The frequency output of the controller is adjustable over its design speed range. Therefore, the speed of the motor is adjustable over this same range. Because an electronic means of generating variable frequencies is being used, the speed range often exceeds the 60 hertz (Hz) rated speed of the motor.

When variable-frequency speed control is employed, the motor supply voltage cannot be allowed to remain at a steady value. The magnitude of the motor voltage must be increased or decreased in proportion to the frequency. That is, the voltage-to-frequency ratio, V/f, must remain approximately constant.

For instance, if the motor has a nameplate rating of 240V at 60Hz, the voltage-to-frequency ratio is 4 (240 ÷ 60 = 4). If the motor is speeded up by adjusting its variable-frequency inverter to 90Hz, the voltage magnitude must be increased to 360V, since 4 × 90 = 360. If the motor is slowed down by adjusting the inverter frequency to 45Hz, the voltage magnitude must be decreased to 180V, since 4 × 45 = 180.

The stator's magnetic field strength must remain constant under all operating conditions. If the stator field strength should happen to rise much above the design value, the motor's core material would go into magnetic saturation. This would effectively lower the core's permeability, thereby inhibiting proper induction of voltage and current in the rotor loops (or bars), thus detracting from the torque-producing capability of the motor. On the other hand, if the stator field strength should happen to fall much below the design value, the weakened magnetic field would simply induce lower values of voltage and current in the rotor loops. This would also detract from the torque-producing ability of the motor.

Therefore, the magnetic field produced by the stator windings must hold a constant rms value, regardless of frequency. The magnetizing current of an induction motor is the current that flows through the stator winding when the rotor is spinning at steady-state speed with no torque load. The magnetizing current for an induction motor is given by Ohm's law:

$$I_{mag} = \frac{V}{X_L}$$

Where:

V = rms value of the applied stator voltage

$X_L$ = inductive reactance of the stator winding

In the equation, $X_L$ does not remain constant as the supply frequency is adjusted; it varies in proportion to the frequency ($X_L = 2\pi fL$). Therefore V must also be varied in proportion to the frequency, so that the Ohm's law division operation yields an unvarying value of magnetizing current.

Alternatively, using $X_L = 2\pi fL$, we can rewrite the equation:

$$I_{mag} = \frac{V}{X_L}$$

$$I_{mag} = \frac{V}{2\pi fL}$$

$$I_{mag} = \frac{1}{2\pi L} \times \frac{V}{f}$$

Since $1 \div 2\pi L$ is a constant determined by the motor's construction, the magnetizing current is kept constant by maintaining the V/f ratio.

The controller can automatically maintain the required volts/cycle (V/Hz) ratio to the motor at any speed. This provides maximum motor capability throughout the speed range.

The V/Hz setting is typically preset at the factory. However, on many controllers it can be adjusted or changed to fine tune controller operation.

## 7.0.0 ◆ MOTOR ENCLOSURES

Motors are usually designed with covers over the moving parts. These covers, called enclosures, are classified by NEMA (National Electrical Manufacturers Association) according to the degree of environmental protection provided and the method of cooling. If the cover has openings, the motor is classified as an open motor; if the enclosure is complete, the motor is classified as an enclosed motor. Each of these types of motors has many modifications. *Table 1* lists the various types for both open and totally enclosed motors.

**Table 1**  Motor Enclosures

| Open | Totally Enclosed |
| --- | --- |
| General purpose | Nonventilated |
| Drip-proof | Fan-cooled |
| Splash-proof | Fan-cooled guarded |
| Guarded | Explosion-proof |
| Semi-guarded | Dust- and ignition-proof |
| Drip-proof guarded | Pipe-ventilated |
| Externally ventilated | Water-cooled |
| Pipe-ventilated | Water-to-air-cooled |
| Weather-protected (Type I & Type II) | |
| Encapsulated windings | |
| Sealed windings | |

The different standard types as explained and defined by NEMA are as follows:

- *General purpose* – Has ventilating openings which permit the passage of external cooling air over and around the windings of the machine.
- *Drip-proof* – Ventilating openings are so constructed that successful operation is not interfered with when drops of liquid or solid particles strike or enter the enclosure at any angle from 0° to 15° downward from the vertical.
- *Splash-proof* – Ventilating openings are so constructed that successful operation is not interfered with when drops of liquid or solid particles strike or enter the enclosure at any angle not greater than 100° downward from the vertical.
- *Guarded* – Openings giving direct access to live metal or rotating parts (except smooth surfaces) are limited in size by the structural parts or by screens, baffles, grills, expanded metal, or other means to prevent accidental contact with hazardous parts.
- *Semi-guarded* – Some of the ventilating openings, usually in the top half, are guarded as in the case of a guarded machine, but the others are left open.
- *Drip-proof guarded* – This type of machine has ventilating openings as in a guarded machine.
- *Externally ventilated* – Designating a machine that is ventilated by a separate motor-driven blower mounted on the machine enclosure. Mechanical protection may be as defined above. This machine is sometimes known as a blower-ventilated or force-ventilated machine.
- *Pipe-ventilated* – Openings for the admission of ventilating air are so arranged that inlet ducts or pipes can be connected to them.
- *Weather-protected* – Type I: Ventilation passages are so designed as to minimize the entrance of rain, snow, and airborne particles to the electrical parts. Type II: In addition to the enclosure described for a Type I machine, ventilating passages at both intake and discharge are so arranged that high-velocity air and airborne particles blown into the machine by storms or high winds can be discharged without entering the internal ventilating passages leading directly to the electric parts.
- *Encapsulated windings* – An AC squirrel cage machine having random windings filled with an insulating resin, which also forms a protective coating.
- *Sealed windings* – An AC squirrel cage machine making use of form-wound coils and an insulation system that, through the use of materials, processes, or a combination of materials and processes, results in a sealing of the windings and connections against contaminants.

## 7.1.0 Totally Enclosed

- *Nonventilated* – Not equipped for cooling by means external to the enclosing parts.
- *Fan-cooled* – Equipped for exterior cooling by means of a fan or fans that are integral with the machine but external to the enclosing parts.
- *Fan-cooled guarded* – All openings giving direct access to the fan are limited in size by design of the structural parts or by screens, grills, expanded metal, etc. to prevent accidental contact with the fan.
- *Explosion-proof* – Designed and constructed to withstand an explosion of a specified gas or vapor that may occur within it and to prevent the ignition of the specified gas or vapor surrounding the machine by sparks, flashes, or explosions of the specified gas or vapor that may occur within the machine casing.
- *Dust- and ignition-proof* – Designed and constructed in a manner that will exclude ignitable amounts of dust or amounts which might affect performance or rating, and that will not permit arcs, sparks, or heat otherwise generated or liberated inside the enclosure to cause ignition of exterior accumulations or atmospheric suspensions of a specific dust on or in the vicinity of the enclosure.
- *Pipe-ventilated* – Openings are so arranged that when inlet and outlet ducts or pipes are connected to them there is no free exchange of the internal air and the air outside the case.
- *Water-cooled* – Cooled by circulating water, with the water or water conductors coming in direct contact with the machine parts.
- *Water-to-air-cooled* – Cooled by circulating air, which in turn is cooled by circulating water.

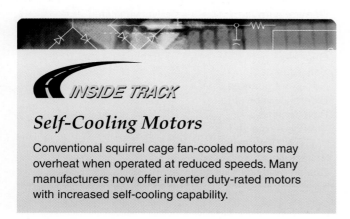

### INSIDE TRACK

#### Self-Cooling Motors

Conventional squirrel cage fan-cooled motors may overheat when operated at reduced speeds. Many manufacturers now offer inverter duty-rated motors with increased self-cooling capability.

## 7.2.0 Open Motor

The most common type of motor is the open motor. It has ventilating openings that permit the passage of external cooling air over and around its windings. If these are limited in size and shape, the motor is called a protected motor, since it is protected from any large pieces of material that may somehow enter the motor, thus damaging its internal parts. A protected motor also prevents a person from touching the rotating or electrically-energized parts of the motor. Drip-proof and splash-proof motors are constructed such that drops of liquid cannot enter the motor.

## 7.3.0 Enclosed Motor

The totally enclosed motor is designed to prevent the free exchange of air between the inside and outside of the actual motor housing. It is used where hostile environmental conditions and the motor application require maximum protection of the internal parts of the motor.

## 8.0.0 ◆ NEMA FRAME DESIGNATIONS

Frame sizes were developed by NEMA to ensure interchangeability of motors among manufacturers. They appear on motor nameplates to give information about the machine's physical dimensions. Key dimensions are:

- Distance from motor feet to shaft centerline
- Bolt-hole center-to-center distance between front and back feet
  Exposed shaft distance from shaft end to shaft shoulder

Tables are available to correlate frame size to dimensions. The system for designating the frames of motors and generators consists of a series of numbers in combination with letters.

## 8.1.0 Small Machines

The frame number for small machines is the D dimension in inches multiplied by 16. The following letters shall immediately follow the frame number to denote variations:

B – Carbonator pump motors

C – Type C face-mounting motors

G – Gasoline pump motors

H – A frame having an F dimension larger than that of the same frame without the suffix H

J – Jet pump motors

K – Sump pump motors

M – Oil burner motors

N – Oil burner motors

Y – Special mounting dimensions (must obtain dimensional diagram from manufacturer)

Z – All mounting dimensions are standard except the shaft extension

## 8.2.0 Medium Machines

The system for numbering frames of medium machines is as follows:

- The first two digits of the frame number are equal to four times the D dimension in inches. (If this product is not a whole number, the first two digits of the frame number shall be the next higher whole number.)
- The third and, when required, the fourth digit of the frame number are obtained from the value of 2F in inches.

*Figure 57* shows a typical end view of a foot-mounted machine. The many different dimensions can be found on a dimension sheet for that machine (*Figure 58*). The NEMA frame designation will provide information relating to both the D and 2F dimensions.

*Table 2* may be used to determine the D dimension and 2F dimension for medium-size motors. The D dimension is the distance from the centerline of the shaft to the bottom of the feet. The 2F dimension is the distance between the centerlines of the mounting holes in the feet or base of the machine.

Medium machines also use letters that denote variations. These letters follow the frame number. Since there are many more varieties of medium-size machines, the letter relates to the different aspects of mounting and shaft orientation.

For example, to understand the NEMA frame designation, we will take a typical motor frame designation and determine the D and 2F dimensions. Then we will use a different set of dimensions to determine the frame designation number.

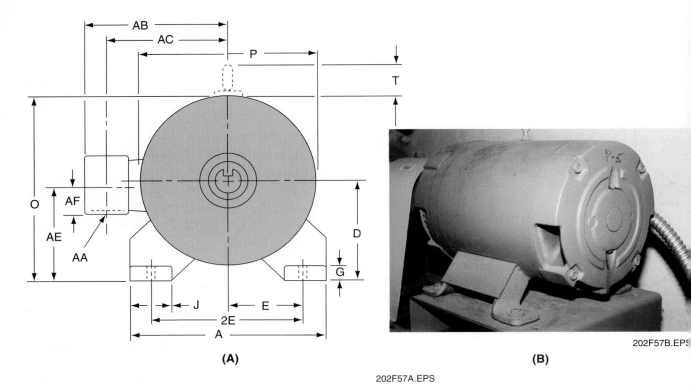

202F57A.EPS

202F57B.EPS

(A)

(B)

*Figure 57* ◆ End view of a foot-mounted motor.

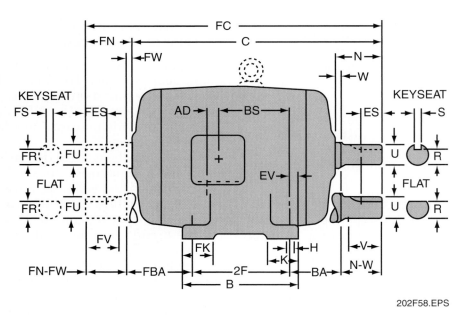

202F58.EPS

*Figure 58* ◆ Lettering of dimension sheets for foot-mounted machines (side view).

**Table 2**    Frame Dimension Chart

| Frame Number Series | D | Third/Fourth Digit in Frame Number | | | | | | |
|---|---|---|---|---|---|---|---|---|
| | | 1 | 2 | 3 | 4 | 5 | 6 | 7 |
| | | **2F Dimensions** | | | | | | |
| 140 | 3.50 | 3.00 | 3.50 | 4.00 | 4.50 | 5.00 | 5.50 | 6.25 |
| 160 | 4.00 | 3.50 | 4.00 | 4.50 | 5.00 | 5.50 | 6.25 | 7.00 |
| 180 | 4.50 | 4.00 | 4.50 | 5.00 | 5.50 | 6.25 | 7.00 | 8.00 |
| 200 | 4.50 | 4.50 | 5.00 | 5.50 | 6.50 | 7.00 | 8.00 | 9.00 |
| 210 | 5.00 | 4.50 | 5.00 | 5.50 | 6.50 | 7.00 | 8.00 | 9.00 |
| 220 | 5.50 | 5.00 | 5.50 | 6.25 | 6.75 | 7.50 | 9.00 | 10.00 |
| 250 | 6.25 | 5.50 | 6.25 | 7.00 | 8.25 | 9.00 | 10.00 | 11.00 |
| 280 | 7.00 | 6.25 | 7.00 | 8.00 | 9.50 | 10.00 | 11.00 | 12.50 |
| 320 | 8.00 | 7.00 | 8.00 | 9.00 | 10.50 | 11.00 | 12.00 | 14.00 |
| 360 | 9.00 | 8.00 | 9.00 | 10.00 | 11.25 | 12.25 | 14.00 | 16.00 |
| 400 | 10.00 | 9.00 | 10.00 | 11.00 | 12.25 | 13.75 | 16.00 | 18.00 |
| 440 | 11.00 | 10.00 | 11.00 | 12.50 | 14.50 | 16.50 | 18.00 | 20.00 |
| 500 | 12.50 | 11.00 | 12.50 | 14.00 | 16.00 | 18.00 | 20.00 | 22.00 |
| 580 | 14.50 | 12.50 | 14.00 | 16.00 | 18.00 | 20.00 | 22.00 | 25.00 |
| 680 | 17.00 | 16.00 | 18.00 | 20.00 | 22.00 | 25.00 | 28.00 | 32.00 |

| Frame Number Series | D | Third/Fourth Digit in Frame Number | | | | | | |
|---|---|---|---|---|---|---|---|---|
| | | 8 | 9 | 10 | 11 | 12 | 13 | 14 | 15 |
| | | **2F Dimensions** | | | | | | |
| 140 | 3.50 | 7.00 | 8.00 | 9.00 | 10.00 | 11.00 | 12.50 | 14.00 | 16.00 |
| 160 | 4.00 | 8.00 | 9.00 | 10.00 | 11.00 | 12.50 | 14.00 | 16.00 | 18.00 |
| 180 | 4.50 | 9.00 | 10.00 | 11.00 | 12.50 | 14.00 | 16.00 | 18.00 | 20.00 |
| 200 | 5.00 | 10.00 | 11.00 | ... | ... | ... | ... | ... | ... |
| 210 | 5.25 | 10.00 | 11.00 | 12.50 | 14.00 | 16.00 | 18.00 | 20.00 | 22.00 |
| 220 | 5.50 | 11.00 | 12.50 | ... | ... | ... | ... | ... | ... |
| 250 | 6.25 | 12.50 | 14.00 | 16.00 | 18.00 | 20.00 | 22.00 | 25.00 | 28.00 |
| 280 | 7.00 | 14.00 | 16.00 | 18.00 | 20.00 | 22.00 | 25.00 | 28.00 | 32.00 |
| 320 | 8.00 | 16.00 | 18.00 | 20.00 | 22.00 | 25.00 | 28.00 | 32.00 | 36.00 |
| 360 | 9.00 | 18.00 | 20.00 | 22.00 | 25.00 | 28.00 | 32.00 | 36.00 | 40.00 |
| 400 | 10.00 | 20.00 | 22.00 | 25.00 | 28.00 | 32.00 | 36.00 | 40.00 | 45.00 |
| 440 | 11.00 | 22.00 | 25.00 | 28.00 | 32.00 | 36.00 | 40.00 | 45.00 | 50.00 |
| 500 | 12.50 | 25.00 | 28.00 | 32.00 | 36.00 | 40.00 | 45.00 | 50.00 | 56.00 |
| 580 | 14.50 | 28.00 | 32.00 | 36.00 | 40.00 | 45.00 | 50.00 | 56.00 | 63.00 |
| 680 | 17.00 | 36.00 | 40.00 | 45.00 | 50.00 | 56.00 | 63.00 | 71.00 | 80.00 |

*Example 1:*

A typical medium-size frame number is a 256T. Since we know this is a medium frame, we divide the first two digits by 4:

$$25 \div 4 = 6.25$$

Therefore, the D dimension is 6.25 inches.

To determine the 2F dimension, we use *Table 2* and the third digit in the frame number. The third digit is 6 and the frame is a 250 series. Using the table, the 2F dimension is 10 inches. The T in the frame number is included as part of a frame designation for which standard dimensions have been established.

Medium-size frames can have multiple letters that denote a variety of different applications and arrangements. A 256AT has the same dimensions, with the A added to denote an industrial DC machine.

*Example 2:*

A frame has a D dimension of 3.5 inches and a 2F dimension of 4 inches, and all standard dimensions have been established. Multiplying the

D dimension by 4 will give the first two digits of the frame designation:

$$3.5 \times 4 = 14$$

Using the table, a 140 frame series and a 2F dimension of 4 inches provides a third digit of 3. Since it is a standard dimension frame, the letter will be the suffix. This frame has a designation of 143T.

Full-load torque (rather than horsepower) determines the frame size required to house the motor. Thus, a motor developing a large amount of horsepower at high speed will have the same frame size as a machine developing less horsepower at a slower speed.

More compact design, better ventilation, and insulation systems with higher temperature ratings have enabled manufacturers to house motors in increasingly smaller frame sizes. NEMA re-rates occurred in 1952 and 1964. Motors manufactured before 1952 are generally referred to as pre-U-frame motors. Those manufactured between 1952 and 1964 are called U-frame motors; those manufactured since 1964 are called T-frame motors.

## 9.0.0 ◆ MOTOR RATINGS AND NAMEPLATE DATA

The ratings of an electric motor include:

- Voltage
- Full-load current
- Speed
- Number of phases and frequency
- Full-load horsepower
- Service classification

Except for full-load horsepower and service classification, these are self-explanatory units. The horsepower rating that is stamped on the motor nameplate by the manufacturer is the horsepower load the motor will carry without damaging any part of the motor.

Electric motor service classification depends on the type of service for which the motor is designed. A motor will usually fall into one of two classifications. General-purpose motors are those motors designed for use without restriction to a particular application. They meet certain specifications as standardized by NEMA. A definite-purpose motor is one that is designed in standard ratings and with standard operating characteristics for use under service conditions other than usual or for use on a particular type of application. A special-purpose motor is one with special operating characteristics or special mechanical construction, or both, that is designed for a particular application and that does not meet the definition of a general-purpose or a definite-purpose motor.

The most common machine rating is the **continuous duty** rating defining the output (in kilowatts for DC generators, kilovolt-amperes at a specified power factor for AC generators, and horsepower for motors) that can be carried indefinitely without exceeding established limitations. For **intermittent duty, periodic duty,** or **varying duty,** a machine may be given a short-time rating defining the load that can be carried for a specific time. Standard periods for short-time ratings are 5, 15, 30, and 60 minutes. Speeds, voltages, and frequencies are also specified in ratings, and provision is made for possible variations in voltage and frequency.

For example, motors must operate successfully at voltages 10% above and below rated voltage and, for AC motors, at frequencies 5% above and below rated frequency; the combined variation of voltage and frequency may not exceed 10%. Other performance conditions are so established that reasonable short-time **overloads** can be carried. Thus, the user of a motor can expect to be able to apply an overload of 25% for a short time at 90% of normal voltage with an ample margin of safety.

## 9.1.0 Nameplate Data

The *NEC Section 430.7* has specified information that must be listed on a motor nameplate based on its type. Requirements can also be found in *NEMA Standards MG-1* and *MG-2*. Required information plus additional information is shown on the nameplate in *Figure 59*.

### 9.1.1 Rated Voltage

Power plant induction motors are designed to operate with a balanced three-phase voltage source applied at the terminals. The rated voltage on the nameplate is usually lower than the voltage of the electrical system. For example, a 460V motor is designed to operate in a 480V system. Here, an assumption is made by motor manufacturers that there will be a voltage drop of 20V from the transformer down to the motor terminals (see *Table 3*). The rated or nameplate voltage is the voltage at which the motor will operate most effectively. When other than rated voltage is applied, performance will change and motor life may be reduced.

Many three-phase motors have two voltages listed on the nameplate. For example, 230/460V means the motor can be connected for either 230V or 460V operation. In these cases, a connection diagram is usually found on the nameplate, as shown in *Figure 60*. These diagrams refer to low voltage and high-voltage connections.

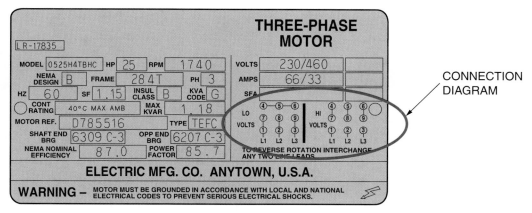

## THREE-PHASE MOTOR

LR-13758

| | | | | | | | | |
|---|---|---|---|---|---|---|---|---|
| MODEL | 3N346B | HP | 5 | RPM | 1740 | VOLTS | 230 | |
| NEMA DESIGN | B | FRAME | K184TC | PH | 3 | AMPS | 13.0 | |
| HZ | 60 | SF | 1.0 | INSUL CLASS | BR | KVA CODE | H | SFA |
| CONT RATING | 40°C MAX AMB | | MAX KVAR | 1.18 | | | | |
| MOTOR REF. | R72986BH891 | TYPE | PF | | | | | |
| SHAFT END BRG | 6206 | OPP END BRG | 6204 | | | | | |
| NEMA NOMINAL EFFICIENCY | 86.5 | POWER FACTOR | 85.7 | | | | | |

LO VOLTS · HI VOLTS

TO REVERSE ROTATION INTERCHANGE ANY TWO LINE LEADS.

### ELECTRIC MFG. CO. ANYTOWN, U.S.A.

WARNING – MOTOR MUST BE GROUNDED IN ACCORDANCE WITH LOCAL AND NATIONAL ELECTRICAL CODES TO PREVENT SERIOUS ELECTRICAL SHOCKS.

*Figure 59* ◆ Nameplate data.

202F69.EPS

## 9.1.2  Full-Load Amps (FLA)

The FLA rating appearing on the nameplate indicates the current the motor will draw at nameplate horsepower, frequency, and voltage. Most manufacturers test to determine this value on a periodic basis during production, ensuring reasonable accuracy. The *NEC®* requires that the rated full-load current be the basis for determining the proper sizing of cable, overload protective devices, and other **overcurrent** protection in the motor circuit. Since many motors can be connected for one of two voltage ratings, they have two FLA ratings.

The FLA ratings are guaranteed if the induction motor is operating at full-load conditions and the applied voltage and frequency are the same as stated on the nameplate. When voltage or frequency are not the same, however, the current drawn by the motor at full-load conditions will be different from the nameplate indication (see *Table 4*). It is possible to damage a motor operated below its rated voltage or frequency, since the current the motor draws at full-load conditions increases in both cases. If the overload protective device is not sized properly, motor life may be shortened by this overcurrent condition.

**Table 3**  Induction Motor Voltages

| System Voltage | Rated Voltage |
|---|---|
| 216 | 208 |
| 240 | 230 |
| 480 | 460 |
| 600 | 575 |
| 2,400 | 2,300 |
| 4,160 | 4,000 |
| 4,800 | 4,600 |
| 6,900 and 7,200 | 6,600 |
| 13,200 and 13,800 | 13,200 |

**Table 4**  Motor Operation

| Mode | Full-Load Current |
|---|---|
| 110% of rated volts | 7% decrease |
| 90% of rated volts | 11% increase |
| 105% of rated frequency | 5%–6% decrease |
| 95% of rated frequency | 5%–6% increase |

## THREE-PHASE MOTOR

LR-17835

| | | | | | | | |
|---|---|---|---|---|---|---|---|
| MODEL | 0525H4TBHC | HP | 25 | RPM | 1740 | VOLTS | 230/460 |
| NEMA DESIGN | B | FRAME | 284T | PH | 3 | AMPS | 66/33 |
| HZ | 60 | SF | 1.15 | INSUL CLASS | B | KVA CODE | G | SFA |
| CONT RATING | 40°C MAX AMB | | MAX KVAR | 1.18 | | |
| MOTOR REF. | D785516 | TYPE | TEFC | | |
| SHAFT END BRG | 6309 C-3 | OPP END BRG | 6207 C-3 | | |
| NEMA NOMINAL EFFICIENCY | 87.0 | POWER FACTOR | 85.7 | | |

LO VOLTS · HI VOLTS

TO REVERSE ROTATION INTERCHANGE ANY TWO LINE LEADS.

CONNECTION DIAGRAM

### ELECTRIC MFG. CO. ANYTOWN, U.S.A.

WARNING – MOTOR MUST BE GROUNDED IN ACCORDANCE WITH LOCAL AND NATIONAL ELECTRICAL CODES TO PREVENT SERIOUS ELECTRICAL SHOCKS.

*Figure 60* ◆ High-voltage and low-voltage connection diagrams shown on motor nameplate.

202F60.EPS

### 9.1.3 Rated Full-Load Speed

The rated full-load speed is the value indicated in rpm on the nameplate. It is the speed at which the shaft will turn at the nameplate horsepower when supplied with power at the nameplate voltage and frequency. If the driven load is less than the nameplate horsepower, the shaft will turn faster than full-load speed.

If the motor is operating unloaded, the shaft will turn very close to synchronous speed. For example, with a full-load speed of 1,750 rpm, it can be inferred that the motor's synchronous speed is 1,800 rpm. The machine will operate from close to 1,800 rpm down to 1,750 rpm, from no-load to full-load conditions.

Common synchronous speeds are 3,600, 1,800, 1,200, 900, and 600 rpm. Synchronous speed is rarely found on the motor nameplate unless the machine has been retrofitted and has not yet been tested for new full-load speed.

### 9.1.4 Rated Horsepower

An induction motor is really a torque generator. It delivers a needed torque to a driven machine at a certain speed. Thus:

$$\text{Horsepower} = \frac{\text{load torque in ft.-lbs} \times \text{rpm}}{5,250}$$

For induction motors that are built to NEMA standards, the ratings will range from ½hp to 400hp, with 24 categories in all. If horsepower requirements fall between any two ratings, the larger motor size should be selected.

Remember, an induction motor will try to deliver any amount of horsepower the load requires. If properly sized, most motors operate at something less than the motor nameplate horsepower. Standard motors are designed to operate at nameplate values from sea level up to an altitude of 3,300 feet if the ambient temperature does not exceed 104°F (40°C). Above this altitude, the nameplate horsepower no longer applies.

NEMA standards provide a method for determining the proper temperature rise, or the new maximum ambient temperature, at higher elevations. However, the standards do not provide a direct method for deriving the horsepower. Several methods are available to estimate true motor horsepower output.

### 9.1.5 Duty or Time Rating

All polyphase induction motors have either a duty or a time rating, which is the elapsed time the motor can operate at nameplate horsepower without shortening its life. The time rating of a motor is determined by operating the machine at full-load conditions and measuring the time it takes for the windings to heat up to the temperature rating of the insulation.

Standard time ratings are 5, 15, 30, and 60 minutes, and continuous or 24 **hours.** A motor with a time (or duty) rating other than continuous is a smaller motor that is given a higher horsepower rating for a shorter period of time, thus reducing size and cost. In power plant uses, most motor ratings are continuous at 104°F (40°C).

### 9.1.6 NEMA Design Letters

The NEMA design letter defines the starting torque characteristics of an induction motor. It is one of the most important pieces of information on the nameplate; unfortunately, when a motor is replaced, the NEMA design letter is usually ignored, often leading to misapplication of the new machine. For fans or centrifugal pumps, starting torque requirements increase with the square of the change in speed. For mixers or loaded conveyor belts, however, starting torque requirements change very little with speed.

*Motor Horsepower and Speed*

Can you replace a fan motor rated at a specific horsepower and speed with a motor rated at the same horsepower but a higher speed to increase airflow? If not, why not?

To account for these differences, NEMA has formulated design letters A, B, C, D, and F. The difference between motors with these letters is mainly in the design of the rotor, although there are also a few external differences. Design A and B motors are intended to drive conventional loads such as fans, blowers, and centrifugal pumps. About 80% of industrial motors are NEMA Design B.

Generally, the starting current is about five to seven times the rated full-load current. From *Table 5*, it can be seen that for larger motors, the starting current can be very significant, and across-the-line starting of larger motors could result in objectionable line-voltage dips. These voltage dips could result in other control equipment dropping out on low voltage and could even cause lights to dim.

### 9.1.7  Insulation Class

The electrical insulation system in a motor determines the machine's ultimate life span more than any other component. By some estimates, over 80% of all motors brought to repair shops are there because of premature failure of the insulation system.

The insulation class is a NEMA designation that identifies the class of material used to insulate the windings. Four letters designate the four classifications. They are A, B, F, and H. The insulation class defines the temperature that the insulation can be subjected to without suffering damage. The insulation class is shown on the nameplate in *Figure 61*.

Class A is now obsolete insofar as industrial motors are concerned. Class A was once the most

| | | Starting (Maximum) Current | |
|---|---|---|---|
| HP | Rated Full-Load Current | Classes B, C, D | Class F |
| ½ | 2.0 | 12 | — |
| 1 | 3.5 | 24 | — |
| 1½ | 5.0 | 35 | — |
| 2 | 6.5 | 45 | — |
| 3 | 9 | 60 | — |
| 5 | 15 | 90 | — |
| 7½ | 22 | 120 | — |
| 10 | 27 | 150 | — |
| 15 | 40 | 220 | — |
| 20 | 52 | 290 | — |
| 25 | 64 | 365 | — |
| 30 | 78 | 435 | 270 |
| 40 | 104 | 580 | 360 |
| 50 | 125 | 725 | 450 |
| 60 | 150 | 870 | 540 |
| 75 | 185 | 1,085 | 675 |
| 100 | 246 | 1,450 | 900 |
| 125 | 310 | 1,815 | 1,125 |
| 150 | 360 | 2,170 | 1,350 |
| 200 | 480 | 2,900 | 1,800 |

**Table 5**  Current for 220V, 60-Cycle Squirrel Cage Motors

common classification for motor insulation, especially for small motors. Class A comprises materials or combinations of materials such as cotton or paper, when suitably impregnated or coated, or other materials capable of operation at the temperature rise assigned for Class A insulation for the particular machine.

Class B is the predominant class of insulation used in motor manufacturing and rewinding

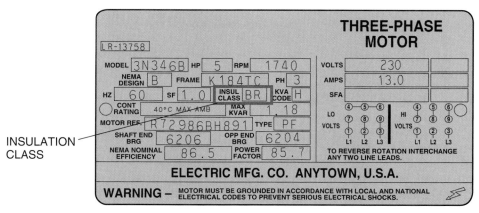

INSULATION CLASS

202F61.EPS

*Figure 61* ◆ Nameplate showing insulation class.

today. This class is the basic standard of the industry. It includes materials such as mica, glass fiber, polyester, and aramid laminates, etc., with suitable bonding substances, or other materials, not necessarily inorganic, capable of operation at the temperature rise assigned for Class B insulation for the particular machine. (The insulation class may be designated more specifically by the use of additional letters, such as the BR shown in *Figure 61*.)

Class F incorporates materials that are similar to those in Class B but are capable of operation at the temperature rise assigned for Class F for the particular machine.

Class H insulation systems comprise materials or combinations of materials such as silicone elastomer, mica, glass fiber, polyester, and aramid laminates, etc., with suitable bonding substances such as silicone resins, or other materials capable of operation at the temperature rise assigned for Class H insulation for the particular machine.

When replacing motors, ensure that the insulation class is equal to or better than that of the motor removed from service.

### 9.1.8 Nominal Rated Voltage

Nominal rated voltage is defined as the voltage rating at which the motor is designed to operate.

### 9.1.9 Minimum Starting Voltage

Minimum starting voltage may be defined as the lowest voltage at which a motor will start without drawing an excessive/trip current.

### 9.1.10 Frequency

Frequency is given for AC motors in hertz or cycles per second. Standard frequencies for AC motors are 50Hz and 60Hz. Alternating current in the U.S. is 60Hz.

### 9.1.11 Service Factor

The service factor is a multiplier for the nameplate horsepower rating that determines the amount of overload the motor can withstand. This extra horsepower is available if the motor is already operating at rated voltage and frequency and is in an environment that does not exceed the ambient temperature rating. The most common service factor appearing on a motor nameplate is 1.15.

### 9.1.12 NEMA Code Letters

The high current draw of the motor during the first moments of startup is called the in-rush or

locked-rotor current. It can be derived from the kVA code letter on the motor nameplate. The letter corresponds to the kilovolt-amperes per rated horsepower (kVA/hp) required during the first moments of motor startup. *Table 6* provides the kVA/hp value for each kVA code—a letter from A to V, excluding I, O, and Q. The locked-rotor current is required when sizing fuses or determining a **circuit breaker** setting in an induction motor circuit.

### 9.1.13 Bearings

Polyphase induction motors require either anti-friction or sleeve bearings. Anti-friction bearings are standard in medium (integral) horsepower motor sizes through 125hp/1,800 rpm. They are optional in 150 to 600hp/1,800 rpm sizes. Sleeve bearings are standard in 500hp/3,600 rpm and larger sizes.

Since radial loads are higher at the drive end of the motor, the drive-end bearing has a higher load rating than the bearing at the opposite end. A typical nameplate (*Figure 62*) might depict both bearing duties as:

- Shaft end brg: 6,206
- Opp end brg: 6,204

Bearing internal clearances are: C1 and C2 (smaller-than-normal clearance); standard clearance (normal); and C3, C4, and C5 (larger-than-normal clearance). Electric motors usually require a C3 internal clearance. Some bearing manufacturers have a different designation for motor bearings that have a larger-than-normal internal clearance.

### 9.1.14 Rated Amperage

Rated amperage may be defined as the full-load current required to produce full-rated horsepower at the motor's rated voltage and frequency. *Figure 62* shows the amperage for a typical motor.

### 9.1.15 Rated Horsepower

Horsepower is a rating used to specify the capacity of an electric motor to produce mechanical power to drive a specific piece of equipment (see *Figure 62*).

### 9.1.16 Locked-Rotor Current

The locked-rotor current is the steady-state current of a motor with the rotor locked and with rated voltage applied at rated frequency. NEMA has designated a set of code letters (*NEC Section 430.7*) to define locked-rotor kilovolt-amperes

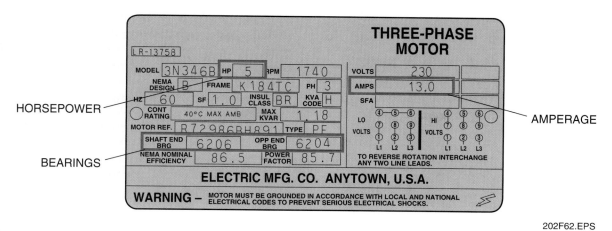

HORSEPOWER

BEARINGS

AMPERAGE

202F62.EPS

*gure 62* ◆ Nameplate showing bearings, horsepower, and amperage.

VA) per horsepower (*Table 6*). This code letter ppears on the nameplate of all AC squirrel cage duction motors. The kVA rating is an indication f the current draw and, indirectly, the impedance f the locked rotor.

The current drawn by the motor under stall onditions can be calculated using the values

given in *Table 6*. The current drawn by the motor under stalled conditions must be considered when selecting the motor protection and starting package and in coordination with the power system protective devices.

### 9.1.17 Starting Current

The total instantaneous starting current comprises the locked-rotor current plus the transient in-rush that flows until the motor magnetic circuit stabilizes.

### 9.1.18 Temperature Rise

The temperature rise may be defined as the measure of the heat produced by the operation of the motor. Several conditions contribute to temperature rise. Examples include running current, hysteresis losses, and friction of rotating parts.

### 9.1.19 Power Factor

The power factor (pf) is the ratio of active power of an alternating or pulsating current (when measured with a wattmeter) to the apparent power indicated by an ammeter and voltmeter. It is also referred to as the phase factor. The power factor is the measure of the system or equipment efficiency.

## 9.2.0 Motor Protection

Fuses are normally used for motor overload protection. When used, fuses must be provided in each ungrounded conductor and also the grounded conductor of a three-wire, three-phase AC system with one conductor grounded. When non-fuse overload protective devices are used (*NEC Section 430.37*), follow the guidelines as

**Table 6**   Locked-Rotor Code Letters

| Code Letter | kVA Per Horsepower with Locked Rotor |
|---|---|
| A | 0–3.14 |
| B | 3.15–3.54 |
| C | 3.55–3.99 |
| D | 4.0–4.49 |
| E | 4.5–4.99 |
| F | 5.0–5.59 |
| G | 5.6–6.29 |
| H | 6.3–7.09 |
| J | 7.1–7.99 |
| K | 8.0–8.99 |
| L | 9.0–9.99 |
| M | 10.0–11.19 |
| N | 11.2–12.49 |
| P | 12.5–13.99 |
| R | 14.0–15.99 |
| S | 16.0–17.99 |
| T | 18.0–19.99 |
| U | 20.0–22.39 |
| V | 22.4–AND UP |

stated in *Table 7*. Note that each motor winding must be individually protected against short circuits and ground faults.

In general, when providing overcurrent protection for motor circuits against overcurrents due to grounds and short circuits (*NEC Section 430.52*), follow the guidance listed in *Table 8*. *Table 8* provides time delay and instantaneous trip values for various types of motors as a percentage of full-load current.

When sizing the overload protection for continuous duty motors, refer to *NEC Section 430.32*. Motors that have a service factor of 1.15 and/or a maximum temperature rise of 40°C shall be provided with overload protection limited to 125% of the full-load current of the motor (this also applies to the secondary circuit of a wound rotor motor). All other motors shall be limited to 115% of the full-load current. Motors that are rated at less than 1hp have exceptions to this rule. Refer to *NEC Article 430* for these exceptions.

If the desired overload ratings are not available when sizing overload protection for the motor, then use the next highest available overload rating. This is allowed provided that 140% of full-load current is not exceeded by motors that have a service factor of 1.15 and/or a maximum temperature rise of 40°C. For all other motors, this maximum value would be 130% rather than 115% as stated earlier.

Additionally, in certain situations, motors wit installed overloads rated as discussed previousl may not start or be able to carry system load. I these instances, it is permissible to increase th overload settings to the respective 140%/130 values. When motor starting is still a problem, th overload protective device may be shorted ou during the equipment startup sequence provide that the circuit breaker or fuse protecting th branch is not set at greater than 400% of the ful load current value and the motor does not have a automatic starter.

Overload protection for adjustable spee drives is based on the rated input to the powe conversion equipment. If overload protection supplied with the equipment, then no furthe overload protection is required. The rating of th disconnecting means shall be no less than 115% c the power conversion equipment rated input cu rent and it shall be physically located in the i coming line. Overload protection, if not shunte should allow a sufficient time delay for the moto to start and accelerate.

### 9.2.1 Thermal Protectors

**Thermal protectors** that are integral with the moto are often used to protect the motor from overloac and starting failures. All motors with a voltag rating greater than 600V must have a therm

**Table 7**    Minimum Number of Overload Units

| Type of Motor | Supply System | Number and Location of Overloac Units (such as trip coils or relays) |
|---|---|---|
| Single-phase AC or DC | Two-wire, single-phase AC or DC, ungrounded | One in either conductor |
| Single-phase AC or DC | Two-wire, single-phase AC or DC, one grounded conductor | One in ungrounded conductor |
| Single-phase AC or DC | Three-wire, single-phase AC or DC, grounded neutral | One in either ungrounded conducto |
| Single-phase AC | Any three-phase supply | One in ungrounded conductor |
| Two-phase AC | Three-wire, two-phase AC, ungrounded | Two, one in each phase |
| Two-phase AC | Three-wire, two-phase AC, one grounded conductor | Two, one in each ungrounded conductor |
| Two-phase AC | Four-wire, two-phase AC, grounded or ungrounded | Two, one per phase in ungrounded conductors |
| Two-phase AC | Five-wire, two-phase AC, grounded neutral or ungrounded | Two, one per phase in any ungrounded phase wire |
| Three-phase AC | Any three-phase supply | Three, one in each phase* |

*Exception: An overload unit in each phase shall not be required where overload protection is provided by other approved means.

**Table 8** Motor Protection

| Type of Motor | Percent of Full-Load Current | | | |
|---|---|---|---|---|
| | Nontime Delay Fuse | Dual Element (Time Delay) Fuse** | Instantaneous Trip Breaker | Inverse Time Breaker* |
| Single-phase motors | 300 | 175 | 800 | 250 |
| AC polyphase motors other than wound-rotor: | | | | |
| Squirrel cage: | | | | |
| Other than Design B, energy efficient | 300 | 175 | 800 | 250 |
| Design B, energy-efficient | 300 | 175 | 1,100 | 250 |
| Synchronous† | 300 | 175 | 800 | 250 |
| Wound rotor | 150 | 150 | 800 | 150 |
| Direct-current (constant voltage) | 150 | 150 | 250 | 150 |

For certain exceptions to the values specified, see *NEC Section 430.54.*

The values given in the last column also cover the ratings of nonadjustable inverse time types of circuit breakers that may be modified per *NEC Section 430.52.*

*The values in the Nontime Delay Fuse column apply to time delay Class CC fuses.

Synchronous motors of the low-torque, low-speed type (usually 450 rpm or lower), such as are used to drive reciprocating compressors, pumps, etc., that start unloaded, do not require a fuse rating or circuit breaker setting in excess of 200% of the full-load current.

protector and its overload must not have an automatic reset feature. They shall trip no higher than the following percentage of full-load current:

- Motor full-load current not exceeding 9 amps—170%
- Motor full-load current between 9.1 and 20 amps—156%
- Motor full-load current greater than 20.1 amps—140%

This requirement is based on the maximum full-load motor current as listed in the tables provided in *NEC Article 430.*

Motors that are rated 1,500hp include a device that is set to de-energize the motor once the actual temperature rise of the motor equals the rated temperature rise of the motor insulation. Thermal protectors are usually sized and installed by the motor manufacturer.

### 9.2.2 Branch Considerations

According to *NEC Section 430.22,* when a single motor used in a continuous duty application is supplied from a **branch circuit,** the ampacity of the branch circuit must be not less than 125% of the motor full-load current as determined by *NEC Section 430.6(A)(1).* If a multiple-speed motor is used, then the ampacity shall be based on the highest of the full-load current ratings on the motor nameplate. Where motors have unusual duty cycle requirements, use the requirements listed in *Table 9,* as referenced in *NEC Section 430.22(E).*

Per *NEC Section 430.24,* when sizing conductors supplying several motors, the capacity shall not be less than 125% of the largest motor plus the sum of the full-load current ratings of all other motors in the group. Values for the full-load amps are taken from *NEC Tables 430.247 through 430.250.* Several motors or loads are permitted to be provided for on one branch circuit if:

- The system voltage is <600 volts.
- The branch protective device protects the smallest installed motor.
- All motors are 1hp, <20A (15A) on 120V (600V) circuits where each motor draws <6A, overloads are installed on the motor, and short circuit current and ground fault current do not exceed the branch circuit rating.
- It is part of a factory-listed assembly.

In instances where taps are used, short circuit current and ground fault current protection may not be required for the taps used. This is true provided that the tap used has the same ampacity as the branch circuit it is connected to. Additionally, the tap cannot be longer than 25' and it must also be physically protected from damage.

**Table 9** Duty Cycle Service

| Classification of Service | Percentages of Nameplate Current Rating | | | |
| --- | --- | --- | --- | --- |
| | 5-Minute Rated Motor | 15-Minute Rated Motor | 30- and 60-Minute Rated Motor | Continuous Rated Motor |
| Short-Time Duty | | | | |
|   Operating valves, raising or lowering rolls, etc. | 110 | 120 | 150 | — |
| Intermittent Duty | | | | |
|   Freight and passenger elevators, tool heads, pumps, drawbridges, turntables, etc. | | | | |
|   For arc welders, see *NEC Section 630.11* | 85 | 85 | 90 | 140 |
| Periodic Duty | | | | |
|   Rolls, ore- and coal-handling machines, etc. | 85 | 90 | 95 | 140 |
| Varying Duty | 110 | 120 | 150 | 200 |

Any motor application shall be considered as continuous duty unless the nature of the apparatus it drives is such that the motor will not operate continuously with load under any condition of use.

Reprinted with permission from NFPA 70, the *National Electrical Code*®. Copyright © 2004, National Fire Protection Association, Quincy, MA 02269. This reprinted material is not the complete and official position of the National Fire Protection Association on the referenced subject, which is represented only by the standard in its entirety.

## 10.0.0 ◆ CONNECTIONS AND TERMINAL MARKINGS FOR AC MOTORS

The markings on the external leads of an induction motor are sometimes missing or illegible, and proper identification must be made before the motor can be connected to the line. This section describes the procedures for identifying leads in either a wye-connected or delta-connected, three-phase, nine-lead motor.

The required materials for this procedure are:

- Appropriate personal protective equipment
- 12V battery such as an automotive battery
- Analog meter with a large scale and low range (digital meters may not clearly capture the voltage kick)

- Test leads and jumpers
- Momentary contact, normally open (N.O.) pushbutton switch
- Labels to mark leads as they are identified
- Three-phase, nine-lead induction motor

Before starting, identify whether the motor to be tagged is wye-connected or delta-connected. Compare the two connection diagrams in *Figure 63* and *Figure 64*. You will see that both types of motors have nine leads and six coils. In a wye-connected motor, three coils are connected together and three coils are isolated. A delta-connected motor has three sets of two coils connected together. Using an ohmmeter, insulate all motor leads from one another and check for continuity between each lead. Start by placing one probe on one lead and check through the remaining leads. As you identify which leads show

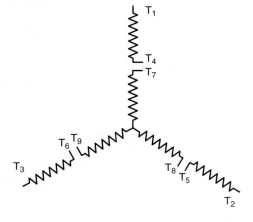

202F63.EPS

*Figure 63* ◆ Dual-voltage, three-phase wye connection.

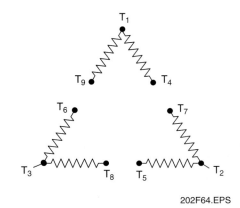

202F64.EPS

*Figure 64* ◆ Dual-voltage, three-phase delta connection.

continuity, group them together. Continue this procedure with each lead until all leads are grouped. When you have completed this procedure, you should have either three wires in one group and three sets of two wires grouped together, which would indicate a wye-connected motor, or three sets of three wires grouped together, indicating a delta-connected motor.

**NOTE**

If the leads are partially tied together, mark or identify them in a way that will allow you to reconnect them after the testing procedure is completed.

## 0.1.0 Identifying the Terminals of Wye-Connected Motors

Figure 65 shows the coil arrangement for a three-phase, wye-connected motor. To identify the terminals of a wye-connected motor, proceed as follows:

*Step 1* Taking the group of three common leads, arbitrarily identify them as leads 7, 8, and 9.

*Step 2* Using the diagram in *Figure 66* as a guide, connect the positive lead from the battery to lead 7. Connect the lead from the battery negative through the N.O. switch to leads 8 and 9 simultaneously.

*Step 3* Connect one of the three remaining lead pairs to the voltmeter terminals.

*Step 4* Close the N.O. switch while observing the DC voltmeter. Use the lowest scale practical without over-ranging the meter. If the meter deflection is upward, note the voltage reading. Observe that the reading

occurs only on the initial energization of the windings and then decays. Note the peak reading only and ignore the deflection in the opposite direction that occurs when the switch is opened. If the meter initially deflects downward, reverse the test lead connections.

*Step 5* Continue with the remaining two lead pairs. The pair with the highest voltage reading is the winding associated with lead 7. The lead with positive polarity is identified as lead 4 and the lead with negative polarity is lead 1.

*Step 6* Repeat Step 3, but apply the positive lead of the battery to lead 8 and the negative lead of the battery to leads 7 and 9. The positive lead of the pair with the highest voltage is identified as lead 5 and the lead with negative polarity is lead 2.

*Step 7* Repeat Step 3, but apply the positive lead of the battery to lead 9 and the negative lead of the battery to leads 7 and 8. The positive lead of the pair with the highest voltage is marked lead 6 and the negative lead is lead 3.

*Step 8* To confirm that all leads are correctly identified, connect the motor to the circuit. Be sure to observe proper connection procedures for the applied voltage. Once connected to the circuit, start the motor and take current readings on all three lines. If the motor starts correctly and the current readings are approximately equal, the procedure was a success.

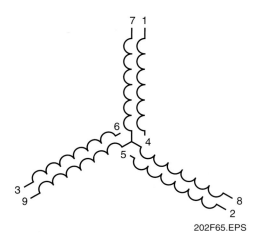

202F65.EPS

*Figure 65* ◆ Coil arrangement in a wye-connected motor.

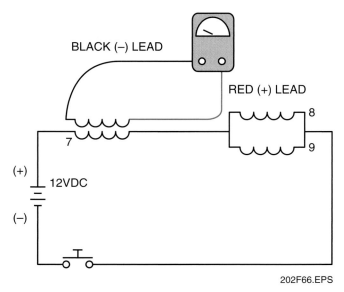

202F66.EPS

*Figure 66* ◆ Battery hookup for wye-connected motor lead identification.

## Motor Lead Identification

Refer to the procedure for identifying the leads in a wye-connected motor and answer the following questions:

- In Step 2, what would happen if 8 and 9 were connected one at a time?
- In Step 4, why does the voltage reading decay and later deflect downward?
- In Step 5, how much larger is the high voltage reading than the lower readings? Why?

### 10.2.0 Identifying the Terminals of Delta-Connected Motors

A delta-connected motor has three sets of three leads. *Figure 67* shows how the coils are arranged in a delta-connected, three-phase motor. In this figure, the coils that are side by side are actually wound on the same poles on the motor. As discussed previously, this will allow some transformer interaction between adjacent coils. To identify the terminals of a delta-connected motor, proceed as follows:

*Step 1* Using an ohmmeter on a low scale, measure the resistance between each of the three leads in one group. When performing this measurement, you should see that the resistance between two of the leads is about twice that between either of those two and the third. The lead that shows the least resistance to the other two will be lead 1. Refer to all three wires in this set as set 1.

*Step 2* Repeat Step 1 with the second set to identify the lead with the least resistance as lead 2. Refer to all three wires in this set as set 2.

*Step 3* Repeat Step 1 with the final set to identify the lead with the least resistance as lead 3. Refer to all three wires in this set as set 3.

*Step 4* Using the diagram in *Figure 68* as a guide, connect lead 1 to the positive terminal of a DC voltage source and one of the remaining leads in that set (set 1) to the negative terminal. Attach the red lead of the volt meter to lead 2 and the black lead to one of the two unknown leads in set 2. Press the pushbutton and observe the meter needle. If the correct leads have been selected, a voltage will be induced into this coil. If not, connect the second lead to the volt meter and repeat the test. If there is still no induced voltage, disconnect the unknown lead in set 1 from the DC voltage and connect the remaining unknown lead to the negative source. Repeat the test until the leads with an induced voltage have been identified. Once these leads are located, identify the lead connected to the negative terminal of the DC voltage source as lead and the lead connected to the negative voltmeter probe as lead 7. Identify the other lead in set 2 as lead 5.

*Step 5* The remaining lead in set 1 will be lead 9. Leaving lead 1 on the positive DC terminal, connect the negative terminal to lead 9. Attach the red lead of the voltmeter to lead 3 and the black lead to one of the two unknown leads in set 3. Press the pushbutton and observe the meter needle. If the correct leads have been selected, a voltage will be induced into this coil. If not, connect the second lead to the volt meter and repeat the test. Once these leads are located, identify the lead connected to the negative voltmeter probe as lead 6.

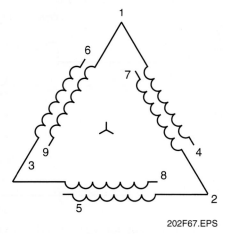

202F67.EPS

*Figure 67* ◆ Coil arrangement in a delta-connected motor.

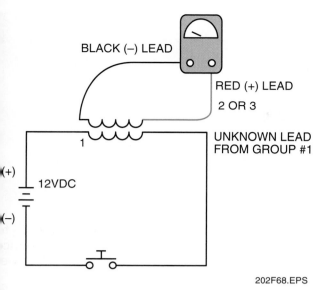

BLACK (–) LEAD

RED (+) LEAD

2 OR 3

UNKNOWN LEAD
FROM GROUP #1

1

(+)

12VDC

(–)

202F68.EPS

Figure 68 ◆ Battery hookup for delta-connected motor lead identification.

**Step 6** The remaining lead in set 3 is lead 8. To verify this, connect lead 3 to the positive terminal of the DC voltage source and lead 8 to the negative terminal. Attach the red lead of the voltmeter to lead 2 and the black lead to lead 5. Press the pushbutton and observe the meter needle. If the results are correct, a voltage will be induced into this coil, resulting in meter needle deflection.

**Step 7** To confirm that all leads are correctly identified, connect the motor to the circuit. Be sure to observe proper connection procedures for the applied voltage. Once connected to the circuit, start the motor and take current readings on all three lines. If the motor starts correctly and the current readings are approximately equal, the procedure was a success.

# 11.0.0 ◆ NEC® REQUIREMENTS

*NEC Article 430* covers the application and installation of motors, motor circuits, and motor control connections, including conductors, short circuit and ground fault protection, starters, disconnects, and overload protection.

*NEC Article 440* contains provisions for motor-driven equipment and for branch circuits and controllers for HVAC equipment.

All motors must be installed in a location that allows adequate ventilation to cool the motors. Furthermore, the motors should be located so that maintenance, troubleshooting, and repairs can be readily performed. Such work could consist of lubricating the motor bearings or perhaps replacing worn brushes. Testing the motor for open circuits and ground faults is also necessary from time to time.

When motors must be installed in locations where combustible material, dust, or similar material may be present, special precautions must be taken in selecting and installing the motors.

Any exposed live parts of motors operating at 50V or more between terminals must be guarded; that is, they must be installed in a room, enclosure, or location so as to allow access only by qualified persons (electrical maintenance personnel). If such a room, enclosure, or location is not feasible, an alternative is to elevate the motors not less than 8' above the floor. In all cases, adequate space must be provided around motors with exposed live parts, even when properly grounded, to allow for maintenance, troubleshooting, and repairs.

The chart in *Table 10* summarizes *NEC®* installation rules.

A summary of *NEC Article 430* is shown in *Figure 69*. Detailed information may be found in the *NEC®* under the articles or sections indicated.

**Table 10** Summary of *NEC*® Requirements for Motor Installations

| Application | Requirement | *NEC*® Reference |
|---|---|---|
| Location | Motors must be installed in areas with adequate ventilation. They must also be arranged so that sufficient work space is provided for replacement and maintenance. | *NEC Section 430.14(A)* |
| | Open motors must be located or protected so that sparks cannot reach combustible materials. | *NEC Section 430.14(B)* |
| | In locations where dust or flying material will collect on or in motors in such quantities as to seriously interfere with the ventilation or cooling of motors and thereby cause dangerous temperatures, suitable types of enclosed motors that will not overheat under the prevailing conditions must be used. | *NEC Section 430.16* |
| Disconnecting means | A motor disconnecting means must be within sight from the controller location (with exceptions) and disconnect both the motor and controller. The disconnect must be readily accessible and clearly indicate the OFF/ON positions (open/closed). | *NEC Article 430, Part IX* <br> *NEC Section 430.104* |
| | Motor control circuits require a disconnecting means to disconnect them from all supply sources. | *NEC Section 430.74* |
| | The disconnecting means must be as specified in the code. | *NEC Section 430.109* |
| Wiring methods | Flexible connections such as Type AC cable, Greenfield, flexible metal tubing, etc., are standard for motor connections. | *NEC Articles 300 and 430* |
| Motor control circuits | All conductors of a remote motor control circuit outside of the control device must be installed in a raceway or otherwise protected. The circuit must be wired so that an accidental ground in the control device will not start the motor. | *NEC Section 430.73* |
| Guards | Exposed live parts of motors and controllers operating at 50 volts or more must be guarded by installation in a room, enclosure, or other location so as to allow access by only qualified persons, or elevated 8 feet or more above the floor. | *NEC Section 430.232* |
| Adjustable speed drive systems | Requirements for adjustable speed drives and their motors. | *NEC Article 430, Part X* |
| Motors operating over 600 volts | Special installation rules apply to motors operating at over 600 volts. | *NEC Article 430, Part XI* |
| Controller grounding | Motor controllers must have their enclosures grounded. | *NEC Section 430.244* |

## Motor Connections

On dual-voltage and/or multi-speed motors, always check the wiring connection diagrams given on the motor nameplate to wire the motor for the correct voltage and/or speed.

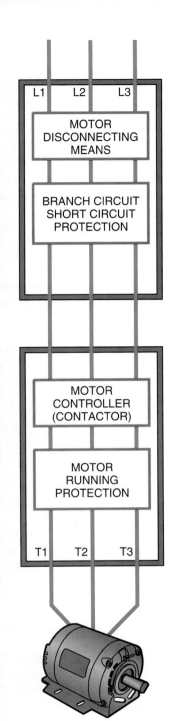

**NEC Article 430, Part IX**
*Sections 430.101*
*through 430.113*

**Disconnects motor and controllers from circuit.**
1. Continuous rating of 115% or more of motor FLC. Also see *NEC Article 430, Part II*.
2. Disconnecting means shall be as listed in *NEC Section 430.109*.
3. Must be located in sight of motor location and driven machinery. The controller disconnecting means can serve as the disconnecting means if the controller disconnect is located in sight of the motor location and driven machinery.

**NEC Article 430, Part IV**
*Sections 430.51*
*through 430.58*

**Protects branch circuit from short circuits or grounds.**
1. Must carry starting current of motor.
2. Rating must not exceed values in *NEC Table 430.52* unless not sufficient to carry starting current of motor.
3. Values of branch circuit protective devices shall in no case exceed exceptions listed in *NEC Section 430.52*.

**NEC Article 430, Part VII**
*Sections 430.81*
*through 430.91*

**Used to start and stop motors.**
1. Must have current rating of 100% or more of motor FLC.
2. Must be able to interrupt LRC.
3. Must be rated as specified in *NEC Section 430.83*.

**NEC Article 430, Part III**
*Sections 430.31*
*through 430.44*

**Protects motor and controller against excessive heat due to motor overload.**
1. Must trip at following percent or less of motor FLC for continuous motors rated more than one horsepower.
   a) 125% FLC for motors with a marked service factor of not less than 1.15 or a marked temperature rise of not over 40°C.
   b) 115% FLC for all others. (See the *NEC®* for other types of protection.)
2. Three thermal units required for any three-phase AC motor.
3. Must allow motor to start.
4. Select size from FLC on motor nameplate.

**NEC Article 430, Part II**
*Sections 430.21*
*through 430.29*

**Specifies the sizes of conductors capable of carrying the motor current without overheating.**
1. To determine the ampacity of conductors, switches, branch circuit overcurrent devices, etc., the full-load current values given in *NEC Tables 430.247 thru 430.250* shall be used instead of the actual current rating marked on the motor nameplate. *(See NEC Section 430.6.)*
2. According to *NEC Section 430.22*, branch circuit conductors supplying a single motor used in a continuous duty application shall have an ampacity of not less than 125% of motor FLC, as determined by *NEC Section 430.6(A)(1)*.

202F69.EPS

*Figure 69* ◆ Summary of requirements for motors, motor circuits, and controllers.

# 12.0.0 ◆ TROUBLESHOOTING

The useful life of an induction motor depends largely on the condition of its insulation. In general, the insulation should be suitable for the operating requirements.

## 12.1.0 Stator Windings

The stator (stationary) windings appear to be so simple and rugged as to cause one to frequently overlook the necessity for certain maintenance procedures. However, a glance into the average motor repair shop will make it apparent that the induction motor stator is a vulnerable piece of equipment. Most of the work going on will be involved with replacing or repairing stator windings.

Stator troubles can usually be traced to one or more of the following causes:

- Worn bearings
- Moisture
- Overloading
- Operating single phase
- Poor insulation

Dust and dirt are usually contributing factors. Some forms of dust are highly conductive and contribute materially to insulation breakdown. The effect of dust on the motor temperature through restriction of ventilation is another reason for keeping the machine clean, either by periodically blowing it out with compressed air or by dismantling and cleaning it. The compressed air must be dry and throttled down to a low pressure that will not endanger the insulation.

*Moisture* – One of the most subtle enemies of motor insulation is moisture. Needless to say, motor insulation must be kept reasonably dry, although many applications make this practically impossible unless the motor is totally enclosed or otherwise protected from the direct effects of moisture. If operated in a damp place, a special moisture-resistant coating should be applied to the windings.

*Dipping and baking* – The life of a winding depends on keeping it in its original (or new) condition for as long as possible. In a new machine, the winding is snug in the slots and the insulation is fresh and flexible, being newly treated with varnish and therefore resistant to the deteriorating effects of moisture and other foreign matter. This condition is best maintained by periodic cleaning, followed by varnish and oven treatments.

One condition that frequently hastens winding failure is movement of the coils because of vibration during operation. After insulation dries out it loses its flexibility and the mechanical stresses caused by starting, plugging, and stopping, as well as the natural stresses in operation under load, will precipitate short circuits in the coils and possibly failures from coil to ground, usually at the point where the coil leaves the slot. The effect of periodic varnish and oven treatments that are properly carried out so as to fill all air spaces caused by drying and shrinkage of the insulation, thereby maintaining a solid winding, will also provide an effective seal against moisture.

*Rotor windings* – The rotors of wound rotor motors have many features in common with the stators; therefore, the same comments apply to the care of rotor windings as are given for the care of stator windings. However, the rotor introduces some additional problems because it is a rotating element.

Most wound rotors have a three-phase winding, and are, therefore, susceptible to trouble from single-phase operation. The first symptom of an open-rotor circuit is lack of torque, with a decrease in speed accompanied by a growling noise, or perhaps a complete failure to start the load. The first place to look for an open secondary circuit is in the resistance bank or the control circuit external to the rotor. Short circuiting the rotor circuit at the slip rings and then operating the motor will usually determine whether the trouble is in the control circuit or in the rotor itself. It may be one of the stud connections to the slip rings.

If the rotor is wave wound with the winding made up of copper strap coils with clips connecting the top and bottom halves of the coil, inspect these end connections for possible signs of heating, which would be an indication of a partially open circuit. Faulty or improperly made end connections are a common source of open circuits in rotor windings.

A ground in a rotor circuit will not affect the performance of the motor unless another ground should also develop, which might cause the equivalent of a short circuit, in which case it would have the effect of unbalancing the rotor electrically. In addition to reduced torque, another symptom of this condition might be excessive vibration of the motor. There might also be sparking and uneven wear of the collector rings.

Another method of checking for short circuits in the rotor windings is to raise the brushes off the slip rings and energize the stator. If the rotor winding is free from short circuits, it should have little or no tendency to rotate, even when disconnected from the load. If it does show evidence of considerable torque or the tendency to come up to speed, the rotor should be removed and the winding opened and examined for a fault. In making this test, note that some rotors having a wide tooth design may show a tendency to rotate even though the windings are in good condition.

Still another check that can be made when the rotor is in place and the stator is energized (also with the brushes raised) is to check the voltage across the rings to see if they are balanced. When making this check, be sure that any inequality in voltage measurements is not due to the relative position of the rotor and stator phases. To avoid inaccurate measurements, the rotor should be moved to several positions during the voltage test.

## 12.2.0 Squirrel Cage Rotors

Squirrel cage rotors are more rugged and in general require less maintenance than wound rotors, but may have trouble because of open circuits or high resistance points in the rotor circuit. The symptoms of such conditions are generally the same as with wound rotor motors: slowing down under load and reduced starting torque. Such conditions can usually be detected by looking for evidence of heating at the end ring connections, which is particularly noticeable when shutting down after operating under load.

In brazed rotors, any fractures in the rotor bars will usually be found either at the point of connection to the end ring or at the point where the bar leaves the laminations. Discolored rotor bars are also evidence of excessive heating.

Brazing broken bars or replacing bars should only be done by a qualified person. Considerable technique is required for this kind of work, and it is recommended that the manufacturer's nearest district sales office be consulted before attempting such repairs in the shop or plant, unless an experienced operator is available.

With die-case rotors, look for cracks or other imperfections that may have developed in the end rings. A faulty die-case rotor can rarely be effectively repaired and should be replaced if defective.

## 12.3.0 The Air Gap

A small air gap is characteristic of the induction motor. The size of the air gap has an important bearing on the power factor of the motor. Doing anything to affect it, such as grinding the rotor laminations or filing the stator teeth, results in increased magnetizing current with a resultant lower power factor.

Good maintenance procedures call for periodically checking the air gap with a feeler gauge to ensure against a worn sleeve bearing that might permit the rotor to rub the laminations. (A very light rub can produce enough heat to destroy the coil insulation.) Gap measurements should be made on the shaft end of the motor.

On large machines, it is desirable to keep a record of these checks. Four measurements should be taken approximately 90° apart, with one of these points being the load side; that is, the point on the rotor periphery that corresponds with the load side of the bearing.

A comparison of the new measurements with previously-recorded measurements will permit the early detection of bearing wear.

## 12.4.0 Overloading and Single-Phase Operation

Often, a motor of adequate capacity that was properly applied in the original application is later found to be overloaded or otherwise unsuited for the job. This usually happens because of one or more of the following:

• More severe duty imposed on the motor
• A change in equipment
• A change in equipment parts
• A change in operating time

Connecting measuring instruments to the motor circuit will quickly disclose the reason for motor overheating, failure to start the load, or other abnormal symptoms.

Control circuits for many older systems were not provided with relay protection, and single-phase operation of polyphase induction motors on such circuits has frequently been responsible for motor burnout. Usually this has resulted from one of the fuses blowing while the motor is up to speed and under load. Under such conditions, the portion of winding that remains in the circuit will endeavor to carry the load until it fails due to overheating.

The effect of increasing the load on the motor beyond its rated capacity is simply to increase the operating temperature, which shortens the life of the insulation. Momentary overloads usually do no damage; consequently, the tendency is to use the thermal type of overload protection in present-day controls. Obviously, the ideal place to measure the thermal effect of overload is on the motor itself.

The polyphase induction motor is the simplest and most foolproof piece of rotating electrical apparatus. The largest single cause of winding failures is probably the rotor rubbing the stator iron, usually because of a worn or failed bearing.

## 13.0.0 ◆ TESTING ELECTRIC MOTORS

A simple test light or continuity tester may be used to test for an open motor coil. With all power circuits shut off, connect the continuity test leads across each motor coil in turn. If the coil is operational, the light will glow or the dial of the ohmmeter will swing to full scale.

To test for a grounded coil, connect one of the test leads to the motor frame and the other lead to one of the field coil wires. If the light glows or the ohmmeter dial swings toward zero, the coil is grounded.

To prepare for an insulation resistance test, first take the equipment or circuit to be tested out of service. Check between the equipment terminals and ground using a voltmeter (at the proper range setting) to be sure there is no voltage present. If possible, disconnect all leads to the motor being tested. When a motor or circuit is not completely isolated, make sure you are aware of all the components that will be tested when the meg ohmmeter (megger) is connected. Should an interconnected circuit be overlooked, the instrument readings may be lower than expected.

The testing of wiring can be performed on all types of systems if two rules are kept in mind:

- Be sure all wiring is de-energized.
- Know what wiring is included in the test and make a record of it.

When a distribution panel is present, check the entire system to ground by attaching one megger

### Testing with a Megohmmeter

*INSIDE TRACK*

While multimeters or ohmmeters can be used to check for open or short circuits in a motor, they can't be used to test the insulation resistance of a motor because the resistance to be measured is in the megohm range. A megohmmeter (megger) is designed to apply a high voltage to the motor to check the insulation resistance under load. Because all motor insulation degrades over time, many industrial/commercial facilities conduct a periodic maintenance program that includes checking the insulation resistance of motors on a regular schedule so that the rate of degradation can be used to predict motor failures before they occur.

202P0206.EPS

lead to the dead (de-energized) post of the open main power switch and the other lead to a grounded portion of the system such as the panel housing or an incoming conduit.

Individual circuits are tested to ground by opening distribution panel switches, fuses, or circuit breakers and testing each circuit in turn.

Once all power has been disconnected, disconnect the motor from the line, either by using the switch or by disconnecting the wiring at the motor terminals. If the switch is used, remember that the insulation resistance of the connecting wire, switch panel, and contacts will all be measured at the same time. Connect the positive megger lead to one of the motor lines and the negative test lead to the frame of the motor. If insulation resistance minimums have been established, the reading can be checked against them. Always check with your supervisor before using a megger. Since every brand of megger operates somewhat differently, always refer to the operating manual or seek assistance from your supervisor as to the proper operation of the instrument.

## 14.0.0 ◆ MOTOR INSTALLATION

The best motors on the market will operate improperly if they are installed incorrectly. Therefore, all personnel involved with the installation of electric motors should understand the procedures for installing the various types of motors that will be used.

**WARNING!**

When a motor is received at the job site, always refer to the manufacturer's instructions and follow them to the letter. Failure to do so could result in serious injury or death. Install and ground according to *NEC®* requirements and good practices. Consult qualified personnel with any questions or problems.

Keep the following in mind when installing new motors:

- *Uncrating* – Once the motor has been carefully uncrated, check to see if any damage has occurred during handling. Be sure that the motor shaft and armature turn freely. This is also a good time to check to determine if the motor has been exposed to dirt, grease, grit, or excessive moisture during shipment or storage. Motors in storage should have shafts turned over once each month to redistribute grease in the bearings. The measure of insulation resistance is a good dampness test. Clean the motor of any dirt or grit.

**WARNING!**

Never start a motor that has been wet until it has been completely dried and thoroughly tested.

- *Lifting* – Eyebolts or lifting lugs on motors are intended only for lifting the motor and factory motor-mounted standard accessories. These lifting provisions should never be used when lifting or handling the motor when the motor is attached to other equipment as a single unit. The eyebolt lifting capacity rating is based on a lifting alignment coincident with the eyebolt centerline. The eyebolt capacity reduces as deviation from this alignment increases.
- *Guards* – Rotating parts such as pulleys, couplings, external fans, and shaft extensions must be permanently guarded against accidental contact with clothing or body extremities.
- *Requirements* – All motors must be installed, protected, and fused in accordance with *NEC Article 430.* For general information on grounding, refer to *NEC Article 250* and *NEC Article 430, Part XIII.*
- *Thermal protector information* – The motor nameplate may or may not be stamped to indicate thermal protection.

## Installing Motors

The shaft of this air conditioner motor must be aligned precisely with the shaft of the driven device. Note the micrometer attached to the motor and the load to achieve exact alignment.

202P0207.EPS

## Putting It All Together

Count the motors in your home. The typical home may easily have over 30 motors (including electronic equipment and tools). A century ago, a typical home might have had none. Determine what types of motors you have. Are they AC or DC? What identifying information can you determine by examining each motor nameplate?

1. The name of the motor part that rotates during operation is the _____.
   a. stator
   b. shunt/capacitor
   c. brushes/commutator
   d. armature/rotor

2. The electrical energy required to produce one horsepower of mechanical energy is _____.
   a. 476W
   b. 647W
   c. 746W
   d. 864W

3. The principal reason for developing the brushless DC motor was to _____.
   a. eliminate commutator problems
   b. improve efficiency
   c. increase horsepower
   d. improve airplanes

4. The name of the stationary motor part that produces the magnetic field during operation is the _____.
   a. stator
   b. shunt/capacitor
   c. brushes/commutator
   d. armature/rotor

5. The name of the most popular rotor in use is the _____ rotor.
   a. wound
   b. squirrel cage
   c. multiphase
   d. induction

6. The starting torque characteristics of an induction motor are defined by _____.
   a. rotor resistance
   b. starting current
   c. load
   d. stator resistance

7. The speed of an induction motor depends on the power supply frequency and _____.
   a. current
   b. voltage
   c. size
   d. number of pairs of poles

8. The NEMA frame designation for gasoline pump motors is _____.
   a. B
   b. C
   c. G
   d. H

9. The letters FLA on a motor nameplate stand for _____.
   a. fused last application
   b. fast lower arm
   c. full-load amps
   d. full-load armature

10. To determine the horsepower rating of a motor that was already installed and in place, you would _____.
    a. multiply the rated voltage times the FLA
    b. divide the nominal efficiency by the power factor
    c. check the nameplate data
    d. use a torque wrench and horsepower data

11. The multiplier to the nameplate horsepower rating is called the _____.
    a. maximum kVAR
    b. service factor
    c. power factor
    d. NEMA nominal efficiency

12. A _____ is used to protect the motor from overloads and starting failures.
    a. fuse
    b. circuit breaker
    c. centrifugal switch
    d. thermal protector

13. The code requirements for motor disconnects are covered in _____.
    a. *NEC Article 430, Part VIII*
    b. *NEC Article 430, Part IX*
    c. *NEC Article 430, Part X*
    d. *NEC Article 430, Part XI*

**14.** One of the five causes of stator problems in motors is _____.
   a. no motor protection device
   b. worn bearings
   c. torque
   d. no air circulation

**15.** Before starting a motor that has been wet, _____.
   a. clean it with alcohol
   b. thoroughly dry it
   c. rotate it by hand
   d. heat it

# Summary

This module discussed AC and DC motor theory, construction, and various motor types and applications. This discussion included torque, speed, and speed regulations as well as the fundamental concepts associated with variable speed drive systems. Motor enclosures were described, including open and totally enclosed motors and motor frame designations. Discussions of horsepower and calculation of load under various conditions were included. *NEC®* requirements and basic troubleshooting techniques were also discussed.

# Notes

# Trade Terms
# Introduced in This Module

*Armature:* The rotating windings of a DC motor.

*Branch circuit:* The circuit conductors between the final overcurrent device protecting the circuit and the outlet(s).

*Brush:* A conductor between the stationary and rotating parts of a machine. It is usually made of carbon.

*Circuit breaker:* A device designed to open and close a circuit by nonautomatic means and to open the circuit automatically on a predetermined overcurrent without injury to itself when properly applied within its rating.

*Commutator:* A device used on electric motors or generators to maintain a unidirectional current.

*Continuous duty:* Operation at a substantially constant load for an indefinitely long time.

*Controller:* A device that serves to govern, in some predetermined manner, the electric power delivered to the apparatus to which it is connected.

*Duty:* Describes the length of operation. There are four designations for circuit duty: continuous, periodic, intermittent, and varying.

*Equipment:* A general term including material, fittings, devices, appliances, fixtures, apparatus, and the like used as a part of, or in connection with, an electrical installation.

*Field poles:* The stationary portion of a DC motor that produces the magnetic field.

*Horsepower:* The rated output capacity of the motor. It is based on breakdown torque, which is the maximum torque a motor will develop without an abrupt drop in speed.

*Hours:* The duty cycle of a motor. Most fractional horsepower motors are marked continuous for around-the-clock operation at the nameplate rating in the rated ambient conditions. Motors marked one-half are for ½-hour ratings, and those marked one are for 1-hour ratings.

*Intermittent duty:* Operation for alternate intervals of (1) load and no load; or (2) load and rest; or (3) load, no load, and rest.

*Overcurrent:* Any current in excess of the rated current of equipment or the ampacity of a conductor. It may result from an overload, short circuit, or ground fault.

*Overload:* Operation of equipment in excess of the normal, full-load rating, or of a conductor in excess of rated ampacity, which, after a sufficient length of time, will cause damage or dangerous overheating. A fault, such as a short circuit or ground fault, is not an overload.

*Periodic duty:* Intermittent operation at a substantially constant load for a short and definitely specified time.

*Revolutions per minute (rpm):* The approximate full-load speed at the rated power line frequency. The speed of a motor is determined by the number of poles in the winding. A four-pole, 60Hz motor runs at an approximate speed of 1,725 rpm. A six-pole, 60Hz motor runs at an approximate speed of 1,140 rpm.

*Rotation:* For single-phase motors, the standard rotation, unless otherwise noted, is counterclockwise facing the lead or opposite shaft end. All motors can be reconnected at the terminal board for opposite rotation unless otherwise indicated.

*Synchronous speed:* When the speed of the rotor is equal to the speed of the stator. The speed is determined by multiplying 120 times the frequency divided by the number of poles.

*Thermal protector:* A protective device for assembly as an integral part of a motor or motor compressor that, when properly applied, protects the motor against dangerous overheating due to overload or failure to start.

*Varying duty:* Operation at varying loads and/or intervals of time.

This module is intended to present thorough resources for task training. The following reference works are suggested for further study. These are optional materials for continued education rather than for task training.

*American Electricians' Handbook,* Latest Edition. New York: Croft and Summers, McGraw-Hill.

*National Electrical Code® Handbook,* Latest Edition. Quincy, MA: National Fire Protection Association.

The NCCER makes every effort to keep these textbooks up-to-date and free of technical errors. We appreciate your help in this process. If you have an idea for improving this textbook, or if you find an error, a typographical mistake, or an inaccuracy in NCCER's *Contren®* textbooks, please write us, using this form or a photocopy. Be sure to include the exact module number, page number, a detailed description, and the correction, if applicable. Your input will be brought to the attention of the Technical Review Committee. Thank you for your assistance.

*Instructors* – If you found that additional materials were necessary in order to teach this module effectively, please let us know so that we may include them in the Equipment/Materials list in the Annotated Instructor's Guide.

**Write:** Product Development
National Center for Construction Education and Research
P.O. Box 141104, Gainesville, FL 32614-1104

**Fax:** 352-334-0932

**E-mail:** curriculum@nccer.org

Craft _____  Module Name _____

Copyright Date _____  Module Number _____  Page Number(s) _____

Description _____

(Optional) Correction _____

(Optional) Your Name and Address _____

# Motor Calculations
## 26309-05

**Steven F. Udvar-Hazy Center**
**National Air and Space Museum**
Chantilly, Virginia
Mega-Projects Over $100 Million Award Winner
Hensel Phelps Construction Co.

# 26309-05
# *Motor Calculations*

*Topics to be presented in this module include:*

# Overview

There are three basic types of motors: squirrel cage induction, wound-rotor induction, and synchronous. Motors may be single-phase or three-phase. There are two basic parts to an alternating current motor, the rotor and the stator. The rotor is the part that turns or spins. The stator is the stationary winding assembly in which the rotor turns.

In order to calculate conductor sizes and overcurrent protection for motor circuits, you must know the full load amperage (FLA) of the motor. FLAs for motors may be found on the nameplate of the motor or approximated by referring to the full load amperage tables located in *NEC Article 430*. Multiple motors connected to a single feeder circuit require the application of specific formulas in order to determine circuit ratings. Conductor sizing and branch circuit ratings for all motors and motor controllers are also regulated by *NEC Article 430*. Motor overload protection should be calculated based on the FLA of the motor when running in a normal state. Fuses protecting motor circuits must be selected based on the starting amperage of the motor. Some motors draw as much as five or six times normal FLA during startup. This is called locked rotor amperes or LRA. Time delay fuses are typically used in these motor circuits to allow the motor to reach full running speed without opening the circuit.

## Objectives

When you have completed this module, you will be able to do the following:

1. Size branch circuits and feeders for electric motors.
2. Size and select overcurrent protective devices for motors.
3. Size and select overload relays for electric motors.
4. Size and select devices to improve the power factor at motor locations.
5. Size motor short circuit protectors.
6. Size multi-motor branch circuits.
7. Size motor disconnects.

## Trade Terms

Circuit interrupter
Rating
Service factor
Terminal
Torque

## Required Trainee Materials

1. Pencil and paper
2. Appropriate personal protective equipment
3. Copy of the latest edition of the *National Electrical Code®*

## Prerequisites

Before you begin this module, it is recommended that you successfully complete *Core Curriculum, Electrical Level One; Electrical Level Two; Electrical Level Three*, Modules 26301-05 through 26308-05.

This course map shows all of the modules in *Electrical Level Three*. The suggested training order begins at the bottom and proceeds up. Skill levels increase as you advance on the course map. The local Training Program Sponsor may adjust the training order.

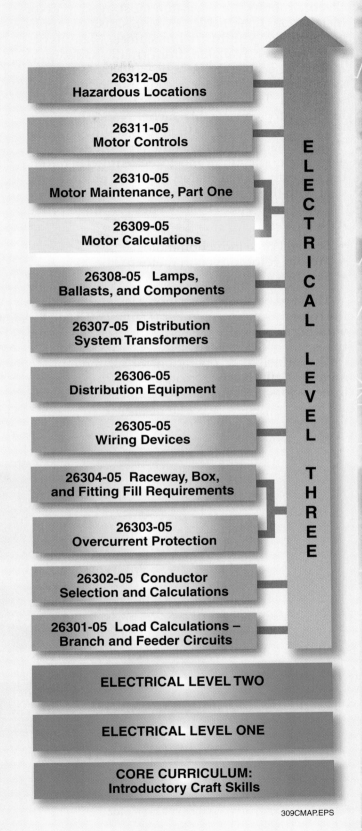

309CMAP.EPS

## 1.0.0 ◆ INTRODUCTION

Electric motors are used in almost every type of installation imaginable, from residential appliances to heavy industrial machines. Many types of motors are available, from small shaded-pole motors (used mostly in household fans) to huge synchronous motors for use in large industrial installations. There are numerous types in between to fill every conceivable niche. None, however, have the wide application possibilities of the three-phase motor. This is the type of motor that electricians encounter most frequently. Therefore, the majority of the material in this module will deal with three-phase motors.

There are three basic types of three-phase motors:

• Squirrel cage induction motor
• Wound-rotor induction motor
• Synchronous motor

The type of three-phase motor is determined by the rotor or rotating member (*Figure 1*). The stator winding is basically the same for all three motor types.

The principle of operation for all three-phase motors is the rotating magnetic field. There are three factors that cause the magnetic field to rotate:

• The voltages of a three-phase electrical system are 120° out of phase with each other.
• The three voltages change polarity at regular intervals.
• The stator windings around the inside of the motor are arranged in a specific manner to induce rotation.

The *National Electrical Code® (NEC®)* plays an important role in the installation of electric motors. *NEC Article 430* covers the application and installation of motor circuits and motor control connections, including conductors, short-circuit and ground-fault protection, controllers, disconnects, and overload protection.

*NEC Article 440* contains provisions for motor-driven air conditioning and refrigerating equipment, including the branch circuits and controllers for the equipment. It also takes into account the special considerations involved with sealed (hermetic) motor compressors, in which the motor operates under the cooling effect of the refrigeration. When referring to *NEC Article 440*, be aware that the rules in this article are in addition to, or are amendments to, the rules given in *NEC Article 430*. Motors are also covered to some degree in *NEC Articles 422 and 424*.

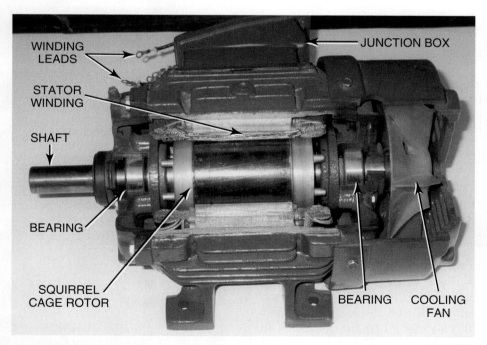

WINDING LEADS

JUNCTION BOX

STATOR WINDING

SHAFT

BEARING

SQUIRREL CAGE ROTOR

BEARING

COOLING FAN

309F01.TIF

*Figure 1* ◆ Basic parts of a three-phase motor.

# .0.0 ◆ MOTOR BASICS

he rotor of an AC squirrel cage induction motor *Figure 2*) consists of a structure of steel lamina- ons mounted on a shaft. Embedded in the rotor the rotor winding, which is a series of copper or luminum bars, short circuited at each end by a netallic end ring. The stator consists of steel lam- nations mounted in a frame. Slots in the stator old stator windings that can be either copper or luminum coils or bars. These are connected to orm a circuit.

Energizing the stator coils with an AC supply oltage causes current to flow in the coils. The cur- ent produces an electromagnetic field that causes nagnetic poles to be created in the stator iron. The trength and polarity of these poles vary as the AC urrent flows in one direction, then the other. This nange causes the poles around the stator to alter- ate between being south and north poles, thus roducing a rotating magnetic field.

The rotating magnetic field cuts through the ro- or, inducing a current in the rotor bars. This in- uced current only circulates in the rotor, which in urn causes a rotor magnetic field. As with two onventional bar magnets, the north pole of the otor field attempts to line up with the south pole f the stator magnetic field, and the south pole at- mpts to line up with the north pole. However, ecause the stator magnetic field is rotating, the otor chases the stator field. The rotor field never uite catches up due to the need to furnish **torque** the mechanical load.

## 2.1.0 Synchronous Speed

The speed at which the magnetic field rotates is known as the synchronous speed. The synchro- nous speed of a three-phase motor is determined by two factors:

- Number of stator poles
- Frequency of the AC line in hertz (Hz)

The synchronous speeds for various 60Hz mo- tors are as follows:

- Two poles–3,600 rpm
- Four poles–1,800 rpm
- Six poles–1,200 rpm
- Eight poles–900 rpm

These speeds illustrate that the rpm of a three- phase motor decreases as the number of poles in- creases.

## 2.2.0 Stator Windings

The stator windings of three-phase motors are connected in either a wye or a delta configuration (*Figure 3*). Some motor stators are designed to op- erate both ways; that is, they are started as a wye- connected motor to help reduce starting current, and then changed to a delta configuration for running.

Many three-phase motors have dual-voltage stators. These stators are designed to be connected to either 240V or 480V. The leads of a dual-voltage stator use a standard numbering system. *Figure 4* shows a dual-voltage, wye-connected stator.

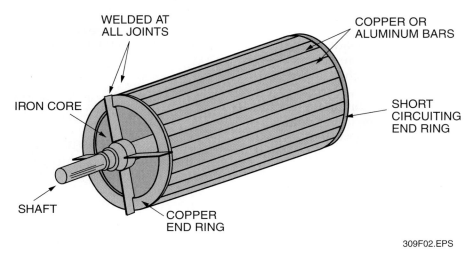

WELDED AT ALL JOINTS

COPPER OR ALUMINUM BARS

IRON CORE

SHORT CIRCUITING END RING

SHAFT

COPPER END RING

309F02.EPS

*'gure 2* ◆ Squirrel cage rotor.

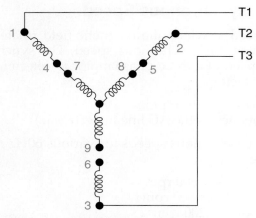

WYE-CONNECTED MOTOR WINDINGS
(SERIES CONNECTED)

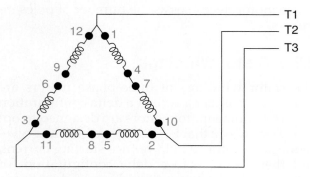

DELTA-CONNECTED MOTOR WINDINGS
(SERIES CONNECTED)

309F03.EPS

*Figure 3* ◆ Types of windings found in three-phase motors.

Note that the nine motor leads are numbered in a spiral. The leads are connected in series for use on the higher voltage and in parallel for use on the lower voltage. Therefore, for the higher voltage, leads 4 and 7, 5 and 8, and 6 and 9 are connected together. For the lower voltage, leads 4, 5, and 6 are connected together; further connections are 1 and 7, 2 and 8, and 3 and 9, which are then connected to the three-phase power source. *Figure 5* shows the equivalent parallel circuit when the motor is connected for use on the lower voltage.

The same standard numbering system is used for delta-connected motors, and many delta-wound motors also have nine leads, as shown in *Figure 6.* However, there are only three circuits of three leads each. The high-voltage and low-voltage connections for a three-phase, delta-wound, dual-voltage motor are shown in *Figure 7.*

In some instances, a dual-voltage motor connected in a delta configuration will have 12 leads instead of nine. *Figure 8* shows the high-voltage and low-voltage connections for a dual-voltage, 12-lead, delta-wound motor.

### 2.2.1 Principles of Dual-Voltage Connections

When a motor is operated at 240V, the current draw of the motor is double the current draw of 480V connection. For example, if a motor draws 10A of current when connected to 240V, it will draw only 5A when connected to 480V. The reason for this is the difference of impedance in the windings between a 240V connection and a 480V connection. Remember that the low-voltage windings are always connected in parallel, while the high-voltage windings are connected in series.

For instance, assume that the stator windings of a motor (R1 and R2) both have a resistance of 48Ω. If the stator windings are connected in parallel, the total resistance ($R_t$) may be found as follows:

$$R_t = \frac{R1 \times R2}{R1 + R2}$$

$$R_t = \frac{48\Omega \times 48\Omega}{48\Omega + 48\Omega}$$

$$R_t = \frac{2,304\Omega}{96\Omega}$$

$$R_t = 24\Omega$$

Therefore, the total resistance (R) of the motor winding connected in parallel is 24Ω, and if a voltage (E) of 240V is applied to this connection, the following current (I) will flow:

$$I = \frac{E}{R}$$

$$I = \frac{240V}{24\Omega}$$

$$I = 10A$$

If the windings are connected in series for operation on 480V, the total resistance of the winding is:

$$R_t = R1 + R2$$

$$R_t = 48\Omega + 48\Omega$$

$$R_t = 96\Omega$$

Consequently, if 480V is applied to this winding, the following current will flow:

$$I = \frac{E}{R}$$

$$I = \frac{480V}{96\Omega}$$

$$I = 5A$$

It is obvious that twice the voltage means half the current flow, or vice versa.

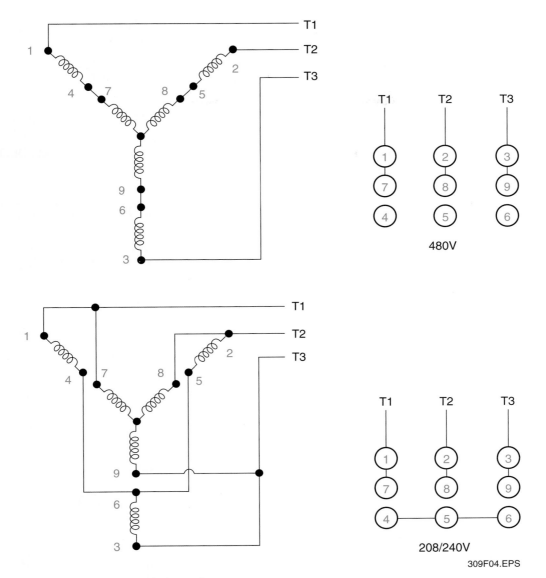

Figure 4 ◆ Dual-voltage, wye-connected, three-phase motors.

309F04.EPS

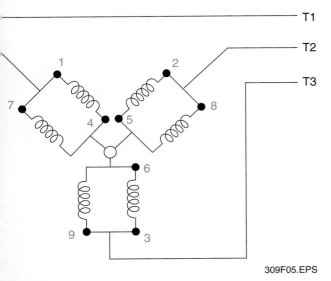

309F05.EPS

Figure 5 ◆ Equivalent parallel circuit.

Figure 6 ◆ Arrangement of leads in a nine-lead, delta-wound, dual-voltage motor.

309F06.EPS

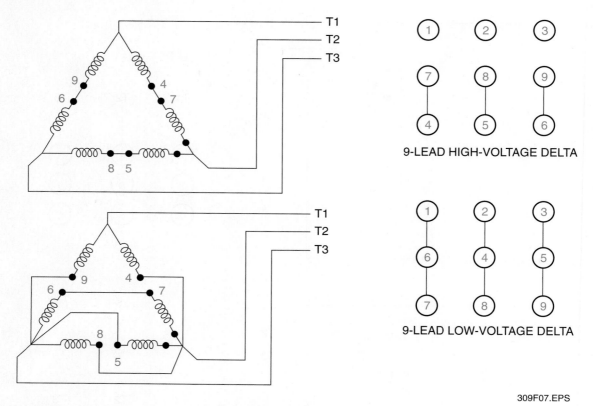

9-LEAD HIGH-VOLTAGE DELTA

9-LEAD LOW-VOLTAGE DELTA

309F07.EPS

*Figure 7* ◆ Lead connections for a three-phase, dual-voltage, delta-wound motor.

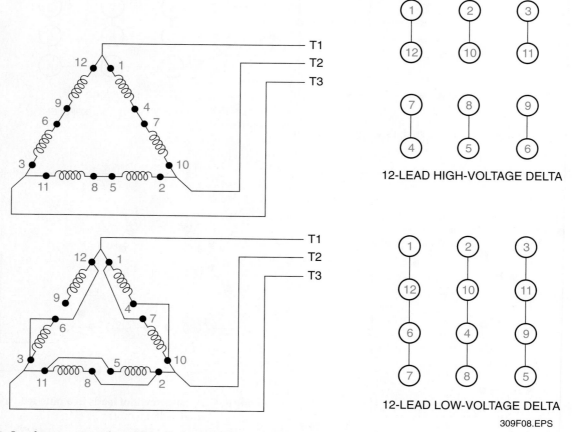

12-LEAD HIGH-VOLTAGE DELTA

12-LEAD LOW-VOLTAGE DELTA

309F08.EPS

*Figure 8* ◆ Lead connections for a 12-lead, dual-voltage, delta-wound motor.

## 2.3.0 Special Connections

Some three-phase motors designed for operation on voltages higher than 600V may have more than 12 leads. Motors with 15 or 18 leads are common in high-voltage installations. A 15-lead motor has three coils per phase, as shown in *Figure 9*. Notice that the leads are numbered in the same spiral sequence as a nine-lead, wye-wound motor.

## 3.0.0 ◆ CALCULATING MOTOR CIRCUIT CONDUCTORS

The basic elements of a motor circuit are shown in *Figure 10*. Although these elements are shown separately in this illustration, there are certain cases in which the *NEC®* permits a single device to serve more than one function. For example, in some cases, one switch can serve as both the disconnecting means and the controller. In other cases, short circuit protection and overload protection can be combined in a single circuit breaker or set of fuses.

**NOTE**

*NEC Section 430.22(A)* states that when sizing conductors supplying a single motor used for continuous duty, the conductors must have a current-carrying capacity of not less than 125% of the motor full-load current rating. Conductors on the line side of the controller supplying multi-speed motors must be based on the highest of the full-load current ratings shown on the motor nameplate. Conductors between the controller and the motor must have a current-carrying rating based on the current rating for the speed of the motor being fed by each set of conductors.

## *NEC®* Motor Sizes

How is the largest motor in a group determined by the *NEC®*? Is it by frame size, horsepower, weight, or the motor's full-load amps (FLA)?

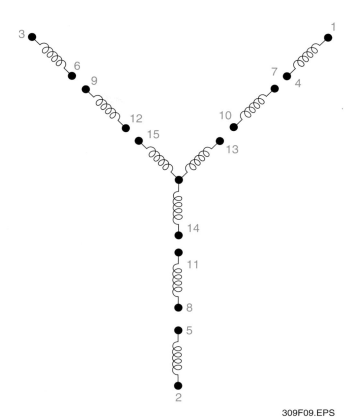

309F09.EPS

*Figure 9* ◆ Fifteen-lead motor.

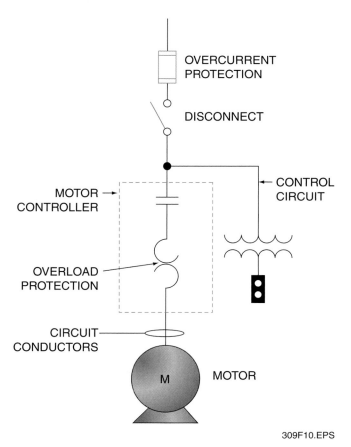

309F10.EPS

*Figure 10* ◆ Basic elements of any motor circuit.

A typical motor control center and branch circuits feeding four different motors are shown in *Figure 11*. We will see how the feeder and branch circuit conductors are sized for these motors.

***Step 1*** Refer to *NEC Table 430.250* for the full-load current of each motor.

***Step 2*** Determine the full-load current of the largest motor in the group.

***Step 3*** Calculate the sum of the full-load current ratings for the remaining motors in the group.

***Step 4*** Multiply the full-load current of th largest motor by 1.25 (125%) and then ad the sum of the remaining motors to the re sult *(NEC Section 430.24)*. The combine total will give the minimum feeder size.

When sizing feeder conductors for motors, b aware that the procedure previously describe will give the minimum conductor rating based o the *NEC®* minimum only. Consequently, it is ofte necessary to increase the size of conductors t compensate for voltage drop and power loss i the circuit.

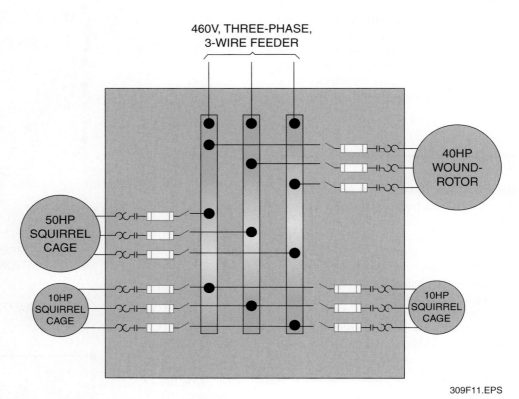

309F11.EPS

*Figure 11* ◆ Typical motor control center.

## Voltage Ratings

**INSIDE TRACK** The motor voltage ratings used in the *NEC*® can be somewhat confusing. Motors are built and tested at various voltages. For example, the 460V referenced in *NEC Tables 430.248 and 430.250* is based on rated motor voltages; however, in order to standardize calculations and maintain minimum safety standards, the *NEC*® uses a higher value of 480V for motor calculations. See *NEC Section 220.5(A)*.

Now we will complete the conductor calculations for the motor circuits in *Figure 11*.

Referring to *NEC Table 430.250,* the motor horsepower is shown in the far left-hand column. Follow across the appropriate row until you come to the column titled *460V,* which is the voltage of the motor circuits in *Figure 11*. We find that the ampere ratings for the motors in question are as follows:

50hp = 65A
40hp = 52A
10hp = 14A

The largest motor in this group is the 50hp squirrel cage motor, which has a full-load current of 65A.

The sum of the remaining motors is:

52A + 14A + 14A = 80A

Now, multiply the full-load current of the largest motor by 125% (1.25) and then add the total amperage of the remaining motors:

(1.25 × 65A) + 80A = 161.25A

Therefore, the feeders for the 460V, three-phase, three-wire motor control center will have a minimum ampacity of 161.25A. Referring to *NEC Table 310.16* under the column headed 75°C, the closest conductor size is 2/0 copper (rated at 175A) or 4/0 aluminum (rated at 180A).

The branch circuit conductors feeding the individual motors are calculated somewhat differently. *NEC Section 430.22(A)* requires that the ampacity of branch circuit conductors supplying a single continuous-duty motor must not be less than 125% of the motor full-load current rating. Therefore, the current-carrying capacity of the branch circuit conductors feeding the four motors in question are calculated as follows:

50hp motor = 65A × 1.25 = 81.25A
40hp motor = 52A × 1.25 = 65A
10hp motor = 14A × 1.25 = 17.5A

Referring to *NEC Table 310.16,* the closest size 75°C THWN copper conductors permitted to

be used on these various branch circuits are as follows:

- A 50hp motor at 81.25A requires No. 4 AWG THWN conductors.
- A 40hp motor at 65A requires No. 6 AWG THWN conductors.
- A 10hp motor at 17.5A requires No. 12 AWG THWN conductors per *NEC Section 240.4(D)*.

Refer to *Figure 12* for a summary of the conductors used to feed our example motor control center, along with the branch circuits supplying the individual motors.

If voltage drop and/or power loss must be taken into consideration, please refer to the Level Three module, *Conductor Selection and Calculations.*

For motors with other voltages (up to 2,300V) or for synchronous motors, refer to *NEC Table 430.250.*

In accordance with *NEC Section 430.22(E),* branch circuit conductors serving motors used for short-time, intermittent, or other varying duty must have an ampacity not less than the percentage of the motor nameplate current rating shown in *NEC Table 430.22(E).* However, to qualify as a short-time, intermittent motor, the nature of the apparatus that the motor drives must be arranged so that the motor cannot operate continuously with a load under any condition of use. Otherwise, the motor must be considered continuous duty. Consequently, the majority of motors encountered in the electrical trade must be rated for continuous duty, and the branch circuit conductors sized accordingly.

### 3.1.0 Wound-Rotor Motors

The primary full-load current ratings for wound-rotor motors are listed in *NEC Table 430.250* and are the same as those for squirrel cage motors. Conductors connecting the secondary leads of wound-rotor induction motors to their controllers must have a current-carrying capacity at least equal to 125% of the motor full-load secondary

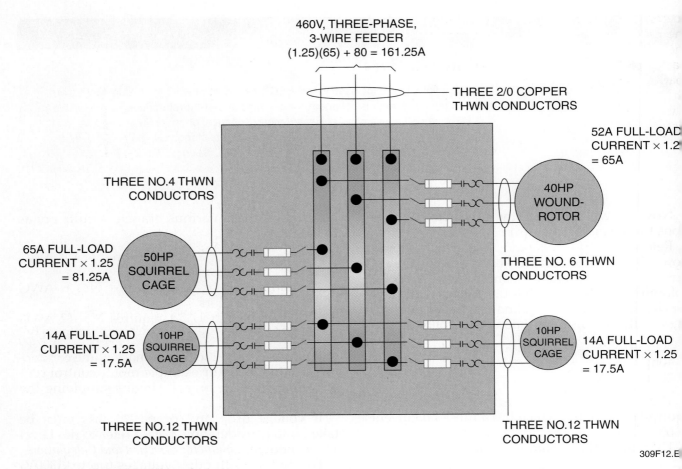

*Figure 12* ◆ Sizing motor branch circuits.

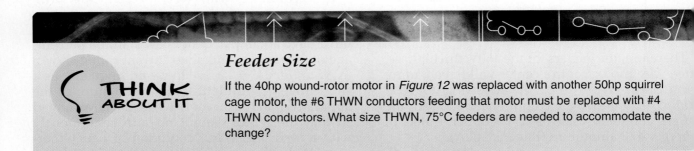

### Feeder Size

If the 40hp wound-rotor motor in *Figure 12* was replaced with another 50hp squirrel cage motor, the #6 THWN conductors feeding that motor must be replaced with #4 THWN conductors. What size THWN, 75°C feeders are needed to accommodate the change?

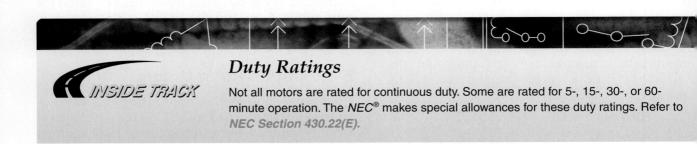

### Duty Ratings

Not all motors are rated for continuous duty. Some are rated for 5-, 15-, 30-, or 60-minute operation. The *NEC®* makes special allowances for these duty ratings. Refer to *NEC Section 430.22(E)*.

current if the motor is used for continuous duty. If the motor is used for less than continuous duty, the conductors must have a current-carrying capacity of not less than the percentage of the full-load secondary nameplate current given in *NEC Table 430.22(E)*. Conductors from the controller of a wound-rotor induction motor to its starting resistors must have an ampacity in accordance with *NEC Table 430.23(C)*.

> **NOTE**
>
> *NEC Section 430.6(A)(1)* specifies that for general motor applications (excluding applications of torque motors and sealed hermetic-type refrigeration compressor motors), the values given in *NEC Tables 430.247, 430.248, 430.249, and 430.250* should be used instead of the actual current rating marked on the motor nameplate when sizing conductors, switches, and overcurrent protection. Overload protection, however, is based on the marked motor nameplate.

## 2.0 Conductors for DC Motors

*NEC Sections 430.22(A), Exception 1 and 430.29* cover the rules governing the sizing of conductors from a power source to a DC motor controller and from the controller to separate resistors for power accelerating and dynamic braking. *NEC Section 430.29*, with its table of conductor ampacity percentages, assures proper application of DC constant-potential motor controls and power resistors. However, when selecting overload protection, the actual motor nameplate current rating must be used.

## 3.0 Conductors for Miscellaneous Motor Applications

*NEC Section 430.6* should be referred to for torque motors, shaded-pole motors, permanent split capacitor motors, and AC adjustable-voltage motors.

*NEC Section 430.6(B)* specifically states that the motor's nameplate full-load current rating is used to size ground-fault protection for a torque motor. However, both the branch circuit conductors and the overcurrent protection are sized by the provisions listed in *NEC Article 430, Part II* and *NEC Section 430.52*.

For sealed (hermetic) refrigeration compressor motors, the actual nameplate full-load running current of the motor must be used in determining the current rating of the disconnecting means, controller, branch circuit conductor, overcurrent protective devices, and motor overload protection.

## 4.0.0 ◆ MOTOR PROTECTIVE DEVICES

*NEC Sections 430.51 through 430.58* require that the branch circuit protection for motor controls protect the circuit conductors, control apparatus, and the motor itself against overcurrent due to short circuits or ground faults.

Motors and motor circuits have unique operating characteristics and circuit components. Therefore, these circuits must be dealt with differently from other types of loads. Generally, two levels of overcurrent protection are required for motor branch circuits:

- *Overload protection* – Motor running overload protection is intended to protect the system components and motor from damaging overload currents.
- *Short circuit protection (includes ground fault protection)* – Short-circuit protection is intended to protect the motor circuit components such as the conductors, switches, controllers, overload relays, motor, etc., against short circuit currents or grounds. This level of protection is commonly referred to as motor branch circuit protection. Dual-element fuses are designed to give this protection, provided they are sized correctly.

There are a variety of ways to protect a motor circuit, depending upon the application. The ampere rating of a fuse selected for motor protection depends on whether the fuse is of the dual-element, time-delay type or the nontime-delay type.

In general, *NEC Table 430.52* specifies that short-circuit/ground-fault protection nontime-delay fuses can be sized at 300% of the motor full-load current for ordinary motors, while those for wound-rotor or direct current motors may be sized at 150% of the motor full-load current. The sizes of nontime-delay fuses for the four motors previously mentioned are listed in *Figure 13*. Because none of these sizes are standard, *NEC Section 430.52(C)(1), Exception No. 1* permits the size of the fuses to be increased to a standard size. Also, where absolutely necessary to permit motor starting, the size of the overcurrent device may be further increased, but must never be more than 400% of the full-load current [*NEC Section 430.52(C)(1), Exception No. 2(a)*]. In actual practice, most electricians would use a 200A nontime-delay fuse for the 50hp motor, a 175A fuse for the 40hp motor, and 45A fuses for the 10hp motors. If any of these fuses do not allow the motor to start without blowing, the fuses for the 50hp motor may be increased to a maximum of 400% of the full-load currents, which are 360A for the 50hp

motor, 208A for the 40hp motor, and 56A for th 10hp motors.

Per *NEC Table 430.52,* dual-element, time-dela fuses are able to withstand normal motor startin current and can be sized closer to the actual moto rating than nontime-delay fuses. If necessary fo proper motor operation, dual-element, time-dela fuses may be sized up to 175% of the motor's ful load current for all standard motors with the ex ception of wound-rotor and direct current motor These motors must not have fuses sized for mo than 150% of the motor's full-load current ratin; Where absolutely necessary for proper operatio the rating of dual-element, time-delay fuses ma be increased, but must never be more than 225% of the motor full-load current rating [*NEC Sectio 430.52(C)(1), Exception No. 2(b)*]. To size dua element fuses at 175% for the four motors in *Figu 13,* proceed as follows:

$$50\text{hp motor} = 65\text{A} \times 175 = 113.75\text{A}$$
$$40\text{hp motor} = 52\text{A} \times 175 = 91\text{A}$$
$$10\text{hp motors} = 14\text{A} \times 175 = 24.5\text{A}$$

*Figure 14* gives general fuse application guid lines for motor branch circuits (*NEC Article 43 Part IV*). Bear in mind that in many cases, th maximum fuse size depends on the motor desig letter, motor type, and starting method.

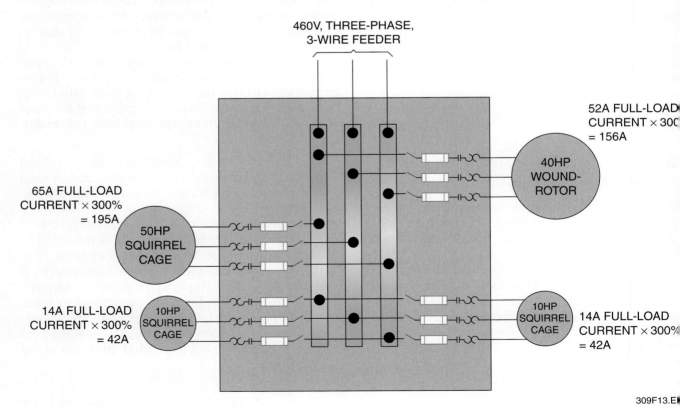

*Figure 13* ◆ Ratings of nontime-delay fuses for typical motor circuits.

## Overload Protection

In a 230V/460V motor such as the one shown here, which applied voltage requires the larger overload protection device?

309P0901.EPS

## 1.0 Practical Applications

For various reasons, motors are often oversized. For instance, a 5hp motor may be installed when the load demand is only 3hp. In these cases, a much higher degree of overload protection can be obtained by sizing the overload relay elements and/or dual-element, time-delay fuses based on the actual full-load current draw. In existing installations, the procedure for providing the maximum overcurrent protection for oversized motors is as follows:

*Step 1* With a clamp-on ammeter, determine the running rms current when the motor is at normal full-load, as shown in *Figure 15*. Be sure this current does not exceed the nameplate current rating. The advantage of this method is realized when a lightly loaded motor (especially those over 50hp) experiences a single-phase condition. Even though the relays and fuses may be sized correctly based on the motor nameplate, circulating currents within the motor may cause damage. If unable to meter the motor current, take the current rating off the motor nameplate.

*Step 2* Size the overload relay elements and/or overcurrent protection based on this current.

*Step 3* Use a labeling system to mark the type and ampere rating of the fuse that should be in the fuse clips. This simple system makes it easy to run spot checks for proper fuse replacements.

**NOTE**

When installing the proper fuses in the switch to give the desired level of protection, it is often advisable to leave spare fuses on top of the disconnect or starter enclosure, or in a cabinet adjacent to the motor control center. This way, if the fuses open, the proper fuses can be readily reinstalled.

Individual motor disconnect switches must have an ampere rating of at least 115% of the motor full-load ampere rating *[NEC Section 430.110(A)]* or sized as specified in *NEC Section 430.109*. The next larger size switches with fuse reducers may sometimes be required.

Some installations may require larger dual-element fuses when:

- The motor uses dual-element fuses in high ambient temperature environments.
- The motor is started frequently or rapidly reversed.
- The motor is directly connected to a machine that cannot be brought up to full speed quickly (e.g., centrifugal machines such as extractors and pulverizers, machines having large fly wheels such as large punch presses, etc.).
- This is a Design B energy-efficient motor with full-voltage start.

## 4.2.0 Motor Overload Protection

A high-quality electric motor that is properly cooled and protected against overloads can be

| Type of Motor | Dual-Element, Time-Delay Fuses | | | Nontime-Delay Fuses |
|---|---|---|---|---|
| | Motor Overload and Short Circuit | Backup Overload and Short Circuit | Short Circuit Only (Based on *NEC* *Tables 430.247 through 430.250* current ratings) | Short Circuit Only (Based on *NEC* *Tables 430.247 through 430.250* current ratings) |
| Service Factor 1.15 or Greater or 40°C Temp. Rise or Less | 125% or less of motor nameplate current | 125% or next standard size (not to exceed 140% of motor nameplate current) | 150% to 175% | 150% to 300% |
| Service Factor Less Than 1.15 or Greater Than 40°C Temp. Rise | 115% or less of motor nameplate current | 115% or next standard size (not to exceed 130% of motor nameplate current) | 150% to 175% | 150% to 300% |

| Fuses give overload and short circuit protection. | Overload relay gives overload protection and fuses provide backup overload protection. | Overload relay provides overload protection and fuses provide only short circuit protection. | Overload relay provides overload protection and fuses provide only short circuit protection. |

309F14.E

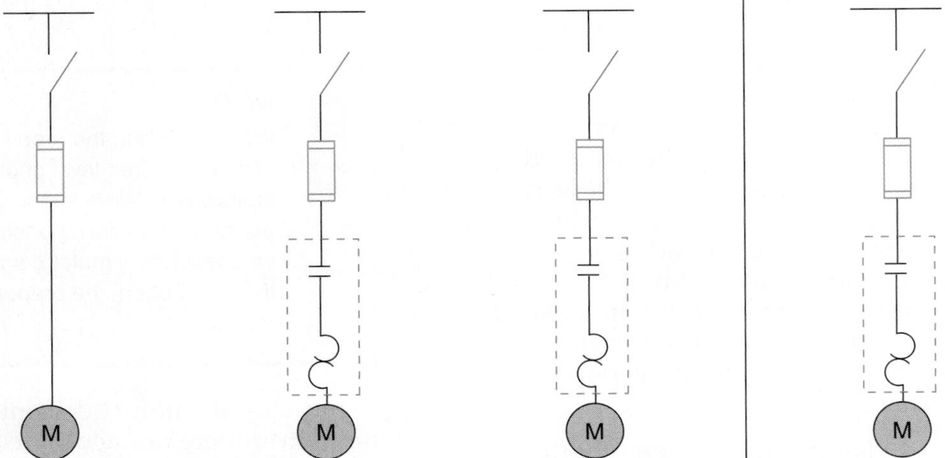

*Figure 14* ◆ Fuse application guidelines for motor branch circuits.

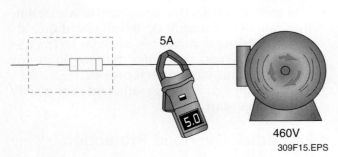

5A

460V

309F15.EPS

*Figure 15* ◆ Determining running current with an ammeter.

expected to have a long life. The goal of prop motor protection is to prolong motor life and po: pone the failure that ultimately takes place. Goc electrical protection consists of providing bo proper overload protection and current-limitir short-circuit protection. AC motors and oth types of high inrush loads require protective d vices with special characteristics. Normal, fu load running currents of motors are substantial less than the currents that result when moto start or are subjected to temporary mechanic overloads. This is illustrated by the typical mot starting current curve shown in *Figure 16*.

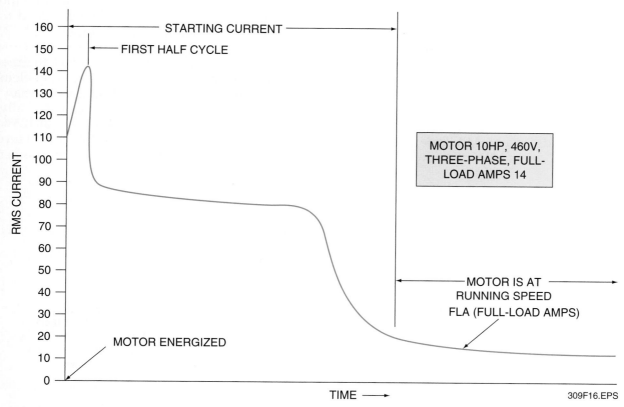

*ure 16* ◆ Motor starting current characteristics.

At the moment an AC motor circuit is energized, the starting current rapidly rises to many times the normal running current and the rotor begins to rotate. As the rotor accelerates and reaches running speed, the current declines to the normal running current. Thus, for a period of time, the overcurrent protective devices in the motor circuit must be able to tolerate the rather substantial temporary overload. Motor starting currents can vary substantially, depending on the motor type, load type, starting methods, and other factors. For the first half cycle, the momentary transient rms current may be 11 times the normal current, or even higher. After this first half cycle, the starting current subsides to 4 to 8 times (typically 6 times) the normal current and remains there for several seconds. This is called the locked-rotor current. When the motor reaches running speed, the current then subsides to its normal running level.

Motor overload protective devices must withstand the temporary overload caused by motor starting currents, and, at the same time, protect the motor from continuous or damaging overloads. The main types of devices used to provide motor overload protection include:

- Overload relays
- Fuses
- Circuit breakers

There are numerous causes of overloads, but if the overload protective devices are properly responsive, such overloads can be removed before damage occurs. To ensure this protection, the motor running protective devices should have time-current characteristics similar to motor damage curves but should be slightly faster. This is illustrated in *Figure 17*.

For example, we will take a 10hp motor and determine the proper circuit components that should be employed (refer to *Figure 18*).

To begin, select the proper size overload relays. Typically, the overload relay is rated to trip at about 115% of the rated current (in this case, 1.15 × 14A = 16.1A). The correct starter size (using NEMA standards) is a NEMA Type 1. The switch size that should be used is 30A. Switch sizes are

based on *NEC®* requirements; dual-element, time delay fuses allow the use of smaller switches.

For short-circuit protection on large motor with currents in excess of 600A, low-peak time delay fuses are recommended. Most motors of this size will have reduced voltage starters, and the in rush currents are not as rigorous. Low-peak fuse should be sized at approximately 150% to 175% of the motor full-load current.

Motor controllers with overload relays commonly used on motor circuits provide motor running overload protection. The overload relay setting or selection must comply with *NE Section 430.32*. On overload conditions, the overload relays should operate to protect the motor. For motor backup protection, size dual-element fuses at the next ampere rating greater than the overload relay trip setting. This can typically be achieved by sizing dual-element fuses at 125% for 1.15 **service factor** motors and 115% for 1.0 service factor motors. The service factor is the number b

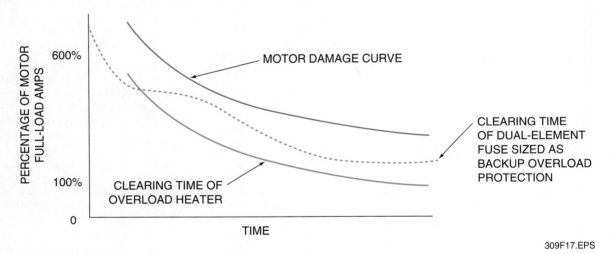

309F17.EPS

*Figure 17* ◆ Time-current characteristics of dual-element fuses and overload heaters.

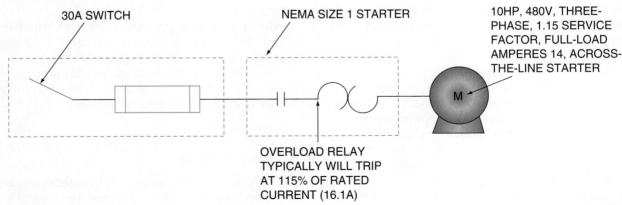

309F18.EPS

*Figure 18* ◆ Circuit components of a typical 10-horsepower motor.

which the horsepower rating is multiplied to determine the maximum safe load that a motor may be expected to carry continuously at its rated voltage and frequency.

## .0.0 ◆ CIRCUIT BREAKERS

The *NEC®* recognizes the use of instantaneous trip circuit breakers (without time delay) for short circuit protection of motor branch circuits. Such breakers are acceptable only if they are adjustable and are used in combination motor starters. Such starters must have coordinated overload, short-circuit, and ground-fault protection for each conductor and must be approved for the purpose in accordance with *NEC Section*

*430.52(C)(3).* This permits the use of smaller circuit breakers than would be allowed if a standard thermal-magnetic circuit breaker was used. In this case, smaller circuit breakers offer faster operation for greater protection against grounds and short circuits. *Figure 19* shows a schematic diagram of magnetic-only circuit breakers used in a combination motor starter.

The use of magnetic-only circuit breakers in motor branch circuits requires careful consideration due to the absence of overload protection up to the short circuit trip rating that is normally available in thermal elements in circuit breakers. However, heaters in the motor starter protect the entire circuit and all equipment against overloads up to and including locked-rotor current. Heaters

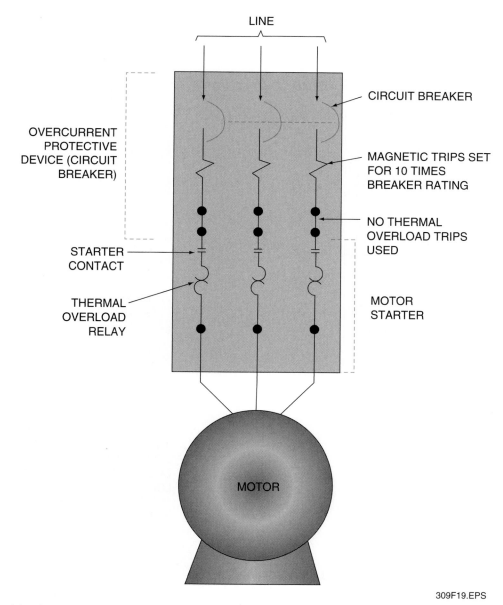

309F19.EPS

*Figure 19* ◆ Combination motor starter with magnetic-only circuit breakers.

(thermal overload relays) are commonly set at 115% to 125% of the motor full-load current.

In dealing with such circuits, an adjustable circuit breaker can be set to take over the interrupting task at currents above locked-rotor current and up to the short circuit duty of the supply system at the point of the installation. The magnetic trip in such breakers can typically be adjusted from 3 to 13 times the breaker current rating. For example, a 100A circuit breaker can be adjusted to trip anywhere between 300A and 1,300A. Consequently, the circuit breaker may serve as motor short circuit protection. However, instantaneous trip circuit breakers used in these installations cannot be adjusted to more than the value specified in *NEC Table 430.52.*

## 5.1.0 Application of Magnetic-Only Circuit Breakers

We will compare the use of both thermal magnetic and magnetic-only circuit breakers in the motor circuit shown in *Figure 20.* In doing so, our job is to select a circuit breaker that will provide short-circuit protection and also qualify as the motor circuit disconnecting means.

*Step 1* Determine the motor full-load current from *NEC Table 430.250.* This is found to be 80A.

*Step 2* A circuit breaker suitable for use as a motor disconnecting means must have a current rating of at least 115% of the motor full-load current. Therefore:

$$1.15 \times 80A = 92A$$

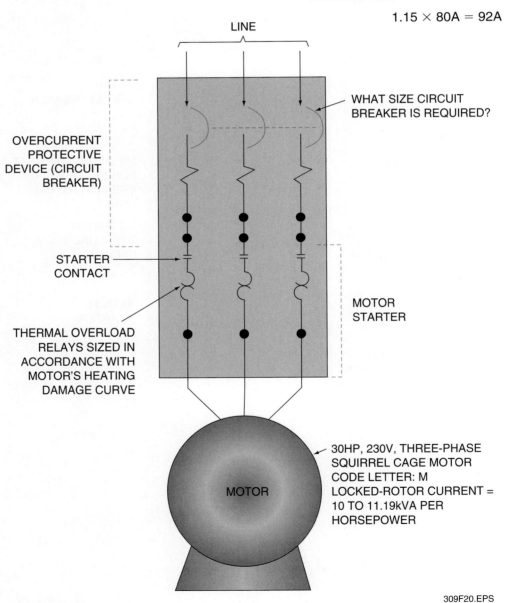

LINE

WHAT SIZE CIRCUIT
BREAKER IS REQUIRED?

OVERCURRENT
PROTECTIVE
DEVICE (CIRCUIT
BREAKER)

STARTER
CONTACT

MOTOR
STARTER

THERMAL OVERLOAD
RELAYS SIZED IN
ACCORDANCE WITH
MOTOR'S HEATING
DAMAGE CURVE

MOTOR

30HP, 230V, THREE-PHASE
SQUIRREL CAGE MOTOR
CODE LETTER: M
LOCKED-ROTOR CURRENT =
10 TO 11.19kVA PER
HORSEPOWER

309F20.EPS

*Figure 20* ◆ Typical 30-horsepower Design B energy-efficient motor circuit.

**NOTE**

*NEC Table 430.52* permits the use of an inverse-time circuit breaker rated at not more than 250% of the motor full-load current. However, a circuit breaker could be rated as high as 400% of the motor full-load current if necessary to hold the motor starting current without opening, according to *NEC Section 430.52(C)(1), Exception 2(c).*

*ep 3*   Assuming that a circuit breaker rated at 250% of the motor full-load current will be used, perform the following calculation:

$$2.5 \times 80A = 200A$$

*ep 4*   Select a regular thermal-magnetic circuit breaker with a 225A frame that is set to trip at 200A.

*ep 5*   Refer to *Figure 20* and note that this is a NEMA Design B energy-efficient motor. Refer to *NEC Table 430.52* and note that an instantaneous breaker for a Design B energy-efficient motor should be no more than 1,100% of the motor full-load current.

*ep 6*   Determine the circuit breaker rating by multiplying the full-load current by 1,100%:

$$80A \times 1,100\% \ (11.00) = 880A$$

The thermal-magnetic circuit breaker selected Step 4 will provide protection for grounds and ort circuits without interfering with motor erload protection. Note, however, that the in-ntaneous trip setting of a 200A circuit breaker ll be about 10 times the current rating, or:

$$200A \times 10 = 2,000A$$

Now consider the use of a 100A circuit breaker th thermal and adjustable magnetic trips. The tantaneous trip setting at 10 times the normal rrent rating would be:

$$100A \times 10 = 1,000A$$

Although this 1,000A instantaneous trip setting bove the 880A locked-rotor current of the 30hp tor in question, the starting current would bably trip the thermal element and open the cuit breaker.

This problem can be solved by removing the cuit breaker's thermal element and leaving ly the magnetic element in the circuit breaker. en the conditions of overload can be cleared by overload devices (heaters) in the motor starter. the setting of the instantaneous trip circuit aker will not hold under the starting load in

*NEC Section 430.52(C)(3),* then *Exception No. 1* will, under engineering evaluation, permit increasing the trip setting up to, but not exceeding, 1,300% (1,700% for NEMA Design B energy-efficient motors).

Therefore, since it has been determined that the 30hp motor in question has a full-load ampere rating of 80A, the maximum trip must not be set higher than:

$$80A \times 17 = 1,360A \text{ or about } 1,300A$$

This circuit breaker would qualify as the circuit disconnect because it has a rating higher than 115% of the motor full-load current (80A × 1.15 = 92A). However, the use of a magnetic-only circuit breaker does not protect against low-level grounds and short circuits in the branch circuit conductors on the line side of the motor starter overload relays—such an application must be made only where the circuit breaker and motor starter are installed as a combination motor starter in a single enclosure.

### 5.2.0 Motor Short Circuit Protectors

Motor short circuit protectors (MSCPs) are fuse-like devices designed for use only in a special type of fusible-switch combination motor starter. The combination offers short-circuit protection, overload protection, disconnecting means, and motor control, all with assured coordination between the short **circuit interrupter** and the overload devices.

The *NEC*® recognizes MSCPs in *NEC Section 430.52(C)(7),* provided the combination is identified for the purpose (i.e., a combination motor starter equipped with an MSCP and listed by Underwriters Laboratories or another nationally recognized third-party testing lab as a package called an MSCP starter).

### 6.0.0 ◆ MULTI-MOTOR BRANCH CIRCUITS

*NEC Sections 430.53(A),(B), and (C)* permit the use of more than one motor on a branch circuit, provided the following conditions are met:

• Two or more motors, each rated at not more than 1hp, and each drawing a full-load current not exceeding 6A, may be used on a branch circuit protected at not more than 20A at 120V or less, or 15A at 600V or less. The rating of the branch circuit protective device marked on any of the controllers must not be exceeded. Individual overload protection is necessary in such circuits unless the motor is not permanently installed, or is manually started and is within sight of the controller location, or has sufficient winding impedance to prevent overheating due to locked-rotor current, or is part of an approved assembly which does not subject the motor to overloads and which incorporates protection for the motor against locked-rotor current, or the motor cannot operate continuously under load.

- Two or more motors of any rating, each having individual overload protection, may be connected to a single branch circuit that is protected by a short circuit protective device (MSCP). The protective device must be selected in accordance with the maximum rating or setting that could protect an individual circuit to the motor of the smallest rating. This may be done only where it can be determined that the branch circuit device so selected will not open under the most severe normal conditions of service that might be encountered. This *NEC*® section offers wide application of more than one motor on a single circuit, particularly in the use of small integral-horsepower motors installed on 208V, 240V, and 480V, three-phase industrial and commercial systems. Only such three-phase motors have full-load operating currents low enough to permit more than one motor on circuits fed from 15A protective devices.

Using these *NEC*® rules, we will take a typica branch circuit (*Figure 21*) with more than one mo tor connected and see how the calculations a made.

The full-load current of each motor is take from *NEC Table 430.250* as required by *NE Section 430.6(A)*. A circuit breaker must be chose that does not exceed the maximum value of sho circuit protection (250%) required by *NEC Secti 430.52* and *NEC Table 430.52* for the smallest mo tor in the group (in this case, 1.5hp). Since t listed full-load current for the smallest mot (1.5hp) is 3A, the calculation is made as follows

$$3A \times 2.5\ (250\%) = 7.5A$$

**NOTE**

*NEC Section 430.52, Exception No. 1* allows the next higher size rating or setting for a standard circuit breaker. Since a 15A circuit breaker is the smallest standard rating recognized by *NEC Section 240.6*, a 15A, three pole circuit breaker may be used.

The total load of the motor currents must be ca culated as follows:

$$4.8A + 3.4A + 3.0A = 11.2A$$

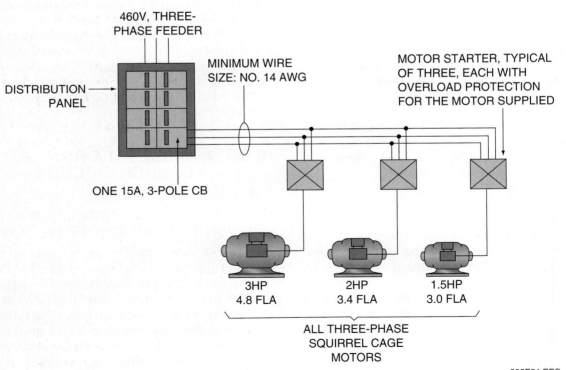

460V, THREE-PHASE FEEDER

MINIMUM WIRE SIZE: NO. 14 AWG

MOTOR STARTER, TYPICAL OF THREE, EACH WITH OVERLOAD PROTECTION FOR THE MOTOR SUPPLIED

DISTRIBUTION PANEL

ONE 15A, 3-POLE CB

3HP
4.8 FLA

2HP
3.4 FLA

1.5HP
3.0 FLA

ALL THREE-PHASE SQUIRREL CAGE MOTORS

309F21.EPS

*Figure 21* ◆ Several motors on one branch circuit.

The total full-load current for the three motors (11.2A) is well within the 15A circuit breaker rating, which has a sufficient time delay in its operation to permit starting of any one of these motors with the other two already operating. The torque characteristics of the loads on starting are not high. Therefore, the circuit breaker will not open under the most severe normal service.

Make certain that each motor is provided with the properly rated individual overload protection in the motor starter.

Branch circuit conductors are sized in accordance with *NEC Section 430.24.* In this case:

4.8A + 3.4A + 3.0A + [25% of the largest motor
(4.8A × 0.25 = 1.2A)] = 12.4A

No. 14 AWG conductors rated at 75°C will fully satisfy this application, as long as the overcurrent protection device does not exceed 15A, according to *NEC Section 240.4(D).*

Another multi-motor situation is shown in *Figure 22.* In this case, smaller motors are used. In general, *NEC Section 430.53(B)* requires branch circuit protection to be no greater than the maximum amperes permitted by *NEC Section 430.52* for the lowest rated motor of the group, which in this case is 1.1A for the ½hp motors. With this information in mind, we will size the circuit components for this application.

From *NEC Section 430.52* and *NEC Table 430.52,* the maximum protection rating for a circuit breaker is 250% of the lowest rated motor. Since this rating is 1.1A, the calculation is performed as follows:

2.5 × 1.1A = 2.75A

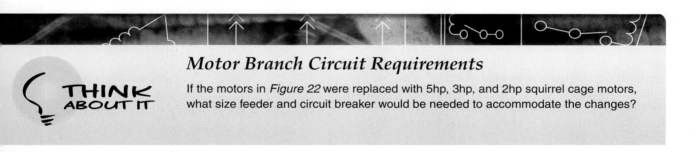

## Motor Branch Circuit Requirements

**THINK ABOUT IT**

If the motors in *Figure 22* were replaced with 5hp, 3hp, and 2hp squirrel cage motors, what size feeder and circuit breaker would be needed to accommodate the changes?

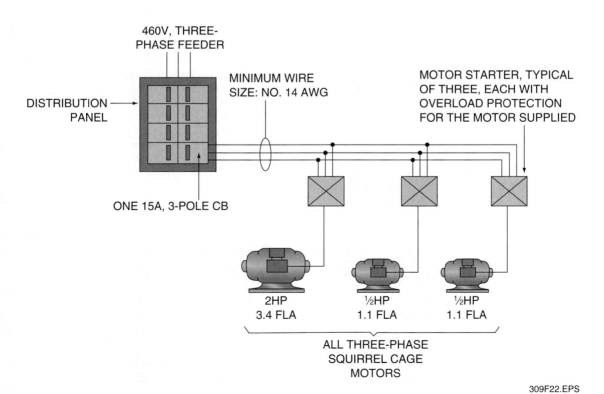

*Figure 22* ◆ Several smaller motors supplied by one branch circuit.

These two previous applications permit the use of several motors up to the circuit capacity, based on *NEC Sections 430.24 and 430.53(B)* and on starting torque characteristics, operating duty cycles of the motors and their loads, and the time delay of the circuit breaker. Such applications greatly reduce the number of circuit breakers and panels and the amount of wire used in the total system. One limitation, however, is placed on this practice in *NEC Section 430.52(C)(2),* which specifies that where maximum branch circuit short circuit and ground fault protective device ratings are shown in the manufacturer's overload relay table for use with a motor controller or are otherwise marked on the equipment, they shall not be exceeded even if higher values are allowed, as shown in the preceding examples.

## 7.0.0 ◆ POWER FACTOR CORRECTION AT MOTOR TERMINALS

Generally, the most effective method of power factor correction is the installation of capacitors at the cause of the poor power factor—the induction motor. This not only increases the power factor, but also releases system capacity, improves voltage stability, and reduces power losses.

When power factor correction capacitors are used, the total corrective kVAR on the load side of the motor controller should not exceed the value required to raise the no-load power factor to unity. Corrective kVAR in excess of this value may cause over-excitation that results in high transient voltages, currents, and torques that can increase safety hazards to personnel and possibly damage the motor or driven equipment.

Do not connect power factor correction capacitors at motor **terminals** on elevator motors; multi-speed motors; plugging or jogging applications; or open transition, wye-delta, autotransformer starting, and some part-winding start motors.

If possible, capacitors should be located at position No. 2, as shown in *Figure 23.* This does not

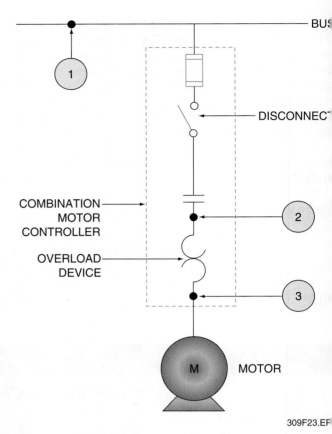

*Figure 23* ◆ Placement of capacitors in motor circuit.

change the current flowing through the motor overload protectors.

The connection of capacitors at position No. requires a change of overload protectors. Capacitors should be located at position No. 1 for any of the following applications:

• Elevator motors
• Multi-speed motors
• Plugging or jogging applications
• Open transition, wye-delta, autotransformer starting motors
• Some part-winding motors

*Table 1* allows the determination of corrective kVAR required where capacitors are individually connected at motor leads. These values should be considered the maximum capacitor rating when the motor and capacitor are switched as a unit. The figures given are for three-phase, 60Hz, NEMA Class B motors to raise the full-load power factor to 95%.

**Table 1** Motor Power Factor Correction Table

| Induction Motor Horsepower Rating | Nominal Motor Speed in RPM | | | | | | | | | | | | | |
| --- | --- | --- | --- | --- | --- | --- | --- | --- | --- | --- | --- | --- | --- | --- |
| | 3600 | | 1800 | | 1200 | | 900 | | 720 | | 600 | |
| | Capacitor Rating kVAR | Line Current Reduction % | Capacitor Rating kVAR | Line Current Reduction % | Capacitor Rating kVAR | Line Current Reduction % | Capacitor Rating kVAR | Line Current Reduction % | Capacitor Rating kVAR | Line Current Reduction % | Capacitor Rating kVAR | Line Current Reduction % |
| 3 | 1.5 | 14 | 1.5 | 15 | 1.5 | 20 | 2 | 27 | 2.5 | 35 | 3.5 | 41 |
| 5 | 2 | 12 | 2 | 13 | 2 | 17 | 3 | 25 | 4 | 32 | 4.5 | 37 |
| 7½ | 2.5 | 11 | 2.5 | 12 | 3 | 15 | 4 | 22 | 5.5 | 30 | 6 | 34 |
| 10 | 3 | 10 | 3 | 11 | 3.5 | 14 | 5 | 21 | 6.5 | 27 | 7.5 | 31 |
| 15 | 4 | 9 | 4 | 10 | 5 | 13 | 6.5 | 18 | 8 | 23 | 9.5 | 27 |
| 20 | 5 | 9 | 5 | 10 | 6.5 | 12 | 7.5 | 16 | 9 | 21 | 12 | 25 |
| 25 | 6 | 9 | 6 | 10 | 7.5 | 11 | 9 | 15 | 11 | 20 | 14 | 23 |
| 30 | 7 | 8 | 7 | 9 | 9 | 11 | 10 | 14 | 12 | 18 | 16 | 22 |
| 40 | 9 | 8 | 9 | 9 | 11 | 10 | 12 | 13 | 15 | 16 | 20 | 20 |
| 50 | 12 | 8 | 11 | 9 | 13 | 10 | 15 | 12 | 19 | 15 | 24 | 19 |
| 60 | 14 | 8 | 14 | 8 | 15 | 10 | 18 | 11 | 22 | 15 | 27 | 19 |
| 75 | 17 | 8 | 16 | 8 | 18 | 10 | 21 | 10 | 26 | 14 | 32.5 | 18 |
| 100 | 22 | 8 | 21 | 8 | 25 | 9 | 27 | 10 | 32.5 | 13 | 40 | 17 |
| 125 | 27 | 8 | 26 | 8 | 30 | 9 | 32.5 | 10 | 40 | 13 | 47.5 | 16 |
| 150 | 32.5 | 8 | 30 | 8 | 35 | 9 | 37.5 | 10 | 47.5 | 12 | 52.5 | 15 |
| 200 | 40 | 8 | 37.5 | 8 | 42.5 | 9 | 47.5 | 10 | 60 | 12 | 65 | 14 |
| 250 | 50 | 8 | 45 | 7 | 52.5 | 8 | 57.5 | 9 | 70 | 11 | 77.5 | 13 |

1. Stator windings can best be described as _____.
   a. a structure of copper or aluminum wire coils
   b. insulating fibers mounted on a shaft
   c. copper bars mounted on a spindle
   d. steel wires mounted on a shaft

2. The synchronous speed of a 60Hz, three-phase induction motor with two poles is _____.
   a. 3,600 rpm
   b. 1,800 rpm
   c. 1,200 rpm
   d. 900 rpm

3. The two most common three-phase motor configurations are _____.
   a. synchronous and rms
   b. box and star
   c. wye and delta
   d. star and wye

4. The most common number of motor leads found on a three-phase, wye-wound motor is _____.
   a. 3
   b. 6
   c. 9
   d. 12

5. Doubling the voltage on a dual-voltage motor _____.
   a. doubles the synchronous speed
   b. doubles the full-load current
   c. halves the full-load current
   d. halves the synchronous speed

6. The total resistance of the stator windings in a three-phase motor, if the windings are connected in parallel and the resistance of each winding is 96Ω, is _____.
   a. 48Ω
   b. 96Ω
   c. 192Ω
   d. 220Ω

7. If a squirrel cage induction motor draws 2A of current at 240V, the amperage will be _____ if connected for use on 480V.
   a. 1A
   b. 2A
   c. 3A
   d. 4A

8. Of the following motors, the one most likely to have 15 or 18 motor leads is the _____.
   a. single-phase capacitor-start motor
   b. 120V shaded-pole motor
   c. 480V three-phase squirrel cage motor
   d. 2,400V three-phase motor

9. The main purpose of motor overload protection is to protect the motor _____.
   a. against short circuits
   b. against ground faults
   c. from damaging overload currents
   d. against locked-rotor current

10. A circuit breaker suitable for use as a motor disconnecting means must have a current rating of at least _____% of the motor full-load current.
    a. 250
    b. 175
    c. 300
    d. 115

## Summary

The *NEC®* plays an important role in the selection and application of motors, including branch circuit conductors, disconnects, controllers, overcurrent protection, and overload protection. For example, *NEC Article 430* covers the application and installation of motor circuits and motor control connections, including conductors, short-circuit and ground-fault protection, controllers, disconnects, and overload protection.

*NEC Article 440* contains provisions for motor-driven air conditioning and refrigerating equipment, including the branch circuits and controllers for the equipment. It also takes into account the special considerations involved with sealed (hermetic) motor compressors, in which the motor operates under the cooling effect of the refrigeration. When referring to *NEC Article 440*, be aware that the rules in this article are in addition to, or are amendments to, the rules given in *NEC Article 430*.

## Notes

# Trade Terms
# Introduced in This Module

*Circuit interrupter:* A non-automatic, manually operated device designed to open a current-carrying circuit without injury to itself.

*Rating:* A designated limit of operating characteristics based on definite conditions. Such operating characteristics as load, voltage, frequency, etc., may be given in the rating.

*Service factor:* The number by which the horsepower rating is multiplied to determine the maximum safe load that a motor may be expected to carry continuously at its rated voltage and frequency.

*Terminal:* A point at which an electrical component may be connected to another electrical component.

*Torque:* A force that produces or tends to produce rotation. Common units of measurement of torque are foot-pounds and inch-pounds.

This module is intended to present thorough resources for task training. The following reference works are suggested for further study. These are optional materials for continued education rather than for task training.

*American Electrician's Handbook.* Terrell Croft and Wilfred I. Summers. New York, NY: McGraw-Hill, 1996.

*National Electrical Code® Handbook,* Latest Edition. Quincy, MA: National Fire Protection Association.

# *CONTREN® LEARNING SERIES* — USER FEEDBACK

The NCCER makes every effort to keep these textbooks up-to-date and free of technical errors. We appreciate your help in this process. If you have an idea for improving this textbook, or if you find an error, a typographical mistake, or an inaccuracy in NCCER's *Contren®* textbooks, please write us, using this form or a photocopy. Be sure to include the exact module number, page number, a detailed description, and the correction, if applicable. Your input will be brought to the attention of the Technical Review Committee. Thank you for your assistance.

*Instructors* – If you found that additional materials were necessary in order to teach this module effectively, please let us know so that we may include them in the Equipment/Materials list in the Annotated Instructor's Guide.

**Write:**   Product Development
National Center for Construction Education and Research
P.O. Box 141104, Gainesville, FL  32614-1104

**Fax:**   352-334-0932

**E-mail:**   curriculum@nccer.org

Craft                                        Module Name

Copyright Date              Module Number                     Page Number(s)

Description

(Optional) Correction

(Optional) Your Name and Address

Trainee Guide

# Advanced Electrical Topics

**National Center for
Construction Education and Research**

# Medical Systems

*Module 20506*

*Wheels of Learning
Standardized Craft Training*

Prentice Hall
Columbus, Ohio
Upper Saddle River, New Jersey

Printed in the United States of America

10 9 8 7 6 5

ISBN: 0-13-909904-2


Prentice-Hall International (UK) Limited, *London*
Prentice-Hall of Australia Pty. Limited, *Sydney*
Prentice-Hall of Canada, Inc., *Toronto*
Prentice-Hall Hispanoamericana, S. A., *Mexico*
Prentice-Hall of India Private Limited, *New Delhi*
Prentice-Hall of Japan, Inc., *Tokyo*
Pearson Education Asia, *Singapore*
Editora Prentice-Hall do Brasil, Ltda., *Rio de Janeiro*

This volume is one of many in the *Wheels of Learning* craft training program. This program, covering more than 20 standardized craft areas, including all major construction skills, was developed over a period of years by industry and education specialists. Sixteen of the largest construction and maintenance firms in the U.S. committed financial and human resources to the teams that wrote the curricula and planned the national accredited training process. These materials are industry-proven and consist of competency-based textbooks and instructor guides.

The *Wheels of Learning* was developed by the National Center for Construction Education and Research in response to the training needs of the construction and maintenance industries. The NCCER is a nonprofit educational entity affiliated with the University of Florida and supported by the following industry and craft associations:

## Partnering Associations
- American Fire Sprinkler Association
- American Society for Training and Development
- American Vocational Association
- American Welding Society
- Associated Builders and Contractors, Inc.
- Associated General Contractors of America
- Carolinas AGC
- Carolinas Electrical Contractors Association
- Construction Industry Institute
- Merit Contractors Association of Canada
- Metal Building Manufacturers Association
- National Association of Minority Contractors
- National Association of Women in Construction
- National Insulation Association
- National Ready Mixed Concrete Association
- National Utility Contractors Association
- National VoTech Honor Society
- Painting and Decorating Contractors of America
- Portland Cement Association
- Texas Gulf Coast ABC

Some of the features of the *Wheels of Learning* program include:

- A proven record of success over many years of use by industry companies.
- National standardization providing "portability" of learned job skills and educational credits that will be of tremendous value to trainees.
- Recognition: upon successful completion of training with an accredited sponsor, trainees receive an industry-recognized certificate and transcript from NCCER.
- Approval by the U.S. Department of Labor for use in formal apprenticeship programs.
- Well illustrated, up-to-date, and practical information. All standardized manuals are reviewed annually in a continuous improvement process.

## Acknowledgments

This manual would not exist were it not for the dedication and unselfish energy of those volunteers who served on the Technical Review Committee. A sincere thanks is extended to:

Bane Allman

Barney Barnette

Mike Basham

Jerry Bass

Michael E. Dahl

Gary Edgington

Tim Ely

Al Hamilton

Donald Hostetler

L.J. LeBlanc

Jim Mitchem

Robert Mueller

Mike Powers

Don Singleton

Rob Soileau

Joe Sullivan

**Advanced Electrical Topics**
**Electrical Trainee Task Module 20506**

# MEDICAL SYSTEMS

## OBJECTIVES

Upon completion of this module, the trainee will be able to:

1. List the types of electrical distribution systems used in the medical industry.
2. Describe the use of electrical closets and their requirements.
3. Understand the requirements of transfer switches when used in emergency/backup systems.
4. Explain the different electrical distribution systems and list their advantages and disadvantages.
5. Describe the categories and branch portions of the distribution circuits.
6. List the items allowed in the life safety branch and critical branch.
7. Determine electrical system voltage, current, and grounding considerations.
8. Describe ground system testing required for the distribution system.
9. Describe ground fault protection required to ensure a safe environment.
10. List the required wiring devices in a health care facility.
11. Explain the use of wiring devices in inhalation anesthetizing locations.
12. Describe the requirements for the installation of X-ray equipment.
13. Describe the operation of isolated power systems.

### Required Trainee Material

1. Trainee Task Module
2. Appropriate Personal Protective Equipment
3. National Electrical Code and Standard for Health Care Facilities, Latest Editions

*Note:*    The designations "National Electrical Code," "NE Code," and "NEC," where used in this document, refer to the National Electrical Code®, which is a registered trademark of the National Fire Protection Association, Quincy, MA. *All National Electrical Code (NEC) references in this module refer to the 1999 edition of the NEC.*

## ADVANCED ELECTRICAL TOPICS

The National Center for Construction Education and Research offers the following Advanced Electrical Topics for continuing education and/or specialized instruction:

*Module 20501, Advanced Electronic Theory*
*Module 20502, Voice and Data Systems*
*Module 20503, Busses and Networks*
*Module 20504, Fiber Optics*
*Module 20505, Programmable Logic Controllers*
*Module 20506, Medical Systems*
*Module 20507, TV and Antenna Systems*
*Module 20508, Medium Voltage*
*Module 20509, Power Quality*
*Module 20510, Energy Management Systems*
*Module 20511, Traffic Signals*
*Module 20512, Sound and Signal Systems*
*Module 20513, Process and Distributed Control Systems*
*Module 20514, Advanced Test Equipment*

For ordering information, contact Prentice Hall Publishers at 800-922-0579.

The following books are also recommended as suitable texts for advanced electrical instruction:

*Basic Leadership Skills for the Advanced Craftperson*
*Understanding the NEC®* (Latest Edition, Holt)
*Understanding NEC® Calculations* (Latest Edition, Holt)

*Basic Leadership Skills* is available from NCCER at 352-334-0920. NEC® titles are available from the Construction Bookstore© at 800-253-0541.

# TABLE OF CONTENTS

# TABLE OF CONTENTS (Continued)

## Trade Terms Introduced In This Module

**Equipotential ground plane:** A mass of conducting material that, when bonded together, provides a low impedance to current flow over a wide range of frequencies.

**ICEA:** Insulated Cable Engineers Association.

**IEEE:** Institute of Electronics and Electrical Engineers.

**NEMA:** National Electrical Manufacturers Association.

**Throwover:** Switches for supplying temporary power.

## 1.0.0    INTRODUCTION

This module covers electric distribution systems for health care facilities. It incorporates the basic National Electrical Code (NEC) requirements for these systems; however, state and local codes vary and may impose different standards than those listed here. Always check state and local codes before beginning any installation.

Power, electricity, and the growing need for electronic apparatus is becoming more and more prevalent within the health care industry. Power is necessary to operate the refrigeration units used to safeguard and store living tissue, bone, and blood. The need for specific lighting in strategic areas to perform delicate operations and associated procedures must be obtained. Every year we see more cardiac operations performed in which the patient's circulation of blood is artificially induced, electrical impulses that stimulate and regulate heart action are employed to sustain life, and electrical equipment is routinely utilized to develop suction in order to evacuate body fluids and mucus that might otherwise cause suffocation and death.

Electrical service to a health care facility is of vital importance. The loss of electrical service can be devastating. Phenomena such as earthquakes, hurricanes, floods, and tornados can interrupt electrical service. Also, fires, explosions, and electrical failures within the facility due to shorts, blown fuses, or overloading of equipment can prevent the successful transfer of electric service. In order to prevent or limit the internal disruption of power within these facilities, a well-planned electrical system must be designed. Loss of power can be corrected in seconds versus hours depending on the system employed. Systems should be designed to cope with the longest probable power outage.

Safeguards are needed to ensure the proper operation and maintenance of electrical circuitry and mechanical components in vital areas.

## 2.0.0    ELECTRICAL DISTRIBUTION SYSTEMS

In order to provide the facility with a reliable electrical power system, significant attention should be paid to the proper design, arrangement, and installation of the system.

An electrical service system consisting of dedicated tandem utility service feeders supplied from distinct and separate distribution busses will provide greater reliability than a single utility service feeder. Reliability of this system is enhanced when each service feeder is installed in parallel so faults within one feeder will not affect or produce faults in another. This form of installation will promote a higher reliability of equipment during high usage periods, substantially improving the operation and efficiency of patient care.

To minimize interruptions to a facility electrical system due to internal failures caused by equipment, the distribution system arrangement should be designed and installed per the factors outlined in ANSI/NFPA 99-1996, Standard for Health Care Facilities. Items to be considered are:

- Current-sensing devices (phase and ground) should be selected and installed to minimize the extent of interruption to the electrical system due to abnormal current caused by overloads or overcurrent situations.
- The system design must account for abnormal voltages such as single phasing of three-phase utilization equipment, switching and/or lightning surges, voltage reductions, etc.
- The system must have the capability of achieving the fastest possible restoration after clearing a fault.
- The system design must account for effects of further changes such as increased loading and/or supply capacity.
- The system design must account for the stability and power capability of the prime mover during and after abnormal conditions.
- The system must provide for sequence reconnecting of loads to avoid large current inrushes that could trip overcurrent devices or overload the generator(s) in the alternate power supply.

Branch and feeder circuits should have minimum power ratings adequate to supply power to the electrical loads and a sufficient number of branches to compensate and distribute load requirements in case of outages within the branch or feeder circuits.

Electrical closets house a large portion of the electrical distribution system. The location of electrical closets within the health care facility should be identified in the initial phase of development. Electrical closets are ideally located in the middle core of the facility or at a midpoint on lengthy wings so branch circuits can be run in various directions. However, these runs should not exceed 75 feet in length. Electrical power circuit risers should not be designed to bend or have inaccessible taps. Therefore, electrical closets on all floors should be aligned in order to allow for this. Electrical closets should have adequate space to accommodate transformers and electrical service panels and sufficient area to allow access and maintainability. Electrical closets which will contain dry transformers should be ventilated to prevent heat buildup. In order to prevent the loss of normal and emergency power, sprinkler heads should not be installed within an electrical closet. However, where local jurisdictions insist upon installing sprinkler heads in electrical closets, the highest permissible temperature head should be used for the installation.

Motors with high inrush current feed are commonly connected to the same supply as voltage-sensitive equipment when installed in a health care facility. Preventive measures should be taken when inrush current could electrically harm voltage-sensitive devices. One method used to provide protection is to connect a separate feeder line supply to the voltage-sensitive equipment. It is common for health care facilities to install a system with motor feeders apart from the power feeders and lighting feeders within a doubled-ended switchboard or switchgear or separate power bus in order to minimize the motor loading effects on other electrical devices. One such motor is the elevator motor, specifically one which is hydraulic. These motors should be installed with the proper code letter from **NEMA** [e.g., ANSI/NFPA 70-1996, National Electrical Code, Article 430, Table 430-7(b)] specifying the maximum inrush current permitted and proper starting method at full or reduced voltage. Another health care facility motor that may create loading problems is the chiller motor, but because of the infrequent starting of these motors, they seldom initiate a problem.

## 2.1.0  RADIAL SYSTEM ARRANGEMENT

Small panelboards or single service panelboard systems may be utilized when power is needed in residential care facilities, smaller health care facilities, or small to mid-size nursing homes, as shown in *Figure 1*. Nonessential overcurrent devices normally feed panelboards within smaller facilities. The restoration of a generator whose output powers a motor load can be delayed utilizing a relay in an autotransfer switch or the addition of a time delay relay installed with the motor starter. These relays are powered by energizing peripheral contacts inside the transfer switch, as shown in *Figure 2*.

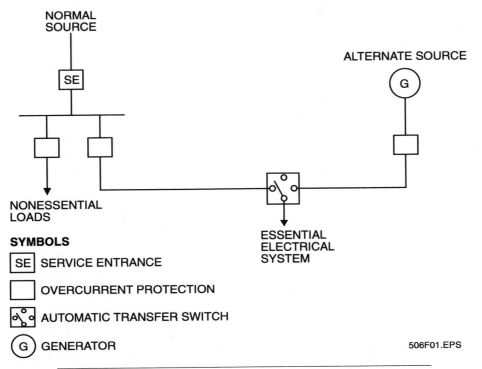

506F01.EPS

Figure 1.  Major Components Of The Electrical System

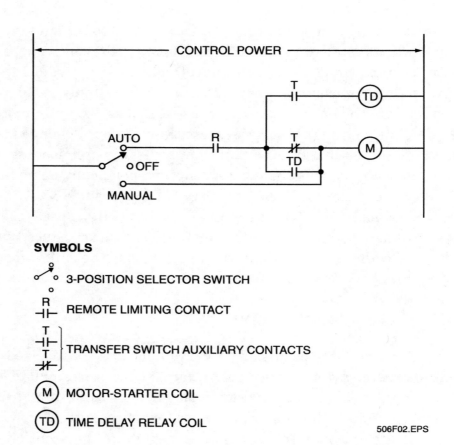

SYMBOLS

3-POSITION SELECTOR SWITCH

R — REMOTE LIMITING CONTACT

T / T — TRANSFER SWITCH AUXILIARY CONTACTS

(M) MOTOR-STARTER COIL

(TD) TIME DELAY RELAY COIL

506F02.EPS

Figure 2.  Time Delay Relay In Transfer Switch Of Motor Starter

In order to improve reliability when the need for significant emergency power arises, the use of several transfer switches may be employed. Transfer switches can be adjusted to sequentially transfer, therefore lessoning the generator inrush requirements. However, when transfer switches are utilized in this manner, the transfer must take place within ten seconds.

ANSI/NFPA 70-1996 (Article 517) requires that the emergency system be automatically transferred to an alternate power source following an interruption of the normal source. However, equipment such as elevators, heating units, or heating and ventilating fans may be manually transferred following a power outage. Where trained personnel are available on a 24-hour basis, manual transfer switching of certain equipment loads may be a less expensive method of applying emergency power than automatic switching. Manual switching also allows equipment to be energized as generator loading permits. ANSI/NFPA 99-1996 (Chapter 8) specifies where manual switching is allowable.

As health care facilities grow, supplementary feeders for nonessential loads and essential electrical systems will become necessary. The requisite electrical system will contain several transfer switches, some of which could be non-automatic. Several smaller transfer switches in place of a large switch will contribute to system reliability as well as stability, but at a significant cost. Additional reliability can be achieved by placing the transfer switches as close to the final load as possible.

*Figure 3* shows two diagrams for distributing power through vertical risers. When power is lost in the normal power supply of either diagram, transfer switches will direct an alternate supply to the electrical power panels where required, but if a specific regular feeder outage occurs, only Scheme A can recognize the specific loss and restore power to the affected panel via the alternate power supply. Scheme A is more reliable than Scheme B; however, it is also more expensive. Loss of normal power is sensed at the transfer device to initiate start-up of the emergency power unit via auxiliary contacts. When nominal emergency power becomes available, it is felt at the transfer device to initiate start-up of the emergency power unit via auxiliary contacts. When adequate emergency power is available, it is switched to the alternate power source. Restoration of power causes the transfer switches to reset to the normal power source while beginning a shutdown of the emergency power unit. ANSI/NFPA 99-1996 (Chapter 8) documents the time requirements between switching regular and emergency supplies.

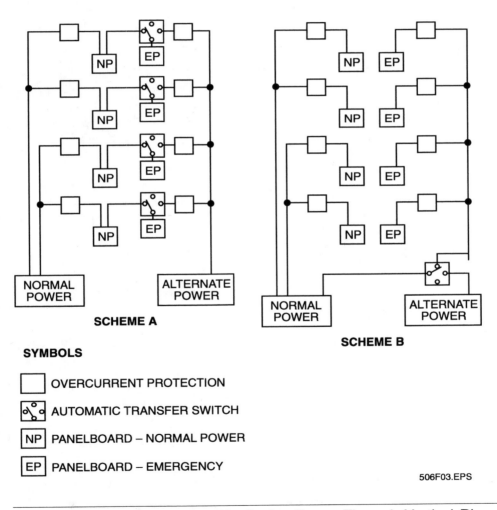

Figure 3. Two Schemes For Distributing Power Through Vertical Risers

## 2.2.0 DOUBLE-ENDED SYSTEM ARRANGEMENT

When transformation in excess of 750 kVA is necessary, a double-ended substation should be considered. *Figure 4* uses a normally open tie protector interlocked with main protectors so that all three cannot be simultaneously closed. When a single transformer or its feeder has loss, the tie protector may be closed, manually adding additional load to the remaining transformer. Double-ended substations have additional benefits such as lower fault current and the ability to differentiate between motor loads that require specific voltage regulation.

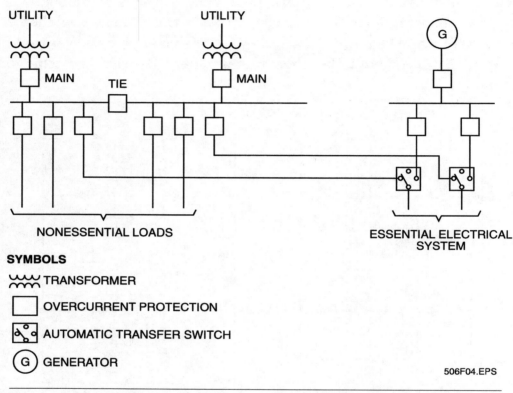

506F04.EPS

Figure 4. Normally Open Tie Protector Interlocked With Main Protectors

If the double-ended substation design utilizes a normally open, electrically-operated tie protector that will automatically close upon loss of either incoming feeder, then control and protective relaying must be added to prevent the bus tie protector from closing when a main protector has tripped due to overload or short circuit conditions.

Utility companies may allow double-ended substations to operate with a closed tie and main protectors. Double-ended substations with mains and normally closed ties have distinct advantages such as better voltage regulation, transfer capabilities when power loss occurs, immediate switching when a power source is lost, and greater reliability of system operation. However, the disadvantages are greater fault current, greater cost, and a more complex design. An engineer can specify and coordinate additional protection for the system.

## 2.3.0  NETWORK SYSTEM ARRANGEMENT

*Figure 5* depicts a network consisting of two or more transformers having their secondaries bussed together through network protectors.

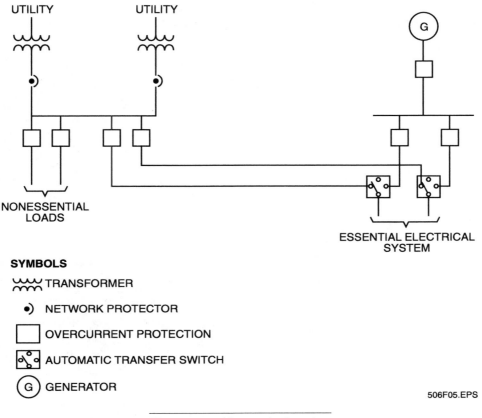

SYMBOLS

〰 TRANSFORMER

•) NETWORK PROTECTOR

☐ OVERCURRENT PROTECTION

⧉ AUTOMATIC TRANSFER SWITCH

Ⓖ GENERATOR

506F05.EPS

Figure 5.  Network Service

Network designs have some distinct advantages such as excellent voltage regulation, lack of service interruption when a feeder is lost, and a high degree of reliability. Disadvantages are large fault current, increased cost, and lack of network expansion without interrupt ratings or having to increase the existing component size.

Electric service is provided by utility-operated networks in metropolitan areas. Urban areas are fed from many network transformers with their secondaries tied into the grid of secondary cables encompassing a large area. This network commonly permits a single primary feeder to be removed from service during all hours. Two primary feeders may be removed during low load periods without creating low voltages on the secondary grid. However, if demand exceeds 500 kVA, utilities may require a spot network that provides two to four network transformers within a small space and has the secondaries bussed together but not connected to the general urban area network.

Though network service is the most expensive, it is also considered the most reliable. In order to lower costs, hospitals may opt to own the network transformer in order to qualify for a primary service discount.

The trend has been to employ open tie substations with automatic transfer of required circuits to onsite generation over that of network closed tie substations. This trend is due to the initial cost and complexity of the closed tie network system. Hospitals can also receive onsite power generation when normal power is lost.

## 2.4.0 HIGH-VOLTAGE SYSTEM ARRANGEMENT

The loop and primary selective systems are the most common methods used for high voltage in hospitals. These systems permit the removal of the feeder or a single cable section from service without prolonged loss of power. Utilizing preconstructed connectors which are separable at transformers and manholes can assist in the isolation of cable section loss. Within these manholes, current detectors can be connected to cables to assist in isolating cable loss. **IEEE** Standard 141-1976 (Chapter 1) provides a detailed description of loop and selective primary systems.

## 2.5.0 EXISTING SYSTEM ARRANGEMENT

In hospitals where an existing substation and new load requirements exist, it is often more convenient to add a transformer rather than update the existing substation if the substation is adequately rated for the load addition. *Figure 6* is an example of a good way to introduce 480V distribution if the existing substation has a lower voltage rating.

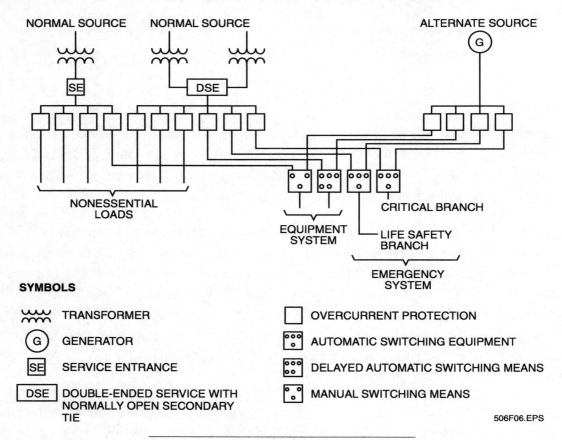

506F06.EPS

Figure 6. Adequately-Rated Substation

## 2.6.0 METERING ARRANGEMENT

When designing an electrical system with multiple primary transformers, it is best to obtain totalized, singular metering from the utility, which will result in lower electrical costs. Electrical utilities commonly price additional blocks of power lower than prior blocks. Therefore, a single meter displays the more expensive blocks once per month.

A hospital may have to purchase all power at a single point and single voltage in order to be permitted by the utility to incorporate totalized metering. Hospitals owning and maintaining their own primary system and purchasing power at primary voltage levels cannot only use a single meter but may also be eligible for lower rate or utility discounts. Initial purchase cost and maintenance of a high-voltage system versus the savings must be evaluated prior to deciding on the electrical service.

## 3.0.0 TYPES OF ELECTRICAL POWER SYSTEMS

A high degree of reliability and safety is required by a health care facility's power system. Health care facilities may require supplemental electrical design within particular areas as documented in IEEE Standard 241-1983. Many areas have additional requirements established by:

- Governing codes and standards
- Complex and electrically-sensitive medical equipment utilization
- Electrical hazards which may harm medical personnel or patients within the health care facility

Extreme caution should be exercised when combustible anesthetics are utilized in order to prevent explosion and fire. ANSI/NFPA 70-1996 (Articles 500 through 503) and ANSI/NFPA 99-1996 (Chapters 3 and 4), as well as all other national and local codes which are applicable to hazardous materials, should be referred to by designers. General purpose overhead lighting used in operating rooms is normally powered from a standard ground distribution system. These lights are not normally manipulated by personnel during operating procedures. Lighting apparatus and other equipment that must be manipulated during surgical procedures such as surgical instrumentation, monitors, X-ray devices, and direct intense light should be isolated from other supplies using an isolation transformer and line-isolation monitor. Therefore, particular attention should be directed to areas such as these.

Typical power sourcing in a system is supplied by electric companies and the necessary alternate power source by the onsite power source (battery system or generators). Naturally, this depends on the specifics of the health care facility. However, when normal sourcing consists of onsite power generators, the alternate power source can be either the utility or other generators. Conditions must be met if utilizing battery systems in assisted-living facilities, nursing homes, and primary health care facilities as documented in ANSI/NFPA 99-1996. A generator set is required as the alternate power source for hospitals.

## 3.1.0 DISTRIBUTION CIRCUITS

Health care facility distribution systems are divided into two categories: the essential emergency system and the nonessential (normal) electrical system. These systems are supplied by the normal power sources, but the essential emergency electrical system is switched to an alternate supply when the normal power sources experience momentary loss or complete power failure.

The essential emergency system consists of the alternate power supply, as well as the transfer equipment, distribution equipment, and circuitry necessary to ensure continuity of electrical service to those loads designated as essential to life safety, critical patient care, and the effective operation of the health care facility.

The nonessential (normal) electrical system consists of the distribution equipment and circuitry necessary to supply electrical power from the standard power supply to loads which are not designated as essential to life safety or the effective operation of the health care facility.

The essential electrical system is divided into two subsystems when designed for hospitals: the equipment system and the emergency system.

The equipment system utilizes electrical equipment and circuits for three-phase distribution including manual transfer or delayed automatic devices to feed equipment loads essential to the effective operation of the hospital as documented in ANSI/NFPA 99-1996 (Chapter 8).

The emergency system is composed of two distinct branches: the life safety branch and the critical branch. These branches incorporate distribution equipment and circuitry, including the automatic transfer devices required to enable emergency loads to be transferred from normal to emergency power sources. To improve reliability of the system, each circuit must be installed separately from all other electrical circuits as well as each other. In addition, ANSI/NFPA 99-1996 and ANSI/NFPA 70-1996 require that this system be designed to allow automatic restoration of electrical power within ten seconds of power interruption or loss and define the electrical loads to be served by the life safety branch and critical branch. Section 517-63(a)(9) of ANSI/NFPA 70-1996 allows the designer to install "other equipment and devices necessary for the effective operation of the hospital" on the critical branch of the emergency system. This permits the designer a degree of flexibility in customizing the design to the specific needs of the hospital. The designer should use his/her good judgement, experience, and hospital staff input when applying this standard to the design of the system.

In addition to the above, the Joint Commission on Accreditation of Hospitals requires that a hospital which incorporates a fire pump connect the fire pump to the essential system. NEC Article 517.30(b) requires that:

- Essential electrical systems for hospitals shall be comprised of two separate systems capable of supplying a limited amount of lighting and power service, which is considered essential for life safety and effective hospital operation during the time the normal electrical service is interrupted for any reason. These two systems shall be the emergency system and the equipment system.

- The emergency system shall be limited to circuits essential to life safety and critical patient care. These are designated the life safety branch and the critical branch.
- The equipment system shall supply major electric equipment necessary for patient care and basic hospital operation.
- The number of transfer switches to be used shall be based upon reliability, design, and load considerations. Each branch of the essential electrical system shall be served by one or more transfer switches, as shown in *Figures 7* and *8*. One transfer switch shall be permitted to serve one or more branches or systems in a facility with a maximum demand on the essential electrical system of 150 kVA, as shown in *Figure 9*.

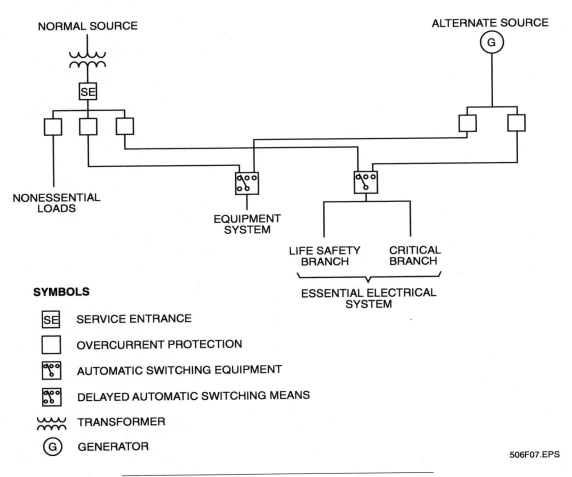

Figure 7. Small Electrical System – Hospitals

*Figures 7, 8,* and *9* indicate possible electrical system connections for hospitals. *Figure 8* depicts a typical design, where the enlargement of the facility requires the addition of a normal supply source to one that is already installed. As depicted in the diagram, this may not require an additional alternate source. However, the alternate source must have the capacity to supply all intended loads.

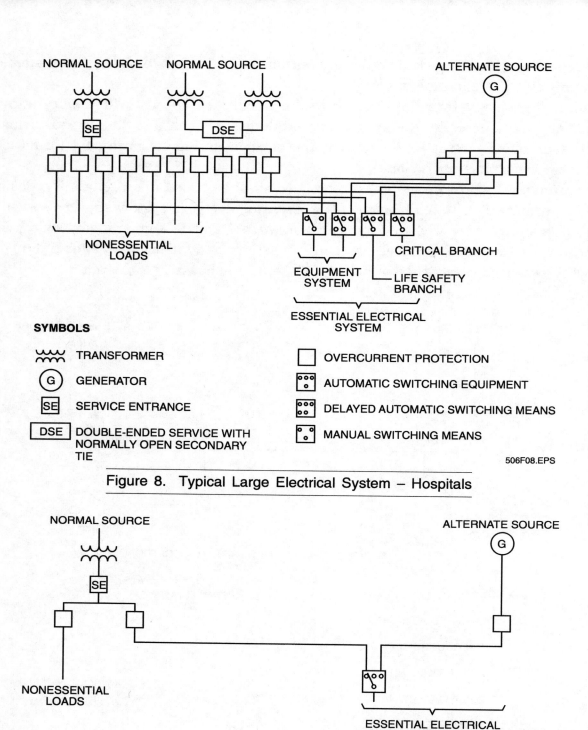

SYMBOLS

~~~ TRANSFORMER                OVERCURRENT PROTECTION

(G) GENERATOR                 AUTOMATIC SWITCHING EQUIPMENT

SE SERVICE ENTRANCE          DELAYED AUTOMATIC SWITCHING MEANS

DSE DOUBLE-ENDED SERVICE WITH    MANUAL SWITCHING MEANS
    NORMALLY OPEN SECONDARY
    TIE

506F08.EPS

Figure 8.  Typical Large Electrical System – Hospitals

SYMBOLS

SE SERVICE ENTRANCE

    OVERCURRENT PROTECTION

    AUTOMATIC SWITCHING EQUIPMENT

~~~ TRANSFORMER

(G) GENERATOR

506F09.EPS

Figure 9.  Small Electrical System – Hospitals (Single Transfer Switch)

For an electrical system having a maximum demand on the essential electrical system of 150 kVA as depicted in *Figure 9*, a small load can be serviced by a single transfer switch that can handle the loads associated with both the emergency system and the equipment system. Naturally, this is assuming that the transfer switch has sufficient capacity to serve the combined additional loads and that the alternate source of power is sufficiently large enough to govern the force of the simultaneous transfer of both systems in the event of a normal power loss.

### 3.1.1 Life Safety Branch

The life safety branch of the emergency system shall supply power for the following equipment, lighting, and receptacles:

- Hospital communications systems, where used for dissemination of instructions during emergencies.
- Task illumination battery charger for emergency battery-powered lighting unit(s) and selected receptacles at the generator set location.
- Illumination of means of exiting, such as lighting required for corridors, passageways, stairways, and landings at exit doors, and all obligatory ways of approach to exits. Arrangements for switching to transfer patient corridor lighting in hospitals from general illumination circuits to night illumination circuits will be authorized provided only one of two circuits can be selected, and both circuits cannot be extinguished simultaneously.
- Exit direction and exit signs.
- Alarm and alerting systems, including fire alarms and alarms required for systems utilized for the piping of nonflammable medical gases.
- Elevator cab communication, control, lighting, and signal systems.

*CAUTION:*  No capacity or service other than those listed above may be connected to the life safety branch electrical system.

### 3.1.2 Critical Branch

The critical branch should be designed to service a finite number of receptacles and locations in order to reduce the load demand and minimize the chances of a fault condition. Receptacles in general patient care corridors are allowed on the critical branch; however, they are required to be identified in some way (labeled or color-coded) as part of the critical branch, in compliance with Sections 3 through 4.2.2.4(b)(2) of ANSI/NFPA 99-1996.

*Task illumination and selected receptacles* – The emergency system's critical branch shall supply power for task illumination, selected receptacles, fixed equipment, and special power circuits feeding the following locations and functions related to patient care:

- Critical care areas that utilize anesthetizing gases—task illumination, selected receptacles, and fixed equipment.
- The isolated power systems located in special environments.
- Patient care areas—task illumination and selected receptacles in:
  - Infant nurseries
  - Medication preparation areas
  - Pharmacy dispensing areas
  - Selected acute nursing areas
  - Psychiatric bed areas (omit receptacles)
  - Ward treatment rooms
  - Nurses' stations (unless adequately lighted by corridor luminaires)
- Additional specialized patient care task illumination and receptacles, where needed.
- Nurse call systems.
- Blood, bone, and tissue banks.
- Telephone equipment room(s) and closet(s).
- Task illumination, selected receptacles, and selected power circuits for:
  - General care beds (at least one duplex receptacle per patient bedroom)
  - Angiographic labs
  - Cardiac catheterization labs
  - Coronary care units
  - Hemodialysis rooms or areas
  - Emergency room treatment areas (selected)
  - Human physiology labs
  - Intensive care units
  - Postoperative recovery rooms (selected)
- Additional task illumination, receptacles, and selected power circuits needed for effective hospital operation. Single-phase fractional horsepower exhaust fan motors that are interlocked with three-phase motors on the equipment shall be permitted to be connected to the critical branch.

### 3.2.0 ESSENTIAL ELECTRICAL SYSTEMS FOR NURSING HOMES AND LIMITED CARE FACILITIES

ANSI/NFPA 99-1996 recognizes two classes of nursing homes for limited care facilities. Only a minimum of alternate lighting and alarm service need be outfitted for the smaller, less complex facilities.

Requirements of NEC Sections 517-41 through 517-44 are to be exercised where treatment of patients is provided. Branches of the emergency system within this class of occupants have identical titles to their counterparts for occupants within hospitals.

*Exception:* Freestanding buildings used as nursing homes and limited care facilities, provided that:

- The facility maintains admitting and discharge policies that preclude the provision of care for any patient or resident who may need to be sustained by electrical life-support equipment.
- The facility offers no surgical treatment requiring general anesthesia.
- The facility provides automatic battery-operated system(s) or equipment that shall be effective for at least 1½ hours and operate in accordance with NEC Section 700-12. The backup system(s) shall be capable of supplying lighting for exit lights, exit corridors, stairways, nursing stations, medical preparation areas, boiler rooms, communication areas, and all alarm systems.

Limited care facilities and nursing homes which furnish inpatient hospital care shall comply with the requirements of NEC Sections 517-30 through 517-35.

Regardless of the name given to the facility, the category of electrical system will depend on the type of patient care. Where care is evidently inpatient hospital care, a hospital-type electrical system is required to be installed.

Nursing homes and limited care facilities that are contiguous with a hospital shall be permitted to have their essential electrical systems supplied by that of the hospital.

Where a limited care facility or nursing home shares fundamentally the same building with a hospital, the nursing home is not required to incorporate its own essential electrical system if it procures its power from the hospital. It should be noted, however, that this rule does not permit the sharing of transfer devices.

NEC Section 517-50 and ANSI/NFPA 99-1996 require an alternate source of power for any and all health care facilities where patients are treated in primarily the same manner as in hospitals, even though the facility may not be designated a hospital.

Essential electrical systems for limited care facilities and nursing homes shall have two separate branches that are able to supply the lighting and power requisite for the protection of life safety and the effective operation of the facility during the interruption of normal electrical service. These two separate branches shall be the life safety branch and the critical branch.

The number of transfer switches used will be based upon reliability, load considerations, and design. Every branch of the essential electrical system shall be served by one or more transfer switches as shown in *Figures 10* and *11*. A single transfer switch will be sanctioned to serve one or more branches or systems in a facility with a maximum demand on the essential electrical system of 150 kVa, as shown in *Figure 12*.

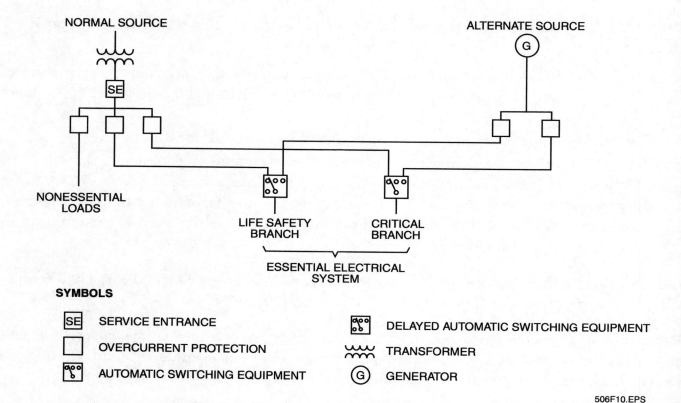

**SYMBOLS**

| | | | |
|---|---|---|---|
| SE | SERVICE ENTRANCE | | DELAYED AUTOMATIC SWITCHING EQUIPMENT |
| | OVERCURRENT PROTECTION | | TRANSFORMER |
| | AUTOMATIC SWITCHING EQUIPMENT | G | GENERATOR |

506F10.EPS

Figure 10.  Small Electrical System – Nursing Homes And Limited Care Facilities

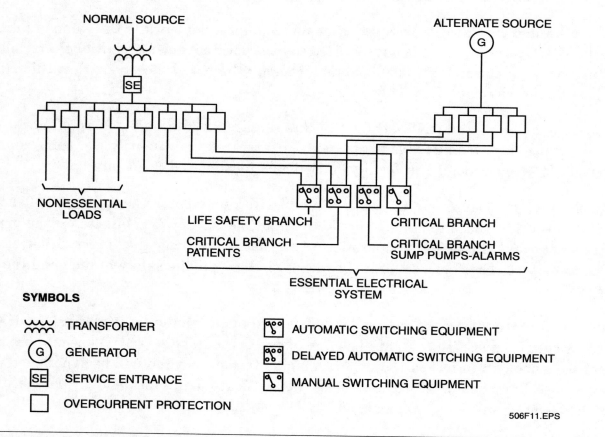

**SYMBOLS**

| | | | |
|---|---|---|---|
| | TRANSFORMER | | AUTOMATIC SWITCHING EQUIPMENT |
| G | GENERATOR | | DELAYED AUTOMATIC SWITCHING EQUIPMENT |
| SE | SERVICE ENTRANCE | | MANUAL SWITCHING EQUIPMENT |
| | OVERCURRENT PROTECTION | | |

506F11.EPS

Figure 11.  Typical Large Electrical System – Nursing Homes And Limited Care Facilities

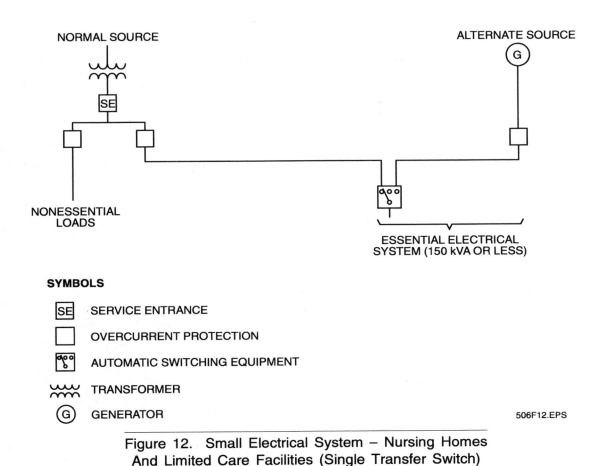

NORMAL SOURCE

ALTERNATE SOURCE

SE

NONESSENTIAL
LOADS

ESSENTIAL ELECTRICAL
SYSTEM (150 kVA OR LESS)

**SYMBOLS**

SE   SERVICE ENTRANCE

☐   OVERCURRENT PROTECTION

AUTOMATIC SWITCHING EQUIPMENT

TRANSFORMER

Ⓖ   GENERATOR

506F12.EPS

Figure 12.  Small Electrical System – Nursing Homes
And Limited Care Facilities (Single Transfer Switch)

The life safety branch shall be kept completely independent of all other equipment and wiring and will not enter the same cabinets, boxes, or raceways with other wiring except as follows:

- In a common junction box attached to exit or emergency lighting fixtures supplied from two sources
- In transfer switches
- In exit or emergency lighting fixtures supplied from two sources

The wiring of the critical branch will be authorized to reside in the same cabinets, boxes, or raceways of other circuits that are not part of the life safety branch.

The life safety branch must be installed and connected to the alternate power source to ensure that all specified functions in the applicable standards will be automatically restored to operation within ten seconds after the interruption of the normal source. The life safety branch supplies power for the following equipment, lighting, and receptacles:

- Hospital communications systems, where used for dissemination of instructions during emergencies.
- Task illumination battery charger for emergency battery-powered lighting unit(s) and selected receptacles at the generator set location.

- Illumination of means of exiting as is necessary for corridors, passageways, stairways and landings at exit doors, and all obligatory ways of approach to exits. Arrangements for switching to transfer patient corridor lighting in hospitals from general illumination circuits to night illumination circuits will be authorized provided only one of two circuits can be selected, and both circuits cannot be extinguished simultaneously.
- Exit direction and exit signs.
- Alarm and alerting systems, including fire alarms and alarms required for systems utilized for the piping of nonflammable medical gases.
- Elevator cab communication, control, lighting, and signal systems.
- Lighting in recreation and dining areas must be sufficient to illuminate exitways.

*CAUTION:*   No function other than those listed above may be connected to the life safety branch.

The critical branch must be installed and connected to the alternate power source in order that the equipment listed in NEC Section 517-43(a) shall be automatically restored to operation at appropriate time-lag intervals following the restoration of the life safety branch to operation. Its arrangement shall also provide for the additional connection of equipment listed in NEC Section 517-43(b) by either delayed automatic or manual operation.

The following equipment must be connected to the critical branch and arranged for delayed automatic connection to the alternate power source:

- Patient care areas—task illumination and selected receptacles in:
  – Medication preparation areas
  – Pharmacy dispensing areas
  – Nurses' stations (unless adequately lighted by corridor luminaires)
- Some pumps and other equipment required to operate for the safety of major apparatus and associated control systems and alarms.
- Smoke control and stair pressurization systems.
- Kitchen hood supply and/or exhaust systems, if required to operate during a fire in or under the hood.

The following equipment must be connected to the critical branch and arranged for either delayed automatic or manual connection to the alternate power source:

- Equipment to provide heating for patient rooms.

*Exception:* Heating of patient rooms during disruption of the normal source shall not be required under any of the following conditions:

- The outside design temperature is higher than +20°F (-6.7°C).
- The outside design temperature is lower than +20°F (-6.7°C) and where selected areas are provided for the needs of all confined patients, then only such areas need be heated.
- The facility is served by a dual source of normal power as described in NEC Section 517-44(c), Fine Print Note.
- In instances where disruption of power would result in elevators stopping between floors, **throwover** facilities shall be provided to allow temporary operation of any elevator for the release of passengers. For elevator cab lighting, control, and signal system requirements, see NEC Section 517-42(g).
- Additional illumination, receptacles, and equipment shall be permitted to be connected only to the critical branch.

## 4.0.0   SYSTEM CONSIDERATIONS

Additional considerations for health care facilities include voltage, current, and grounding requirements.

### 4.1.0   VOLTAGE

The proper selection, regulation, and utilization of voltages throughout health care facilities is of vital importance due to the extensive use of voltage-sensitive medical equipment where significant voltage rating variances exist. Medical equipment may be used for life-sustaining functions or diagnostics where it is imperative that the integrity of the equipment not be harmed by poorly regulated or applied voltages. The attributes and dynamics of the electrical system must enforce proper voltage control and regulation in order for adequate voltages to be supplied to all equipment under any operating condition.

### 4.1.1   Select System Voltages

The onsite utility voltage, loads served, facility size, building layout, requirements for expansion, voltage regulation requirements, and cost will determine the voltage levels selected at a health care facility. The system must be able to provide the proper voltage and regulation to all equipment under any circumstance.

Health care facilities will normally have power supplied at a medium-voltage level from the utility and then stepped down to either 480/277V or 208/120V. A 480V or 208V source is used to supply mechanical equipment such as fans, pumps, chillers, and medical equipment, including radiological apparatus, medical air pumps, and other support equipment (e.g., laboratory and kitchen equipment). 120V is the primary supply voltage and is used to supply receptacle and lighting loads throughout the hospital. 277V can be used to supply some equipment loads and/or lighting loads. In large health care facilities, 277V may be used to supply lighting in lieu of 120V, but this is a major decision and should be considered carefully.

The application of 277V lighting in hospitals differs from other commercial facilities because of the requirement for the four divisions of the electrical system (normal, critical branch, life safety branch, and equipment system). Applying 277V lighting results in having both 120/208V and 277/480V panels for all these systems on each floor or in each electrical room. There are no specific rules or regulations for the application of 277V lighting. Every application should be examined thoroughly to determine its plausibility.

### 4.1.2 Nominal Voltage

Once the nominal utilization voltages have been selected, the voltages of all medical equipment to be installed in the facility should be carefully checked to ensure proper application. If the equipment is not available in the system voltage, then "buck/boost" transformers should be used to supply the rated voltage to the equipment.

Equipment used in radiological functions is available in various three-phase as well as single-phase voltages. In order to plan for the proper installation of equipment, the manufacturer's data sheet is required to verify the voltage and tolerance requirements. A typical error in design is the use of single-phase, 230V-rated equipment on 208V systems. Another typical error occurs in the application of 380V European-manufactured radiological equipment in the United States. This equipment requires a dedicated transformer when applied on 480V or 208V systems.

### 4.1.3 Voltage Variations And Disturbances

Voltage variations in the sinusoidal waveform may be caused by numerous types of power system disturbances. Transient overvoltages and surges (spikes) are created by lightning strikes, capacitive switching, fault switching, arcing grounds, brush-type motors, or switching of inductive loads such as motors and radiological equipment. Voltage sags and dips are created by utility faults, motor starting, or improper grounding. Complete momentary loss of voltage is the result of utility switching operations, reclosing of the utility circuit breaker, surge arresting operations, or equipment failure.

The market maintains a wide variety of voltage protection, regulation, and conditioning equipment and devices. Surge arresters, voltage relays, transient voltage suppressors, shielded isolation transformers, voltage regulators, power conditioners, uninterruptible power supplies, or any combination of these devices may be incorporated to extinguish voltage variation problems. The type of equipment to install depends primarily on the nature of the voltage variation and the characteristic of the equipment to be protected.

Transient voltage suppressors, voltage relays, and surge arrestors are designed to eradicate overvoltages in order to protect distribution and utilization equipment. Shielded isolation transformers provide a clean, noise-free ground. They are generally unproductive in rejecting transients, but will provide some attenuation. Constant voltage transformers or voltage regulators are designed to control the output voltage regardless of variations of input voltage. The typical range of input voltage for which the output voltage will stay regulated is +10% to -20% or +15% to -15%. Other considerations for installing a voltage regulator, in addition to input voltage range, are regulator load sensitivity, load compatibility impedance, energy efficiency, and electrical isolation. Power conditioners typically combine isolation and/or transient suppression and regulation into one package. Uninterruptible power supplies provide a clean, constant voltage with a standby capacity for power failure and brief outages.

The first step toward solving a voltage variation problem is to accurately diagnose the exact problem. The application and installation of various voltage regulating, protection, or conditioning equipment without knowing exactly what the problem is and what is causing it will most likely not rectify the problem and could worsen the situation. A high-accuracy powerline analyzer is an effective tool for diagnosing voltage problems. The electrical service or a segment of the electrical system may be observed over a period of time so that voltage variations, including signal magnitude, variation duration, and time of occurrence can be recorded. The information from the analyzer is then processed and matched with medical equipment operational failure logs or reports to determine the exact problem.

Voltage variations in a health care facility will typically be recognized first in the operation or output of radiology, laboratory, and computerized equipment.

Current demands in radiological equipment are only momentary during an exposure. To ensure that voltage drops are within acceptable limits (normally 3% to 5%), a low impedance source should be used. When voltage regulation is not adequately maintained, X-ray tubes experience loss of life and equipment may malfunction.

Voltage regulators applied on radiology equipment feeders may not improve regulation because the pulse width of the equipment may be less than the response time of the regulator.

In hospitals, voltage variations and dips caused by motor starting must be maintained within the parameters dictated by computerized equipment and radiology. This is typically accomplished by installing diminished voltage starters on large motors. The designer should carefully study the installation of motor starters to minimize system voltage losses within reasonable costs.

## 4.2.0  CURRENT

Load equipment is the determining factor for full load and overload current requirements in a health care facility power system. However, short circuit current requirements are established principally by the power sources and, to a small degree, by the load equipment.

The current flow during a fault at any point in a system is not directly related to the load on the system, but is controlled by the impedance of circuits and equipment from the source or sources to the point of fault. System additions increase the capacity to handle a growing load while not affecting the normal load at existing portions of the system, but may significantly increase the number of fault currents.

The fault current contribution in some health care facilities can differ in magnitude and decay rate between the normal and alternate power sources. This can occur when:

- The normal power source from a public utility experiences a high fault current capability, and the common service point is removed by several modifications and transmission circuits from the utility generation sources.
- The alternate power supply incorporates a relatively small onsite generator or generators and relatively short distribution circuits between the alternate electrical power supply and essential electrical power circuitry.

In order for a fault to occur within the essential electrical power system, the fault current magnitude from the normal power source would be significant and have a slow decay rate. For all practical purposes, the decay rate of the alternating current rms portion of the total fault current could be considered insignificant, while for the same fault conditions the fault current magnitude from the alternate power source would be proportionately small and have a fast decay rate. Since the essential electrical system can be fed power from either source, these factors should be taken into account when rating and setting protective devices.

In order to correctly apply protective equipment, choose adequately-rated system operating equipment and calculate the voltage dips of impact loads such as motor starting, the nature and calculations of short-circuit current must be understood. More information can be found in IEEE Standard 141-1976 (Chapter 5) [17] and IEEE Standard 241-1983 (Chapter 9) [8] on the fundamentals and procedures of fault current calculations.

## 4.3.0  GROUNDING

The term *grounding* is typically used in electrical power systems to encompass both equipment grounding and system grounding. ANSI/NFPA 70-1996 defines these and other terms used when discussing this topic. Becoming familiar with these definitions will establish a more thorough understanding of grounding principles.

Both the electrical system and the equipment are grounded in a health care facility. Special attention to grounding requirements is needed for subsystems and equipment involved in operating rooms, anesthetizing areas, patient care locations, and other special locations.

## 4.3.1 Equipment Grounding

The grounding of equipment is the interconnection and grounding of non-electrical conducting material that either envelopes or is close to electrical power components. The purpose of grounding is to prevent electrical shock hazards and fire hazards caused by electrical discharges. In order to obtain equipment grounding, the grounding conductor circuit must be designed and properly installed to provide a sufficiently low impedance path and an acceptable ground fault current-carrying capability both in magnitude and duration.

Alternating current (AC) flows in the path of least impedance; direct current (DC) flows in the path of least resistance. The lowest impedance path will be closest to the power conductors, as in a ground conductor installed with the power conductors or the metal raceway surrounding the power conductors. In order to obtain and maintain a low impedance ground current return circuit, junctions and terminations must be properly installed. Metal joints must have good contact to prevent sparking during fault conditions. Adequate connections between equipment ground busses and/or housings and metal raceways have to be provided. Also, the components within the ground return circuit, ground conductor junctions, etc., have to have a sufficient ground fault current displacement potential to avoid thermal distress for any form and durations of fault escalations permitted by the overcurrent protection system.

## 4.3.2 System Grounding

The term *system grounding* signifies the type of grounding applied to the electrical system. The basic reasons for system grounding are:

- It restricts the variances of electrical potential between all uninsulated conductors in a local or specific area.
- It provides isolation of defective equipment and circuits where a fault occurs.
- It restricts overvoltages appearing on the system under various fault conditions.

Systems where no ground is present and a fault condition occurs will, in some circumstances, resonate and create an overvoltage within the system. This overvoltage can be sufficient to produce extreme shock hazard conditions to which health care facility personnel and patients are exposed. It can also cause electrical equipment failure due to insulation breakdown. Equipment lasting through an overvoltage occurrence will most likely have lost a large portion of its useful life. Therefore, it is recommended that system grounding be used for all health care facilities.

Several methods are available to ground a system, including neutral grounding, line grounding, mid-phase grounding, etc. The method for grounding most preferred for health care facilities is neutral grounding, since the system neutral is normally available. This will avoid the special system operating precautions required when using other grounding systems.

- *Selection of system grounding points* – In order to achieve the advantages of neutral grounding in every part of the system, it is essential to ground at every voltage level. Each voltage level may be grounded at the neutral lead of a generator, power transformer bank, or neutral-deriving grounding transformer provided they meet the requirements of NEC Section 250-24(c). When two or more major source bus sections are present, each section should have at least one grounded neutral point. If two or more power sources per bus section exist, provisions should be incorporated for grounding at least two sources on each section.

- *Neutral circuit arrangements* – Once the method of grounding and the grounding point are selected for the individual power system, determine how many source generator or transformer neutrals (or both) will be utilized for grounding and whether every neutral will be connected separately to ground or a neutral bus will be employed with a single ground connection.

- *Source neutral(s), medium voltage* – Within a health care facility power system, the medium-voltage portion is normally the three-phase, three-wire system where the neutral is not used as a conductor. Therefore, the generator, source, or transformer neutrals can be grounded or resistance grounded. In resistance grounding, the system neutral is connected in series with a resistor to ground. Resistance grounding is often preferred when no direct connection to lighting exists. This method has the following advantages:

  - Reduction of electric shock hazard to personnel caused by stray ground fault current in the ground return path.
  - Reduction of burn damage in ground-faulted electric equipment (e.g., motors, generators, switchgear, etc.)
  - Reduction of thermal and mechanical stress in circuits and equipment carrying fault current.

  The disadvantages are as follows:

  - Line-to-line voltage-rated units must be applied, losing some degree of overvoltage protection. Line-to-neutral voltage-rated surge arresters are not usable.
  - Added cost of the resistor and possible additional cost of relaying.

The use of individual resistors is preferred to a common resistor when one or two sources are connected. However, when more than two sources are involved, the ground current is increased each time a source is added, raising current levels to an undesirable high. Each resistor must be rated for sufficient current capabilities to ensure satisfactory relaying when operating independently. Unfortunately, the total ground current with several resistors will be several times the minimum required for effective relaying. A simple solution to this situation is to consider the use of only one resistor.

- *Source neutral(s), low voltage* – A health care facility low-voltage system is usually a three-phase, four-wire system in which the neutral wire is used as a circuit conductor. Therefore, the service source neutral should be grounded to allow neutral loading as well as meet the requirements of NEC Section 250-20(b)-2.

The common neutral conductor can be effectively grounded at one point where the power supply consists of services that are dual-fed in a common enclosure or placed together in separate enclosures and use a secondary tie. At least one of the power supplies—usually normal—is considered the service and its neutral(s) should be effectively grounded. Both power supply neutrals can be effectively grounded if the normal and AC alternate power supply are not electrically connected.

Service continuity can be affected depending on the equipment grounding conductors, system arrangement, and type of grounding system installed. Grounding conductors and connections should be arranged so that any deviate neutral current will not exist and ground fault current will flow in low impedance, anticipated paths in order to protect personnel from electrical shock and provide proper operation of the circuit protective equipment.

Systems are required to be solidly grounded when phase-to-neutral loads are employed. However, 480V and 600V systems may use high-resistance grounding or may be ungrounded where a grounding circuit conductor is not used to supply phase-to-neutral loads. High-resistance grounded systems should afford a higher degree of service continuity than solidly grounded systems. Ungrounded systems are not recommended since they are subject to overvoltage stress due to resonance occurring during ground fault conditions.

NEC Section 250-20(d)-FPN 1 states that when the AC alternate power supply (one or more generators or a separate utility service) and its wiring system are electrically interconnected with the normal power supply, either by the neutral or phase conductors, or both, then the alternate power supply is not a separately derived system. Therefore, its neutral is not permitted to be effectively grounded, as shown in *Figure 13*. This is to prevent objectionable neutral load current from flowing in the system ground conductors. The equipment grounding conductor defined as "EGC" in *Figure 13* is still required; therefore, the generator neutral must still be insulated from the machine frame.

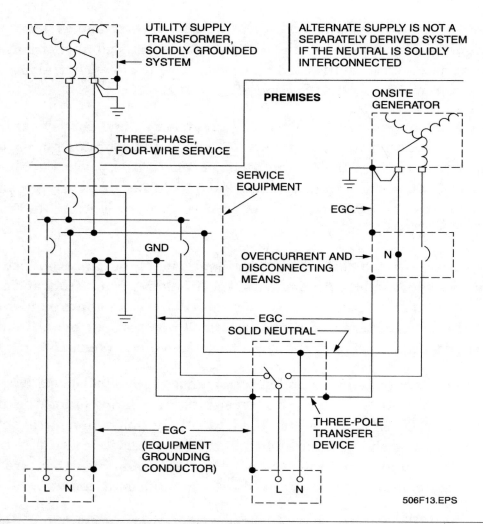

Figure 13. Solidly Interconnected Neutral Conductor Grounded At Service Equipment

NEC Section 250-20(d)-FPN 1 states that when the AC alternate power supply (one or more generators or a separate utility service) and its wiring system are not electrically interconnected with the normal power supply wiring system, either by the neutral or phase conductors, or both, then the alternate power supply is a separately derived system and its neutral is grounded at the alternate power supply in addition to the neutral(s) of the normal power supply. A system in which the neutral and phase conductors between the alternate and normal power supply wiring systems are not electrically interconnected by the use of a four-pole or three-pole transfer device with neutral contacts is shown in *Figure 14*. The onsite generator is considered a separately derived system and its neutral is effectively grounded. Because the neutral conductor is isolated between power systems, grounding of the generator neutral will not provide a path for deviate neutral load current to flow in the system ground conductors.

The decision of whether or not to switch the neutral should be weighed against the cost of employing a transfer device capable of switching all power conductors versus a transfer device capable of switching only the phase conductors and, if required, the necessary additional ground fault monitoring equipment.

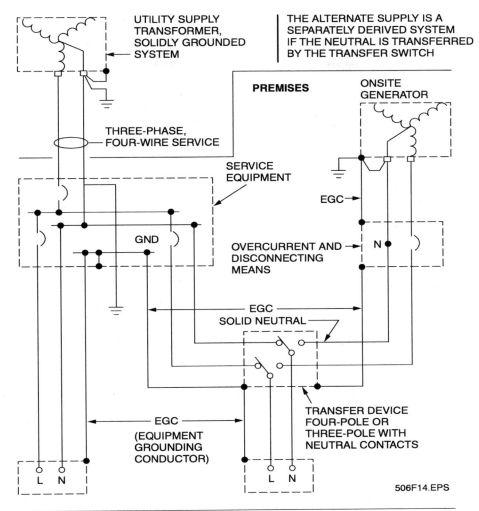

Figure 14. Transferred Neutral Conductor Grounded At
Service Equipment And Source Of Alternate Power Supply

When considering whether or not to switch neutrals, the following application problems should be considered:

- In order to provide maximum service continuity, the transfer device is placed as close to the load as possible. The distance between the normal power source, transfer device, and emergency generator and the neutral conductor would be excessive. For a system not switching the neutral, a direct neutral tie between the normal and emergency system should be used to prevent the load from being transferred to an ungrounded emergency power supply. This requirement would be needed for a system with neutral switching capability.

- A system design in which the neutral is not switched will need additional current sensor monitoring in order to prevent unnecessary tripping of the normal power source protector for a ground fault occurring when the load is supplied from the emergency power source.

The decision of whether or not to ground the AC emergency power supply at its source will not affect the ability to furnish the proper ground fault relaying. However, ground fault protection that is applicable to radial power systems is not necessarily appropriate for multi-source systems.

## 4.4.0 GROUNDING SYSTEM TESTING

One of the line conductors is deliberately grounded in a conventional grounded distribution system, typically at the service entrance or distribution panel. The grounded conductor in this system will be identified as the neutral conductor. The other line conductor(s) is/are the high or hot side of the line. Loads supplied by this particular distribution system are served by both the neutral and high sides of the line.

In this system, a grounding conductor is provided in addition to the high and neutral conductors. One end is connected to the neutral at the point where the neutral is grounded and the other end is connected to the loads. For example, the load connection point may be a convenience receptacle, with the grounding conductor terminating at the grounding terminal of that receptacle.

This grounding conductor can be an independent wire traveling from the receptacle back to the remote grounding connection where it will couple with the neutral conductor. If the conductor does not make any intermediate ground contacts between the receptacle and remote ground, the impedance of the connection between the receptacle and the remote ground is predominantly the resistance of the grounding conductor itself. However, if the receptacle is also interconnected with the remote ground point by any metallic structure or conduit, the impedance of the circuit between the receptacle and remote ground is no longer predictable. Nor is it as easy to measure accurately, although the impedance will be less than that of the grounding wire itself due to the additional parallel paths.

It will soon become clear that it is not necessary to know or measure the absolute value of the apparent impedance between the remote ground point and the grounding contact of an outlet with any great accuracy. This will be covered later in this module.

Ideally, and under no-fault conditions, the grounding system described above is supposed to be carrying no current at all. If that were true, then no voltage differences would be found between the exposed conductive surfaces of any electrical appliances that are grounded to the grounding contacts of the receptacles from which they are powered. Likewise, provided that no current is flowing in these interconnections, there would be no voltage differences between these appliances and any other exposed metal surfaces that are also interconnected with the grounding system.

However, these conditions never occur and, even if there were no "faults" present within an appliance, residual or leakage current does flow in the grounding conductor of each of the appliances. This produces a voltage difference between the chassis of that appliance and the grounding contact of the receptacle that supplies it. This residual current can produce voltage differences between other appliances plugged into other receptacles on the system.

Fortunately, these residual current are tiny, and for reasonably low grounding circuit impedances, the resulting voltage differences are negligible.

Leakage current can become a fault condition when the insulation breaks down between the chassis of an appliance and the high side of the line. The magnitude of the fault depends on the nature of the breakdown or a dead short circuit within an appliance, and is limited only by the resistance of the appliance power line conductors and the power distribution system.

In the case of a short circuit, the impedance of the grounding circuit, as measured between the grounding contact of the receptacle that supplies the defective appliance and the remote ground point where the neutral and grounding conductors are combined, should be so small that a large enough fault current will flow to ensure a rapid fault of the circuit by the overcurrent protection device that serves that receptacle.

For example, in a 15-ampere branch circuit, a fault current of 30 or more amperes would be needed to force a rapid opening of the branch circuit overcurrent protection device. This corresponds to a circuit impedance of three ohms or less, of which one ohm or less is contributed by the grounding system.

The chassis of the defective appliance rises many volts above other grounded surfaces in the same location during the time this large fault current flows in the grounding system. The hazard represented by this condition is minimized by the fact that it exists for only a short period of time. Unless a patient contacts both the faulty appliance and a grounded surface during this period of time, there is no real hazard. The amount of an applied voltage required to produce a serious shock hazard increases as its duration decreases, so the rapidity with which the circuit is interrupted helps reduce shock hazard even if patient contact should occur.

If the appliance defect is not enough to create an immediate circuit interruption, the effect of this intermediate level of fault current appearing on different exposed conductive surfaces in the patient care area must be considered.

Since all fault current flows through the grounding conductor of the defective appliance power cord, the first effect is to raise the potential of this appliance above that of the receptacle that supplies it by an amount proportional to the power cord grounding conductor resistance. This resistance is required to be less than 0.15 ohm, so fault current of 20 amperes or less, which will not trip the branch circuit overcurrent protective device, will increase the potential of the defective appliance above the grounding contact of its supply receptacle by three volts or less. This amount of voltage is not hazardous for casual contact.

Grounding contacts of all receptacles can be affected if a fault current enters the grounding system at the grounding contact of any receptacle within the patient care area. This fault current could produce a significant difference of potential (voltage) between grounding contacts and other grounded surfaces, such as metal building frames and pipes.

If a single grounded spot is picked for reference (for example, a plumbing fixture under the sink in the patient care area), then the voltage variance is measured between that reference and the grounding contact of a receptacle, produced by injecting a known current into that contact. This provides a direct measurement of the effectiveness of the grounding system within the patient care area. This figure can be defined as an amount of volts per fault current ampere. The ratio of volts to amperes is line impedance; but since the exact path taken by the fault current is now known, and since the way in which the reference point is interconnected with the grounding system is not known, it cannot be stated that this value is the impedance between the receptacle and some specific point, such as the joining of the neutral and grounding conductors. However, it can be said that this measured value of effective impedance is characteristic of the effectiveness with which the grounding system minimizes voltage differences between supposedly grounded objects in the patient care area that are produced by ground faults in appliances used in that area. This impedance, which characterizes the ability of the grounding system to maintain nearly equal potential conditions within the patient care area, is of prime importance in the examination of shock hazard. This impedance is not necessarily the same as the impedance between the receptacle and remote ground point, which controls the magnitude of the short circuit current involved in tripping the branch circuit overcurrent protective device.

Neutral-to-ground faults can also produce fault current within the grounding system, which would allow some current to flow in the neutral and some in the ground. This type of fault is often the cause of interference on EKG (electrocardiograph) and EEG (electroencephalograph) electronic equipment. It is not easily recognized because, except for 60 Hz interference, the equipment works properly. It can be found by creating a substantial change in the line-to-line load and noting changes in the ground-to-reference voltage.

### 4.4.1   Grounding, Voltage, And Leakage Current Measurement Circuits

Grounding circuits to handle both fault and leakage current safely requires following Chapter 3 of ANSI/NFPA 99-1996 and NEC Article 250. It also helps to practice good workmanship and to apply some techniques not covered in those manuals.

The effectiveness of the grounding system is produced through the installation of the metal raceway, the green grounding wire, and all of the other building metals. Measurements have shown that it is the metal raceway and the building steel which contribute most of the effective grounding path of less than 10 milliohms at the receptacle. This includes the plug-to-receptacle impedance. The green grounding wire then becomes an alternate (rather than a primary) grounding path.

Each receptacle should have a good jumper grounding connection to the metal raceway at the receptacle location in addition to having the green grounding wire connecting these points to the grounding bus in the distribution panel. These grounding connections must be tight at each receptacle and all metal raceway joints must be secure and tight.

An oscilloscope or spectrum analyzer should be used when measuring the voltage potential in connection with the power distribution grounding system in order to view and measure components of leakage current and voltage differences at any frequency. These instruments may be inconvenient for standard testing. An alternative is to use a metering system that weights the contribution to the meter reading of the different components of the signal being measured in accordance with their probable effect.

A meter designed for this function would have an impedance of approximately 1,000 ohms and a frequency response characteristic that is flat to 1 kHz. It would fall at the rate of 20 decibels per decade to 100 kHz and then remain level to 1 MHz or greater. This frequency response characteristic could be achieved by design of the internal circuits of the amplifier that precedes the indicating instrument, or through the appropriate choice of a feedback network around the amplifier.

When a meter designed for these particular measurements is unavailable, a general purpose millivoltmeter can be created by adding a frequency response shaping network ahead of the meter. *Figure 15* depicts one such suggested network.

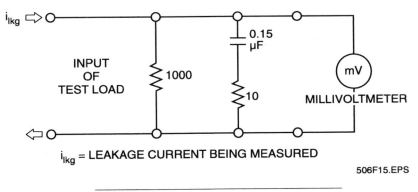

Figure 15.   Basic Current Measuring

The circuit shown in *Figure 15* is particularly useful for the measurement of leakage current, where current measured is acquired from a circuit whose source impedance is high compared to 1,000 ohms. Under these conditions, the voltage developed across the millivoltmeter will be proportional to the impedance of the network. The network impedance will be 1,000 ohms at low frequencies, 10 ohms at high frequencies, and the transition between these two values will occur in the frequency range between one kHz and 1,000 kHz.

The basic low-frequency sensitivity for every microampere of leakage current will deflect one millivolt of meter reading.

The millivoltmeter should have a flat frequency response to well beyond 100 kHz. If the meter impedance is lower than 100 kilohms, then the 1,000-ohm resistor can be raised to a higher value, such that the impedance of that resistor in parallel with the meter will still be 1,000 ohms. The millivoltmeter's own input impedance must be very large compared to 1,000 ohms (one kilohm).

*Figure 15* depicts a circuit which can be employed for most voltage difference measurements because the source impedance will be very low compared to 1,000 ohms; however, the frequency response of the measurement system will remain flat. If any high-frequency components created by pickup from nearby radio frequency transmitters appear on the circuit being measured, they will not be attenuated and the meter reading will be higher than normal.

For meter readings below any defined limits, the possible error is of no consequence. However in borderline cases it could be significant. *Figure 16* provides an example of advanced current measuring in a frequency response shaping network.

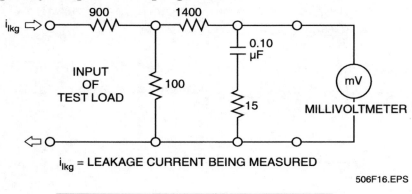

Figure 16.  Advanced Current Measuring

In this example, the source being measured is separated from the frequency response shaping network by the combination of the 900-ohm and 100-ohm resistors. This independence is attained at a loss in signal delivered to the millivoltmeter. The fundamental low-frequency sensitivity of this metering circuit is one millivolt of meter reading for ten microamperes of leakage current or, on a voltage basis, one millivolt of meter reading for ten millivolts at the input terminals of the network.

The input impedance of the millivoltmeter should be at least 150 kilohms with a frequency response that is flat beyond 100 kHz.

The capacitors and resistors should be mounted in a metal container close to the millivoltmeter to avoid stray pickup by the leads going to the meter in either of the networks.

## 4.5.0 SYSTEM PROTECTION AND COORDINATION

The equipment and system protection devices safeguard the health care facility power system from overcurrent and transient overvoltage conditions that can result in equipment loss, system failure, and hazards to patients and personnel. To accomplish this protective function, protective equipment such as surge capacitors, surge arrestors, reactors, and circuit interruption devices are installed. All protection devices must be put to use within their ratings of current, voltage, and frequency. Additionally, factors such as temperature, altitude, seismic activity, etc. at the location or site where the devices are to be installed should be considered. Available standards will provide information such as description, rating applications and limits, and derating factors to which the protective devices must conform.

### 4.5.1 Protection

The protective devices installed in a system are inactive until initiated to clear a fault or some other unplanned problem or disturbance. These devices can be credited with lessening the extent and time period of the interruptions, the hazards of personnel injury, and property damage. Therefore, the protective devices within an electric power system act as a form of insurance.

It would be neither practical nor cost effective to construct a fault-proof power system. Hence, systems today are designed to render reasonable insulation, clearances, etc. to prevent faults from occurring. Even with the best designs, materials deteriorate and the possibility of faults increases with age. All systems are subject to short circuits and ground faults. A knowledge of the effect of faults on system voltage and current values is necessary in order to design suitable protection.

### 4.5.2 Current-Sensing Protectors

Current-sensing detectors within protectors should detect phase to phase and double-phase to ground as well as single-phase to ground and three-phase short circuits. The current strength of those faults involving ground depends to a large extent on the system grounding method (i.e., the magnitude of ground impedance and, in low-voltage systems, the arcing fault impedance).

The design of a protective system involves two independent although interrelated steps:

- The determination of the proper device in order to accomplish the task.
- Selecting the correct protector ampere rating or setting for the devices so they will operate selectively with other devices to disconnect the faulty portion of the system with as little effect on the remainder of the system as possible.

In order for protective devices to be insensitive to conditions such as normal operation, full load current, permissible overload current, and inrush current, they must be properly selected.

These devices should also be chosen for their pickup current and short operating times. Additionally, the devices must be coordinated so that the protective device closest to the fault opens before upstream devices open. Determining the ratings and settings for protective devices requires cognizant knowledge of the NEC requirements for the protection of cables, motors, and transformers. Deciding on the settings for the overcurrent protective devices in a power system can be an overwhelming task. Health care facility electrical service continuity requires that interrupting equipment operates selectively as stated in ANSI/NFPA 99-1996 (Chapter 8) and ANSI/NFPA 70-1996 (Article 517). Complete selectivity and maximum safety to personnel are sometimes competing objectives, so a total study of short circuits, coordination, and device protection should be performed. This study should determine the available short circuit current at each panel and at every component throughout the system. Then, coordination curves are drawn to determine whether or not the overcurrent devices are selectively coordinated at the various available fault current.

The component withstand ratings are then examined to verify if NEC Section 110-10 is met. This form of analysis is used when designing the protection for a new power system, when analyzing protection and coordination conditions in an existing system, or as a valuable maintenance reference when checking the calibration of protective devices. The coordination curves provide a permanent record of the time/current operating relationship of the entire protection system. Normally, the coordination plot is created on graph paper with current as the horizontal (x) axis and time in seconds as the vertical (y) axis. A selection of the most suitable current and time settings must be made for the device to render the best possible protection, safety to personnel and electric equipment, and also to operate selectively with other protective devices in order to disconnect the faulted equipment with as little disturbance as possible to the rest of the system. IEEE Standard 141-1976 (Chapter 4) [17] and IEEE Standard 241-1983 (Chapter 9) [8] provide details and examples of a coordination study for various system equipment and operating conditions.

A logical approach to performing a protective device coordination study is as follows:

- Fabricate a one-line diagram of the system.
- Record pertinent data on the one-line diagram:
  – Distribution equipment ratings
  – Load equipment ratings
  – Impedance data
- Perform calculations to determine short circuit current.
- Determine equipment operating and protection ratings as defined by ANSI/NFPA 70-1996, equipment nameplates, **ICEA** texts or handbooks, manufacturer bulletins, etc. List results on the one-line diagram.
- Ascertain the protective device ratings required to meet the system voltage, frequency, continuous current, and short circuit duty, as well as any unusual conditions due to site application such as altitude, seismic, temperature, etc. Also, take into account any UL, NEC, or local code requirements. List the ratings chosen on the one-line diagram.

- Select a provisional protective device full load rating based on load conditions. List the device on the one-line diagram.
- Acquire characteristic time current curves of all protective device detectors relating to the system under study.
- Create time/current plots to establish device settings and be able to analyze degree of coordination and selectivity concluded.

### 4.5.3 Ground Fault Protection

Phase overcurrent device settings are primarily established by the load requirements. They are set to be insensitive to full load and inrush current and to provide selectivity between downstream and upstream devices. The phase overcurrent device cannot distinguish between normal load current and low magnitude ground fault short circuit current of the same magnitude. Hence, ground fault detection is used to supplement the phase overcurrent devices to provide proper protection.

Health care facilities are required by ANSI/NFPA 70-1996 (Article 517) and ANSI/NFPA 99-1996 (Chapters 8 and 9) to have a normal and emergency power supply. For those health care facilities, the application of ground fault protection requires additional attention.

- When selecting ground fault protective devices, the system wiring configuration and ground current must be considered.
- Numerous types of ground current can exist in any power system:
  - Insulation leakage current from appliances, portable cleaning equipment and/ or tools, etc. Typically, the magnitude of this current is very low (in the order of microamperes in small systems to several amperes in larger systems).
  - Improper connections or metallic objects forced between phase and ground can create bolted-fault ground current. For this type of fault, the current magnitude may be equal to or less than the three-phase fault current.
  - Broken phase conductors touching earth, insulation failure, loose connections, construction accidents, rodents, dirt, debris, etc. can create arcing-fault ground current. The current magnitude may be very low in relation to the three-phase fault current.
  - Lightning discharge through a surge arrester may produce a current that is quite large depending on the energy in the lightning strike.
  - Capacitor charging current and other current surges.
  - Static charge can be produced by many sources.
- Methods of equipping the electrical system to handle or prevent these types of ground current are varied, such as:
  - Use a higher order of insulation and monitor for leakage at low level. When leaks are detected, remove power immediately.
  - Discharge lightning and static charges by applying properly-rated grounding conductors and grids.

- For bolted and/or arcing faults, solutions involve a dual approach. First, minimize the probability of fault initiation by:
  - Paying particular attention to system design and to the settings of protective devices
  - Choosing equipment that is isolated by compartments within grounded metal cases
  - Choosing equipment that incorporates rack-out, drawout, or stab-in features, thereby decreasing the need for working on powered components.
  - Outfitting an insulated bus to prevent the occurrence of ground faults, particularly on the line side of mains where the utility does not provide ground fault protection
  - Using appropriate installation practices and supervision.
  - Protecting equipment from unusual environmental conditions or operations.
  - Completing a thorough cleanup immediately before initial energization of equipment
  - Performing regular and thorough maintenance procedures.
  - Practicing good daily housekeeping.

  Second, remove the defective circuit quickly so that damage will be minimized.

- The designer must balance economics against the cost of equipment damage to decide on a pragmatic ground fault protection system. The designer must keep in mind that the amount of equipment damage will increase the extent of power service loss. This will inevitably increase the risk to patients. There is no single solution for all power systems; each should be analyzed individually. In this analysis, the important factors to be considered are:
  - *Selection of the power system* – The ground fault detection plan is a function of system arrangement and voltage level. Most health care facility applications are low voltage with a fundamental arrangement which is the easiest to analyze and provides a straightforward protection system design. The situation becomes more extensive and involved with secondary selective and spot network circuit arrangements.
  - *Neutral circuit* – A three-phase, four-wire power system with a radial neutral exhibits few problems. For a power system neutral that is used as a load conductor and looped or uninterrupted between alternate power sources and grounded only at the sources or grounded downstream, extreme care should be taken in applying ground fault protection. Each circuit should be checked for deviate returning neutral and/or ground fault current that could cause the ground fault unit to become desensitized or faulty. A basic procedure to check the application is to draw a one-line diagram of the power system and superimpose presumed neutral loads and ground faults. Trace the current flow to determine the effects on the ground fault units. Remember, the return current takes the path of least resistance (impedance). A given path, although initially the lowest impedance path, may not remain the lowest as the magnitude of current increases. It might be determined that the neutral conductors present such good paths for deviate returning current that the only solution to providing ground fault protection is to use ground differential or ground summation schemes.

- *Ground return path* – The ground return path should be structured in such a way as to present a low impedance path and provide an adequate ground fault current-carrying capability to hold the voltage gradients along its path to less than shock hazard thresholds. This design will also allow sensitive detection of ground fault current.
- *Desired reliability* – Radial systems are very reliable for general purpose use, but life support and high value continuity uses rate the redundancy exhibited by the higher order systems. The system designer must confront the increased engineering analysis that accompanies the higher levels, including continuity of service, diminished false outages, and improved level of equipment protection. All of these considerations must be balanced against cost.

- *Ground fault detection systems* – Ground fault current can be monitored either as it flows out to the fault or on its return to the neutral point of the source transformer or generator. When monitoring the return fault current only, the ground return conductor is monitored. Caution is required to ensure that the returning ground fault current bypasses the outgoing monitoring current transformer but does not bypass the current transformer monitoring the return ground fault current. When monitoring the outgoing fault current, the current values of all power conductors are monitored either individually or collectively. The ground fault relay pickup level is variable and may be outfitted with an adjustable time delay. Operation of the relay energizes a trip mechanism on the interrupting device. Selectivity is accomplished by way of a time delay and/or current setting or blocking function. Zone selectivity can be achieved by using a differential or blocking scheme.
- *Medium-voltage systems* – Medium-voltage systems for health care facilities are typically three-phase, three-wire systems with the neutrals solidly grounded or resistance grounded. When the neutral is solidly grounded, the ground fault current magnitude is relatively high and a residually-connected ground fault relay is usually applied. This residually-connected ground fault relay, as shown in *Figure 17*, will monitor the outgoing ground fault current.

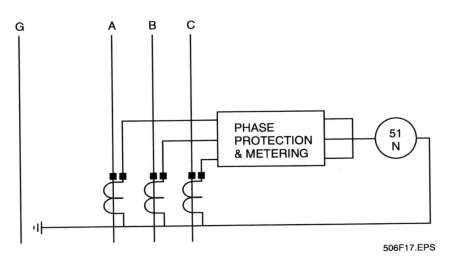

506F17.EPS

Figure 17.  Residually-Connected Ground Fault Relay

When the neutral is resistance grounded, the ground fault current magnitude is comparatively low—1,200 amps or less—and a ground sensor-coupled ground fault relay is normally utilized. *Figure 18* depicts a ground sensor relay that monitors the returning ground fault current.

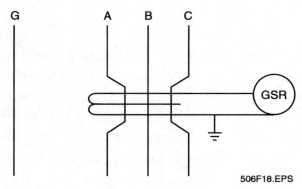

506F18.EPS

Figure 18.   Ground Sensor Ground Fault Relay

*Figure 19* depicts a ground sensor relay that monitors the returning ground fault current in a resistance grounded circuit.

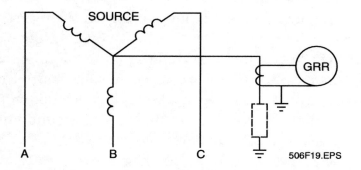

506F19.EPS

Figure 19.   Ground Sensor Ground Fault Relay With Ground Resistor

- *Low-voltage systems* – Low-voltage systems for health care facilities are generally three-phase, four-wire systems. The normal power source neutral is effectively grounded. When required, the AC alternate power source neutral may or may not be effectively grounded at the alternate source. The ground fault scheme selected will depend on how the AC alternate power supply is grounded.

For feeder circuits having no neutral conductor requirements and three-phase, three-wire loads, or for three-phase, four-wire loads where the neutral conductors are not electrically intercoupled between power sources on the load side of the feeder breaker, residually connected, ground sensor, or integral ground fault relays (*Figures 20, 21,* and *22*) are appropriate for the feeder breakers.

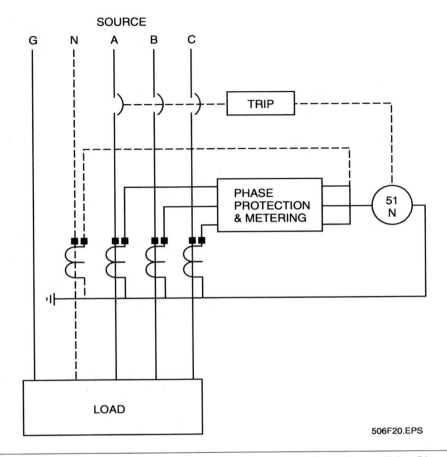

Figure 20. Residually-Connected Ground Fault Relay With Shunt Trip Circuit Breaker

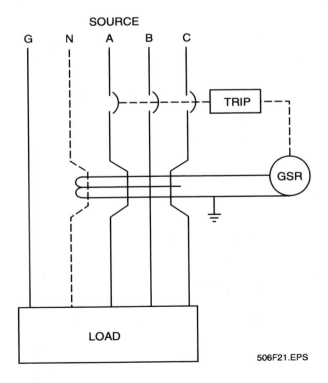

Figure 21. Ground Sensor Fault Relay

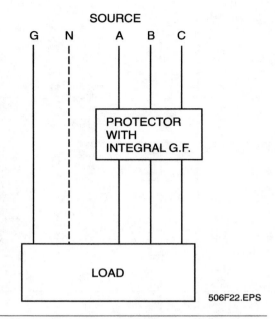

Figure 22.   Integral Ground Fault Relay

For feeder circuits with neutral conductors, where the neutral conductors are electrically intercoupled amid power sources on the load side of the feeder breaker, ground fault summation plans will be applicable. *Figure 23* is an example of such a circuit.

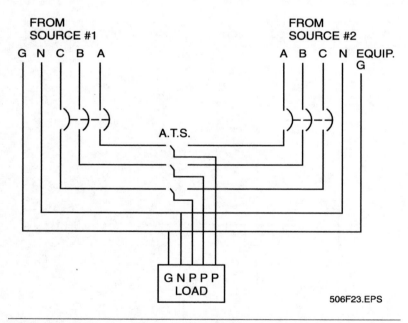

Figure 23.   Dual Source Electrically Interconnected Circuit

When power systems have no neutral conductor requirements (three-phase, three-wire systems), or when the necessary neutral conductors for the system are radial down to the loads (no neutral interconnections or *interties* exist, except through ground connections at the sources), ground sensor, residually-connected, or integral ground fault relays *(Figures 19, 20,* and *21)* may be used for main and tie breakers.

For power systems utilizing neutral conductor interties or several interties amid power sources within the system, standard ground fault relaying will not operate properly for the main, tie, or feeders supplying loads whose power source can be fulfilled from the normal or emergency power supply. Summation plans will be needed for these circuits. Referring to *Figure 24* as an example, the ground fault current return path from the transferable load to the onsite generator is through the main bonding jumper in the service equipment and the neutral conductor from the service equipment to the generator. When a fault occurs as shown at the load equipment, the ground fault current following the return path described earlier will flow through the current sensor. If adequate in magnitude, it will energize the ground fault relay, tripping the main service disconnect even though the ground fault is on a circuit supplied by the generator. To prevent this outage, a summation plan should be initiated in preference to the ground return scheme presently applied.

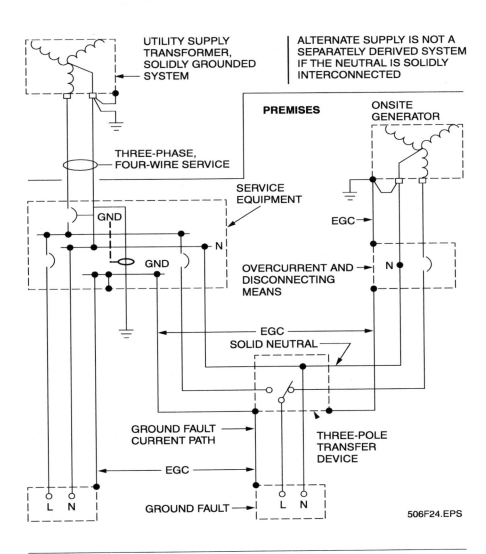

Figure 24.  Ground Fault Current Return Path To Alternate Supply (Neutral Conductor Grounded At Service Equipment Only)

Numerous summation designs are applicable and when taking into account all system coupling possibilities, it becomes impractical to list all relevant schemes and their modifications. However, a common ground fault relaying system is depicted in *Figures 25* and *26* for a health care facility power system which consists of normal and alternate power supplies. The power systems shown in *Figure 25* incorporate an electrical power conductor interconnection between power supplies. Note the ground fault relaying scheme required for the power system shown in *Figure 25*. In both *Figures 25* and *26*, ground fault relay R2 is optional.

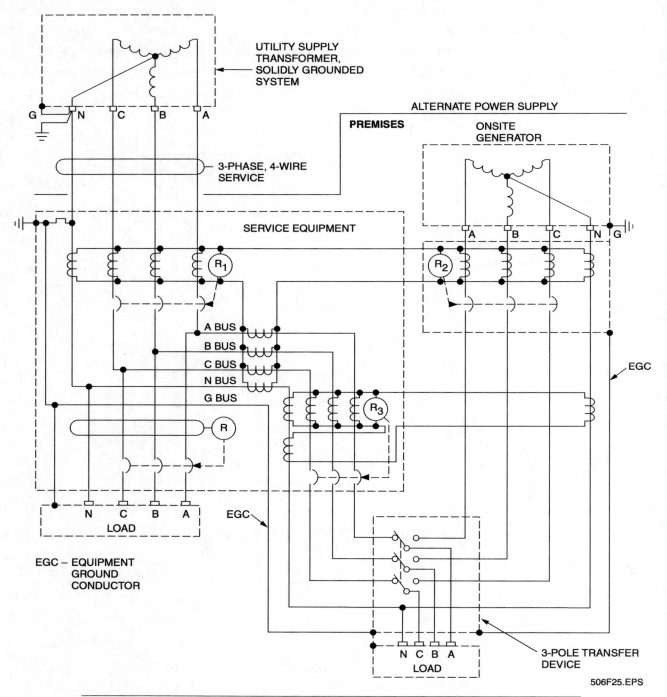

Figure 25.  Ground Fault For A Normal And Alternate Power Supply With An Electrical Power Conductor (Neutral) Interconnection Between Supplies

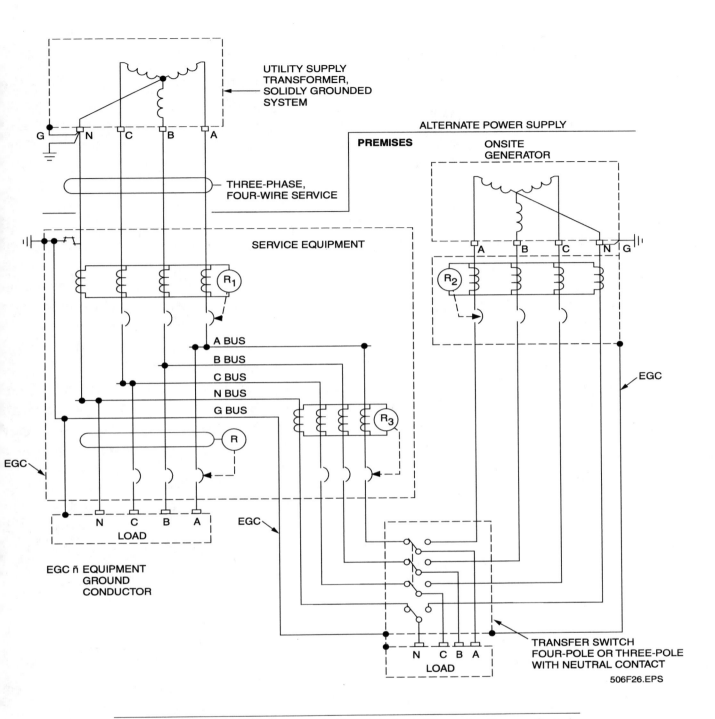

Figure 26. Ground Fault For A Normal And Alternate Power Supply With No Electrical Power Conductor Interconnection Between Supplies

A primary factor in the design and planning of hospitals and health care facilities is the electrical power system. In recognition of this, it is vitally important that the electrical engineer designing a hospital find the correct electrical power sources, both normal and emergency, because this can affect life-and-death situations.

### 5.1.0    GENERAL

Generally, hospitals have two sources of available power: normal and emergency. It is vital that the wiring devices on emergency power be easily identified. This reduces the time wasted in locating receptacles to power life support equipment when seconds can be critical. Devices are identified by using a distinctive color such as red, or by labeling. Identification using a distinctive color is not only easier and less expensive than labeling, but may prevent later confusion. For example, when painters remove the lettered emergency and normal coverplates, there is no longer a distinction between devices. Also, since receptacles in critical care areas must have panelboard and circuit number labels, the device coverplates tend to become cluttered. The distinctive color is also easily spread into other portions of the emergency systems (such as lighting control) to preserve uniformity. Thought should be given to using lighted emergency power receptacles in patient areas that do not have emergency lighting, making the receptacle easier to locate in the near-darkness of a power outage.

Devices in a hospital should be mounted for easy use by staff and patients. Because a large number of hospital patients spend time in wheelchairs, particular attention should be given to handicapped requirements. These requirements are typical of occupational therapy areas. All receptacles should be mounted approximately 24 inches above the floor in order to be convenient to patients as well as staff.

### 5.2.0    HOSPITAL GRADE RECEPTACLES—HIGH ABUSE

In accordance with the National Electrical Code, hospital grade receptacles are listed as suitable for use in health care facilities. Health care facilities are defined in ANSI/NFPA 70-1996 (Article 517) as: "Buildings or parts of buildings that contain, but are not limited to, hospitals, nursing homes, extended-care facilities, clinics, and medical and dental offices, whether fixed or mobile."

All receptacles and plugs should be UL-listed as hospital grade. The hospital grade receptacle meets UL test criteria for superior electrical characteristics and mechanical strength. Within these criteria, and of primary importance to the health care facility, are stringent minimum retention and ground resistance specifications. While it is true that some spec. grade receptacles are of high quality and fully equal to those UL-listed as hospital grade, no formalized standards exist for a spec. grade receptacle. Unfortunately, it is very difficult to control the desired quality level and minimum standards when a project or purchase specification lists spec. grade receptacles as its only requirement.

Some localities require that parallel-blade receptacles be mounted neutral blade or ground pin up. In this configuration, any metal which might drop between the wall and the plug will in most cases come in contact with a non-energized blade.

When only one receptacle is wired to a 20A circuit, it must be a 20A receptacle. If all the receptacles specified are 20A, it may be more convenient for the maintenance department to stock and store these receptacles.

Because housekeeping equipment such as floor buffers, which draw in excess of 15A, are utilized in all areas of a hospital, the use of 15A receptacles is extremely limited.

## 5.3.0 HOSPITAL GRADE ISOLATED GROUND RECEPTACLES

These receptacles are used where separation of the device ground and the building ground is desired. This is normally when digital electronic equipment is used, including computer cash registers, computer peripherals, and digital processing equipment. Transient voltages on the ground system can cause malfunctions in digital circuits.

## 5.4.0 HOSPITAL GRADE SAFETY RECEPTACLES

Safety receptacles inhibit contact with an energized contact in the receptacle unless a grounding-type plug is inserted. These receptacles, occasionally referred to as *tamper-proof receptacles*, must be used throughout psychiatric and pediatric locations. When choosing safety receptacles, be careful not to use the type which makes and breaks contacts where life support apparatus may be required.

## 5.5.0 PATIENT (GENERAL)

It is difficult to prevent the occurrence of a conductive path from a grounded object to a patient's body in a health care facility. The path may be created accidentally or through instrumentation directly connected to the patient acting as a source of electric current that will travel through the patient. This hazard is intensified as more equipment is used near a patient. Therefore, more extensive precautions must be initiated when these periods occur. Control of electric shock hazard demands the hindrance of electric current that may flow in an electric circuit involving the patient's body by:

- Increasing the resistance of the conductive circuit that contains the patient
- Insulation of exposed surfaces that may become energized
- Lowering the potential difference that can appear between exposed conductive surfaces in the patient's vicinity
- Using a combination of the above methods

One distinct problem is presented by the patient with an externalized direct conductive path to the heart. In this situation, the patient may be electrocuted at current levels so low that supplemental protection in the design of equipment, catheter insulation, and control of operational practices is necessary.

The health care facility increases the probability of sensitivity to electric shock by patients whose body resistance may be compromised either accidentally or by medical procedures which are deemed necessary. Situations such as catheter insertion or incontinence may make a patient much more susceptible to the effects of an electric current. Reasons such as these make it imperative that individuals responsible for the design, installation, and maintenance of the electrical system in patient care facilities be well acquainted with hazards related to health care facilities.

Since the recognition of this hazard in the 1971 NEC, continued evaluation of this problem has provided a better understanding of the extent of the hazard, encouraging the changes in both value and wiring methods now found in the NEC.

The NEC clearly assigns the responsibility for designating patient care areas to the governing body of the health care facility. Therefore, both the design and inspection of a patient care area must be based on the governing body's designation rather than the aesthetic appearance of the area.

## 5.5.1   Patient Bed Location

Every patient bed location will be supplied with no less than two branch circuits, one from the normal system and the other from the emergency system. All branch circuits from the normal system will be derived from the same panelboard.

Patient bed areas within general care areas are not allowed to acquire all their branch circuits from the emergency system. At least one branch circuit for each patient bed location is required to originate in a normal system panelboard. This is a reflection of the requirements in NEC Section 517-33.

*Exception No. 1:* Branch circuits serving only special-purpose outlets or receptacles, such as portable X-ray outlets, shall not be required to be served from the same distribution panel or panels.

*Exception No. 2:* Clinics, medical and dental offices, and outpatient facilities; psychiatric, substance abuse, and rehabilitation hospitals; nursing homes and limited care facilities meeting the requirements of NEC Section 517-10.

### 5.5.2 Patient Bed Location Receptacles

Each patient bed location must have a minimum of four receptacles. Receptacles are allowed to be of the single or duplex types or a combination. All receptacles, whether four or more, shall be grounded by means of an insulated copper conductor sized in accordance with NEC Table 250-122. This was a significant change in the 1990 Code, because it broadened the requirement for hospital grade receptacles to include general care patient bed locations. A hospital grade receptacle is shown in *Figure 27.*

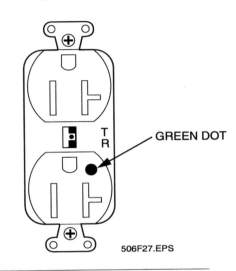

GREEN DOT

506F27.EPS

Figure 27.  Hospital Grade Receptacle

*Exception No. 1:* Psychiatric, substance abuse, and rehabilitation hospitals meeting the requirements of NEC Section 517-10.

*Exception No. 2:* Psychiatric security rooms shall not be required to have receptacle outlets.

Immediate and total replacement of existing non-hospital grade receptacles is not intended here. The intention is that non-hospital grade receptacles be replaced with hospital grade receptacles upon modification of use, renovation, or as existing receptacles need replacement.

### 5.5.3 Pediatric Locations

Both 15A and 20A, 125-volt receptacles meant to supply patient care areas of pediatric wards, rooms, or areas must be tamper resistant. A tamper-resistant receptacle is one that, through its design and construction, limits improper access to its energized contacts.

*Exception:* A receptacle cover shall be permitted to be used in place of a tamper-resistant receptacle provided such cover, by its construction, limits improper access to the energized parts of the receptacle.

An addendum in the 1996 Code, this exception sanctions the use of special receptacle covers over ordinary receptacles instead of tamper-proof receptacles. However, the use of such special receptacle covers must inhibit access to electrified parts.

## 5.6.0  CRITICAL CARE AREAS

Every patient bed location in critical care areas shall be supplied by at least two branch circuits, one or more from the normal system and one or more from the emergency system. At least one branch circuit from the emergency system must supply an outlet(s) only at that bed location. All branch circuits from the normal system shall be from a single panelboard. Emergency system receptacles shall be identified and will also indicate the supply panelboard and circuit number.

*Exception No. 1:* Branch circuits serving only special-purpose receptacles or equipment in critical care areas shall be permitted to be served by other panelboards.

*Exception No. 2:* Critical care locations served from two separate transfer switches on the emergency system shall not be required to have circuits from the normal system.

This new exception was added in the 1996 Code to address a particular case where two individual transfer switches will supply a single patient care area. Branch circuits supplied from two separate transfer switches render the same level of redundancy as required by the main rule.

Each patient bed location shall be provided with a minimum of six receptacles, at least one of which shall be connected to the normal system branch circuit required in NEC Section 517-19(a). They shall be permitted to be of the single or duplex types, or a combination of both. All receptacles, whether six or more, shall be listed as hospital grade and so identified. Each receptacle shall be grounded to the reference grounding point by means of an insulated copper equipment grounding conductor.

NEC Section 517-19(a) covers the branch circuit requirements for patient bed locations in critical care areas. NEC Section 517-19(b) covers the receptacle requirements. Each patient bed location is required to be supplied by at least two branch circuits, one from the normal panel and one from the emergency panel, as shown in *Figure 28*. The normal circuits must be supplied from the same panel (L-1). The emergency circuits are permitted to be supplied from different panels (EML-1 and EML-2). However, the emergency branch circuit to patient bed location A cannot supply emergency receptacles for patient bed location B.

**CRITICAL CARE AREA**

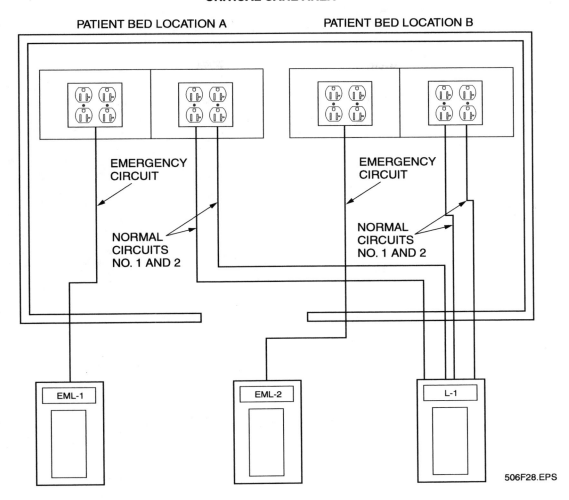

Figure 28. Examples Of Normal And Emergency Circuits
Supplying Patient Bed Locations In A Critical Care Area

Receptacles may be of the single or duplex type, as long as they are listed as hospital grade and are identified as such. A standard method of labeling such receptacles is by a green dot on the outer face of the receptacle. The emergency system receptacles must be marked to indicate the supply panelboard and circuit number.

Requirements such as these are meant to guarantee that critical care patients will not be without electrical power regardless of whether the normal system itself, the branch circuits, or the equipment is at fault.

*Figure 29* depicts a typical bedside configuration for beds where blood pressures will be directly monitored, include transducer mounting poles, etc.

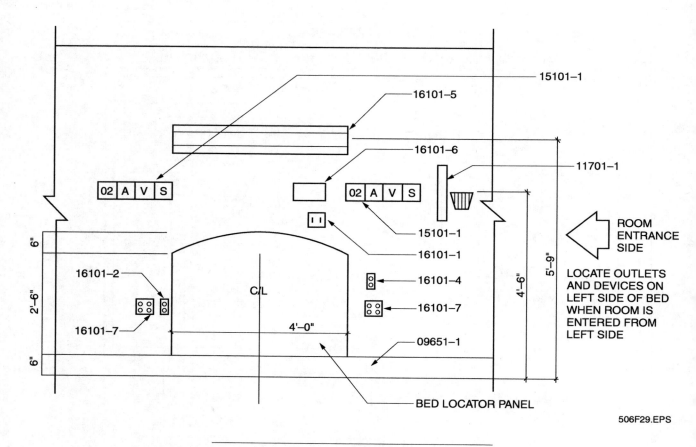

Figure 29.  Typical Bedside Configuration

The required power level for each bedside is typically 90 to 200 VA. The following recommendations are for bedside stations:

- Use only hospital grade permissible power connectors.
- Use no less than two duplex outlets on each side of the patient's bed. The outlets should be breakered in accordance with the ANSI/NFPA 70-1996.
- Use a minimum power rating of 825 VA for each pair of outlets.
- Furnish power outlets within a few feet of the junction boxes and equipment support locations.
- Allocate a grounding system in accordance with ANSI/NFPA 99-1996 and ANSI/NFPA 70-1996.
- Furnish an exposed terminal connected directly to the patient common reference bus for testing purposes. These should be within five feet (1.52 meters) of each bed and each may serve multiple beds.
- Plan and design the system to keep power cables to a minimum length. This contributes both to physical and electrical safety.
- Furnish adequate ventilation in all areas where the patient monitoring equipment is to be installed.

*Note:*　　You will find many other wiring applications in a hospital such as communication and alarm systems as well as vacuum and gas systems.

## 5.7.0 GROUNDING OF RECEPTACLES AND FIXED ELECTRIC EQUIPMENT

In locations used for patient care, the grounding terminals of receptacles and all noncurrent-carrying conductive surfaces of fixed electric equipment likely to become energized that are subject to personal contact and operating at over 100 volts, will be grounded by an insulated copper conductor. The grounding conductor will be sized in accordance with NEC Table 250-122 and installed in metal raceways with the branch circuit conductors supplying these receptacles or fixed electric equipment.

Section 517-13(a) of the NEC pertains to the branch circuits in areas used for patient care and is not limited to patient rooms. Additional areas, such as therapy areas, recreational areas, solaria, and certain patient corridors are also included. It should be understood that this section requires grounding through the use of an insulated copper conductor installed with the branch circuit conductors. This conductor can be either stranded or solid wire. An individual insulated equipment grounding conductor does not need to be run to the branch circuit panelboard with the feeder conductors in a metal raceway.

NEC Section 517-13(a) includes the exceptions listed below:

*Exception No. 1:* Metal raceways shall not be required where listed types MI, MC, or AC cables are used, provided the outer metal armor or sheath of the cable is identified as an acceptable grounding return path.

Exception No. 1 permits certain listed cable types to be used in lieu of metal raceways only where the cable is specifically identified as an acceptable grounding path. The redundant grounding conductor required by NEC Section 517-13(a) would still be required.

*Exception No. 2:* Metal faceplates shall be permitted to be grounded by means of metal mounting screws securing the faceplate to a grounded outlet box or grounded wiring device.

Exception No. 2 permits metal faceplates to be grounded by means of the metal mounting screws rather than by having a separate equipment grounding conductor run to the metal plate.

*Exception No. 3:* Light fixtures more than $7^{1}/_{2}$ feet (2.2 meters) above the floor and switches located outside of the patient vicinity shall not be required to be grounded by an insulated grounding conductor.

Exception No. 3 eliminates light fixtures mounted $7^{1}/_{2}$ feet above the floor from redundant grounding requirements because it is unlikely that they will contact the patient or any equipment connected to the patient.

In addition to the requirements of NEC Section 517-13(a), all branch circuits serving patient care areas shall be provided with a ground path for fault current by installation in a metal raceway system or cable assembly. The metal raceway system, or cable armor or sheath assembly, shall qualify as an equipment grounding return path in accordance with NEC Section 250-118. Type MC and MI cable shall have an outer metal armor or sheath that is identified as an acceptable grounding return path.

The intention of this section is that a redundant ground path through the cable or metal raceway be provided with branch circuits serving patient care areas. This path is in addition to the path through the insulated grounding conductor required in NEC Section 517-13(a).

Patient care areas are not limited to hospitals. They can also be found in other health care facilities such as clinics, nursing homes, medical and dental offices, etc. The outer metal jacket of interlocking tape for Type MC cable does not qualify as an equipment grounding return path in accordance with NEC Section 250-118 and would not be accepted for this purpose in the patient care area.

Metal-sheathed cable assemblies are not authorized for emergency circuits in the patient vicinity because NEC Section 517-30(c)(3) requires such wiring to be protected by installation in a metal raceway.

Equipotential grounding is one method of grounding used for sensitive equipment. An **equipotential ground plane** is a mass of conducting material that, when bonded together, provides a low impedance to current flow over a wide range of frequencies.

Equipotential plane advantages are:

- Shielding of adjacent sensitive circuits or equipment
- Containment of electromagnetic (EM) noise fields between their source (cable, etc.) and the plane
- Increased filtering effectiveness of contained EM fields
- Low-impedance return path for radio frequency (RF) noise current

Equipotential plane structures include the following:

- Metallic screen or sheet metal under floor tile
- Supporting grid of raised access flooring (computer rooms, etc.)
- Conductive grid rooted in or attached to a concrete floor
- Ceiling grid above sensitive equipment

The concept of an equipotential reference plane can be utilized within a section of a single sensitive equipment enclosure, among various pieces of interconnected equipment, or over an entire facility. In all cases, the equipotential plane is bonded to both the local building ground and to the grounding electrode conductor.

Within sensitive equipment cabinets, all significant components, signal return leads, backplanes, etc., must be connected via short (less than 5% to 10% of the wavelength of the highest frequency) conductors to the equipment chassis that forms the equipotential plane. All similar equipment-level equipotential planes should be coupled to a room-level equipotential plane by way of multiple (short) conductors and to the grounding electrode conductor. The room-level equipotential plane must, in turn, be linked to one or more building-level equipotential plane(s) via multiple (short) conductors. This process is continued until the total sensitive electronic equipment system is interconnected to one large continuous equipotential plane. It is best to interlink conductors with single thin-wire cross sections to minimize their impedance at higher frequencies.

## 5.8.0   INHALATION ANESTHETIZING LOCATIONS

In areas where flammable anesthetics are utilized, the entire location will be considered a Class I, Division 1 location that will continue upwards to a level five feet (1.52 meters) above the floor. The area remaining up to the structural ceiling will be designated to be above a hazardous (classified) location.

Any location or room in which flammable anesthetics or volatile flammable disinfecting agents are stored shall be considered a Class I, Division 1 location from floor to ceiling.

Any inhalation anesthetizing location assigned for the exclusive use of nonflammable anesthetizing agents shall be considered to be an other-than-hazardous (classified) location.

This portion of the module divides anesthetizing locations into hazardous (classified) locations, where flammable or nonflammable anesthetics may be interchangeably used, and other-than-hazardous locations, where only nonflammable anesthetics are used. In a flammable anesthetizing location, the entire volume of the room, extending upward from a level five feet above the floor to the surface of the structural ceiling, and including the space between a drop ceiling and the structural ceiling, is considered to be above a hazardous (classified) location.

### 5.8.1   Wiring And Equipment Within Hazardous (Classified) Anesthetizing Locations

Wiring and equipment within hazardous anesthetizing locations must comply with the following:

- Except as sanctioned in NEC Section 517-160, each power circuit within, or partially within, a flammable anesthetizing location as referred to in NEC Section 517-60 shall be isolated from any distribution system by the use of an isolated power system.
- Isolated power system equipment will be listed for the purpose and the system so designed and installed that it meets the provisions and is in accordance with NEC Section 517-60.
- In hazardous (classified) locations referred to in NEC Section 517-60, all fixed wiring and equipment, and all portable equipment, including lamps and other utilization equipment operating at more than ten volts between conductors shall comply with the requirements

of NEC Sections 501-1 through 501-15 and NEC Sections 501-16(a) and (b) for Class I Division 1 locations. All such equipment shall be specifically approved for the hazardous atmospheres involved.

- Where a box, fitting, or enclosure is partially, but not entirely, within a hazardous (classified) location, the hazardous (classified) location shall be considered to be extended to include the entire box, fitting, or enclosure.

- Attachment plugs and receptacles in hazardous (classified) locations will be listed for use in Class I, Group C hazardous (classified) locations and will have provision for the connection of a grounding conductor.

- Flexi-cords used in hazardous (classified) locations for connection to portable utilization equipment, including lamps operating at more than eight volts between conductors, will be typed and authorized for extra-hard usage in accordance with NEC Table 400-4 and will include an additional grounding conductor.

- A storage device for the flexible cord will be provided and will not subject the cord to bending at a radius of less than three inches (76 millimeters).

### 5.8.2    Wiring And Equipment Above Hazardous (Classified) Anesthetizing Locations

Wiring and equipment above hazardous anesthetizing locations must comply with the following:

- Wiring above a hazardous (classified) location referred to in NEC Section 517-60 shall be installed in rigid metal conduit, electrical metallic tubing, intermediate metal conduit, Type MI cable, or Type MC cable that employs a continuous, gas/vapor-tight metal sheath.

- Equipment installed which may produce sparks, arcs, or particles of hot metal, such as lamps and lampholders for fixed lighting, switches, generators, motors, cutouts, or other equipment having sliding contacts, shall be of the totally enclosed type or constructed in such a manner as to prevent the escape of sparks or hot metal particles.

  *Exception*: Wall-mounted receptacles installed above the hazardous (classified) location in flammable anesthetizing locations shall not be required to be totally enclosed or have openings guarded or screened to prevent dispersion of particles.

- Surgical and other lighting fixtures shall conform to Section 501-9(b).

  *Exception No. 1:* The surface temperature limitations set forth for fixed lighting in NEC Section 501-9(b)(2) shall not apply.

  *Exception No. 2:* Integral or pendant switches that are located above and cannot be lowered into the hazardous (classified) location(s) shall not be required to be explosion-proof.

- Only authorized seals shall be provided in conformance with NEC Section 501-5, and NEC Section 501-5(a)(4) shall apply to horizontal as well as to vertical boundaries of the defined hazardous (classified) locations.

- Attachment plugs and receptacles positioned over hazardous (classified) anesthetizing locations will be documented for hospital use for services of prescribed voltage, frequency, rating, and number of conductors with provision for the connection of the grounding conductor. This requirement shall apply to attachment plugs and receptacles of the two-pole, three-wire grounding type for single-phase, 120-volt, nominal, AC service. (See commentary following NEC Section 517-19(b) regarding receptacles listed for hospital use.)

- Plugs and receptacles rated at 250V for connection of 50A and 60A, AC medical equipment for use above hazardous (classified) locations shall be so arranged that the 60A receptacle will accept either the 50A or the 60A plug. 50A receptacles shall be designed so as not to accept the 60A attachment plug. The plugs shall be of the two-pole, three-wire design with a third contact connecting to the insulated (green or green with yellow stripe) equipment grounding conductor of the electrical system.

### 5.8.3 Wiring In Other-Than-Hazardous (Classified) Anesthetizing Locations

Wiring in other-than-hazardous anesthetizing locations must comply with the following:

- Wiring serving other-than-hazardous (classified) locations, as defined in NEC Section 517-60, shall be installed in a metal raceway system or cable assembly. The metal raceway system, or cable armor or sheath assembly, shall qualify as an equipment grounding return path in accordance with NEC Section 250-118. Type MC and MI cable shall have an outer metal armor or sheath that is identified as an acceptable grounding return path.
*Exception:* Pendant receptacle constructions employing at least Type S or equivalent flexible cords suspended not less than six feet (1.83 meters) from the floor.
- Receptacles and attachment plugs installed and used in other-than-hazardous (classified) locations shall be listed for hospital use of services of prescribed voltage, frequency, rating, and number of conductors with provision for connection of the grounding conductor. This requirement shall apply to the two-pole, three-wire grounding type for single-phase 120V, 208V, or 240V nominal AC service.
- Plugs and receptacles rated at 250V for connection of 50A and 60A, AC medical equipment for use in other-than-hazardous (classified) locations shall be so arranged that the 60A receptacle will accept either the 50A or the 60A plug. 50A receptacles shall be designed so as not to accept the 60A attachment plug. The plugs shall be of the two-pole, three-wire design with a third contact connecting to the insulated (green or green with yellow stripe) equipment grounding conductor of the electrical system.

### 5.8.4 Grounding

In any anesthetizing area, all metal raceways and metal-sheathed cables, and all noncurrent-carrying conductive portions of fixed electric equipment shall be grounded. Grounding in Class I locations shall comply with NEC Section 501-16.

*Exception:* Equipment operating at not more than ten volts between conductors shall not be required to be grounded.

Grounding specification and requirements for anesthetizing areas apply only to metal sheathed cables, metal raceways, and electric equipment. It is not a requirement to ground tables, carts, or any other non-electrical items. However, in anesthetizing locations where flammables are present, portable carts and tables usually have a resistance to ground of not more than 1,000,000 ohms, through the use of conductive tires and wheels and conductive flooring to avoid the buildup of static electrical charges. See NFPA 99-1996, Chapter 3, for information on static grounding.

## 5.8.5   Grounded Power Systems In Anesthetizing Locations

A general purpose lighting circuit linked to the normal grounded service will be installed in every operating room.

*Exception:* Circuits connected to any alternate source permitted in NEC Section 700-12 that is separate from the source serving the emergency system.

Failure of the emergency circuit feeder which supplies the operating room with power will commonly place the room in darkness. The requirement of a general purpose lighting circuit supplied by a normal source feeder will inhibit the effect of this kind of failure.

Branch circuits supplying only listed, stationary, diagnostic, and therapeutic equipment permanently installed above the hazardous (classified) area or in other-than-hazardous (classified) locations shall be authorized to be fed from a normal grounded service (single or three-phase system), provided that:

*   All conductive surfaces of the equipment are grounded.
*   Equipment (except enclosed X-ray tubes and the leads to the tubes) are located at least eight feet (2.44 meters) above the floor or outside the anesthetizing location.
*   Wiring for isolated and grounded circuits does not occupy the same cable or raceway.
*   Switches for the grounded branch circuit are located outside the hazardous (classified) location.

*Exception:* NEC Sections 517-63(b)(3) and (b)(4) shall not apply in other-than-hazardous (classified) locations.

Fixed lighting branch circuits feeding *only* fixed lighting shall be permitted to be supplied by a normal grounded service, provided that:

*   All conductive surfaces of fixtures are grounded.
*   Switches are wall-mounted and located above hazardous (classified) locations.
*   Such fixtures are located at least eight feet (2.44 meters) above the floor.
*   Wiring for circuits supplying power to fixtures does not occupy the same raceway or cable as circuits supplying isolated power.

*Exception:* NEC Sections 517-63(c)(1) and (c)(4) shall not apply in other-than-hazardous (classified) locations.

An isolated power supply and its grounded primary feeder will be allowed to be placed in an anesthetizing location, providing it is installed above a hazardous (classified) location or in an other-than-hazardous (classified) location and is listed for the purpose.

Wall-mounted remote control stations will be permitted to be installed in any anesthetizing location for the operation of remote control switching operating at 24V or less.

Except as permitted above, each power circuit within, or partially within, a flammable anesthetizing location as referred to in NEC Section 517-60 shall be isolated from any distribution system supplying other-than-anesthetizing locations.

## 5.8.6 Low-Voltage Equipment And Instruments

Low-voltage equipment that is typically in contact with the bodies of persons or has exposed current-carrying elements shall:

- Operate on an electrical potential of ten volts or less, *or*
- Be approved as intrinsically safe or double-insulated equipment, *and*
- Be moisture-resistant.

Electrical power shall be supplied to low-voltage equipment from:

- An individual portable isolation transformer (autotransformers cannot be used) connected to an isolated power circuit receptacle by means of an appropriate cord and attachment plug, *or*
- A standard low-voltage isolation transformer installed in an other-than-hazardous (classified) location, *or*
- Individual dry-cell batteries, *or*
- Common batteries made up of storage cells located in an other-than-hazardous (classified) location.

Isolating-type transformers for supplying low-voltage circuits shall:

- Have approved means for insulating the secondary circuit from the primary circuit, *and*
- Have grounding of the case and core.

Impedance and resistance devices are allowed to control low-voltage equipment. However, they cannot be used to limit the maximum available voltage supplied to the equipment.

Battery-supplied appliances shall not be capable of being charged during operation unless the charging circuitry utilizes an integral isolating-type transformer.

Receptacles and attachment plugs placed on low-voltage circuits shall be of a type that does not permit interchangeable connection with circuits of higher voltage.

Any circuit interruptions (even in circuits as low as ten volts), caused by a switch or loose or defective connections anywhere in the circuit, may produce a spark sufficient to ignite flammable anesthetic gases.

## 5.9.0  X-RAY INSTALLATIONS

Nothing in this section shall be construed as an indication of safeguards against the useful beam or stray X-ray radiation. Radiation safety and performance requirements of several classes of X-ray equipment are regulated under Public Law 90-602 and are enforced by the Department of Health and Human Services. In addition, information on radiation protection by the National Council on Radiation Protection and Measurements is published as *Reports of the National Council on Radiation Protection and Measurement*. These reports are obtainable from NCRP Publications, P.O. Box 30175, Washington, D.C. 20014.

### 5.9.1  Connection To Supply Circuit

X-ray equipment, whether fixed or stationary, will be connected to the power supply in such a way that the wiring methods meet the general requirements of the NEC.

Equipment shall be permitted to be supplied through a suitable attachment plug and hard-service cable or cord if properly supplied by a branch circuit rated at no more than 30 amperes.

Individual branch circuits will not be required for portable, mobile, and transportable medical X-ray equipment requiring a capacity of no more than 60 amperes.

Circuits and equipment functioning on a supply circuit of over 600 volts will conform with NEC Article 490.

### 5.9.2  Disconnecting Means

A disconnecting means of adequate capacity for at least 50% of the input required for the momentary rating, or 100% of the input required for the long-term rating of the X-ray equipment (whichever is greater) shall be provided in the supply circuit.

Means of disconnection will be feasible from a location readily accessible from the X-ray control.

A grounding-type attachment plug and receptacle of proper rating shall be permitted to serve as a disconnecting means for equipment supplied by a 120-volt branch circuit of 30 amperes or less.

### 5.9.3    Rating Of Supply Conductors And Overcurrent Protection

For diagnostic equipment, the amperage of supply branch circuit conductors and the current rating of overcurrent protective devices shall not be less than 50% of the momentary rating or 100% of the long-term rating, whichever is greater.

The amperage rating of supply feeders and the current rating of overcurrent protective devices feeding two or more branch circuits supplying X-ray units shall not be less than 50% of the momentary demand rating of the largest unit, in addition to 25% of the momentary demand rating of the next largest unit, and 10% of the momentary demand rating of each additional unit. Where concurrent bi-plane tests are undertaken with the X-ray units, the supply conductors and overcurrent protective devices shall be 100% of the momentary demand rating of each X-ray unit.

The minimum conductor sizes for branch and feeder circuits are governed by voltage regulation requirements. In specific installations, manufacturers typically specify the minimum distribution transformer and conductor sizes required, rating of disconnecting means, and overcurrent protection.

For therapeutic equipment, the amperage rating of conductors and rating of overcurrent protective devices shall not be less than 100% of the current rating of medical X-ray therapy equipment.

The amperage rating of the branch circuit conductors and the ratings of disconnecting means and overcurrent protection for X-ray equipment are usually designated by the manufacturer for the specific installation.

### 5.9.4    Control Circuit Conductors

The number of control circuit conductors installed in a raceway shall be determined in accordance with NEC Section 300-17.

Size No. 18 or No. 16 fixture wires as specified in NEC Section 725-27 and flexible cords shall be permitted for the control and operating circuits of X-ray and auxiliary equipment where protected by overcurrent devices of no more than 20 amperes.

### 5.9.5    Equipment Installations

Any equipment for new X-ray installations and all used or reconditioned X-ray equipment transported to and reinstalled in a new location must be of an approved type.

### 5.9.6 Transformers And Capacitors

Transformers and capacitors which are a part of X-ray equipment are not required to comply with NEC Articles 450 and 460. However, capacitors must be mounted within enclosures of insulating material or grounded metal.

### 5.9.7 Installation Of High Tension X-Ray Cables

It is permissible for cables with grounded shields connecting X-ray tubes and image intensifiers to be installed in cable trays or cable troughs along with X-ray equipment control and power supply conductors without the necessity of barriers to separate the wiring.

### 5.9.8 Guarding And Grounding

All high-voltage parts, including X-ray tubes, will be mounted within grounded enclosures. The link from high-voltage equipment to the X-ray tubes and other high-voltage devices will be fashioned with high-voltage shielded cables. Air, oil, gas, or other suitable insulating material will be required to insulate the high voltages from the grounded enclosure.

Cables providing low voltages and connecting to oil-filled units that are not completely sealed (e.g., transformers, condensers, oil coolers, and high-voltage switches) shall have insulation of the oil-resistant type.

## 6.0.0  ISOLATED POWER SYSTEMS

Every isolated power circuit must be controlled by a switch having a disconnecting pole in each isolated circuit conductor to concurrently disengage all power. Such isolation will be achieved by means of one or more transformers having no electrical connection between the primary and secondary windings, motor generator sets, or suitably isolated batteries.

Circuits feeding the primaries of isolation transformers shall function at not more than 600 volts between conductors and must be furnished with the proper overcurrent protection. The secondary voltage of isolation transformers must not exceed 600 volts between conductors of each circuit. All circuits fed from these secondaries will be ungrounded and have an approved overcurrent device of the proper rating in each conductor. Circuits supplied directly from batteries or from motor generator sets shall be ungrounded and protected against overcurrent in the same way as transformer-fed secondary circuits. If an electrostatic shield is present, it shall be connected to the reference grounding point.

The motor generator sets, batteries and battery chargers, isolation transformers, and associated primary and secondary overcurrent devices may not be installed in hazardous (classified) locations. The isolated secondary circuit wiring extending into a hazardous anesthetizing location shall be installed in accordance with NEC Section 501-4.

An isolated branch circuit supplying an anesthetizing location shall not supply any other location.

Per NEC Section 517-160(a)(5), the isolated circuit conductors shall be identified as follows:

Isolated Conductor No. 1 – Orange
Isolated Conductor No. 2 – Brown

For three-phase systems, the third conductor shall be identified as yellow.

No wire-pulling compounds that increase the dielectric constant of a conductor may be used on the secondary conductors of the isolated power supply.

In order to meet impedance requirements, it may be desirable to limit the size of the isolation transformer to 10 kVA and to use conductor insulation with low leakage.

In order to reduce leakage from line to ground, steps should be taken to minimize the length of branch circuit conductors and use conductor insulation with a dielectric constant of less than 3.5 and an insulation resistance constant greater than 20,000 megohm-feet (6,100 megohm-meters) at 60°F (16°C).

## 6.1.0  LINE ISOLATION MONITOR

Every isolated power system shall be provided with an approved continually functioning line isolation monitor that indicates possible leakage or fault current from either isolated conductor to ground, in addition to the usual control and protective devices.

Grounding systems are the primary protection devices for patients. The ungrounded secondary of an isolation transformer reduces the maximum current in the grounding system in the event of a single fault between either isolated power conductor and ground. The line isolation monitor provides a warning when a single fault occurs, or when excessively low impedance to ground develops, which might expose the patient to an unsafe condition should an additional fault occur. Excessive current in the grounding conductors will not result from an initial fault. A hazard exists if a second fault occurs before the first fault is cleared.

Monitors will be designed with a green signal lamp, visible to individuals in the anesthetizing area, which will remain illuminated when the system is sufficiently isolated from ground. An adjacent red signal lamp will illuminate with an audible warning siren when total hazard current (consisting of possible capacitive and resistive leakage current) from either isolated conductor to ground reaches a threshold value of 5.0 mA under normal line voltage conditions. The line isolation monitor should not alarm for any hazard fault current of 3.7 mA or less.

The capability to turn off the audible alarm while leaving the red warning lamp activated should be provided. When the fault is corrected and the green signal lamp is reactivated, the audible alarm silencing circuit shall reset automatically, or an audible or distinctive visual signal shall indicate that the audible alarm has been silenced.

The assumed specification for the line isolation monitor is a 120V, 60 Hz AC system with a moderate ampere rating. When other systems are considered, modifications will be required for different voltages or frequencies as well as installation impedance. However, sensitivity (alarm) levels remain the same.

A line isolation monitor must have enough internal impedance so that when it is properly connected to the isolated system, the maximum internal current that will flow through the line isolation monitor when any point of the isolated system is grounded shall be one milliamp.

Line isolation monitors are permitted to be of the low-impedance type so that the current through the line isolation monitor, when any point of the isolated system is grounded, will not exceed twice the alarm threshold value for a duration not to exceed five milliseconds.

It is also beneficial in reducing this monitor hazard current provided this reduction will result in a heightened "not alarm" threshold value for the fault hazard current.

The line isolation monitor may be a composite unit with a sensing section connected to a separate display panel which displays the alarm and test functions, if the two sections are contained within the same electric enclosure.

An ammeter connected in series to verify the total hazard current of the system (the fault hazard current and monitor hazard current) shall be mounted in a visible place on the line isolation monitor with the Alarm On zone at approximately the center of the scale (total hazard current = 5.0 mA). Locate the ammeter where it is visible to persons in the anesthetizing location.

In order to test the operability of the line isolation monitor, a reliable test switch shall be mounted on the chassis of the line isolation monitor. This test switch shall transfer the grounding connection within the line isolation monitor from reference ground to test ground, a resistive network arrangement across the isolated line producing a test impedance. This test impedance must be significant enough to induce a meter reading with the magnitude sufficient for total hazard current at nominal line voltages, or to a lesser alarm hazard current if the line isolation monitor is rated in such a way (test must create alarms to function and deflect meter to indicate that the alarm is on). The operation of this test will break the grounding connecting point prior to transferring the grounding connector to the test impedance(s); therefore, the test will not add to the hazard of the system.

Line isolation monitors shall not generate energy with enough amplitude and/or frequency to create interference or artifacts on human physiological signals (as measured by a physiological monitor with a gain of at least $10^4$ with a source impedance of 1,000 ohms connected to the balanced differential input of the monitor). The output voltage from the amplifier shall not exceed 30 mV when the gain is $10^4$. The 1,000-ohm impedance shall be connected to the ends of typical unshielded electrode leads (which are a normal part of the cable assembly furnished with physiological monitors). A 60 Hz notch filter shall be used to reduce ambient interference (as is typical in physiological monitor design).

## SUMMARY

This module overviewed the requirements for the development of an electrical distribution system in a health care facility, provided information on the advantages and disadvantages of various systems, and reviewed the items that are allowed on the essential and non-essential electrical systems. Also, we discussed the other considerations that are required to be addressed in the design process to ensure that the system operates safely and effectively.

## References

For advanced study of the topics covered in this task module, the following books are suggested:

*Reports of the National Council on Radiation Protection and Measurement*, NCRP Publications, Washington, D.C.

## SELF CHECK REVIEW/PRACTICE QUESTIONS

1. Which electrical distribution design would be more reliable and safe as far as maintaining continuous electrical power in a medical facility?
   a. Two or more separate utility service feeders
   b. One utility service feeder
   c. Power system fault protection (protective relays/fuses)
   d. Adequately-rated power system

2. What is the maximum length allowed for a branch circuit in the electrical system of a medical facility?
   a. 50 feet
   b. 75 meters
   c. 75 feet
   d. 25 feet

3. What is the maximum time allowed for transfer switches to engage an emergency power system?
   a. 10 minutes
   b. 10 seconds
   c. 5 seconds
   d. 2 minutes

4. What is the maximum demand that can be imposed on one transfer switch in the essential electrical system?
   a. 150 kVA
   b. 100 VA
   c. 150 VA
   d. 100 MVA

5. Which of the following is *not* a function of the life safety branch for a hospital or nursing home?
   a. Elevator cab lighting
   b. Emergency communication system
   c. Coronary care unit
   d. Exit signs

6. Which of the following must be connected to the critical branch and arranged for delayed automatic connection to the alternate power source?
   a. Medication preparation areas
   b. Pharmacy dispensing areas
   c. Nurses' stations
   d. All of the above

7. What type of device is effective in diagnosing voltage problems?
a. Oscilloscope
b. Voltmeter
c. Ammeter
d. Powerline analyzer

8. A Class I, Division 1 location shall extend upward to a level of _____ above the floor in an area where flammables are employed.
a. 5 feet
b. 5 meters
c. 8 feet
d. 2 feet

9. For AC systems, the return ground current will flow through the lowest _____.
a. impedance path.
b. resistance path.
c. reactance path.
d. none of the above.

10. Which of these is *not* a basic reason for system grounding?
a. To limit the differences of electrical potential between all uninsulated conducting objects in a local area
b. To isolate faulty equipment and circuits
c. To increase ground current handling capabilities
d. To limit overvoltages

11. What is the preferred grounding method for health care facilities?
a. Line grounding
b. Neutral grounding
c. Mid-phase grounding
d. None of the above

12. In a medical facility, receptacles should be mounted _____ inches above the floor.
a. 18
b. 24
c. 30
d. 36

13. Where receptacles will support computer equipment, _____ receptacles should be used.
a. spec. grade
b. high abuse
c. safety
d. isolated ground

14. What is the minimum number of receptacles required in a critical care area?
a.  3
b.  4
c.  5
d.  6

15. It is desirable to limit the size of the isolation transformer to _____ or less.
a.  12 kVA
b.  10 VA
c.  10 kVA
d.  20 kVA

# notes

## ANSWERS TO REVIEW/PRACTICE QUESTIONS

| Answer | | Section |
|--------|-----|---------|
| 1. | a | 2.0.0 |
| 2. | c | 2.0.0 |
| 3. | b | 2.1.0 |
| 4. | a | 3.1.0 |
| 5. | c | 3.1.1 |
| 6. | d | 3.2.0 |
| 7. | d | 4.1.3 |
| 8. | a | 5.8.0 |
| 9. | a | 4.3.1 |
| 10. | c | 4.3.2 |
| 11. | b | 4.3.2 |
| 12. | b | 4.3.2 |
| 13. | b | 5.1.0 |
| 14. | d | 5.2.0 |
| 15. | d | 5.6.0 |

NCCER makes every effort to keep these manuals complete, up-to-date, and free of technical errors. We appreciate your help in this process. If you have an idea for improving this manual, or if you find an error, a typographical mistake, or an inaccuracy in NCCER's Craft Training Manuals, please write us, using this form or a photocopy. Be sure to include the exact module number, page number, a description of the problem, and the correction, if possible. Your input will be brought to the attention of the Technical Review Committee. Thank you for your assistance.

*Instructors* – If you found that additional materials were necessary in order to teach this module effectively, please let us know so that we may include them in the Equipment/ Materials list in the Instructor's Guide.

**Write:** Curriculum and Revision Department
National Center for Construction Education and Research
P.O. Box 141104
Gainesville, FL 32614-1104
**Fax:** 352-334-0932

Craft _____ Module Name _____

Module Number _____ Page Number(s) _____

Description of Problem _____

_____

_____

_____

(Optional) Correction of Problem _____

_____

_____

(Optional) Your Name and Address _____

_____

_____

# notes

## Walt Disney World's Wilderness Lodge

Walt Disney World's Wilderness Lodge is modeled after the Old Faithful Inn that was built inside Yellowstone National Park in 1902; it even includes a functional reproduction of Old Faithful Geyser. Installation of the electrical work involved highly detailed coordination to ensure that the various lighting and power systems would be concealed and not detract from the period feel of the building.

# 26312-05
# *Hazardous Locations*

*Topics to be presented in this module include:*

## Overview

Hazardous locations are those that contain both combustible materials and energized electrical components. The *NEC*® uses a system of classes and divisions to identify hazardous locations. Classes identify the type of combustible material, while divisions define the state or presence of the material. Class I locations contain combustible gases or vapors; combustible dust is present in Class II locations; and Class III locations contain combustible fibers or flyings.

Equipment that houses electrical components in hazardous locations must meet certain standards or guidelines depending on the division to which it is assigned. Special fittings are available for conduit systems to physically seal off the passage through the interior of the conduit in order to prevent combustible material from traveling from the hazardous area to potential ignition points. *NEC Chapter 5* contains rules and regulations that apply to hazardous locations.

## Objectives

When you have completed this module, you will be able to do the following:

1. Define the various classifications of hazardous locations.
2. Describe the wiring methods permitted for branch circuits and feeders in specific hazardous locations.
3. Select seals and drains for specific hazardous locations.
4. Select wiring methods for Class I, Class II, and Class III hazardous locations.
5. Follow *National Electrical Code*® (*NEC*®) requirements for installing explosionproof fittings in specific hazardous locations.

## Trade Terms

Approved
Conduit
Conduit body
Equipment
Explosionproof
Explosionproof
  apparatus

Hazardous (classified)
  location
Sealing compound
Sealoff fittings

## Required Trainee Materials

1. Pencil and paper
2. Appropriate personal protective equipment
3. Copy of the latest edition of the *National Electrical Code*®

## Prerequisites

Before you begin this module, it is recommended that you successfully complete *Core Curriculum; Electrical Level One; Electrical Level Two; Electrical Level Three*, Modules 26301-05 through 26311-05.

This course map shows all of the modules in *Electrical Level Three*. The suggested training order begins at the bottom and proceeds up. Skill levels increase as you advance on the course map. The local Training Program Sponsor may adjust the training order.

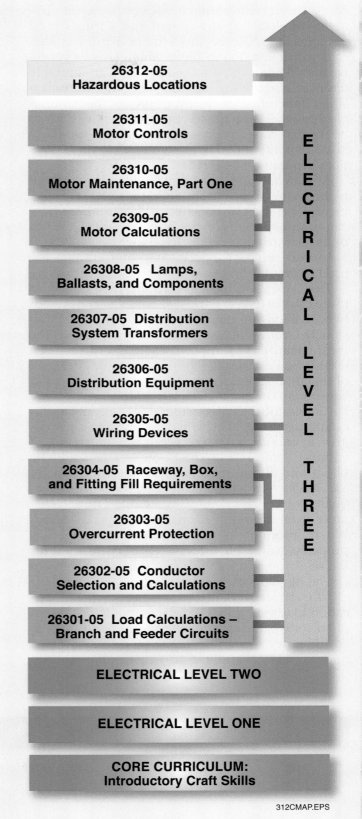

26312-05
Hazardous Locations

26311-05
Motor Controls

26310-05
Motor Maintenance, Part One

26309-05
Motor Calculations

26308-05 Lamps,
Ballasts, and Components

26307-05 Distribution
System Transformers

26306-05
Distribution Equipment

26305-05
Wiring Devices

26304-05 Raceway, Box,
and Fitting Fill Requirements

26303-05
Overcurrent Protection

26302-05 Conductor
Selection and Calculations

26301-05 Load Calculations –
Branch and Feeder Circuits

ELECTRICAL LEVEL TWO

ELECTRICAL LEVEL ONE

CORE CURRICULUM:
Introductory Craft Skills

ELECTRICAL LEVEL THREE

312CMAP.EPS

## 1.0.0 ◆ INTRODUCTION

*NEC Articles 500 through 504* cover the requirements of electrical **equipment** and wiring for all voltages in locations where fire or explosion hazards may exist due to flammable gases or vapor, flammable liquids, combustible dust, or ignitable fibers or other flying materials. Locations are classified depending on the properties of the flammable vapors, liquids, gases, or combustible dusts or fibers that may be present, as well as the likelihood that a flammable or combustible concentration or quantity is present.

Any area in which the atmosphere or a material in the area is such that the arcing of operating electrical contacts, components, and equipment may cause an explosion or fire is considered a **hazardous (classified) location.** In all such cases, **explosionproof apparatus,** raceways, and fittings are used to provide an **explosionproof** wiring system.

The *NEC*® divides hazardous materials into three classes (Class I, Class II, and Class III), with two divisions for each class (Division 1 and Division 2). Of these, Class I, Division 1 represents the most hazardous location. These classes have been established on the basis of the explosive character of the atmosphere for the testing and approval of equipment for use in each class. However, it must be understood that considerable skill and judgment must be applied when deciding to what degree an area contains hazardous concentrations of vapors, combustible dusts, or easily ignitable fibers and flying materials. Furthermore, many factors, such as temperature, barometric pressure, quantity of release, humidity, ventilation, and distance from the vapor source, must be considered. When information on all factors concerned is properly evaluated, a consistent classification for the selection and location of electrical equipment can be developed.

*NEC Article 505* allows classification and application to international standards, but it will be applied only under engineering supervision. In addition, few American-made products are listed for international application. As a result, this module will not cover *NEC Article 505* in any detail.

## 1.1.0 Class I Locations

Class I atmospheric hazards are divided into Divisions 1 and 2, and also into four groups (A, B, C and D). Group A represents the most hazardous location.

Those locations in which flammable gases or vapors may be present in the air in quantities sufficient to produce explosive or ignitable mixtures are identified as Class I locations. If these gases or vapors are present during normal operation, frequent repair or maintenance operations, or where breakdown or faulty operation of process equipment might also cause simultaneous failure of electrical equipment, the area is designated a Class I, Division 1. Examples of such locations are interiors of paint spray booths where volatile flammable solvents are used, inadequately ventilated pump rooms where flammable gas is pumped, anesthetizing locations of hospitals (to a height of 5' above floor level), and drying rooms for the evaporation of flammable solvents (see *Figure 1*).

Class I, Division 2 covers locations in which volatile flammable gases, vapors, or liquids are handled either in a closed system or confined within suitable enclosures, or where hazardous concentrations are normally prevented by positive mechanical ventilation. Areas adjacent to Division 1 locations, into which gases might occasionally flow, also belong in Division 2.

## 1.2.0 Class II Locations

Class II locations are those that are hazardous because of the presence of combustible dust. Class II Division 1 locations are areas in which combustible dust may be present in the air under normal operating conditions in quantities sufficient to produce explosive or ignitable mixtures; examples are working areas of grain-handling and storage plants and rooms containing grinders or pulverizers (*Figure 2*). Class II, Division 2 locations are areas in which dangerous concentrations of suspended dust are not likely, but where dust might accumulate.

### Zone Classifications

**INSIDE TRACK**

The zone system covered in *NEC Article 505* is an alternative to the division classification covered in *NEC Article 500.* All electrical components and devices must be rated for the specific zone or division in which they are installed, regardless of the level of protection provided by the device.

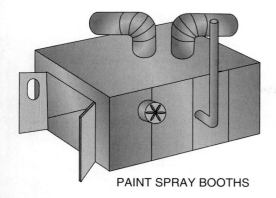

PAINT SPRAY BOOTHS

ANESTHETIZING
LOCATIONS
IN HOSPITALS

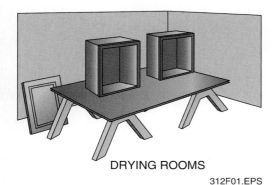

DRYING ROOMS

312F01.EPS

*Figure 1* ◆ Typical *NEC*® Class I locations.

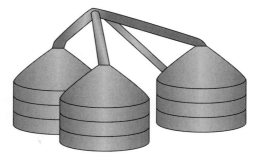

GRAIN-HANDLING AND STORAGE PLANTS

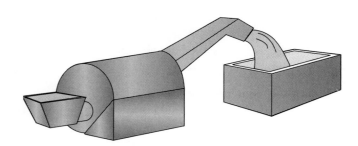

ROOMS CONTAINING GRINDERS AND PULVERIZERS

312F02.EPS

*Figure 2* ◆ Typical *NEC*® Class II locations.

Besides the two divisions, Class II atmospheric hazards also cover three groups of combustible dusts (E, F, and G). The groupings are based on the resistivity of the dust. Group E is always Division 1. Groups F and G may be either Division 1 or 2, depending on their resistivity. Because the *NEC*® is considered the definitive classification tool and contains explanatory data about hazardous atmospheres, refer to *NEC Section 500.5* for exact definitions of Class II, Divisions 1 and 2.

## .3.0 Class III Locations

Class III locations are those areas that are hazardous because of the presence of easily ignitable fibers or other flying materials, but such materials are not likely to be in suspension in the air in

quantities sufficient to produce ignitable mixtures. Such locations usually include certain areas of rayon, cotton, and textile mills, clothing manufacturing plants, and woodworking plants (*Figure 3*).

## 1.4.0 Applications

Hazardous atmospheres are summarized in *Table 1*. For a more complete listing of flammable liquids, gases, and solids, see *Recommended Practice for the Classification of Flammable Liquids, Gases, or Vapors and of Hazardous (Classified) Locations for Electrical Installations in Chemical Process Areas*, National Fire Protection Association Publication No. 497.

Once the class of an area is determined, the conditions under which the hazardous material may be present determine the division. In Class I and Class II, Division 1 locations, the hazardous gas or dust may be present in the air under normal operating conditions in dangerous concentrations. In Division 2 locations, the hazardous material is not normally in the air, but it might be released if there is an accident or if there is faulty operation of equipment.

*Tables 2* through 6 provide a summary of the various classes of hazardous locations as defined by the *NEC*®.

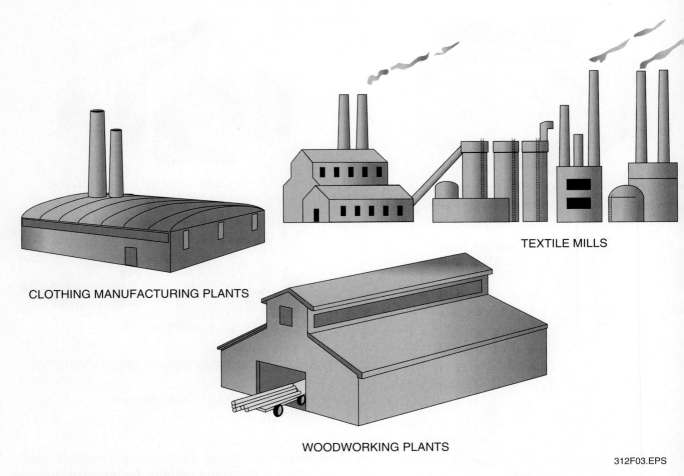

CLOTHING MANUFACTURING PLANTS

TEXTILE MILLS

WOODWORKING PLANTS

312F03.EPS

*Figure 3* ◆ Typical *NEC*® Class III locations.

**Table 1** Summary of Hazardous Atmospheres

| Hazardous Area | Class Subdivisions | Groups |
|---|---|---|
| | **Class I Divisions** | **Class I, Division Groups** |
| Class I: Material present is a flammable gas or vapor | Division 1: Locations in which hazardous concentrations of flammable gases or vapors are present normally or frequently | Group A: Atmospheres containing acetylene |
| | Division 2: Locations in which hazardous concentrations of flammable gases or vapors are present as a result of infrequent failure of equipment or containers | Group B: Atmospheres containing hydrogen, manufactured gases containing more than 30% hydrogen by volume, or gases or vapors of equivalent hazard<br>Group C: Atmospheres containing ethylene, cyclopropane, or gases or vapors of equivalent hazard<br>Group D: Atmospheres containing propane, gasoline, or gases or vapors of equivalent hazard |
| | **Class I Zones** | **Class I, Zone Groups** |
| | Zone 0: Locations in which combustible material is present continuously or for long periods | Group IIC: Atmospheres containing acetylene or hydrogen or other gases or vapors meeting Group IIC criteria |
| | Zone 1: Locations in which combustible material is likely to be present normally or frequently because of repair or maintenance operations or leakage | Group IIB: Atmospheres containing acetaldehyde, ethylene, or other gases or vapors meeting Group IIB criteria |
| | Zone 2: Locations in which combustible material is not likely to occur in a normal operation and, if it does occur, will exist only for a short period | Group IIA: Atmospheres containing propane, gasoline, or other gases or vapors meeting Group IIA criteria |
| | | **Class II, Division Groups** |
| Class II: Material present is a combustible dust | Division 1: Locations in which hazardous concentrations of combustible dust are present normally or may exist because of equipment breakdown or where electrically conductive combustible dusts are present in hazardous quantities | Group E: Atmospheres containing combustible metal dusts including aluminum, magnesium, and other metals of similar hazards |
| | Division 2: Locations in which hazardous concentrations of combustible dust are not normally suspended in the air but may occur as a result of infrequent malfunction of equipment or where dust accumulation may interfere with safe dissipation of heat or may be ignitable by abnormal operation of electrical equipment | Group F: Atmospheres containing combustible carbonaceous dusts, including carbon black, charcoal, coals, or dusts that have been sensitized by other materials so that they present an explosion hazard |
| Class III: Material present is an ignitable fiber or flying | Division 1: Locations in which easily ignitable fibers or materials producing combustible flyings are handled, manufactured, or used | Group G: Atmospheres containing combustible nonconductive dusts not included in Group E or F, including flour, grain, wood, and plastic<br>No Groups |
| | Division 2: Locations in which easily ignitable fibers are stored or handled, except in the manufacturing process | |

**Table 2** Application Rules for Class I, Division 1

| Components | Characteristics | NEC® Reference |
|---|---|---|
| Boxes, fittings | Explosionproof and threaded for connection to conduit | NEC Section 501.10(A) |
| Sealoffs | Approved for purpose | NEC Section 501.15(A) |
| Wiring methods | Rigid metal conduit, steel intermediate metal conduit, Type MI cable, and, under certain conditions, ITC and MC cable | NEC Section 501.10(A) |
| Receptacles | Approved for the location | NEC Section 501.145 |
| Lighting fixtures | Approved for Class I, Division 1 | NEC Section 501.130(A) |
| Panelboards | Class I enclosure | NEC Section 501.115(A) |
| Circuit breakers | Class I enclosure | NEC Section 501.115(A) |
| Fuses | Class I enclosure | NEC Section 501.115(A) |
| Switches | Class I enclosure | NEC Section 501.115(A) |
| Motors | Class I, Division 1, totally-enclosed or submerged | NEC Section 501.125(A) |
| Liquid-filled transformers | Installed in an approved vault | NEC Section 501.100(A) |
| Dry-type transformers | Class I, Division 1 enclosure | NEC Section 501.120(A) |
| Utilization equipment | Class I, Division 1 | NEC Section 501.135(A) |
| Flexible connections | Class I, explosionproof | NEC Section 501.10(A) |
| Portable lamps | Class I, Division 1, approved as a portable assembly | NEC Section 501.130(A) |
| Generators | Class I, Division 1, totally enclosed or submerged | NEC Section 501.125(A) |
| Alarm systems | Class I, Division 1 | NEC Section 501.150(A) |

**Table 3** Application Rules for Class I, Division 2

| Components | Characteristics | NEC® Reference |
|---|---|---|
| Boxes, fittings | Do not have to be explosionproof unless current interrupting contacts are exposed | NEC Section 501.15(C) |
| Sealoffs | Approved for purpose | NEC Section 501.15(B) |
| Wiring methods | Rigid metal conduit, steel intermediate metal conduit, Types MI, MC, MV, TC, ITC, or PLTC cables, or enclosed gasketed busways or wireways | NEC Section 501.10(B) |
| Receptacles | Approved for the location | NEC Section 501.145 |
| Lighting fixtures | Protected from physical damage | NEC Section 501.130(B) |
| Panelboards | General purpose with exceptions | NEC Section 501.115(B) |
| Circuit breakers | Class I enclosure | NEC Section 501.115(B)(1) |
| Fuses | Class I enclosure | NEC Section 501.105(B)(3) |
| Switches | Class I enclosure | NEC Section 501.115(B) |
| Motors | General purpose unless motor has sliding contacts, switching contacts, or integral resistance devices; if so, use Class I, Division 1 | NEC Section 501.125(B) |
| Motor controls | Class I, Division 2 | NEC Section 501.115(B) |
| Liquid-filled transformers | General purpose | NEC Section 501.100(B) |
| Dry-type transformers | Class I, general purpose except switching mechanism Division 1 enclosures | NEC Section 501.120(B) |
| Utilization equipment | Class I, Division 2 | NEC Section 501.135(B) |
| Flexible connections | Class I, explosionproof | NEC Section 501.10(B) |
| Portable lamps | Explosionproof | NEC Section 501.130(B) |
| Generators | Class I, totally enclosed or submerged | NEC Section 501.125(B) |
| Alarm systems | Class I, Division 2 | NEC Section 501.150(B) |

**Table 4** Application Rules for Class II, Division 1

| Components | Characteristics | NEC® Reference |
|---|---|---|
| Boxes, fittings | Class II boxes required when using taps, joints, or other connections; otherwise, use dust-tight boxes with no openings | *NEC Section 502.10(A)(4)* |
| Wiring methods | Rigid metal conduit, steel intermediate metal conduit, or Types MI and, under certain conditions, MC cables listed for use in Class II, Division 1 locations | *NEC Section 502.10(A)* |
| Receptacles | Class II | *NEC Section 502.145(A)* |
| Lighting fixtures | Class II | *NEC Section 502.130(A)* |
| Panelboards | Dust/ignitionproof | *NEC Section 502.115(A)(1)* |
| Circuit breakers | Dust/ignitionproof enclosure | *NEC Section 502.115(A)* |
| Fuses | Dust/ignitionproof enclosure | *NEC Section 502.115(A)* |
| Switches | Dust/ignitionproof enclosure | *NEC Section 502.115(A)* |
| Motors | Class II, Division 1 or totally enclosed | *NEC Section 502.125(A)* |
| Motor controls | Dust/ignitionproof | *NEC Section 502.115(A)* |
| Liquid-filled transformers | Install in an approved vault | *NEC Section 502.100(A)* |
| Dry-type transformers | Class II, vault | *NEC Section 502.100(A)* |
| Utilization equipment | Class II | *NEC Section 502.135(A)* |
| Flexible connections | Extra-hard usage cord, liquid-tight, and others | *NEC Section 502.10(A)(2)* |
| Portable lamps | Class II | *NEC Section 502.130(A)* |
| Generators | Class II, Division 1 or totally enclosed | *NEC Section 502.125(A)* |

**Table 5** Application Rules for Class II, Division 2

| Components | Characteristics | NEC® Reference |
|---|---|---|
| Boxes, fittings | Use tight covers to minimize entrance of dust | *NEC Section 502.10(B)(4)* |
| Wiring methods | Rigid metal conduit, steel intermediate metal conduit, electrical metallic tubing (EMT), Types MI, MC, TC, ITC, or PLTC cables, or enclosed dust-tight busways or wireways | *NEC Section 502.10(B)* |
| Receptacles | Exposed live parts are not allowed | *NEC Section 502.145(B)* |
| Lighting fixtures | Class II | *NEC Section 502.130(B)* |
| Panelboards | Dust-tight enclosure | *NEC Section 502.115(B)* |
| Circuit breakers | Dust-tight enclosure | *NEC Section 502.115(B)* |
| Fuses | Dust-tight enclosure | *NEC Section 502.115(B)* |
| Switches | Dust-tight enclosure | *NEC Section 502.115(B)* |
| Motors | Class II, Division 1 or totally enclosed | *NEC Section 502.125(B)* |
| Motor controls | Dust-tight enclosure | *NEC Section 502.115(B)* |
| Liquid-filled transformers | Install in vault | *NEC Section 502.100(B)* |
| Dry-type transformers | Class II vault | *NEC Section 502.100(B)* |
| Utilization equipment | Class II | *NEC Section 502.135(B)* |
| Flexible connections | Extra-hard usage cord, liquid-tight, and others | *NEC Section 502.10(B)(2)* |
| Portable lamps | Class II | *NEC Section 502.130(B)(1)* |
| Generators | Class II, Division 1 or totally enclosed | *NEC Section 502.125(B)* |

**Table 6** Application Rules for Class III, Divisions 1 and 2

| Components | Characteristics | NEC® Reference |
|---|---|---|
| Boxes, fittings | Dust-tight | *NEC Section 503.10(A)(1)* |
| Wiring methods | Rigid metal conduit, steel intermediate metal conduit, EMT, Types MI and MC cables, or enclosed dust-tight busways or wireways | *NEC Section 503.10(A)* |
| Receptacles | Minimize accumulation of fibers or flyings | *NEC Section 503.145* |
| Lighting fixtures | Tight enclosure with no openings | *NEC Section 503.130* |
| Panelboards | Dust-tight enclosure | *NEC Section 503.115* |
| Circuit breakers | Dust-tight enclosure | *NEC Section 503.115* |
| Fuses | Dust-tight enclosure | *NEC Section 503.115* |
| Switches | Dust-tight enclosure | *NEC Section 503.115* |
| Motors | Totally enclosed | *NEC Section 503.125* |
| Motor controls | Dust-tight enclosure | *NEC Section 503.115* |
| Liquid-filled transformers | Install in an approved vault | *NEC Section 503.100* |
| Dry-type transformers | Dust-tight enclosure | *NEC Section 503.100* |
| Utilization equipment | Class III | *NEC Section 503.135* |
| Flexible connections | Extra-hard usage cord and other flexible conduit/fittings | *NEC Section 503.10(A)(2)* |
| Portable lamps | Unswitched, guarded with tight enclosure for lamp | *NEC Section 503.130* |
| Generators | Totally enclosed | *NEC Section 503.125* |

## Delayed Action Receptacles

The receptacle shown here is rated for Class I, Division 1 and 2 locations and features a delayed action rotating sleeve that prevents complete withdrawal of the plug in one continuous movement. This delay allows any arc-generated heat to be dissipated before the plug is released.

312P1202.EPS

## 2.0.0 ◆ PREVENTION OF EXTERNAL IGNITION/EXPLOSION

The main purpose of using explosionproof fittings and wiring methods in hazardous areas is to prevent ignition of flammable liquids or gases and to prevent an explosion.

### 2.1.0 Sources of Ignition

In certain atmospheric conditions when flammable gases or combustible dusts are mixed in the proper proportion with air, any source of energy is all that is needed to touch off an explosion.

One prime source of energy is electricity. Equipment such as switches, circuit breakers, motor starters, pushbutton stations, or plugs and receptacles can produce arcs or sparks in normal operation when contacts are opened and closed. This could easily cause ignition.

Other hazards are devices that produce heat, such as lighting fixtures and motors. In this case, the surface temperatures may exceed the safe limits of many flammable atmospheres.

Finally, many parts of the electrical system can become potential sources of ignition in the event of insulation failure. This group includes wiring (particularly splices in the wiring), transformers, impedance coils, solenoids, and other low-temperature devices without make-or-break contacts.

Non-electrical hazards such as sparking metal can also easily cause ignition. A hammer, file, or other tool that is dropped on masonry or on a ferrous surface can cause a hazard unless the tool is made of non-sparking material. For this reason, portable electrical equipment is usually made from aluminum or other material that will not produce sparks if the equipment is dropped.

Electrical safety is of crucial importance. The electrical installation must prevent accidental ignition of flammable liquids, vapors, and dusts released to the atmosphere. In addition, because much of this equipment is used outdoors or in corrosive atmospheres, the material and finish must be such that maintenance costs and shutdowns are minimized.

### 2.2.0 Combustion Principles

Three basic conditions must be satisfied for a fire or explosion to occur:

- A flammable liquid, vapor, or combustible dust must be present in sufficient quantity.
- The flammable liquid, vapor, or combustible dust must be mixed with air or oxygen in the proportions required to produce an explosive mixture.
- A source of ignition must be applied to the explosive mixture.

In applying these principles, the quantity of the flammable liquid or vapor that may be liberated and its physical characteristics must be recognized.

Vapors from flammable liquids also have a natural tendency to disperse into the atmosphere and rapidly become diluted to concentrations below the lower explosion limit, particularly when there is natural or mechanical ventilation.

**WARNING!**

The possibility that the gas concentration may be above the upper explosion limit does not afford any degree of safety, because the concentration must first pass through the explosive range to reach the upper explosion limit.

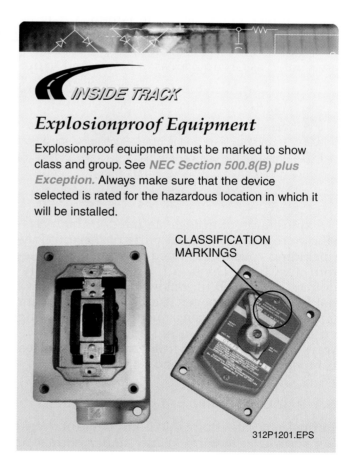

*INSIDE TRACK*

### Explosionproof Equipment

Explosionproof equipment must be marked to show class and group. See *NEC Section 500.8(B) plus Exception.* Always make sure that the device selected is rated for the hazardous location in which it will be installed.

CLASSIFICATION MARKINGS

312P1201.EPS

## 3.0.0 ◆ EXPLOSIONPROOF EQUIPMENT

Each area that contains gases or dusts considered hazardous must be carefully evaluated to make certain the correct electrical equipment is selected. Many hazardous atmospheres are Class I, Group D or Class II, Group G. However, certain areas may involve other groups, particularly Class I, Groups B and C. Conformity with the *NEC®* requires the use of fittings and enclosures **approved** for the specific hazardous gas or dust involved.

The wide assortment of explosionproof equipment now available makes it possible to provide adequate electrical installations under any of the various hazardous conditions. However, you must be thoroughly familiar with all *NEC®* requirements and know what fittings are available, how to install them properly, and where and when to use the various fittings. For example, some electricians are under the false impression that a fitting rated for Class I, Division 1 can be used under any hazardous conditions. However, remember the groups. For example, a fitting rated for Class I, Division 1, Group C cannot be used in areas classified as Groups A or B. On the other hand, fittings rated for use in Group A may be used for any group beneath A; fittings rated for use in Class I, Division 1, Group B can be used in areas rated as Group B areas or below, and so on.

**WARNING!**
Never interchange fittings or covers between one hazardous area and another. Such items must be rated for the appropriate class, division, and group.

Explosionproof fittings are rated for both classification and groups. All parts of these fittings (including covers) are rated accordingly. Therefore, if a Class I, Division 1, Group A fitting is required, a Group B (or below) fitting cover must not be used. The cover itself must be rated for Group A locations. Consequently, when working on electrical systems in hazardous locations, always make certain that fittings and their related components match the condition at hand.

### 3.1.0 Intrinsically Safe Equipment

Intrinsically safe equipment is incapable of releasing sufficient electrical energy under normal or abnormal conditions to cause ignition of a specific hazardous atmospheric mixture in its most easily ignited concentration. The use of intrinsically safe

equipment is primarily limited to process control instrumentation because these electrical systems lend themselves to the low energy requirements.

Installation rules for intrinsically safe equipment are covered in *NEC Article 504*. In general, intrinsically safe equipment and its associated wiring must be installed so that it is positively separated from the non-intrinsically safe circuits because induced voltages could defeat the concept of intrinsically safe circuits. Underwriters Laboratories, Inc. and Factory Mutual list several devices in this category.

### 3.2.0 Explosionproof Conduit and Fittings

A typical floor plan for a hazardous area is shown in *Figure 4*.

In hazardous locations where threaded metal **conduit** is required, the conduit must be threaded with a standard conduit cutting die (*Figure 5*) that provides ¾" taper per foot. The conduit should be made up wrench-tight to prevent sparking in the event fault current flows through the raceway system *[NEC Section 501.10(A)(1)(a)]*. All boxes, fittings, and joints shall be threaded for connection to the conduit system and shall be an approved explosionproof type (*Figure 6*). Threaded joints must be made up with at least five threads fully engaged. Where it becomes necessary to employ flexible connectors at motor or fixture terminals (*Figure 7*), flexible fittings approved for the particular class location shall be used. Unions are provided to facilitate the installation and removal of equipment.

*What's wrong with this picture?*

312P1203.EPS

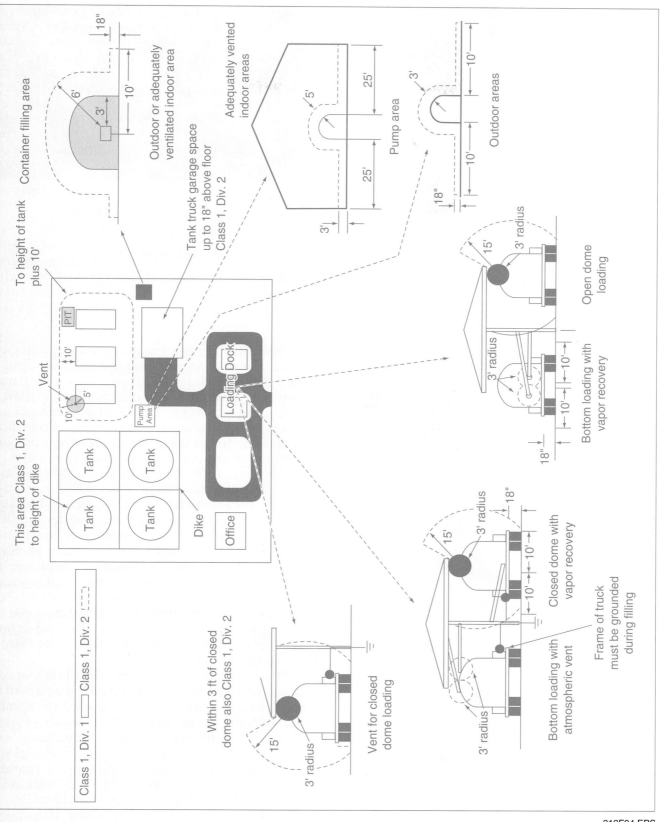

Figure 4 ◆ Floor plan of a hazardous location.

312F04.EPS

PORTABLE CONDUIT
THREADER

STANDARD CONDUIT DIES

312F05.EPS

***Figure 5*** ◆ Portable conduit threader.

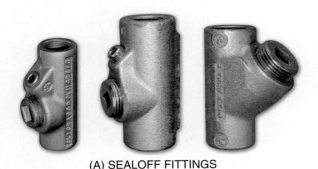

(A) SEALOFF FITTINGS

(B) EXPLOSIONPROOF SEAL

(C) EXPLOSIONPROOF
CONDUIT BODY

312F06.EPS

***Figure 6*** ◆ Typical fittings approved for hazardous areas.

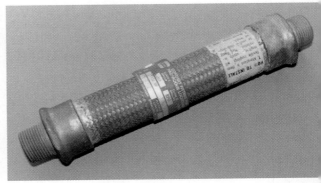

312F07.EP

***Figure 7*** ◆ Explosionproof flexible connector.

### 3.3.0 Seals and Drains

Seals and drains are both used to protect condu
systems.

#### 3.3.1 Seals

**Sealoff fittings,** also known as sealing fittings c
seals *(Figure 8),* are required in conduit systems t
prevent the passage of gases, vapors, or flame
from one portion of the electrical installation t
another at atmospheric pressure and normal an
bient temperatures. Furthermore, sealoffs lim
explosions to the enclosure and prevent precom
pression of pressure piling in conduit systems.

For Class I, Division 1 locations, *NEC Sectio
501.15(A)(1)* states that in each conduit run ente
ing an enclosure for switches, circuit breaker
fuses, relays, resistors, or other apparatus th.
may produce arcs, sparks, or high temperature
seals shall be installed within 18" from such er
closures. Explosionproof unions, couplings, r
ducers, elbows, capped elbows, and **condu
bodies** similar to L, T, and cross types shall be th
only enclosures or fittings permitted between th
sealing fitting and the enclosure. The conduit bo
ies shall not be larger than the largest trade size
the conduit.

However, one exception to this rule is that co.
duits are not required to be sealed if the current i
terrupting contacts are enclosed within a chamb
hermetically sealed against the entrance of gas
or vapors, immersed in oil in accordance wi
*NEC Section 501.15(A)(1), Exception,* or enclose
within a factory-sealed explosionproof chamb
within an enclosure approved for the location ar
marked *FACTORY SEALED* or equivalent.

Seals are also required in Class II locatio
where a raceway provides communication b
tween an enclosure that is required to be dus
ignitionproof and one that is not *(NEC Sectio
502.15).*

## Pressure Piling

Pressure piling occurs when an explosion in one section of a raceway creates expanding gases that cause the vapors to compress further down in the raceway, which will then cause a secondary explosion of a greater magnitude. This explosion will result in additional expanding gases and compressed vapors, continuing to create additional explosions, which may potentially exceed the containment capabilities of the raceway system.

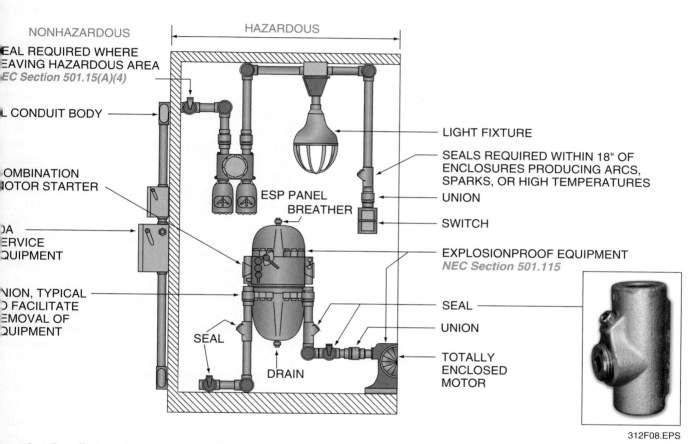

312F08.EPS

*Figure 8* ◆ Installation of seals in Class I, Division 1 locations.

A permanent and effective seal is one method preventing the entrance of dust into the dust/ignitionproof enclosure through the raceway. A horizontal raceway, not less than 10' long, another approved method, as is a vertical raceway not less than 5' long and extending downward from the dust/ignitionproof enclosure.

Where a raceway provides communication between an enclosure that is required to be dust/ignitionproof and an enclosure in an unclassified location, seals are not required.

Where sealing fittings are used, all must be accessible.

While it is not an *NEC®* requirement, many electrical designers sectionalize long conduit runs by inserting seals not more than 50' to 100' apart, depending on the conduit size. This is done in order to minimize the effects of pressure piling.

In general, seals are installed at the same time as the conduit system. However, the conductors are installed after the raceway system is complete and prior to packing and sealing the fittings.

# Fill Requirements

Why do the standards for listing sealoff fittings allow only a 25% fill for these fittings, while conduits are permitted to have a 40% fill?

### 3.3.2   Drains

In humid atmospheres or wet locations where it is likely that water will gain entrance to the raceway system, the raceways should be inclined so that water will not collect in enclosures or on seals, but will be led to low points where it may pass out through integral drains.

If the arrangement of raceway runs makes this impractical, special drain/seal fittings should be used, such as the type shown in *Figure 9*. These fittings prevent water from accumulating above the seal and meet the requirements of *NEC Section 501.15(F)*.

Even if the location is not typically humid or wet, surprising amounts of water may still collect in conduit systems. This is because no conduit system is completely airtight. Alternate increases and decreases in temperature and/or barometric pressure due to weather changes or to the nature of the process carried on in the location where the conduit is installed will cause the introduction of outside air. If this air carries sufficient moisture, it will condense within the system when the temperature drops. Because the internal conditions are unfavorable to evaporation, the resultant water will remain and accumulate over time.

To avoid the accumulation of moisture, install drain/seal fittings with drain covers or fittings with inspection covers. This is a recommended practice even if prevailing conditions at the time of planning or installation do not indicate a moisture problem.

### 3.3.3   Selection and Installation of Seals and Drains

Always select the proper sealoff fitting for the hazardous location (such as Class 1, Groups A, B, C, or D) and for the proper use in respect to its mounting position. This is particularly critical when the conduit run crosses between hazardous and nonhazardous areas. The improper positioning of a seal may permit hazardous gases or vapors to enter the system beyond the seal and escape into another portion of the hazardous area or enter a nonhazardous area. Some seals are designed to be mounted in any position; others are restricted to horizontal or vertical mounting. *Figure 10* shows various types of seals.

Install the seals on the proper side of the partition or wall, as recommended by the manufacturer. The installation of seals should be made only by trained personnel in strict compliance with the instruction sheets furnished with the seals and **sealing compound**. *NEC Section 501.15(C)(4)* prohibits splices or taps in sealoff fittings. Sealoff fittings are listed by UL for use in Class I hazardous locations with approved sealing compound only. This compound, when properly mixed and poured, hardens into a dense, strong mass that is insoluble in water, not attacked by chemicals, and not softened by heat. It is designed to withstand the pressure of the exploding trapped gases or vapors. Conductors sealed in the compound may be any approved thermoplastic or rubber insulated type. Conductors may or may not be lead-covered.

### 3.3.4   Sealing Compounds and Dams

Poured seals should be made only by qualified personnel following the manufacturer's instructions. Improperly poured seals serve no purpose. Sealing compound must be approved for the purpose, not be affected by the surrounding

312F09.EPS

*Figure 9* ◆ Typical drain seal.

ELBOW
SEAL

DRAIN
SEAL

SEAL FOR USE
AT ANY ANGLE

SEAL WITH
DRAIN COVER

312F10.EPS

*Figure 10* ◆ Various types of seals.

mosphere or liquids, and not have a melting
point of less than 200°F (93°C). The sealing compound and dams must also be approved for the
type and manufacturer of the fitting. For example,

Crouse-Hinds CHICO® A sealing compound is
the only sealing compound approved for use with
Crouse-Hinds ECM fittings.

To pack the sealoff, remove the threaded plug
or plugs from the fitting and insert the fiber supplied with the packing kit. Tamp the fiber between
the wires and the hub before pouring the sealing
compound into the fitting, then pour in the sealing cement and reset the threaded plug tightly.
The fiber packing prevents the sealing compound
from entering the conduit lines in the liquid state.

Sealing compound is poured after the conduit
system and seals are installed and the conductors
and packing fiber have been installed. Most sealing compound kits contain a powder in a poly-
ethylene bag within an outer container. Remove
the bag of powder, fill the outside container, pour
in the powder, and mix.

> **CAUTION**
>
> Always make certain that the sealing compound
> is compatible for use with the packing material,
> brand and type of fitting, and type of conductors
> used in the system.

In practical applications, dozens of seals may
be required for a particular installation. Consequently, after the conductors are pulled, each seal
in the system is first packed. To prevent the possibility of overlooking a seal, a certain color of paint
is normally sprayed on the seal hub to indicate

## Sealing Conductors

On a multi-conductor cable traveling between areas where sealoff fittings are required,
strip the insulation from the cable in the middle of the fitting and slightly unravel and
separate (birdcage) the conductors. This ensures that the sealing compound fully
surrounds each conductor to prevent the passage of gas through the seal. See *NEC
Section 501.15(D)(2)*. This may require special consideration when selecting a sealoff
fitting.

## Pouring Vertical Seals

When pouring a vertical seal that penetrates the top of an enclosure, such as starters
or panelboards, open the door while you are pouring the seal to observe whether or not
the seal is leaking into the enclosure.

## Anti-Seize Compound

When preparing sealing fittings, apply an approved anti-seize compound to the screw
threads and interior surfaces of the caps and plugs. This will facilitate removal of the
plugs for inspection purposes.

that the seal has been packed. When the sealing compound is poured, a different color paint is sprayed on the seal hub to indicate a finished job. This method permits the job supervisor to visually inspect the conduit run, and if a seal is not painted the appropriate color, he or she knows that the proper installation on this seal was not done; therefore, action can be taken to correct the situation immediately. The sealoff fittings in *Figure 11* are typical of those used. The type in *Figure 11(A)* is for vertical mounting and is provided with a threaded, plugged opening into which the sealing cement is poured. The sealoff in *Figure 11(B)* has an additional plugged opening in the lower hub to facilitate packing fiber around the conductors to form a dam for the sealing cement. *Figure 11(C)* shows a sealoff fitting along with fiber material and sealing compound.

The following guidelines should be observed when preparing sealing compound:

- Use a clean mix vessel for every batch. Particles of previous batches or dirt will spoil the seal.
- Recommended proportions are by volume— usually two parts powder to one part clean water. Slight deviations in these proportions will not affect the results.

- Do not mix more than can be poured in 15 minutes after water is added. Use cold water; warm water increases the setting speed. Stir immediately and thoroughly.
- If the batch starts to set, do not attempt to thin it by adding water or by stirring. Such a procedure will spoil the seal. Discard the partially set material and make a fresh batch. After pouring, close the opening immediately.
- Do not pour compound in sub-freezing temperatures or when these temperatures are likely to occur during curing.
- Ensure that the compound level is in accordance with the instruction sheet for the specific fitting.

Most other explosionproof fittings are provided with threaded hubs for securing the conduit as described previously. Typical fittings include switch and junction boxes, conduit bodies, unions and connectors, flexible couplings, explosionproof lighting fixtures, receptacles, and panelboard and motor starter enclosures. A practical representation of these and other fittings is shown in *Figure 12* through *14*.

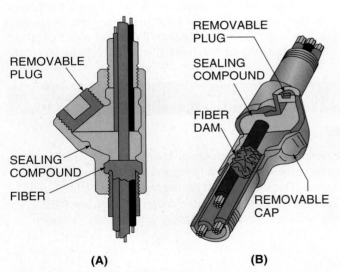

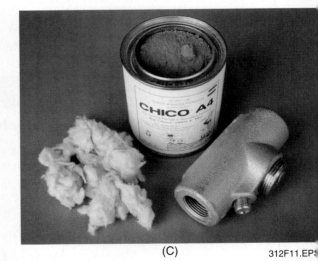

**(A)**          **(B)**          (C)          312F11.EPS

*Figure 11* ◆ Seals made with fiber dams and sealing compound.

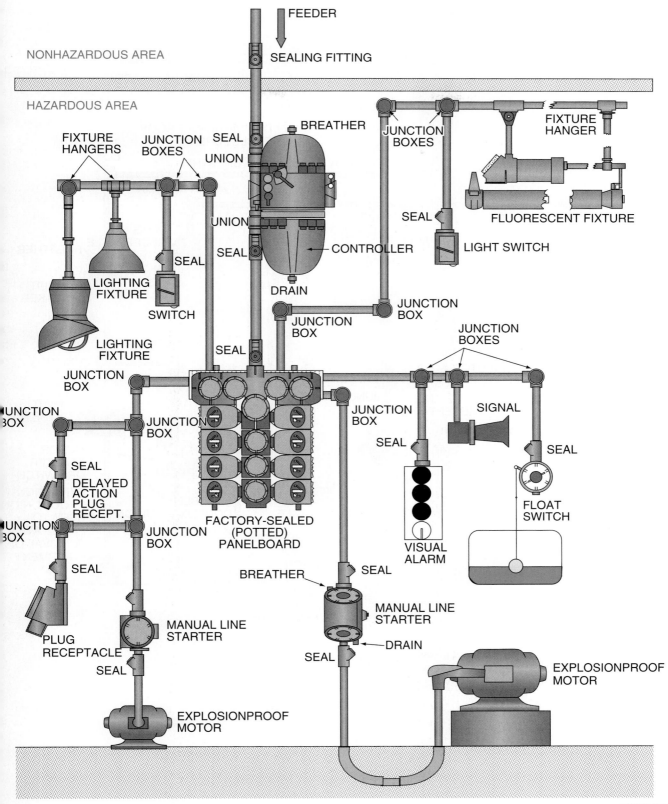

**NONHAZARDOUS AREA**

**HAZARDOUS AREA**

FEEDER

SEALING FITTING

FIXTURE HANGERS

JUNCTION BOXES

SEAL

UNION

BREATHER

JUNCTION BOXES

FIXTURE HANGER

SEAL

FLUORESCENT FIXTURE

LIGHTING FIXTURE

UNION

SEAL

CONTROLLER

LIGHT SWITCH

SEAL

SWITCH

DRAIN

JUNCTION BOX

JUNCTION BOX

LIGHTING FIXTURE

SEAL

JUNCTION BOX

JUNCTION BOX

JUNCTION BOXES

JUNCTION BOX

JUNCTION BOX

SIGNAL

SEAL

SEAL

SEAL

DELAYED ACTION PLUG RECEPT.

FACTORY-SEALED (POTTED) PANELBOARD

FLOAT SWITCH

JUNCTION BOX

JUNCTION BOX

VISUAL ALARM

SEAL

BREATHER

SEAL

MANUAL LINE STARTER

PLUG RECEPTACLE

MANUAL LINE STARTER

DRAIN

EXPLOSIONPROOF MOTOR

SEAL

SEAL

EXPLOSIONPROOF MOTOR

312F12.EPS

*Figure 12* ◆ Class I, Division 1 electrical installation.

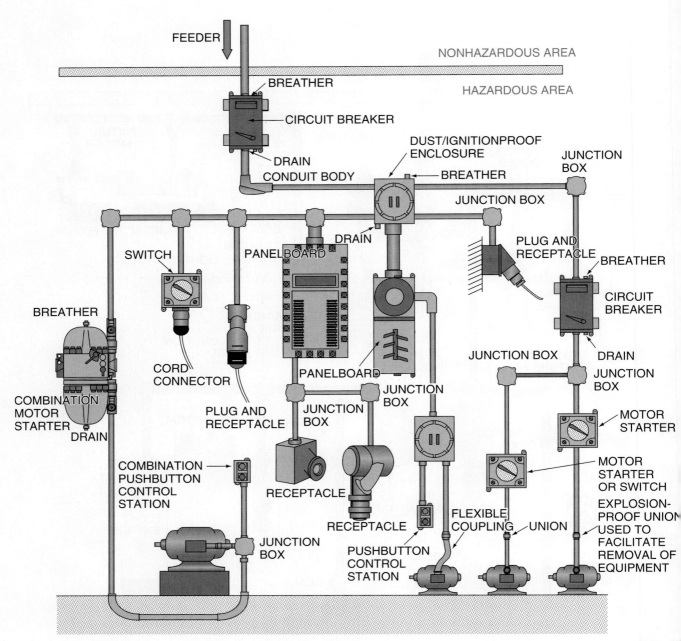

*Figure 13* ◆ Class II, Division 1 electrical installation.

312F13.EPS

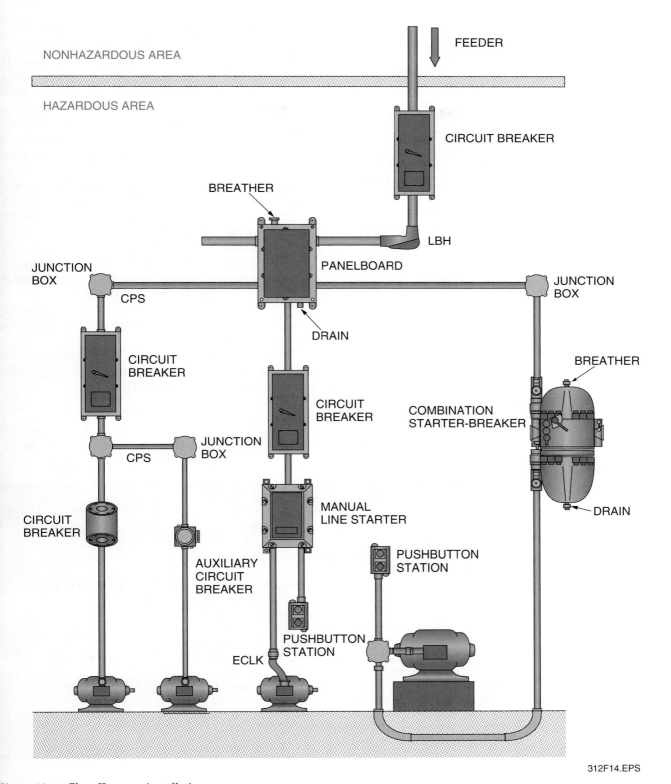

NONHAZARDOUS AREA

HAZARDOUS AREA

FEEDER

CIRCUIT BREAKER

BREATHER

LBH

JUNCTION BOX

CPS

PANELBOARD

DRAIN

JUNCTION BOX

CIRCUIT BREAKER

CIRCUIT BREAKER

BREATHER

COMBINATION STARTER-BREAKER

CPS

JUNCTION BOX

DRAIN

CIRCUIT BREAKER

MANUAL LINE STARTER

PUSHBUTTON STATION

AUXILIARY CIRCUIT BREAKER

PUSHBUTTON STATION

ECLK

312F14.EPS

*Figure 14* ◆ Class II power installation.

# 4.0.0 ◆ GARAGES AND SIMILAR LOCATIONS

Garages and similar locations where volatile or flammable liquids are handled or used as fuel in self-propelled vehicles (including automobiles, buses, trucks, and tractors) are not usually considered critically hazardous locations. However, the entire area up to a level 18" above the floor is considered a Class I, Division 2 location, and certain precautionary measures are required by the *NEC*®. Likewise, any pit or depression below floor level shall be considered a Class I, Division 2 location, and the pit or depression may be judged as a Class I, Division 1 location if it is unvented.

Normal raceway (conduit) and wiring may be used for the wiring method above this hazardous level, except where conditions indicate that the area concerned is more hazardous than usual. In this case, the applicable type of explosionproof wiring may be required.

Approved sealoff fittings should be used on all conduit passing from hazardous areas to nonhazardous areas. The requirements set forth in *NEC Article 501* apply to horizontal as well as vertical boundaries of the defined hazardous areas. Raceways embedded in a masonry floor or buried beneath a floor are considered to be within the hazardous area above the floor if any connection or extensions lead into or through such an area. However, conduit systems terminating to an open raceway in an outdoor unclassified area shall not be required to be sealed between the point at which the conduit leaves the classified location and enters the open raceway.

*Figure 15* shows a typical automotive service station with applicable *NEC*® requirements. The space in the immediate vicinity of the gasoline dispensing island is denoted as Class I, Division 1. The surrounding area, within a radius of 20' of the island, falls under Class I, Division 2 to a height of 18" above grade. Bulk storage plants for gasoline are subject to comparable restrictions.

*NEC Article 514* covers gasoline dispensing and service stations. *NEC Article 511* covers commercial garages.

A summary of *NEC*® rules governing the installation of electrical wiring at and near gasoline dispensing pumps is shown in *Table 7*.

| Table 7 *NEC*® Application Rules for Service Stations | | |
|---|---|---|
| **Application** | ***NEC*® Regulation** | ***NEC*® Reference** |
| Equipment in hazardous locations | All wiring and components must conform to the rules for Class I locations. | *NEC Section 514.4* |
| Equipment above hazardous locations | All wiring must conform to the rules for such equipment in commercial garages. | *NEC Section 514.4* |
| Gasoline dispenser | A disconnecting means must be provided for each circuit leading to or through a dispensing pump to disconnect all voltage sources, including feedback, during periods of service and maintenance. An approved seal (sealoff) is required in each conduit entering or leaving a dispenser. | *NEC Sections 514.7 and 514.13* |
| Grounding | Metal portions of all noncurrent-carrying parts of dispensers must be effectively grounded. | *NEC Section 514.16* |
| Underground wiring | Underground wiring installed within 2' of ground level shall be in threaded rigid metal conduit or IMC. If underground wiring is buried 2' or more, rigid nonmetallic conduit may be used along with the types mentioned above; Type MI cable may also be used in some cases. | *NEC Section 514.8* |

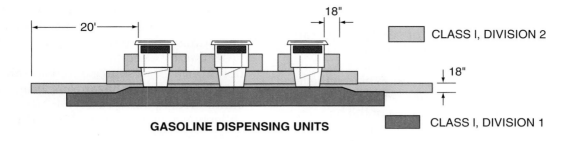

**GASOLINE DISPENSING UNITS**

CLASS I, DIVISION 2

CLASS I, DIVISION 1

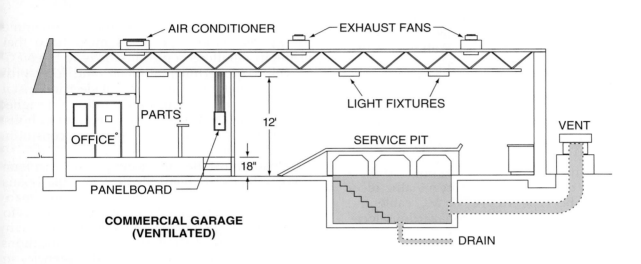

**COMMERCIAL GARAGE
(VENTILATED)**

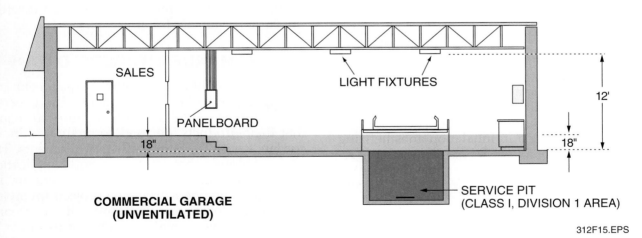

**COMMERCIAL GARAGE
(UNVENTILATED)**

312F15.EPS

*Figure 15* ◆ Commercial service station and garage classifications.

## 5.0.0 ◆ AIRPORT HANGARS

Buildings used for storing or servicing aircraft in which gasoline, jet fuels, or other volatile flammable liquids or gases are used fall under *NEC Article 513*. In general, any depression below the level of the hangar floor is considered to be a Class I, Division 1 location. The entire area of the hangar, including any adjacent and communicating area not suitably cut off from the hangar, is considered to be a Class I, Division 2 location up to a level of 18" above the floor. The area within 5' horizontally from aircraft power plants, fuel tanks, or structures containing fuel is considered to be a Class I, Division 2 hazardous location; this area extends upward from the floor to a level 5' above the upper surface of wings and engine enclosures.

Adjacent areas in which hazardous vapors are not likely to be released, such as stockrooms and electrical control rooms, should not be classified as hazardous when they are adequately ventilated and effectively cut off from the hangar itself by walls or partitions. All fixed wiring in a hangar not within a hazardous area as defined in *NEC Section 513.3* must be installed in metallic raceways or shall be Type MI, TC, or MC cable; the only exception is wiring in nonhazardous locations as defined in *NEC Section 513.3(D)*, which may be of any type recognized in *NEC Chapter 3*. *Figure 16* summarizes the *NEC®* requirements for airport hangars.

## 6.0.0 ◆ HOSPITALS

Hospitals and other healthcare facilities fall under *NEC Article 517*. *NEC Article 517, Part II* covers the general wiring in patient areas of healthcare facilities. *NEC Article 517, Part III* covers essential electrical systems for hospitals. *NEC Article 517, Part IV* gives the performance criteria and wiring methods used in inhalation anesthetizing locations. *NEC Article 517, Part V* covers the requirements for electrical wiring and equipment in X-ray installations. *NEC Article 517, Part VI* covers communications, signaling systems, and fire alarm systems. *NEC Article 517, Part VII* covers isolated power systems.

Anesthetizing locations of hospitals are considered Class I, Division 1 to a height of 5' above the floor. Gas storage rooms are designated as Class I, Division 1 throughout. Most of the wiring in these areas, however, can be limited to lighting fixtures only by locating all switches and other devices outside of the hazardous area.

The *NEC®* recommends that electrical equipment for hazardous locations be located in less hazardous areas wherever possible. It also suggests that by adequate, positive-pressure ventilation from a clean source of outside air, the hazard may be reduced or hazardous locations limited or eliminated. In many cases, the installation of dust collecting systems can greatly reduce the hazard in a Class II area.

## 7.0.0 ◆ PETROCHEMICAL HAZARDOUS LOCATIONS

Most manufacturing facilities involving flammable liquids, vapors, or fibers must have their wiring installations conform strictly to the *NEC* as well as governmental, state, and local ordinances. Therefore, the majority of electrical installations for these facilities are carefully designed by experts in the field—either the plant in-house engineering staff or an independent consulting engineering firm.

Industrial installations dealing with petroleum or some types of chemicals are particularly susceptible to several restrictions involving many governmental agencies. Electrical installations for petrochemical plants will therefore have many pages of electrical drawings and specifications which require approval from all the agencies involved. Once approved, these drawings and specifications must be followed exactly, because any change whatsoever must once again go through the various agencies for approval.

## 8.0.0 ◆ MANUFACTURERS' DATA

Manufacturers of explosionproof equipment and fittings expend a lot of time, energy, and expense in developing guidelines and brochures to ensure that their products are used correctly and in accordance with the latest *NEC®* requirements. The many helpful charts, tables, and application guidelines available from manufacturers are invaluable to anyone working on projects involving hazardous locations. Therefore, it is recommended that you obtain as much of this data as possible. Once obtained, study this data thoroughly. Doing so will enhance your qualification for working in hazardous locations of any type. Manufacturers' data is usually available to qualified personnel at little or no cost and can be obtained from local distributors or directly from the manufacturer.

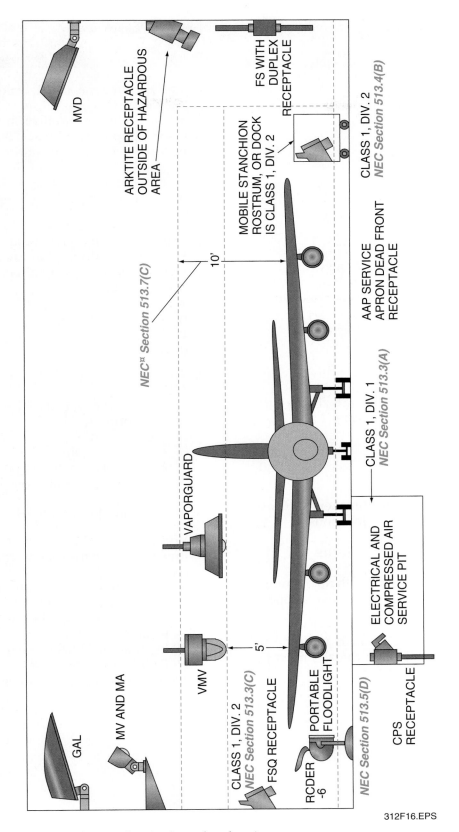

MVD

ARKTITE RECEPTACLE
OUTSIDE OF HAZARDOUS
AREA

FS WITH
DUPLEX
RECEPTACLE

CLASS 1, DIV. 2
*NEC Section 513.4(B)*

MOBILE STANCHION
ROSTRUM, OR DOCK
IS CLASS 1, DIV. 2

*NEC¤ Section 513.7(C)*

10'

AAP SERVICE
APRON DEAD FRONT
RECEPTACLE

CLASS 1, DIV. 1
*NEC Section 513.3(A)*

VAPORGUARD

MV AND MA

GAL

VMV

CLASS 1, DIV. 2
*NEC Section 513.3(C)*

FSQ RECEPTACLE

5'

PORTABLE
FLOODLIGHT

RCDER
-6

*NEC Section 513.5(D)*

CPS
RECEPTACLE

ELECTRICAL AND
COMPRESSED AIR
SERVICE PIT

312F16.EPS

*Figure 16* ◆ Sections of an airport hangar showing hazardous locations.

# Review Questions

1. The *NEC®* lists _____ classification(s) of hazardous atmospheres.
   a. one
   b. two
   c. three
   d. four

2. There is/are _____ division(s) for each classification.
   a. one
   b. two
   c. three
   d. four

3. There is/are _____ group(s) listed under Class I, Division 1.
   a. one
   b. two
   c. three
   d. four

4. Which of the following are the groups listed under Class II, Division 1?
   a. A, B, C, and D
   b. E, F, G
   c. H, I, J
   d. L, M, N

5. When installing circuit breakers in Class II, Division 1 hazardous locations, a _____ must be used.
   a. dust/ignitionproof enclosure
   b. dust-tight enclosure
   c. tight metal enclosure with no openings
   d. standard enclosure with several openings

6. When rigid metal conduit is required in hazardous locations, the threads must be cut at _____ taper per foot.
   a. ½"
   b. ¾"
   c. 1"
   d. 1¼"

7. The main purpose of a union in conduit runs is to _____.
   a. facilitate the installation and removal of equipment
   b. ensure grounding continuity
   c. seal the system from flammable gases or vapors
   d. form tighter joints in the system

8. When installing switches or other arc-producing apparatus in Class I, Division 1 locations, within what distance of the switch (or other apparatus) must sealing fittings be installed?
   a. 6"
   b. 12"
   c. 18"
   d. 24"

9. The purpose of packing fiber in a sealing fitting is to _____.
   a. identify the type of seal and the sealing compound to use
   b. prevent any liquids, gases, or vapors from passing through the fitting
   c. prevent flammable vapors from mixing with the sealing compound
   d. provide a dam to contain the sealing compound until it hardens

10. Which of the following best describes the time to pour in the sealing compound in a sealing fitting?
    a. Within five minutes after it is installed in a raceway system
    b. After the conduit system and seals are installed and the conductors and packing fiber have been installed
    c. Prior to installing the packing fiber
    d. After the threaded plug is set tight

## Summary

ny area in which the atmosphere or a material in he area is such that the arcing of operating electrical contacts, components, and equipment may ause an explosion or fire is considered a hazardous location. In all such cases, explosionproof equipment, raceways, and fittings are used to provide an explosionproof wiring system.

The wide assortment of explosionproof equipment now available makes it possible to provide adequate electrical installations under any of the various hazardous conditions. However, you must be thoroughly familiar with all *NEC*® requirements and know what fittings are available, how to install them properly, and where and when to use the various fittings.

## Notes

# Trade Terms
# Introduced in This Module

*Approved:* Acceptable to the authority having jurisdiction.

*Conduit:* A tubular raceway such as electrical metallic tubing (EMT); rigid metal conduit, rigid nonmetallic conduit, etc.

*Conduit body:* A separate portion of a conduit or tubing system that provides access through removable covers to the interior of the system at a junction of two or more sections of the system or at a terminal point of the system.

*Equipment:* A general term including material, fittings, devices, appliances, fixtures, apparatus, and the like used as a part of (or in connection with) an electrical installation.

*Explosionproof:* Designed and constructed to withstand an internal explosion without creating an external explosion or fire.

*Explosionproof apparatus:* Apparatus enclosed in a case that is capable of withstanding an ex-plosion of a specified gas or vapor that may occur within it; also capable of preventing the ignition of a specified gas or vapor surrounding the enclosure by sparks, flashes, or explosion of the gas or vapor within; which operates at such an external temperature that a surrounding flammable atmosphere will not be ignited thereby.

*Hazardous (classified) location:* A location in which ignitable vapors, dust, or fibers may cause a fire or explosion.

*Sealing compound:* The material poured into an electrical fitting to seal and minimize the passage of vapors.

*Sealoff fittings:* Fittings required in conduit systems to prevent the passage of gases, vapors, or flames from one portion of the electrical installation to another through the conduit. Also referred to as sealing fittings or seals.

## Additional Resources

This module is intended to present thorough resources for task training. The following reference works are suggested for further study. These are optional materials for continued education rather than for task training.

*American Electrician's Handbook.* Terrell Croft and Wilfred I. Summers. New York, NY: McGraw-Hill, 1996.

*Code Digest.* Latest Edition. Syracuse, NY: Crouse-Hinds.

*National Electrical Code® Handbook.* Latest Edition. Quincy, MA: National Fire Protection Association.

*CONTREN® LEARNING SERIES — USER FEEDBACK*

The NCCER makes every effort to keep these textbooks up-to-date and free of technical errors. We appreciate your help in this process. If you have an idea for improving this textbook, or if you find an error, a typographical mistake, or an inaccuracy in NCCER's *Contren®* textbooks, please write us, using this form or a photocopy. Be sure to include the exact module number, page number, a detailed description, and the correction, if applicable. Your input will be brought to the attention of the Technical Review Committee. Thank you for your assistance.

*Instructors* – If you found that additional materials were necessary in order to teach this module effectively, please let us know so that we may include them in the Equipment/Materials list in the Annotated Instructor's Guide.

**Write:**  Product Development
National Center for Construction Education and Research
P.O. Box 141104, Gainesville, FL 32614-1104

**Fax:**  352-334-0932

**E-mail:**  curriculum@nccer.org

Craft _____  Module Name _____

Copyright Date _____  Module Number _____  Page Number(s) _____

Description _____

_____

_____

_____

(Optional) Correction _____

_____

_____

(Optional) Your Name and Address _____

_____

_____

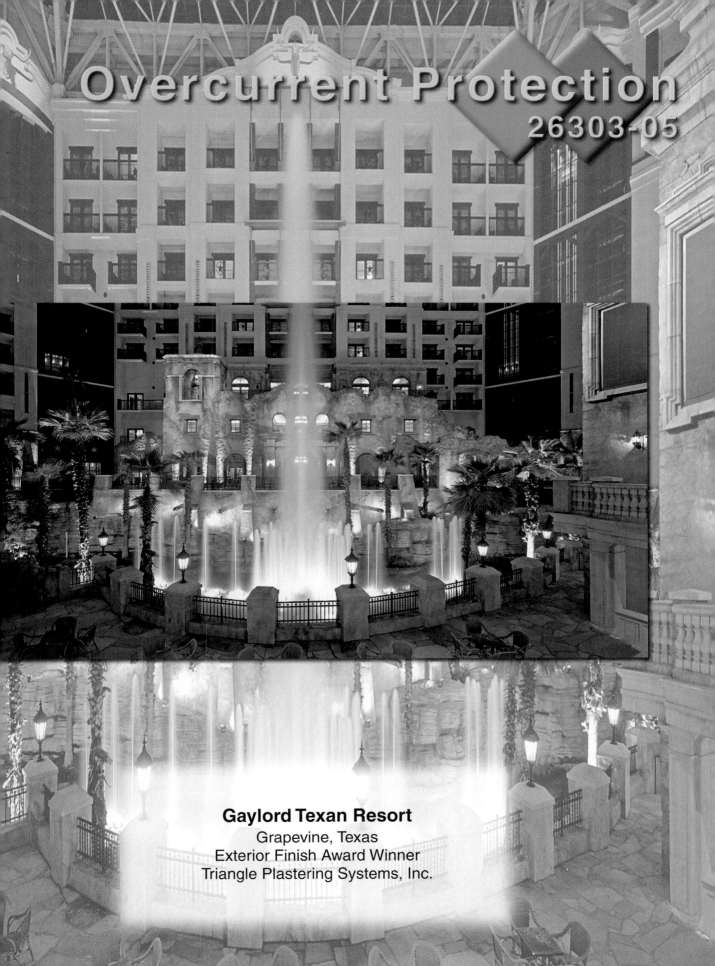

# Overcurrent Protection

## 26303-05

**Gaylord Texan Resort**
Grapevine, Texas
Exterior Finish Award Winner
Triangle Plastering Systems, Inc.

# 26303-05
# *Overcurrent Protection*

*Topics to be presented in this module include:*

## Overview

Overcurrent protective devices are used primarily to protect the conductor from excessive heat caused by overcurrent. However, some overcurrent protective devices also function to protect equipment. There are three categories of overcurrent: overloads, short circuits, and ground faults.

An overload occurs when the load in amperes exceeds the normal operating or intended current level. A short circuit occurs when an unintended path develops from one current-carrying circuit conductor to another, either bypassing the load entirely or in some cases, partially bypassing the load. Ground faults only occur in grounded electrical systems in which one current-carrying conductor is intentionally grounded. In a ground fault situation, an ungrounded current-carrying conductor makes unintended contact with earth ground or a conductive part that is grounded. This condition provides a path for the electrons to get back to the source by using the earth ground as a conductive path back to the point at which the system is grounded.

Overcurrent protective devices must be selected based on the voltage to which they will be exposed, the trip ampere rating for the circuit, and the interrupting rating (in amperes).

## Objectives

When you have completed this module, you will be able to do the following:

1. Apply the key *National Electrical Code®* (*NEC®*) requirements regarding overcurrent protection.
2. Check specific applications for conformance to *NEC®* sections that cover short circuit current, fault currents, interrupting ratings, and other sections relating to overcurrent protection.
3. Determine let-through current values (peak and rms) when current-limiting overcurrent devices are used.
4. Select and size overcurrent protection for specific applications.

## Trade Terms

| | |
|---|---|
| Ampere rating | Melting time |
| Ampere squared seconds ($I^2t$) | *NEC®* dimensions |
| | Overload |
| Amperes interrupting capacity (AIC) | Peak let-through (Ip) |
| | Root-mean-square (rms) |
| Arcing time | Semiconductor fuse |
| Clearing time | Short circuit current |
| Current-limiting device | Single phasing |
| Fast-acting fuse | UL classes |
| Inductive load | Voltage rating |

## Required Trainee Materials

1. Pencil and paper
2. Appropriate personal protective equipment
3. Copy of the latest edition of the *National Electrical Code®*

## Prerequisites

Before you begin this module, it is recommended that you successfully complete *Core Curriculum; Electrical Level One; Electrical Level Two; Electrical Level Three,* Modules 26301-05 and 26302-05.

This course map shows all of the modules in *Electrical Level Three.* The suggested training order begins at the bottom and proceeds up. Skill levels increase as you advance on the course map. The local Training Program Sponsor may adjust the training order.

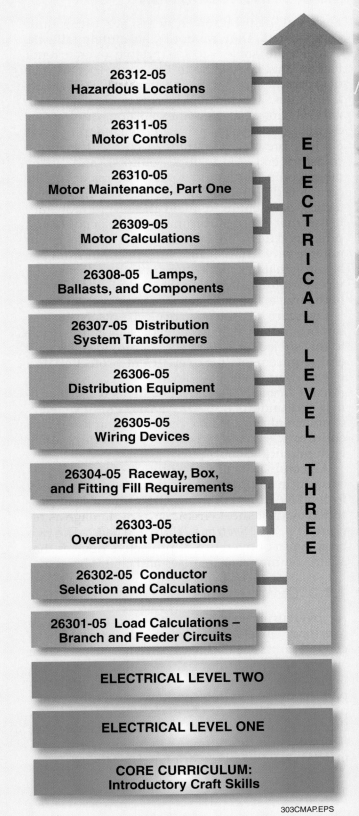

303CMAP.EPS

# 1.0.0 ◆ INTRODUCTION

Electrical distribution systems are often quite complicated. They cannot be absolutely fail-safe. Circuits are subject to destructive overcurrents. Factors that contribute to the occurrence of such overcurrents are harsh environments, general deterioration, accidental damage or damage from natural causes, excessive expansion, or electrical distribution system overload. Reliable protective devices prevent or minimize costly damage to transformers, conductors, motors, and many other components and loads that make up the complete distribution system. Reliable circuit protection is essential to avoid the severe monetary losses that can result from power blackouts and prolonged downtime of facilities. It is the need for reliable protection, safety, and freedom from fire hazards that has made overcurrent protective devices absolutely necessary in all electrical systems, both large and small.

Overcurrent protection of electrical circuits is so important that the *NEC*® devotes an entire article to this subject. *NEC Article 240* provides the general requirements for overcurrent protection and overcurrent protective devices. *NEC Article 240, Parts I through VIII* cover systems 600V (nominal) and under; *NEC Article 240, Part IX* covers overcurrent protection over 600V (nominal). This entire article will be covered in this module, along with practical examples.

All conductors must be protected against overcurrents in accordance with their ampacities as set forth in *NEC Section 240.3.* They must also be protected against **short circuit current** damage as required by *NEC Sections 110.10 and 240.1.* The two basic types of overcurrent protective devices that are in common use are fuses and circuit breakers.

## 1.1.0 Overcurrents

An overcurrent condition may be caused by an **overload** current, a short circuit current, or a ground fault. The overload current is an excessive current relative to normal operating current but one that is confined to the normal conductive paths provided by the conductor and other components and loads of the distribution system. As the name implies, a short circuit current is one that flows outside the normal conducting paths and may be phase-to-phase or phase-to-ground.

### 1.1.1 Overloads

Overloads are most often between one and six times the normal current level. Usually, they are caused by temporary surge currents that occur when motors are started up or transformers are energized. Such overload currents or transient are normal occurrences. Since they are of brief duration, any temperature rise is momentary and has no harmful effect on the circuit component so long as the system is designed to accommodate them.

Continuous overloads can result from defective motors (such as worn motor bearings), overloaded equipment, or too many loads on one circuit. Such sustained overloads are destructive and must be cut off by protective devices before they damage the distribution system or system load. However, since they are of relatively low magnitude compared to short circuit currents, removal of the overload current within a few second will generally prevent equipment damage. A sustained overload current results in overheating of conductors and other components and will cause deterioration of insulation, which may eventually result in severe damage and short circuits if no interrupted.

### 1.1.2 Short Circuits

A short circuit is a conducting connection whether intentional or accidental, between any of the conductors of an electrical system, either line to-line or line-to-ground.

The **amperes interrupting capacity (AIC)** rating of a circuit breaker or fuse is the maximum short circuit current that the breaker will safely interrupt. This AIC rating is at rated voltage and frequency.

Whereas overload currents occur at rather modest levels, a short circuit or fault current can be many hundreds of times larger than the normal operating current. A high-level fault may be 50,000A (or larger). If not cut off within a matter of a few thousandths of a second, damage and destruction can become rampant—there can be severe insulation damage, melting of conductors, vaporization of metal, ionization of gases, arcing, and fires. Simultaneously, high-level short circuit currents can develop huge magnetic field stresses. The magnetic forces between busbars and other conductors can be many hundreds of pounds per lineal foot; even heavy bracing may not be adequate to keep them from being warped or distorted beyond repair.

*NEC Section 110.9* clearly states that equipment intended to interrupt current at fault levels (fuse and circuit breakers) must have an interrupting rating sufficient for the nominal circuit voltage and the current that is available at the line terminals of the equipment.

Equipment intended to interrupt current at other than fault levels must have an interrupting

ting at nominal circuit voltage sufficient for the current that must be interrupted.

These *NEC*® statements mean that fuses and circuit breakers (and their related components) designed to interrupt fault or operating currents (open the circuit) must have a rating sufficient to withstand such currents. This section emphasizes the difference between clearing fault level currents and clearing operating currents. Protective devices such as fuses and circuit breakers are designed to clear fault currents and therefore must have short circuit interrupting ratings sufficient for fault levels. Equipment such as contactors and safety switches have interrupting ratings for currents at other than fault levels. Thus, the interrupting rating of electrical equipment is now divided into two parts:

Current at fault (short circuit) levels
Current at operating levels

Most people are familiar with the normal current-carrying ampere rating of fuses and circuit breakers. For example, if an overcurrent protective device is designed to open a circuit when the circuit load exceeds 20A for a given time period, as the current approaches 20A, the overcurrent protective device begins to overheat. If the current barely exceeds 20A, the circuit breaker will open normally or a fuse link will melt after a given period of time with little, if any, arcing. For example, if 40A of current were instantaneously applied to the circuit, the overcurrent protective device would open, but again with very little arcing. However, if a ground fault occurs on the circuit that ran the amperage up to 5,000A, for example, an explosion effect would occur within the protective device. One simple indication of this is the blackened windows of plug fuses.

If this fault current exceeds the interrupting rating of a fuse or circuit breaker, the protective device can be damaged or destroyed; such current can also cause severe damage to equipment and injure personnel. Therefore, selecting overcurrent protective devices with the proper interrupting capacity is extremely important in all electrical systems.

There are several factors that must be considered when calculating the required interrupting capacity of an overcurrent protective device. *NEC Section 110.10* states that the overcurrent protective devices, total impedance, component short circuit current ratings, and other characteristics of the circuit to be protected shall be selected and coordinated to permit the circuit protective devices used to clear a fault to do so without extensive damage to the electrical components of the circuit. This fault shall be assumed to be either between two or more of the circuit conductors, or between any circuit conductor and the grounding conductor or enclosing metal raceway.

The component short circuit rating is a current rating given to conductors, switches, circuit breakers, and other electrical components, which, if exceeded by fault currents, will result in extensive damage to the component. The rating is expressed in terms of time intervals and/or current values. Short circuit damage can be the result of heat generated or the electromechanical force of a high-intensity magnetic field.

The *NEC*®'s intent is that the design of a system must be such that short circuit currents cannot exceed the short circuit current ratings of the components selected as part of the system. Given specific system components and the level of available short circuit currents that could occur, overcurrent protective devices (mainly fuses and/or circuit breakers) must be used that will limit the energy let-through of fault currents to levels within the withstand ratings of the system components.

### 1.1.3 Ground Faults

A ground fault is a conducting connection, whether intentional or accidental, between any of the conductors of an electrical system and the conducting material that encloses the conductors or any conducting material that is grounded or may become grounded.

## 2.0.0 ◆ FUSES

The fuse is a reliable overcurrent protective device. It consists of a fusible link or links encapsulated in a tube and connected to contact terminals. The electrical resistance of the link is so low that it simply acts as a conductor. However, when destructive currents occur, the link quickly melts and opens the circuit to protect conductors and other circuit components and loads. Fuse characteristics are stable and do not require periodic maintenance or testing.

### 2.1.0 Types of Fuses

*NEC Article 240, Part V* contains the requirements associated with plug fuses, plug fuseholders, and adapters; *NEC Article 240, Part VI* lists those requirements applying to cartridge fuses and cartridge fuseholders. Plug fuses are normally used in general-purpose branch circuits. Cartridge fuses may be found in branch circuits, feeder circuits, motor circuits, and many other special applications.

## Fuseholder Safety

Always verify that the fuseholders are not energized before replacing any fuses. Keep in mind that if the fuseholder is wired backfed, the fuseholder will remain energized even though the disconnect is in the OFF position. Also, if a switch is bleeding through, one knife blade may remain touching, keeping it energized.

## Fuse Position

Always make a point of installing fuses right side up, with the label pointing out. When a fuse requires replacement and the label is upside down or backwards, the typical response would be to reach in and twist it around to read the label. This can result in serious shocks or even death.

Per *NEC Section 240.50(A)*, plug fuses are only permitted in circuits not exceeding 125V between conductors or in circuits supplied by a system having a grounded neutral where the line-to-neutral voltage does not exceed 150V.

Plug fuses rated at 15A or less have hexagonal windows or caps so that they may easily be distinguished from fuses of higher ampere ratings. This is a requirement of *NEC Section 240.50(C)*. Plug fuses with an ampere rating above 15A have a round window.

There are two screw-in configurations associated with plug fuses, Edison-base and Type S. An adapter is available to convert an Edison-base socket to a Type S socket. The Edison-base socket is a standard screw-in base, which allows any ampere-rated Edison fuse to be installed. The Type S socket is matched to a specific-rated fuse and will not accept any other fuse except that rating.

*NEC Section 240.52* prohibits the use of Edison-base fuseholders in new installations except where they are made to accept Type S fuses using the adapter method.

Per *NEC Section 240.60(A)*, cartridge fuses and fuseholders rated at 300V are only permitted to be used in circuits not exceeding 300V between conductors, or in single-phase, line-to-neutral circuits supplied from a three-phase, four-wire, solidly grounded, neutral source where the line-to-neutral voltage does not exceed 300V.

### 2.2.0 Voltage Rating

Most low-voltage power distribution fuses have 250V or 600V ratings. The **voltage rating** of a fuse

must be at least equal to or greater than the circu voltage. It can be higher, but never lower. For e ample, a 600V fuse can be used in a 240V circui

The voltage rating of a fuse is a function of depends upon its capability to open a circuit u der an overcurrent condition. Specifically, t voltage rating determines the ability of the fuse suppress the internal arcing that occurs after fuse link melts and an arc is produced (arci time). If a fuse is used with a voltage rating low than the circuit voltage, arc suppression will impaired and, under some fault current cond tions, the fuse may not safely clear the overcu rent. Special consideration is necessary f **semiconductor fuse** applications in which a fu of a certain voltage rating is used on a lowe voltage circuit.

### 2.3.0 Ampere Rating

Every fuse has a specific ampere rating. When s lecting the ampere rating, consideration must l given to the size and type of load and *NEC* requirements. The ampere rating of a fuse shou normally not exceed the current-carrying capaci of the circuit. For instance, if a conductor is rated carry 20A, a 20A fuse is the largest that should l used. However, there are specific circumstances which the ampere rating is permitted to be great than the current-carrying capacity of the circuit. typical example is the motor circuit; dual-eleme fuses are generally permitted to be sized up 175% and nontime-delay fuses up to 300% of th motor full-load amperes. Generally, the ampe rating of a fuse and switch combination should l lected at 125% of the continuous load current (this usually corresponds to the circuit capacity, which is also selected at 125% of the load current). There are exceptions, such as when the fuse-switch combination is approved for continuous operation at 100% of its rating.

## 2.4.0 Interrupting Rating

A protective device must be able to withstand the destructive energy of short circuit currents. If a fault current exceeds a level beyond the capability of the protective device, the device may actually rupture, causing additional damage. Therefore, it is important to choose a protective device that can sustain the largest potential short circuit currents. The rating that defines the capacity of a protective device to maintain its integrity when reacting to fault currents is called its interrupting rating.

*NEC Section 110.9* requires equipment intended to interrupt current at fault levels to have an interrupting rating sufficient for the current that must be interrupted. Interrupting rating and interrupting capacity were covered in your Level

Two training; more advanced material is presented in this module.

## 2.5.0 Selective Coordination

The coordination of protective devices prevents system power outages or blackouts caused by overcurrent conditions. When only the protective device nearest a faulted circuit opens and larger upstream fuses remain closed, the protective devices are selectively coordinated (they discriminate). The word selective is used to denote total coordination (isolation of a faulted circuit by the opening of only the localized protective device).

*Figure 1* shows the minimum ratios of ampere rating of low peak fuses that are required to provide selective coordination of upstream and downstream fuses.

## 2.6.0 Current Limitation

If a protective device cuts off a short circuit current in less than one half cycle, before it reaches its total available (and highly destructive) value, the

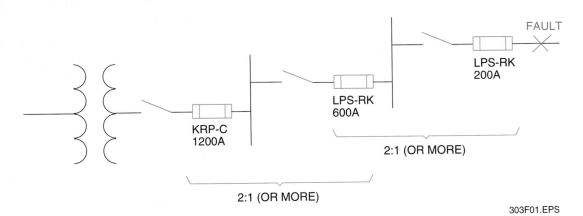

303F01.EPS

*Figure 1* ◆ Selective coordination.

### *Fault Current Protection*

In a fully rated system, each overcurrent protective device has an interrupting rating that is equal to or greater than the available fault current at the service entrance. Fully rated systems are approved for use in all locations.

In a series rated system, the main upstream breaker has an interrupting capacity equal to or greater than the available fault current at the service entrance, but the downstream protective devices can be rated at lower values and therefore, will have a lower installed cost. Series rated systems have their place in the industry in areas where the tripping of a main breaker would cause a nuisance but would not result in an unsafe condition or the interruption of a critical process. For this reason, series rated systems are not approved for use in all locations. (See also *NEC Section 110.22*.)

device is a **current-limiting device.** Most modern fuses are current-limiting devices. They restrict fault currents to such low values that a high degree of protection is given to circuit components against even very high short circuit currents. They permit breakers with lower interrupting ratings to be used and can reduce bracing of bus structures. They also minimize the need for other components to have high short circuit current ratings. If not limited, short circuit currents can reach levels of 30,000A or 40,000A or higher in the first half cycle (0.008 second at 60Hz) after the start of a short circuit. The heat that can be produced in circuit components by the immense energy of short circuit currents can cause severe insulation damage or even an explosion. At the same time, the huge magnetic forces developed between conductors can crack insulators and distort and destroy bracing structures. Thus, it is extremely important that a protective device limit fault currents before they can reach their full potential level.

A noncurrent-limiting protective device, by permitting a short circuit current to build up to its full value, can let an immense amount of destructive short circuit heat energy through before opening the circuit, as shown in *Figure 2*. On the other hand, a current-limiting device (such as a current-limiting fuse) has such a high speed of response that it cuts off a short circuit long before it can build up to its full peak value, as shown in *Figure 3*.

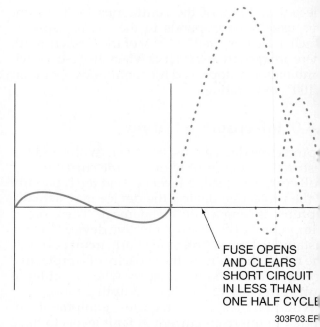

FUSE OPENS
AND CLEARS
SHORT CIRCUIT
IN LESS THAN
ONE HALF CYCLE

303F03.EP

***Figure 3*** ◆ Characteristics of a current-limiting fuse.

### 3.0.0 ◆ OPERATING PRINCIPLES OF FUSES

This section describes the operating characteristics of various types of fuses. These fuses include the nontime-delay and the dual-element, time-delay fuses.

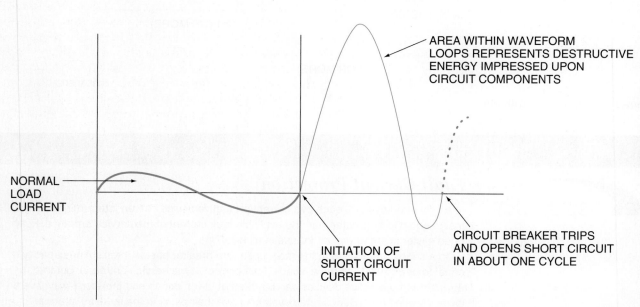

NORMAL
LOAD
CURRENT

AREA WITHIN WAVEFORM
LOOPS REPRESENTS DESTRUCTIVE
ENERGY IMPRESSED UPON
CIRCUIT COMPONENTS

INITIATION OF
SHORT CIRCUIT
CURRENT

CIRCUIT BREAKER TRIPS
AND OPENS SHORT CIRCUIT
IN ABOUT ONE CYCLE

303F02.EPS

***Figure 2*** ◆ Characteristics of a noncurrent-limiting protective device.

# 1.0 Nontime-Delay Fuses

e basic component of a fuse is the link. De-
nding upon the ampere rating of the fuse, the
gle-element, nontime-delay fuse may have one
more links. They are electrically connected to
e end blades (or ferrules) and enclosed in a tube
cartridge surrounded by an arc-quenching
ler material.

Under normal operation, when the fuse is op-
ating at or near its ampere rating, it simply func-
ns as a conductor. However, as illustrated in
*gure 4,* if an overload current occurs and persists
more than a short interval of time, the temper-
ure of the link eventually reaches a level that
uses a restricted segment of the link to melt; as
esult, a gap is formed and an electric arc estab-
hed. As the arc causes the link metal to burn
ck, the gap becomes progressively larger. The

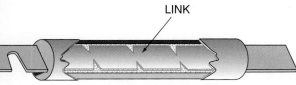

LINK

Cut-away view of single-element fuse.

Under sustained overload, a section of the link
melts and an arc is established.

The open single-element fuse after opening a
circuit overload.

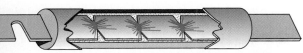

When subjected to a short circuit, several sections
of the fuse link melt almost instantly.

The appearance of an open single-element fuse
after opening a short circuit.

303F04.EPS

*ure 4* ◆ Characteristics of a single-element fuse.

electrical resistance of the arc eventually reaches
such a high level that the arc cannot be sustained
and is extinguished; the fuse will have then completely cut off all current flow in the circuit. Suppression or quenching of the arc is accelerated by
the filler material.

Overload current normally falls within the region of between one and six times normal current,
resulting in currents that are quite high. Consequently, a fuse may be subjected to short circuit
currents of 30,000A to 40,000A or higher. The response of current-limiting fuses to such currents is
extremely fast. The restricted sections of the fuse
link will simultaneously melt within a matter of
two-thousandths or three-thousandths of a second in the event of a high-level fault current.

The high resistance of the multiple arcs, together with the quenching effects of the filler particles, results in rapid arc suppression and
clearing of the circuit. Again, refer to *Figure 3.* The
short circuit current is cut off in less than one half
cycle, long before the short circuit current can
reach its full value.

## 3.2.0 Dual-Element, Time-Delay Fuses

Unlike single-element fuses, the dual-element,
time-delay fuse can be applied in circuits subject
to temporary motor overloads and surge currents
to provide both high-performance short circuit
and overload protection. Oversizing to prevent
nuisance openings is not necessary with this type
of fuse. The dual-element, time-delay fuse contains two distinctly separate types of elements.
Electrically, the two elements are connected in series. The fuse links (similar to those used in the
nontime-delay fuse) perform the short circuit protection function; the overload element provides
protection against low-level overcurrents or overloads and will hold an overload that is five times
greater than the ampere rating of the fuse for a
minimum time of 10 seconds.

As shown in *Figure 5,* the overload section consists of a copper heat absorber and a spring-
operated trigger assembly. The heat absorber bar
is permanently connected to the heat absorber extension and the short circuit link on the opposite
end of the fuse by the S-shaped connector of the
trigger assembly. The connector electrically joins
the short circuit link to the heat absorber in the
overload section of the fuse. These elements are
joined by a calibrated fusing alloy. An overload
current causes heating of the short circuit link connected to the trigger assembly. The transfer of heat
from the short circuit link to the heat absorber

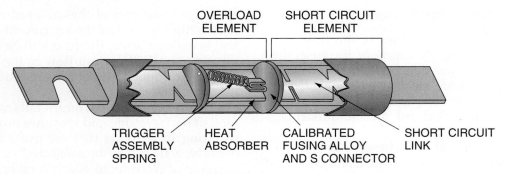

OVERLOAD ELEMENT     SHORT CIRCUIT ELEMENT

TRIGGER ASSEMBLY SPRING     HEAT ABSORBER     CALIBRATED FUSING ALLOY AND S CONNECTOR     SHORT CIRCUIT LINK

The true dual-element fuse has distinct and separate overload and short circuit elements.

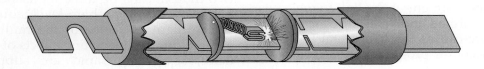

Under sustained overload conditions, the trigger spring fractures the calibrated fusing alloy and releases the connector.

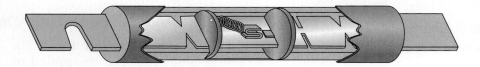

The dual-element fuse after opening under an overload.

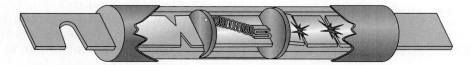

Like the single-element fuse, a short circuit current causes the restricted portions of the short circuit elements to melt and arcing to burn back the resulting gaps until the arcs are suppressed by the arc-quenching material and increased arc resistance.

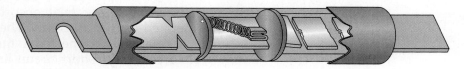

The dual-element fuse after opening under a short circuit condition.

303F05.EPS

*Figure 5* ◆ Characteristics of a dual-element, time-delay fuse.

begins to raise the temperature of the heat absorber. If the overload is sustained, the temperature of the heat absorber eventually reaches a level that permits the trigger spring to fracture the

calibrated fusing alloy and pull the connector fr of the short circuit link and the heat absorber. As result, the short circuit link is electrical disconnected from the heat absorber, t

ducting path through the fuse is opened, and
e overload current is interrupted. A critical as-
ct of the fusing alloy is that it retains its original
aracteristics after repeated temporary over-
ds without degradation.

The advantages of dual-element fuses are:

Provide motor overload, ground fault, and
short circuit protection
Permit the use of smaller and less costly
switches
Give a higher degree of short circuit protection
(greater current limitation) in circuits in which
surge currents or temporary overloads occur
Simplify and improve blackout prevention (selective coordination)

# .0 ◆ UL FUSE CLASSES

fety is the primary consideration of Underwrit-
; Laboratories, Inc. (UL). The proper selection,
erall functional performance, and reliability of
product are factors that are not within the basic
pe of UL activities. However, to develop its
ety test procedures, UL does develop the basic
rformance and physical specifications of stan-
rds of a product. In the case of fuses, these stan-
rds have culminated in the establishment of
stinct UL classes of low-voltage (600V or less)
es. Various UL fuse classes are described in the
lowing paragraphs.

UL Class R (rejection) fuses are high-
rformance ⅒A to 600A units, 250V and 600V,
ving a high degree of current limitation and a
ort circuit interrupting rating of up to 200,000A
ot-mean-square [rms] symmetrical). This type
fuse is designed to be mounted in rejection-type
se clips to prevent older Class H fuses from be-
; installed. Since Class H fuses are not current-
niting devices and are recognized by UL as
ving only a 10,000A interrupting rating, serious
mage could result if a Class H fuse were in-
ted in a system designed for Class R fuses.
nsequently, *NEC Section 240.60(B)* requires
seholders for current-limiting fuses to reject
ncurrent-limiting fuses.

*Figure 6* shows standard Class H and Class R
rtridge fuses. A grooved ring in one ferrule of
e Class R fuse provides the rejection feature of
e Class R fuse in contrast to the lower interrupt-
; capacity, nonrejection type. *Figure 7* shows
se rejection clips for Class R fuses.

Class CC fuses are 600V, 200,000A interrupting
ing, branch circuit fuses with overall dimen-
ns of $^{13}\!/_{32}"$ × 1½". Their design incorporates re-
tion features that allow them to be inserted into
ection fuseholders and fuse blocks that reject all

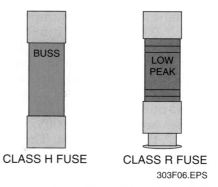

**Figure 6** ◆ Comparison of Class H and Class R fuses.

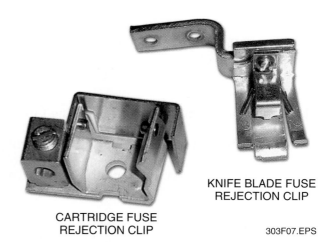

**Figure 7** ◆ Fuse rejection clips.

lower voltage, lower interrupting rating $^{13}\!/_{32}"$ × 1½"
fuses. They are available from ⅒A through 30A.

Class G fuses are 300V, 100,000A interrupting
rating branch circuit fuses that are size rejecting to
eliminate overfusing. The fuse diameter is $^{13}\!/_{32}"$,
while the length varies from 1⅝" to 2¼". They are
available in ratings from 1A through 60A.

Class H fuses are 250V and 600V, 10,000A interrupting rating branch circuit fuses that may be re-
newable or nonrenewable. They are available in
ampere ratings of 1A through 600A.

Class J fuses are rated to interrupt 200,000A.
They are UL labeled as current limiting, are rated
for 600VAC, and are not interchangeable with
other classes.

Class K fuses are listed by UL as K-1, K-5, or
K-9. Each subclass has designated ampere
squared seconds ($I^2t$) and peak let-through (Ip)
maximums. These are dimensionally the same as
Class H fuses (*NEC® dimensions*), and they can
have interrupting ratings of 50,000A, 100,000A, or
200,000A. These fuses are current-limiting devices; however, they are not marked current limiting since they do not have a rejection feature.

Class L fuses are available in ampere ratings of 601A through 6,000A, and are rated to interrupt 200,000A. They are labeled current limiting and are rated for 600VAC. They are intended to be bolted into their mountings and are not normally used in clips. Some Class L fuses have time-delay features for all-purpose use.

Class T fuses are 300V and 600V, with ampere ratings from 1A through 1,200A. They are physically very small and can be applied where space is at a premium. They are fast-acting fuses with an interrupting rating of 200,000A.

## 4.1.0 Branch Circuit Listed Fuses

Branch circuit listed fuses are designed to prevent the installation of fuses that cannot provide a comparable level of protection to equipment. The characteristics of branch circuit fuses are as follows:

- They must have a minimum interrupting rating of 10,000A.
- They must have a minimum voltage rating of 125V.
- They must be size rejecting such that a fuse of a lower voltage rating cannot be installed in the circuit.
- They must be size rejecting such that a fuse with a current rating higher than the fuseholder rating cannot be installed in the circuit.

## 4.2.0 Medium-Voltage Fuses

As defined in *ANSI/IEEE 40-1981*, fuses above 600V are classified as general-purpose, current-limiting; backup current-limiting; or expulsi[on] types.

- *General-purpose current-limiting fuses* – Fus[es] that are capable of interrupting all curre[nt] from the rated interrupting current down to t[he] current that causes melting of the fusible e[le]ment in one hour.
- *Backup current-limiting fuses* – Fuses that are [ca]pable of interrupting all currents from the ma[x]imum rated interrupting current down to t[he] rated minimum interrupting current.
- *Expulsion fuses* – Vented fuses in which the [ex]pulsion effect of gases produced by the arc a[nd] lining of the fuseholder, either alone or aided [by] a spring, extinguishes the arc.

In the definitions just given, the fuses [are] defined as either expulsion or current-limiti[ng] types. A current-limiting fuse is a sealed, n[on] venting fuse that, when melted by a curre[nt] within its interrupting rating, produces arc vo[lt] ages exceeding the system voltage, which in tu[rn] forces the current to zero. The arc voltages [are] produced by introducing a series of high resi[st]ance arcs within the fuse. The result is a fuse t[hat] typically interrupts high fault currents within t[he] first half cycle of the fault.

In contrast, an expulsion fuse depends on [an] arc to initiate the interruption process. The arc a[cts] as a catalyst, causing the generation of de-ionizi[ng] gas from its housing. The arc is then elongated [ei] ther by the force of the gases created or a spri[ng.] At some point, the arc elongates far enough to p[re] vent a restrike after passing through a curre[nt] zero. Therefore, it is not atypical for an expulsi[on] fuse to take many cycles to clear.

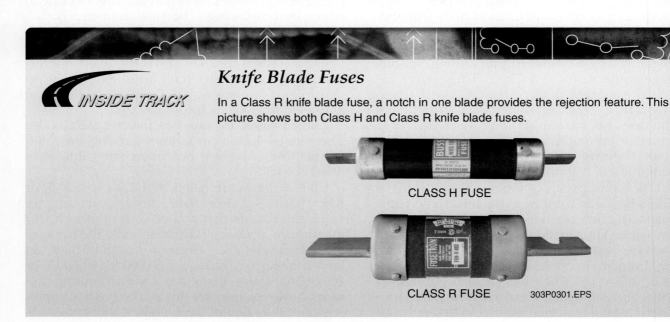

### *INSIDE TRACK*

### *Knife Blade Fuses*

In a Class R knife blade fuse, a notch in one blade provides the rejection feature. This picture shows both Class H and Class R knife blade fuses.

CLASS H FUSE

CLASS R FUSE          303P0301.EPS

any of the rules for applying expulsion fuses
d current-limiting fuses are the same, but be-
use the current-limiting fuse operates much
ster on high fault currents, some additional
les must be applied.

Three basic factors must be considered when
plying any fuse: voltage, continuous current-
rrying capacity, and interrupting rating.

*Voltage* – The fuse must have a voltage rating
that is equal to or greater than the normal frequency recovery voltage that will be seen
across the fuse under all conditions. On three-
phase systems, it is a good rule of thumb
that the voltage rating of the fuse be greater
than or equal to the line-to-line voltage of the
system.

*Continuous current-carrying capacity* – Continuous current values that are shown on the fuse
represent the level of current the fuse can
carry continuously without exceeding the
temperature rises as specified in *ANSI C37.46*.
An application that exposes the fuse to a current slightly above its continuous rating but
below its minimum interrupting rating may
damage the fuse due to excessive heat. This is
the main reason overload relays are used in
series with backup current-limiting fuses for
motor protection.

*Interrupting rating* – All fuses are given a maximum interrupting rating. This rating is the
maximum level of fault current that the fuse
can safely interrupt. Backup current-limiting
fuses are also given a minimum interrupting
rating. When using backup current-limiting
fuses, it is important that other protective devices are used to interrupt currents below this
level.

When choosing a fuse, it is important that the
se be properly coordinated with other protec-
e devices located upstream and downstream.
 accomplish this, one must consider the **melting
ne** and **clearing time** characteristics of the de-
:es. Two curves, the minimum melting curve
d the total clearing curve, provide this informa-
n. To ensure proper coordination, the following
les should be observed:

The total clearing curve of any downstream
protective device must be below a curve representing 75% of the minimum melting curve of
the fuse being applied.

The total clearing curve of the fuse being applied must lie below a curve representing 75%
of the minimum melting curve for any upstream protective device.

## 4.3.0 Current-Limiting Fuses

To ensure proper application of a current-limiting
fuse, it is important that the following additional
rules be applied:

- Current-limiting fuses produce arc voltages
  that exceed the system voltage. Care must be
  taken to ensure that the peak voltages do not
  exceed the insulation level of the system. If the
  fuse voltage rating is not permitted to exceed
  140% of the system voltage, there should not be
  a problem. This does not mean that a higher
  rated fuse cannot be used, but one must be assured that the system insulation level (BIL)
  will handle the peak arc voltage produced. BIL
  stands for basic impulse level, which is the reference impulse insulation strength of an electrical system.
- As with the expulsion fuse, current-limiting
  fuses must be properly coordinated with other
  protective devices on the system. For this to
  happen, the rules for applying an expulsion
  fuse must be used at all currents that cause the
  fuse to interrupt in 0.01 second or greater.

When other current-limiting protective devices
are on the system, it becomes necessary to use $I^2t$
values for coordination at currents causing the
fuse to interrupt in less than 0.01 second. These
values may be supplied as minimum and maximum values or minimum melting and total clearing $I^2t$ curves. In either case, the following rules
should be followed:

- The minimum melting $I^2t$ of the fuse should be
  greater than the total clearing $I^2t$ of the downstream current-limiting device.
- The total clearing $I^2t$ of the fuse should be less
  than the minimum melting $I^2t$ of the upstream
  current-limiting device.

The fuse selection chart in *Figure 8* should serve
as a guide for selecting fuses on circuits of 600V or
less. Other valuable information may be found in
catalogs furnished by manufacturers of overcurrent protective devices. These are usually obtainable from electrical supply houses or from
manufacturers' representatives. You may also
write the various manufacturers for a complete
list (and price, if any) for all reference materials of-
fered by them.

## 4.4.0 Fuses for Selective Coordination

The larger the upstream fuse is relative to a downstream fuse (feeder to branch, etc.), the less possibility there is of an overcurrent in the downstream
circuit causing both fuses to open. Fast action,

| Circuit | Load | Ampere Rating | Fuse Type | Symbol | Voltage Rating (ac) | UL Class | Interrupting Rating (K) | Remarks |
|---|---|---|---|---|---|---|---|---|
| Main, Feeder, and Branch (Conventional dimensions) | All type loads (optimum overcurrent protection) | 0 to 600A | LOW PEAK® (dual-element time-delay) | LPN-RK | 250V | RK1 | 200 | All-purpose fuses. Unequaled for combined short circuit and overload protection. |
| | | | | LPS-RK | 600V | | | |
| | | 601 to 6,000A | LOW PEAK® time-delay | KRP-C | 600V | L | 200 | |
| | Motors, welders, transformers, capacitor banks (circuits with heavy inrush currents) | 0 to 600A | FUSETRON® (dual-element time-delay) | FRN-R | 250V | RK5 | 200 | Moderate degree of current limitation. Time-delay passes surge currents. |
| | | | | FRS-R | 600V | | | |
| | | 601 to 4,000A | LIMITRON® (time-delay) | KLU | 600V | L | 200 | All-purpose fuse. Time-delay passes surge currents. |
| | Non-motor loads (circuits with no heavy inrush currents) | 0 to 600A | LIMITRON® (fast-acting) | KTN-R | 250V | RK1 | 200 | Same short circuit protection as LOW PEAK□ fuses but must be sized larger for circuits with surge currents i.e., up to 300% |
| | | | | KTS-R | 600V | | | |
| | LIMITRON□ fuses particularly suited for circuit breaker protection | 601 to 6,000A | LIMITRON® (fast-acting) | KTU | 600V | L | 200 | A fast-acting, high-performa■ fuse. |
| | All type loads (optimum overcurrent protection) | 0 to 600A | LOW PEAK® (dual-element, time-delay) | LPJ | 600V | J | 200 | All-purpose fuses. Unequaled for combined short circuit and overload protection. |
| | Non-motor loads (circuits with no heavy inrush currents) | 0 to 600A | LIMITRON® (quick-acting) | JKS | 600V | J | 200 | Very similar to KTS-R LIMITRON□, but smaller. |
| | | 0 to 1,200A | T-TRON™ | JJN | 300V | T | 200 | The space sav■ (1/3 the size o■ KTN-R/KTS-R■ |
| | | | | JJS | 600V | | | |

303F08.E■

*Figure 8* ◆ Fuse selection chart (600V or less).

ntime-delay fuses require at least a 3:1 ratio be-
een the ampere rating of a large upstream, line-
le, time-delay fuse to that of the downstream,
ad-side fuse in order to be selectively coordi-
ted. In contrast, the minimum selective coordi-
tion ratio necessary for dual-element fuses is
ly 2:1 when used with low peak load-side fuses
*gure 9*).

The use of dual-element, time-delay fuses af-
rds easy selective coordination, which hardly
quires anything more than a routine check of a
oulation of required selectivity ratios. As shown
*Figure 10*, close sizing of dual-element fuses in
e branch circuit for motor overload protection
ovides a large difference (ratio) in the ampere
tings between the feeder fuse and the branch
se compared to the single-element, nontime-
lay fuse.

## 5.0 Fuse Time-Current Curves

hen a low-level overcurrent occurs, a long in-
val of time will be required for a fuse to open
elt) and clear the fault. On the other hand, if the
ercurrent is large, the fuse will open very
ickly. The opening time is a function of the
agnitude of the level of overcurrent. Overcur-
nt levels and the corresponding intervals of
ening times are logarithmically plotted in
aph form, as shown in *Figure 11*. Levels of overrrent are scaled on the horizontal axis, with
ne intervals on the vertical axis. The curve is
erefore called a time-current curve.

The plot in *Figure 11* reflects the characteristics
a 200A, 600V, dual-element fuse. Note that at
e 1,000A overload level, the time interval that is
quired for the fuse to open is 10 seconds. Yet, at
proximately the 2,200A overcurrent level, the
ening (melt) time of the fuse is only 0.01 second.
is apparent that the time intervals become
orter and shorter as the overcurrent levels be-
me larger. This relationship is called an inverse
ne-to-current characteristic. Time-current curves
e published or are available on most commonly
ed fuses showing minimum melt, average melt,
d/or total clear characteristics. Although up-
eam and downstream fuses are easily coordi-
ted by adhering to simple ampere ratios, these
ne-current curves permit close or critical analy-
 of coordination.

### 5.1  Peak Let-Through Charts

ak let-through charts enable you to determine
th the peak let-through current and the appar-
t prospective rms symmetrical let-through

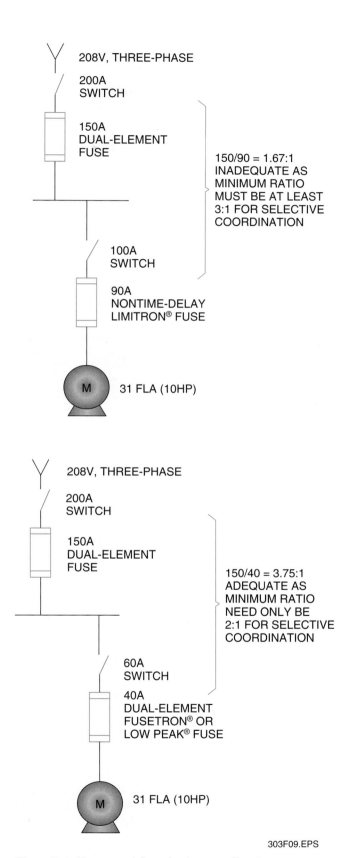

303F09.EPS

*Figure 9* ◆ Fuses used for selective coordination.

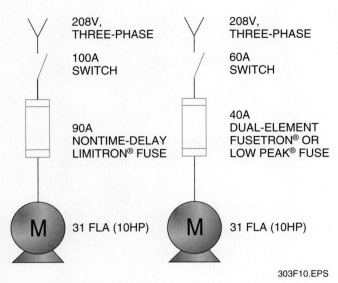

Figure 10 ◆ Comparison of dual-element fuse and single-element, nontime-delay fuse.

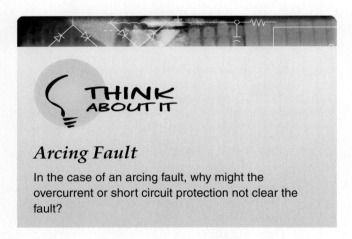

**THINK ABOUT IT**

*Arcing Fault*

In the case of an arcing fault, why might the overcurrent or short circuit protection not clear the fault?

current. Such charts are commonly referred to as current limitation curves. *Figure 12* shows a simplified chart with explanations of the various functions.

**NOTE**

Let-through charts are available in the device manufacturer's literature.

See *Figure 12*. Point 1 shows the system available rms short circuit current of 40,000A. Upward from point 1 is the intersection with the fuse size of 100A (point 2). Follow this left to point 3, the peak let-through current (10,400A). This line represents the point at which the fuse becomes

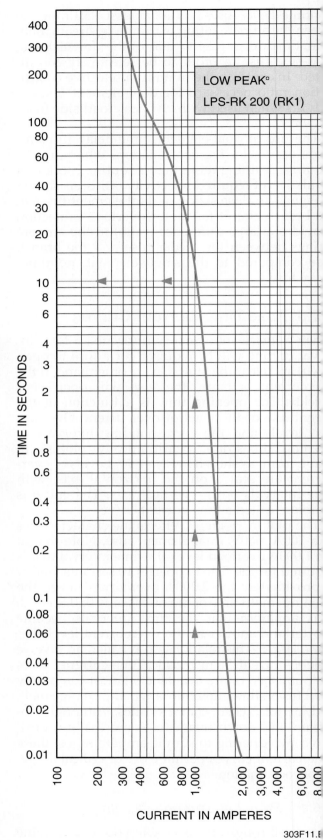

Figure 11 ◆ Typical time-current curve of a fuse.

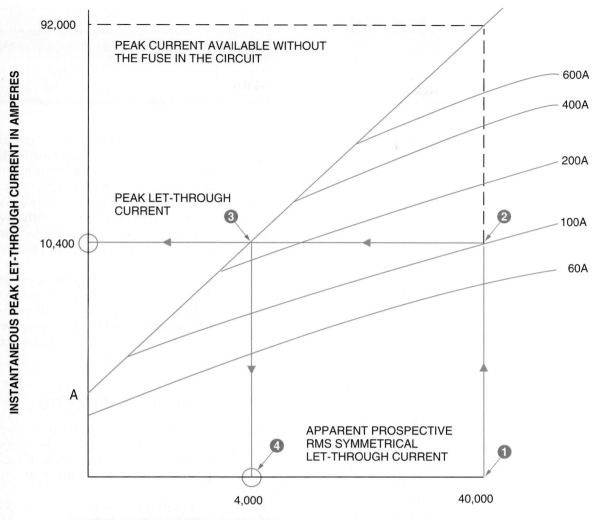

**PROSPECTIVE SHORT CIRCUIT CURRENT – SYMMETRICAL RMS AMPERES**

303F12.EPS

*ure 12* ◆ Principles of forming current limitation curves.

rrent limiting. From point 3, go down to the axis and read the apparent symmetrical rms let-rough current of 4,000A (point 4).

Three factors that affect the let-through per-rmance of a fuse are the short circuit power ctor, the point in the sine wave where fault in-rruption occurs, and the available voltage. The blished charts typically represent worst-case enarios.

**0.0 ◆ MOTOR OVERLOAD AND SHORT CIRCUIT PROTECTION**

hen used in circuits with surge currents such as ose caused by motors, transformers, and other ductive components, dual-element, time-delay

fuses can be sized close to full-load amperes to give maximum overcurrent protection. For exam-ple, assume that a 10hp, 208V three-phase motor with integral thermal protection has a full-load current of 31A. *Table 1* shows the fuse type, size, and switch size required by *NEC Sections 430.52 and 430.110* for a 10hp three-phase motor.

*Table 1* shows that a 45A, dual-element fuse will protect the 31A motor compared to the much larger 100A, single-element fuse necessary. It is apparent that if a sustained, harmful overload of 300% occurred in the motor circuit, the 100A, single-element fuse would never open and the motor could be damaged. The nontime-delay fuse provides only ground fault and short circuit protection—requiring separate overload protec-tion as per the *NEC®*.

**Table 1** Fuse and Switch Size for a 10-Horsepower Motor (208V, 3Ø, 31 FLA)

| Fuse Type | Maximum Fuse Size (Amps) | Required Switch Size (Amps) |
|---|---|---|
| Dual-element, time-delay | 45A | 60A |
| Single-element, nontime-delay | 100A | 100A |

In contrast, the 45A, dual-element fuse provides ground fault and short circuit protection plus a high degree of backup protection against motor burnout from overload or **single phasing** should other overload protective devices fail. If thermal overloads, relays, or contacts should fail to operate, the dual-element fuses will act independently to protect the motor.

Aside from providing only short circuit protection, the single-element fuse also makes it necessary to use larger size switches since a switch rating must be equal to or larger than the ampere rating of the fuse; as a result, the larger switch may cost two or three times more than would be necessary if a dual-element fuse were used (*Figure 13*).

When secondary single phasing occurs, the current in the remaining phases increases to a value of 170% to 200% of the rated full-load current. When primary single phasing occurs, unbalanced voltages that occur in the motor circuit cause excessive current. Dual-element fuses sized for motor overload protection can protect motors against the overload damage caused by single phasing.

The nontime-delay, **fast-acting fuse** must be oversized in circuits in which surge or temporary overload currents occur (**inductive load**). The re-

sponse of the oversized fuse to short circuit currents is slower. Current builds up to a high level before the fuse opens, causing the current-limiting action of the oversized fuse to be less than a fuse whose ampere rating is closer to the normal full load current of the circuit. Consequently, oversizing sacrifices some component protection and although it is permitted by the *NEC®*, the practice is not recommended.

In actual practice, dual-element fuses used to protect motors keep short circuit currents to approximately half the value of the nontime-delay fuses, since the nontime-delay fuses must be oversized to carry the temporary starting current of the motor per *NEC Table 430.52*.

## 6.0.0 ◆ CIRCUIT BREAKERS

Circuit breakers were covered in your Level Two training. However, some of the more important points are worth repeating here before we cover practical applications of both fuses and circuit breakers.

Basically, a circuit breaker is a device for closing and interrupting a circuit between separable contacts under both normal and abnormal conditions. This is done manually (normal conditions) by using its handle to switch it to the ON or OFF positions. However, the circuit breaker is also designed to open a circuit automatically on a predetermined overload or ground fault current without damage to itself or its associated equipment. As long as a circuit breaker is applied within its rating, it will automatically interrupt any fault and is therefore classified as an inherently safe overcurrent protective device.

The internal arrangement of a circuit breaker is shown in *Figure 14*, while its external operating characteristics are shown in *Figure 15*. Note that the handle on a circuit breaker resembles an ordinary toggle switch. On an overload, the circuit breaker opens itself or trips. In a tripped position, the handle jumps to the middle position (*Figure 15*). To reset it, turn the handle to the OFF position and then turn it as far as it will go beyond this position (RESET position); finally, turn it to the ON position.

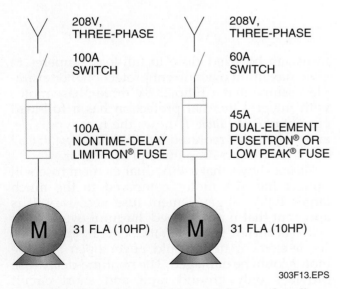

208V,
THREE-PHASE

100A
SWITCH

100A
NONTIME-DELAY
LIMITRON® FUSE

M  31 FLA (10HP)

208V,
THREE-PHASE

60A
SWITCH

45A
DUAL-ELEMENT
FUSETRON® OR
LOW PEAK® FUSE

M  31 FLA (10HP)

303F13.EPS

*Figure 13* ◆ Dual-element fuses permit the use of smaller and less costly switches.

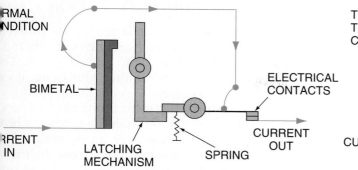

RMAL
NDITION

BIMETAL →

RRENT
IN

LATCHING
MECHANISM

SPRING

ELECTRICAL
CONTACTS

CURRENT
OUT

THERMAL
TRIP
CONDITION

CURRENT
IN

303F14.EPS

*ure 14* ◆ Internal arrangement of a circuit breaker.

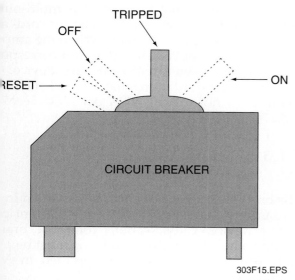

TRIPPED

OFF

RESET →

ON

CIRCUIT BREAKER

303F15.EPS

*re 15* ◆ External characteristics of a circuit breaker.

A standard molded case circuit breaker usually tains:

- A set of contacts
- A magnetic trip element
- A thermal trip element
- Line and load terminals
- Busing used to connect these individual parts
- An enclosing housing of insulating material

The circuit breaker handle manually opens and ses the contacts and resets the automatic trip ts after an interruption. Some circuit breakers b contain a manually operated push-to-trip ing mechanism.

> **CAUTION**
>
> When a breaker trips, always determine why it tripped before resetting it.

## *Molded Case Circuit Breakers*

UL requires that the handles of molded case circuit breakers be trip free. This means that the circuit breaker must open under trip conditions even if the handle is held in the ON position.

## *Arc Fault Circuit Interrupters (AFCIs)*

Arc faults occur as a result of damaged or deteriorated wiring and are a common cause of house fires. AFCIs are special breakers that can detect arcs and eliminate current flow almost immediately. The *NEC*® now requires AFCIs to be installed in all 15A and 20A branch circuits supplying outlets in dwelling unit bedrooms.

Circuit breakers are grouped for identification according to given current ranges. Each group is classified by the largest ampere rating of its range. These groups are:

- 15A–100A
- 125A–225A
- 250A–400A
- 500A–1,000A
- 1,200A–2,000A

Therefore, they are classified as 100A, 225A, 400A, 1,000A, and 2,000A frames. These numbers are commonly referred to as frame classifications or frame sizes and are terms applied to groups of molded case circuit breakers that are physically interchangeable with each other.

## 6.1.0 Interrupting Capacity Rating

In most large commercial and industrial installations, it is necessary to calculate available short circuit currents at various points in a system to determine if the equipment meets the requirements of *NEC Sections 110.9 and 110.10*. There are a number of methods used to determine the short circuit requirements in an electrical system. Some give approximate values; others require extensive computations and are quite exacting.

The breaker interrupting capacity is based on tests to which the breaker is subjected. There are two such tests; one is set up by UL and the other by NEMA. The NEMA tests are self-certification. UL tests are certified by unbiased witnesses. UL tests have been limited to a maximum of 10,000A in the past, so the emphasis was placed on NEMA tests with higher ratings. UL tests now include the NEMA tests plus other ratings. Consequently, the emphasis is now being placed on UL tests.

The interrupting capacity of a circuit breaker is based on its rated voltage. Where the circuit breaker can be used on more than one voltage, the interrupting capacity will be shown for each voltage level. For example, the LA-type circuit breaker has 42,000A symmetrical interrupting capacity at 240V, 30,000A symmetrical at 480V, and 22,000A symmetrical at 600V.

## Arc Flash

A serious injury resulted when a journeyman electrician on an industrial service call attempted to install a three-phase, 400A bolt-in circuit breaker into an energized panel. He carelessly miscalculated the positioning of the bolt-in lugs of the breaker with the breaker handle in the ON position, causing one phase terminal to contact an energized busbar, while contacting the grounded cabinet with another phase terminal. The circuit breaker exploded in his face, in addition to releasing a toxic vapor due to a phenomenon known as arc flash. He survived but sustained severe injuries to his eyes and lungs.

**The Bottom Line:** Working with energized equipment requires the use of properly rated personal protective equipment, including a full-body flash suit, face shield, and glasses.

## 7.0.0 ◆ CIRCUIT PROTECTION

All conductors in a circuit are to be protect against overcurrents in accordance with their a pacities as set forth in *NEC Section 240.4*. Th must also be protected against short circuit c rent damage as required.

Ampere ratings of overcurrent protective vices must not be greater than the ampacity of conductor. There is, however, an exception. N *Section 240.4(B)* states that if such conductor r ing does not correspond to a standard size ov current protective device, the next larger s overcurrent protective device may be used, p vided its rating does not exceed 800A. Likewi the conductor cannot be part of a multi-out branch circuit supplying receptacles for cord- a plug-connected portable loads. When the amp ity of a busway or cablebus does not correspo to a standard overcurrent protective device, next larger standard rating may be used only if rating does not exceed 800A per *NEC Sectio 368.17(A) and 370.5*.

## 7.1.0 Lighting/Appliance Branch Circuits

The branch circuit rating must be classified in cordance with the rating of the overcurrent p tective device. Classifications for those brar circuits other than individual loads must be 1! 20A, 30A, 40A, and 50A, as specified in N *Section 210.3*.

## *Surge Protection*

In addition to the plug-in surge strips that are typically used to protect electronic equipment, some manufacturers are now offering residential surge protection devices that mount directly on the main breaker panel. These devices provide comprehensive protection for AC power in use throughout the residence, and are used in conjunction with surge strips. Surge strips are not rated to handle the higher surges caused by induced lightning, and the comprehensive device reduces the voltage surge to a level that can be handled by the surge protector.

Branch circuit conductors and equipment must protected by an overcurrent protective device h ampere ratings that conform to *NEC Section 0.20*. Basically, the branch circuit conductor and ercurrent protective device must be sized for actual noncontinuous load plus 125% of the itinuous load. The overcurrent protection size ist not be greater than the conductor ampacity. inch circuits rated 15A through 50A with two or re outlets (other than receptacle circuits) must protected at their rating and the branch circuit iductor sized according to *NEC Table 210.24*. s protection is normally installed at the point ere the conductors receive their supply.

## .1 Feeder Circuits

e feeder overcurrent protective device ampere ing and feeder conductor ampacity must be as ows:

*eeder circuit with no motor load* – The overcur-ent protective device size must be at least 125% )f the continuous load plus 100% of the non-:ontinuous load.

*eeder circuit with all motor loads* – Size the over-:urrent protective device at 100% of the largest >ranch circuit protective device plus the sum of he full-load current of all other motors.

*eeder circuit with mixed loads* – Size the overcur-ent protective device at 100% of the largest >ranch circuit protective device plus the sum of he full-load current of all other motors, plus .25% of the continuous, nonmotor load, plus .00% of the noncontinuous, nonmotor load.

## .2 Service Equipment

:h ungrounded service entrance conductor st have an overcurrent device in series with a ng not higher than the ampacity of the con-:tor. The service overcurrent devices shall be 't of the service disconnecting means or be lo-ed immediately adjacent to it (*NEC Section 91*).

iervice disconnecting means can consist of one ix switches or circuit breakers for each service or each set of service-entrance conductors per-ted in *NEC Section 230.2*. When more than one tch is used, the switches must be grouped to-her (*NEC Section 230.72*).

## .3 Transformer Secondary Circuits

ld installations indicate nearly 50% of trans-mers installed do not have secondary protec-1. The *NEC®* requires overcurrent protection for lighting and appliance panelboards and rec-ommends that secondary conductors be protected from damage by applying the proper overcurrent protective device. For example, the primary over-current device protecting a three-wire trans-former cannot offer protection to the secondary conductors. *NEC Section 240.4(F)* and *NEC Section 240.21(C)* discuss protection of trans-former secondary conductors.

### 7.1.4 Motor Circuit Protection

Motors and motor circuits have unique operating characteristics and circuit components. Therefore, these circuits must be dealt with differently from other types of loads. Generally, two levels of over-current protection are required for motor branch circuits:

- *Overload protection* – Motor running overload protection is intended to protect the system components and motor from damaging over-load currents.
- *Short circuit protection (includes ground fault pro-tection)* – Short circuit protection is intended to protect the motor circuit components such as the conductors, switches, controllers, overload relays, motor, etc., against short circuit currents or grounds. This level of protection is com-monly referred to as motor branch circuit pro-tection. Dual-element fuses are designed to provide this protection, as long as they are sized correctly.

There are a variety of ways to protect a motor circuit, depending upon the user's objective. The ampere rating of an overcurrent protective device selected for motor protection depends on whether the overcurrent protective device is of the dual-element, time-delay type or the nontime-delay type.

In general, nontime-delay fuses can be sized at 300% of the motor full-load current for ordinary motors so that the normal motor starting current does not affect the fuse (*NEC Table 430.52*). Dual-element, time-delay fuses are able to withstand normal motor starting current and can be sized closer to the actual motor rating than nontime-delay fuses.

**NOTE**

Design B energy-efficient motors require special circuit protection consideration.

A summary of *NEC*® regulations governing overcurrent protection is covered in *Table 2,* while the table in *Figure 16* gives generalized fuse application guidelines for motor branch circuits. *Table 3* may be used to select dual-element fuses for motor protection.

**NOTE**

In many cases, the overcurrent device size is le than that allowed by the *NEC*®. This is an additional safeguard adopted by many manufacturers and installers.

| Type of Motor | Dual-Element, Time-Delay Fuses | | | Nontime-Delay Fuses |
|---|---|---|---|---|
| | Desired Level of Protection | | | |
| | Motor Overload and Short Circuit | Backup Overload and Short Circuit | Short Circuit Only (Based on *NEC Tables 430.247 through 430.250* current ratings) | Short Circuit Only (Based on *NEC Tables 430.247 through 430.250* current ratings) |
| Service Factor 1.15 or Greater or 40°C Temp. Rise or Less | 125% or less of motor nameplate current | 125% or next standard size (not to exceed 140%) | 150% to 175% | 150% to 300% |
| Service Factor Less Than 1.15 or Greater Than 40°C Temp. Rise | 115% or less of motor nameplate current | 115% or next standard size (not to exceed 130%) | 150% to 175% | 150% to 300% |

Fuses give overload and short circuit protection.

Overload relay gives overload protection and fuses provide backup overload protection.

Overload relay provides overload protection and fuses provide only short circuit protection.

Overload relay provides overloac protection and fus provide only shor circuit protection.

303F16

*Figure 16* ◆ Fuse application guidelines for motor branch circuits.

**Table 2** *NEC*® Regulations for Overcurrent Protection

| Application | Rule | *NEC*® Reference |
|---|---|---|
| Scope | Overcurrent protection for conductors and equipment is provided to open the circuit if the current reaches a value that will cause an excessive or dangerous temperature in conductors or conductor insulation. See also *NEC Sections 110.9 and 110.10* for requirements for interrupting capacity and protection against fault currents. | *NEC Section 240.1 FPN* |
| Protection required | Each ungrounded service-entrance conductor must have overcurrent protection in series with each ungrounded conductor. | *NEC Section 230.90(A)* |
| Number of devices | Up to six circuit breakers or sets of fuses may be considered as the overcurrent device. | *NEC Section 230.90(A),* **Exception No. 3** |
| Location in building | The overcurrent device must be part of the service disconnecting means or be located immediately adjacent to it. | *NEC Section 230.91* |
| Accessibility | In a property comprising more than one building under single management, the ungrounded conductors supplying each building served shall be protected by overcurrent devices, which may be located in the building served or in another building on the same property, provided they are accessible to the occupants of the building served. In a multiple-occupancy building, each occupant shall have access to the overcurrent protective devices. | *NEC Sections 230.92 and 230.72(C),* **Exception** |
| Location in circuit | The overcurrent device must protect all circuits and devices, except equipment which may be connected on the supply side, including: (1) Service switch; (2) Special equipment, such as surge arrestors; (3) Circuits for emergency supply and load management (where separately protected); (4) Circuits for fire alarms or fire pump equipment (where separately protected); (5) Meters with all metal housing grounded (600V or less); (6) Control circuits for automatic service equipment, if suitable overcurrent protection and disconnecting means are provided. | *NEC Section 230.94* **plus Exceptions** |
| Installation and use | Listed or labelled equipment shall be used and installed in accordance with any instructions included in the listing or labeling. | *NEC Section 110.3(B)* |
| Interrupting rating | Equipment intended to interrupt current at fault levels shall have an interrupting rating sufficient for the system voltage and the current which is available at the line terminals of the equipment. | *NEC Section 110.9* |
| Circuit impedance and other characteristics | The overcurrent protective devices, total impedance, component short circuit current ratings, and other characteristics of the circuit to be protected shall be so selected and coordinated as to permit the circuit protective devices used to clear a fault without the occurrence of extensive damage to the electrical components of the circuit. | *NEC Section 110.10* |
| General | Bonding shall be provided where necessary to ensure electrical continuity and the capacity to safely conduct any fault current likely to be imposed. | *NEC Section 250.4(A)(4)* |
| Bonding other enclosures | Metal raceways, cable trays, cable armor, cable sheath, enclosures, frames, fittings, and other metal noncurrent-carrying parts that are to serve as grounding conductors, with or without the use of supplementary equipment grounding conductors, shall be effectively bonded where necessary to ensure electrical continuity and the capacity to safely conduct any fault current likely to be imposed on them. Any nonconductive paint, enamel, or similar coating shall be removed at threads, contact points, and contact surfaces or be connected by means of fittings so designed as to make such removal unnecessary. | *NEC Section 250.96(A)* |

**Table 3**  Selection of Fuses for Motor Protection (1 of 3)

| Dual-Element Fuse Size | Motor Protection (Used without properly sized relays) Motor Full-Load Amps | | Backup Motor Protection (Used with properly sized overload relays) Motor Full-Load Amps | |
|---|---|---|---|---|
| | Motor service factor of 1.15 or greater or with temperature rise not over 40°C | Motor service factor less than 1.15 or with temperature rise not over 40°C | Motor service factor of 1.15 or greater or with temperature rise not over 40°C | Motor service factor of less than 1.15 or with temperature rise not over 40°C |
| $1/10$ | 0.08–0.09 | 0.09–0.10 | 0–0.08 | 0–0.09 |
| $1/8$ | 0.10–0.11 | 0.11–0.15 | 0.09–0.10 | 0.10–0.11 |
| $5/100$ | 0.12–0.15 | 0.14–0.15 | 0.11–0.12 | 0.12–0.13 |
| $2/10$ | 0.16–0.19 | 0.18–0.20 | 0.13–0.16 | 0.14–0.17 |
| $1/4$ | 0.20–0.23 | 0.22–0.25 | 0.17–0.20 | 0.18–0.22 |
| $3/10$ | 0.24–0.30 | 0.27–0.30 | 0.21–0.24 | 0.23–0.26 |
| $4/10$ | 0.32–0.39 | 0.35–0.40 | 0.25–0.32 | 0.27–0.35 |
| $1/2$ | 0.40–0.47 | 0.44–0.50 | 0.33–0.40 | 0.36–0.43 |
| $6/10$ | 0.48–0.60 | 0.53–0.60 | 0.41–0.48 | 0.44–0.52 |
| $8/10$ | 0.64–0.79 | 0.70–0.80 | 0.49–0.64 | 0.53–0.70 |
| 1 | 0.80–0.89 | 0.87–0.97 | 0.65–0.80 | 0.71–0.87 |
| $1 1/8$ | 0.90–0.99 | 0.98–1.08 | 0.81–0.90 | 0.88–0.98 |
| $1 1/4$ | 1.00–1.11 | 1.09–1.21 | 0.91–1.00 | 0.99–1.09 |
| $1 4/10$ | 1.12–1.19 | 1.22–1.30 | 1.01–1.12 | 1.10–1.22 |
| $1 1/2$ | 1.20–1.27 | 1.31–1.39 | 1.13–1.20 | 1.23–1.30 |
| $1 6/10$ | 1.28–1.43 | 1.40–1.56 | 1.21–1.28 | 1.31–1.39 |
| $1 8/10$ | 1.44–1.59 | 1.57–1.73 | 1.29–1.44 | 1.40–1.57 |
| 2 | 1.60–1.79 | 1.74–1.95 | 1.45–1.60 | 1.58–1.74 |
| $2 1/4$ | 1.80–1.99 | 1.96–2.17 | 1.61–1.80 | 1.75–1.96 |
| $2 1/2$ | 2.00–2.23 | 2.18–2.43 | 1.81–2.00 | 1.97–2.17 |

**Table 3**   Selection of Fuses for Motor Protection (2 of 3)

| Dual-Element Fuse Size | Motor Protection (Used without properly sized relays) Motor Full-Load Amps | | Backup Motor Protection (Used with properly sized overload relays) Motor Full-Load Amps | |
|---|---|---|---|---|
| | Motor service factor of 1.15 or greater or with temperature rise not over 40°C | Motor service factor less than 1.15 or with temperature rise not over 40°C | Motor service factor of 1.15 or greater or with temperature rise not over 40°C | Motor service factor of less than 1.15 or with temperature rise not over 40°C |
| 2⁶/₁₀ | 2.24–2.39 | 2.44–2.60 | 2.01–2.24 | 2.18–2.43 |
| 3 | 2.40–2.55 | 2.61–2.78 | 2.25–2.40 | 2.44–2.60 |
| 3²/₁₀ | 2.56–2.79 | 2.79–3.04 | 2.41–2.56 | 2.61–2.78 |
| 3¹/₂ | 2.80–3.19 | 3.05–3.47 | 2.57–2.80 | 2.79–3.04 |
| 4 | 3.20–3.59 | 3.48–3.91 | 2.81–3.20 | 3.05–3.48 |
| 4¹/₂ | 3.60–3.99 | 3.92–4.34 | 3.21–3.60 | 3.49–3.91 |
| 5 | 4.00–4.47 | 4.35–4.86 | 3.61–4.00 | 3.92–4.35 |
| 5⁶/₁₀ | 4.48–4.79 | 4.87–5.21 | 4.01–4.48 | 4.36–4.87 |
| 6 | 4.80–4.99 | 5.22–5.43 | 4.49–4.80 | 4.88–5.22 |
| 6¹/₄ | 5.00–5.59 | 5.44–6.08 | 4.81–5.00 | 5.23–5.43 |
| 7 | 5.60–5.99 | 6.09–6.52 | 5.01–5.60 | 5.44–6.09 |
| 7 | 6.00–6.39 | 6.53–6.95 | 5.61–6.00 | 6.10–6.52 |
| 8 | 6.40–7.19 | 6.96–7.82 | 6.01–6.40 | 6.53–6.96 |
| 9 | 7.20–7.99 | 7.83–8.69 | 6.41–7.20 | 6.97–7.83 |
| 10 | 8.00–9.59 | 8.70–10.00 | 7.21–8.00 | 7.84 –8.70 |
| 12 | 9.60–11.99 | 10.44–12.00 | 8.01–9.60 | 8.71–10.43 |
| 15 | 12.00–13.99 | 13.05–15.00 | 9.61–12.00 | 10.44–13.04 |
| 17¹/₂ | 14.00–15.99 | 15.22–17.39 | 12.01–14.00 | 13.05–15.21 |
| 20 | 16.00–19.99 | 17.40–20.00 | 14.01–16.00 | 15.22–17.39 |
| 25 | 20.00–23.99 | 21.74–25.00 | 16.01–20.00 | 17.40–21.74 |
| 30 | 24.00–27.99 | 26.09–30.00 | 20.01–24.00 | 21.75–26.09 |
| 35 | 28.00–31.99 | 30.44–34.78 | 24.01–28.00 | 26.10–30.43 |

**Table 3** Selection of Fuses for Motor Protection (3 of 3)

| Dual-Element Fuse Size | Motor Protection (Used without properly sized relays) Motor Full-Load Amps | | Backup Motor Protection (Used with properly sized overload relays) Motor Full-Load Amps | |
|---|---|---|---|---|
| | Motor service factor of 1.15 or greater or with temperature rise not over 40°C | Motor service factor less than 1.15 or with temperature rise not over 40°C | Motor service factor of 1.15 or greater or with temperature rise not over 40°C | Motor service factor of less than 1.15 or with temperature rise not over 40°C |
| 40 | 32.00–35.99 | 34.79–39.12 | 28.01–32.00 | 30.44–37.78 |
| 45 | 36.00–39.00 | 39.13–43.47 | 32.01–36.00 | 37.79–39.13 |
| 50 | 40.00–47.99 | 43.48–50.00 | 36.01–40.00 | 39.14–43.48 |
| 60 | 48.00–55.99 | 52.17–60.00 | 40.01–48.00 | 43.49–52.17 |
| 70 | 56.00–59.99 | 60.87–65.21 | 48.01–56.00 | 52.18–60.87 |
| 75 | 60.00–63.99 | 65.22–69.56 | 56.01–60.00 | 60.88–65.22 |
| 80 | 64.00–71.99 | 69.57–78.25 | 60.01–64.00 | 65.23–69.57 |
| 90 | 72.00–79.99 | 78.26–86.95 | 64.01–72.00 | 69.58–78.26 |
| 100 | 80.00–87.99 | 86.96–95.64 | 72.01–80.00 | 78.27–86.96 |
| 110 | 88.00–99.00 | 95.65–108.69 | 80.01–88.00 | 86.97–95.65 |
| 125 | 100.00–119.00 | 108.70–125.00 | 88.01–100.00 | 95.66–108.70 |
| 150 | 120.00–139.99 | 131.30–150.00 | 100.01–120.00 | 108.71–30.43 |
| 175 | 140.00–159.99 | 152.17–173.90 | 120.01–140.00 | 130.44–152.17 |
| 200 | 160.00–179.99 | 173.91–195.64 | 140.01–160.00 | 152.18–173.91 |
| 225 | 180.00–199.99 | 195.65–217.38 | 160.01–180.00 | 173.92–195.62 |
| 250 | 200.00–239.99 | 217.39–250.00 | 180.01–200.00 | 195.63–217.39 |
| 300 | 240.00–279.99 | 260.87–300.00 | 200.01–240.00 | 217.40–260.87 |
| 350 | 280.00–319.99 | 304.35–347.82 | 240.01–280.00 | 260.88–304.35 |
| 400 | 320.00–359.99 | 347.83–391.29 | 280.01–320.00 | 304.36–347.83 |
| 450 | 360.00–399.99 | 391.30–434.77 | 320.01–360.00 | 347.84–391.30 |
| 500 | 400.00–479.99 | 434.78–500.00 | 360.01–400.00 | 391.31–434.78 |
| 600 | 480.00–600.00 | 521.74–600.00 | 400.01–480.00 | 434.79–521.74 |

1. Which of the following best describes the maximum short circuit current that a fuse or circuit breaker will safely interrupt?
   a. CIA
   b. AIC
   c. SOL
   d. ICA

2. The minimum interrupting rating of branch circuit listed fuses is _____.
   a. 5,000A
   b. 10,000A
   c. 15,000A
   d. 20,000A

3. The minimum voltage rating of branch circuit fuses is _____.
   a. 24V
   b. 120V
   c. 125V
   d. 240V

4. All of the following are classifications of medium-voltage fuses *except* _____.
   a. general-purpose current-limiting fuses
   b. backup current-limiting fuses
   c. expulsion fuses
   d. proportion fuses

5. An expulsion fuse is best described as a _____.
   a. fuse capable of interrupting all currents from the rated interrupting current down to the current that causes melting of the fusible element in an hour
   b. fuse capable of interrupting all currents from the maximum rated interrupting current down to the rated minimum interrupting current
   c. strap-mounted device
   d. vented fuse in which the expulsion effect of gases produced by the arc and lining of the fuseholder, either alone or aided by a spring, extinguishes the arc

6. Each of the following is a basic factor to consider when applying any fuse *except* _____.
   a. voltage
   b. continuous current-carrying capacity
   c. interrupting rating
   d. manufacturer's brand name

7. The total clearing time of any downstream protective device must be below a curve representing _____ of the minimum melting curve of the fuse being applied.
   a. 10%
   b. 20%
   c. 50%
   d. 75%

8. When a common circuit breaker trips, the handle is in the _____ position.
   a. OFF
   b. ON
   c. middle
   d. RESET

9. Circuit breakers are grouped for identification according to given current ranges. Each group is classified by the _____.
   a. largest ampere rating of its range
   b. smallest ampere rating of its range
   c. absolute lowest ampere rating of its range
   d. overall average ampere rating of its range

10. When circuit breakers are classified as 100A through 2,000A frames, these numbers are normally referred to as the _____.
   a. frame size
   b. overload protective current
   c. maximum voltage allowed on the circuit
   d. physical size of the circuit breaker

## Summary

Reliable overcurrent protective devices prevent or minimize costly damage to transformers, conductors, motors, and the many other components and electrical loads that make up the complete electrical distribution system. Consequently, reliable circuit protection is essential to avoid the severe monetary losses that can result from power blackouts and prolonged downtime of various types facilities. The *NEC*® has set forth various mumum requirements dealing with overcurrent vices and how they should be installed in varitypes of electrical circuits.

## Notes

# Trade Terms
# Introduced in This Module

*Ampere rating:* The current-carrying capacity of an overcurrent protective device. The fuse or circuit breaker is subjected to a current above its ampere rating; it will open the circuit after a predetermined period of time.

*Ampere squared seconds ($I^2t$):* The measure of heat energy developed within a circuit during the fuse's clearing. It can be expressed as melting $I^2t$, arcing $I^2t$, or the sum of them as clearing $I^2t$. I stands for effective let-through current (rms), which is squared, and t stands for time of opening in seconds.

*Amperes interrupting capacity (AIC):* The maximum short circuit current that a circuit breaker or fuse can safely interrupt.

*Arcing time:* The amount of time from the instant the fuse link has melted until the overcurrent is interrupted or cleared.

*Clearing time:* The total time between the beginning of the overcurrent and the final opening of the circuit at rated voltage by an overcurrent protective device. Clearing time is the total of the melting time and the arcing time.

*Current-limiting device:* A device that will clear a short circuit in less than one half cycle. Also, it will limit the instantaneous peak let-through current to a value substantially less than that obtainable in the same circuit if that device were replaced with a solid conductor of equal impedance.

*Fast-acting fuse:* A fuse that opens on overloads and short circuits very quickly. This type of fuse is not designed to withstand temporary overload currents associated with some electrical loads (inductive loads).

*Inductive load:* An electrical load that pulls a large amount of current—an inrush current—when first energized. After a few cycles or seconds, the current declines to the load current.

*Melting time:* The amount of time required to melt a fuse link during a specified overcurrent.

*NEC® dimensions:* These are dimensions once referenced in the *National Electrical Code®*. They are common to Class H and K fuses and provide interchangeability between manufacturers for fuses and fusible equipment of given ampere and voltage ratings.

*Overload:* Can be classified as an overcurrent that exceeds the normal full-load current of a circuit.

*Peak let-through (Ip):* The instantaneous value of peak current let-through by a current-limiting fuse when it operates in its current-limiting range.

*Root-mean-square (rms):* The effective value of an AC sine wave, which is calculated as the square root of the average of the squares of all the instantaneous values of the current throughout one cycle. Alternating current rms is that value of an alternating current that produces the same heating effect as a given DC value.

*Semiconductor fuse:* Fuse used to protect solid-state devices.

*Short circuit current:* Can be classified as an overcurrent that exceeds the normal full-load current of a circuit by a factor many times greater than normal. Also characteristic of this type of overcurrent is that it leaves the normal current-carrying path of the circuit—it takes a shortcut around the load and back to the source.

*Single phasing:* The condition that occurs when one phase of a three-phase system opens, either in a low-voltage or high-voltage distribution system. Primary or secondary single phasing can be caused by any number of events. This condition results in unbalanced loads in polyphase motors and unless protective measures are taken, it will cause overheating and failure.

**UL classes:** Underwriters Laboratories has developed basic physical specifications and electrical performance requirements for fuses with voltage ratings of 600V or less. These are known as UL standards. If a type of fuse meets with the requirements of a standard, it can fall into that UL class. Typical UL classes are R, K, G, L, H, T, CC, and J.

**Voltage rating:** The maximum value of syste voltage in which a fuse can be used, yet saf interrupt an overcurrent. Exceeding the volta rating of a fuse impairs its ability to safely cl an overload or short circuit.

s module is intended to present thorough re-
rces for task training. The following reference
rks are suggested for further study. These are
ional materials for continued education rather
n for task training.

*American Electrician's Handbook.* Terrell Croft and
Wilfred I. Summers. New York, NY: McGraw-
Hill, 1996.

*National Electrical Code® Handbook,* Latest Edition.
Quincy, MA: National Fire Protection Association.

# *CONTREN® LEARNING SERIES* — USER FEEDBACK

The NCCER makes every effort to keep these textbooks up-to-date and free of technical errors. We appreciate your help in this process. If you have an idea for improving this textbook, or if you find an error, a typographical mistake, or an inaccuracy in NCCER's *Contren®* textbooks, please write us, using this form or a photocopy. Be sure to include the exact module number, page number, a detailed description, and the correction, if applicable. Your input will be brought to the attention of the Technical Review Committee. Thank you for your assistance.

*Instructors* – If you found that additional materials were necessary in order to teach this module effectively, please let us know so that we may include them in the Equipment/Materials list in the Annotated Instructor's Guide.

**Write:**  Product Development
National Center for Construction Education and Research
P.O. Box 141104, Gainesville, FL 32614-1104

**Fax:**  352-334-0932

**E-mail:**  curriculum@nccer.org

---

raft                                Module Name

pyright Date          Module Number                    Page Number(s)

escription

_____

_____

_____

_____

ptional) Correction

_____

_____

_____

ptional) Your Name and Address

_____

_____

_____